# The Chemistry and Physics of Drugs Used in Anesthesia

*Cynthia S. Dowd, PhD, and Lemont B. Kier, PhD*

*Published by*
American Association of Nurse Anesthetists

American Association of Nurse Anesthetists
222 South Prospect Avenue
Park Ridge, IL 60068-4001

Printed in the United States of America

Last digit indicates print number: 10 9 8 7 6 5 4 3 2 1

The authors and publisher have done everything possible to make this book accurate, up to date, and in accord with accepted standards at the time of publication. The authors, editors, and publisher are not responsible for errors or omissions or for consequences from application of the book, and make no warranty, expressed or implied, in regard to the contents of the book. Any practice described in this book should be applied in accordance with professional standards of care used in regard to the unique circumstances that may apply in each situation.

## Library of Congress Cataloging-in-Publication Data

Kier, Lemont B. (Lemont Burwell), author, editor.
  [Chemistry of drugs for nurse anesthetists]
  The chemistry and physics of drugs used in anesthesia / by Cynthia S. Dowd and Lemont B. Kier. -- Second edition.
       p. ; cm.
  Lemont B. Kier's name appears first in the previous edition.
  Preceded by The chemistry of drugs for nurse anesthetists / Lemont B. Kier and Cynthia S. Dowd, with contributions from Michael D. Fallacaro ... [et al.]. c2004.
  Includes bibliographical references and index.
  ISBN 978-0-9829912-2-0 (soft cover)
  I. Dowd, Cynthia S., author, editor. II. American Association of Nurse Anesthetists, issuing body. III. Title.
  [DNLM: 1. Anesthesia--nursing. 2. Anesthetics--pharmacokinetics. 3. Central Nervous System Agents. 4. Nurse Anesthetists. WY 151]
  RS403
  615.1'9--dc23
                            2014016253

# Foreword

Since time immemorial, healthcare professionals have struggled to alleviate pain and suffering in patients. Early experiments with roots and berries ultimately led to sampling extracts from seeds of the poppy. These trials have now blossomed into a growing scientific discipline grounding and validating anesthesia practice. Yet, in the wrong hands, such miraculous therapeutics can inflict suffering and can harm the very patients they are designed to serve.

*The Chemistry and Physics of Drugs Used in Anesthesia* serves as a resource for all anesthetists who seek best-evidence knowledge in therapeutics to inform their practice. This interdisciplinary offering brings art and science together in a unique manner. In this reference, bench researchers, medicinal chemists and pharmacologists, and anesthesia practitioners present the chemical and physical essence of the substances and compounds employed in operating rooms every day. On this scientific foundation, today's art of safe and effective anesthesia delivery is built.

As a Certified Registered Nurse Anesthetist (CRNA) with more than 30 years of clinical and education experience, I can say without a doubt that the drugs used in the discipline today have little resemblance to those used when I entered the field. Many state-of-the-art medications that I was taught to safely employ early in my career are now off the market, and some have been deemed dangerous. Yet, I am surprised to find that some colleagues still practice as they were taught, even if their methods are decades old. All practitioners need to embrace a commitment to best-evidence practice and lifelong learning. This best evidence does not just appear; it must be actively sought by embracing, instilling, and demonstrating a daily spirit of curiosity and inquiry. Why should this therapeutic agent or method be used over another? Am I aware of everything I need to know regarding the medicines I am about to inject? Are there better alternatives to deliver high-quality care?

In today's consumer-driven economy, it is common for people to comparison shop for goods and services. Recently, I recall interviewing 3 companies when considering having yard work done. Cost was not the big issue; quality was the matter of most importance to me. Within days of this exercise, in the preanesthesia hold area, a young mother handed me her child who was in need of a hernia repair. I had never met this woman before and had never seen the child until that moment. Reflecting back, I remain astonished that people like this mother hand over their most precious possession (their child) to strangers like me, whom they know little or nothing about. The trust placed in the hands of those who care for sick individuals is sacred. It is a trust that demands the application of best-evidence knowledge and the highest level of skill from those holding the syringe.

The struggle to alleviate pain and suffering continues, and it is a noble calling to join the ranks of those engaged in this pursuit. It is of paramount importance to patients and their families that providers possess a comprehensive understanding of the substances employed in anesthesia as well as a passion for high-quality care. To care for others at a time when they cannot care for themselves is a privilege that brings with it a promise and challenge for all anesthetists to commit themselves to lifelong learning. It is hoped that the pages of this textbook will enhance such learning in all who watch over those who sleep.

Michael D. Fallacaro, CRNA, DNS
*Professor*
Department of Nurse Anesthesia
Virginia Commonwealth University School of Allied Health Sciences
Richmond, Virginia

# Preface

The past decade has revealed a substantial list of achievements in the development, application, and understanding of drugs and agents used in the nurse anesthesia profession. The introduction of the text by Kier and Dowd in 2004 opened the doors to a vehicle for student registered nurse anesthetists and practitioners to learn of and understand the chemicals used in their profession. So much has been added to those earlier chemical tools of their practice that a new textbook is certainly desirable. We accept the challenge, in this textbook, to bring to the profession an advanced knowledge and understanding of drugs used in nurse anesthesia.

The strategy we have adopted in this text is to describe the category of physiological objectives in use in the profession and to identify the mechanisms at work in each. These objectives are at first described as the necessary goals sought in the treatment of a patient preparing for or undergoing surgery, or recovering from it. For each category there exists a realm of knowledge as to the chemical agents that can achieve modifications desired in an operation or treatment. The drugs are introduced, identified, and portrayed as to their chemical and physical properties, and then described in a physiological setting. Importantly, we include drugs that are in current use clinically as well as those that have been replaced in practice. This approach will give the student a historical basis for understanding the mechanisms of action and structure-activity relationships of current drugs.

In each description, side effects, drug-drug interactions, long-term effects, and safety features are introduced. These attributes are information emerging from recent experiences and are often of value in modifying the use of an agent relative to information available when it was introduced. Each chapter ends with a list of suggested reading, as well as discussion topics intended to inspire further conversation on the subject.

We begin the text with introductions to the medicinal chemistry and physics of molecules that are in use by a professional in his or her practice. This lays the groundwork for descriptions and explanations of the routes of administration, pharmacology, dose effects, side effects, and long-term properties encountered. Our principal objective is that the nurse anesthetist will emerge from these readings with a clear picture of each drug's use, value, precautions, and long-term problems.

In the creation of this text, we have been guided by the introduction and successful use of the 2004 text by Kier and Dowd, *The Chemistry of Drugs for Nurse Anesthetists*. We are also guided by the structure of the course created 20 years ago in the Virginia Commonwealth University Department of Nurse Anesthesia, Richmond, Virginia, and the successful use of that text, under the leadership of Department Chairman Michael D. Fallacaro, CRNA, DNS, and the course lecturers. We are grateful for the collaborative nature of our relationship, which has been both enjoyable and beneficial to the book.

Cynthia S. Dowd, PhD, and Lemont B. Kier, PhD

# Authors

**Rami A. Al-Horani, PhD**
American Heart Association Postdoctoral Associate
Department of Medicinal Chemistry
Virginia Commonwealth University

**May H. Abdel Aziz, PhD**
Postdoctoral Associate
Department of Pharmaceutics
University of Utah

**Chuck Biddle, CRNA, PhD**
Professor
Department of Nurse Anesthesia
Virginia Commonwealth University

**Nicole Damico, CRNA, MSNA**
Assistant Professor
Department of Nurse Anesthesia
Virginia Commonwealth University

**Matthew D'Angelo, CRNA, DNP**
Assistant Professor
Nurse Anesthesia Program
Uniformed Services University of the Health Sciences

**Umesh R. Desai, PhD**
Professor
Department of Medicinal Chemistry and Institute for Structural Biology
and Drug Discovery
Virginia Commonwealth University

**Cynthia S. Dowd, PhD**
Assistant Professor
Department of Chemistry
George Washington University

**Michael D. Fallacaro, CRNA, DNS**
Professor
Department of Nurse Anesthesia
Virginia Commonwealth University

## Lemont B. Kier, PhD
Emeritus Professor of Medicinal Chemistry
School of Pharmacy
Virginia Commonwealth University

## Akul Y. Mehta, PhD
Postdoctoral Associate
Department of Medicinal Chemistry
Virginia Commonwealth University

## Jürgen Venitz, MD, PhD
Professor
Department of Pharmaceutics
Virginia Commonwealth University

## Suzanne M. Wright, CRNA, PhD
Associate Professor
Department of Nurse Anesthesia
Virginia Commonwealth University

# Contents

## The Chemistry and Physics of Drugs Used in Anesthesia

Chapter 1    **The Laws That Govern Gases and Their Transition**
*Matthew D'Angelo, CRNA, DNP, and Chuck Biddle, CRNA, PhD*        1

Chapter 2    **The Basics of Organic Chemistry**
*Cynthia S. Dowd, PhD, and Lemont B. Kier, PhD*        23

Chapter 3    **Biological Macromolecules**
*Cynthia S. Dowd, PhD, and Lemont B. Kier, PhD*        73

Chapter 4    **The Biochemistry of Fundamental Metabolic Processes**
*Cynthia S. Dowd, PhD*        97

Chapter 5    **Drug-Receptor Interactions**
*Lemont B. Kier, PhD, and Cynthia S. Dowd, PhD*        123

Chapter 6    **Pharmacokinetics and Pharmacodynamics**
*Jürgen Venitz, MD, PhD*        139

Chapter 7    **Autonomic Agents: Cholinergics and Adrenergics**
*Cynthia S. Dowd, PhD, and Lemont B. Kier, PhD*        175

Chapter 8    **Cardiovascular Agents**
*Umesh R. Desai, PhD, Rami A. Al-Horani, PhD,*
*Akul Y. Mehta, PhD, and May H. Abdel Aziz, PhD*        201

Chapter 9    **Anesthetic Agents**
*Nicole Damico, CRNA, MSNA, Michael D. Fallacaro, CRNA, DNS,*
*and Lemont B. Kier, PhD*        241

Chapter 10   **Central Nervous System Depressants**
*Lemont B. Kier, PhD, and Cynthia S. Dowd, PhD*        269

Chapter 11   **Analgesic Agents**
*Lemont B. Kier, PhD, and Cynthia S. Dowd, PhD*        289

Chapter 12   **Psychotropic Drugs**
*Cynthia S. Dowd, PhD, and Lemont B. Kier, PhD*        313

Chapter 13   **Antibiotic and Antiviral Agents**
*Suzanne M. Wright, CRNA, PhD, Cynthia S. Dowd, PhD,*
*and Lemont B. Kier, PhD*        341

Glossary        371

Index        383

# Acknowledgments

As with any collaborative work, there are many people who have had a hand in its creation and development. The chapter authors have taken their roles seriously and devoted significant attention and expertise to their chapters. Working with the authors has been enjoyable and we have learned quite a lot from their knowledge. Our spouses, Matthew J. Dowd and Martha Kier, continue to provide encouragement to our professional activities, especially the publication of this book. The students and faculty of the Department of Nurse Anesthesia at VCU have been especially supportive of this book and its contents. Their enthusiasm for the field and help in leading others into the future of patient care is truly inspiring. Without the help and support of these individuals, this book might never have been realized. We are grateful to all of them.

Cynthia S. Dowd, PhD, and Lemont B. Kier, PhD

# Chapter 1

# The Laws That Govern Gases and Their Transition

*by Matthew D'Angelo, CRNA, DNP, and Chuck Biddle, CRNA, PhD*

The delivery of anesthesia requires the use of a variety of compounds. In everyday practice, anesthetists use liquids, gases, and solids to anesthetize patients. Delivery of anesthesia often involves transforming compounds to produce a desired physiologic effect; for example, solids are converted into liquids, and gases are vaporized. *Kinetic theory,* the study of molecular behavior, explains many of the phenomena encountered in the practice of anesthesia.

Unfortunately, much of the "science" of the kinetic theory is easily forgotten and memorized only for examinations. Transition away from the "copper kettle" and technological control of the operative environment has removed a significant portion of provider manipulation of gas laws, making much of this content underwhelming to readers, without significant clinical reinforcement. Although it may seem that the influence of gas laws has limited usefulness in the practice of modern anesthesia, these laws continue to permeate the administration of every anesthetic.

This chapter focuses on the physical laws that are essential to the practice of anesthesia. It is divided into 2 major sections: Section I explores kinetic theory and details individual gas laws and how they relate to clinical practice. Section II describes how gases move from the outside environment and into a patient. Combined, these sections provide theoretical foundations, using practical illustrations, and a solid scientific foundation for clinical practice.

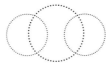

# Section I:

## Compressed Gas in the Operating Room

In this section, we describe how atoms and molecules behave in the environment. As we progress, we will step back from the molecular level and see how a mass of molecules of gas reacts to changes in temperature, pressure, and volume. Ultimately, this journey will clarify how gases behave and react to compression and storage for medical use.

## Kinetic Theory

Atoms and molecules are composed of positive, negative, and neutral forces. These particles exist in various energy states and randomly move in space. Matter, whether it is in the form of a gas, liquid, or solid, is composed of atoms and molecules that are in constant, somewhat chaotic, movement. Molecular motion varies upon the state and its level of energy. A molecule consists of 2 or more atoms moving as a result of internal, thermally induced vibrations. This configuration causes a constant, natural shifting of molecular position with respect to the environment. In the case of a gas, the molecules are not bound to one another in any manner and exhibit random vibration and rotation, freely colliding into one another and against the walls of the container in which they may be confined. Molecules of solids vibrate and move randomly, yet are locked into what might be called an "average" position, producing a rigid form. Between these extremes are liquids, whose molecules vibrate, move, and rotate with more freedom than those of a solid, but with less freedom than those of a gas. Kinetic theory describes molecular behavior in its various states combining Newton's laws of motion and the bulk properties of gases.

Newton's laws of motion describe molecular behavior and are easily visualized when one considers bingo. Imagine a bingo game in which the balls (representing atoms and molecules) are motionless in a glass tank. As the game begins, the balls are "spun" with air. The balls mix in the container. As a ball moves, it does so in a line. Its motion will continue and is limited only by the constraints of the glass tank (Newton's first law). Newton states that an object in motion will remain in motion unless a force is acted on it. A molecule (or bingo ball) will travel until something stops it. In a real bingo game, the balls are of equal size. For this scenario, however, imagine that the bingo balls vary in size, some large and some small. As the game continues, the tank is amassed with balls colliding with one another. Larger balls collide with smaller balls. While each ball has an impact on collision, the larger balls have a greater impact due to their greater (heavier) size (Newton's second law). Newton's second law states that heavier objects have a greater impact than smaller ones. While some bingo balls collide with one another, others collide with the glass tank itself. The momentum (energy) from the collisions between the balls and the tank is not lost, but transferred between the other balls and the walls of the tank itself (Newton's third law).

## Kinetic Energy

Movement in and of itself creates energy. Particles in motion produce kinetic energy. *Kinetic energy* is defined as the energy that a mass (an object) produces from being in motion. If we take the bingo example and move it to a closed container such as a cylinder, the motion of the balls and change of momentum cause energy to transfer, ultimately creating force. *Force* is the change in momentum per unit of time. The faster the balls' momentum changes, the higher the force. In other words, the more the balls (molecules) bounce off each other and the walls, the more energy is transferred. *Pressure* is the result of force that is applied to an area. Therefore, the pressure produced by a gas within the container is a result of the collision of gas molecules with the wall. Simply, the more the molecules collide with the wall, the higher the pressure.

It is only natural to think of the obvious and visualize the bingo scenario. We see a cylinder of gas (or balls moving in a bingo container) and view it in isolation. Yet the external environment may affect what happens inside the cylinder (or the bingo container). If the container walls are warmer than the gas (outside environment is warmer), energy from the wall will be transferred to the gas molecules, making the molecules move faster (increasing pressure). Alternatively, if the gas is warmer than the walls, energy will be transferred to the wall, cooling the gas (decreasing pressure). In either case, the force and pressure of the tank change in relation to environmental temperature. Equilibrium is reached, and pressure stabilizes when energy transfer between the gas and wall is equivalent.

Not all gas molecules have the same kinetic energy. The gas laws presume an average kinetic energy equating to the internal energy in an ideal gas. It follows then that average kinetic energy is directly proportional to the temperature.

## Pressure

As noted, pressure is the force of molecular impact on a surface area. Pressure is measured in many forms, but it is commonly reported in anesthesia as pounds per square inch (psi) and millimeters of mercury (mm Hg). Pressure will be described further in this chapter. It is important to note, however, that when reading a tank pressure gauge (eg, 2,000 psig on an oxygen E cylinder) what is actually measured is a pressure that is in excess of atmospheric pressure. When the gauge of an "empty" tank reads "0," the internal tank is at atmospheric pressure; flow of gas from the tank ceases because there is no driving gradient. The gauge pressure reveals the existence of "added pressure," or pressure above atmospheric pressure.

## Temperature

As noted, ambient temperature has little role in the modern anesthetizing environment. The vast majority of anesthetic cases occur in climate-controlled environments. In addition, technology has been developed to reduce the effect of environmental temperature variation; temperature-compensated vaporizers provide reliably stable gas output in a wide range of temperatures. Despite modern innovation, temperature deserves special consideration in anesthesia because it has such a decisive role in the behavior of gases and liquids. Extremes in temperature and the use of uncompensated equipment (copper kettle) are possible. In general, higher environmental temperatures result in increasing liquid vaporization. Changes in temperature will cause pressure to fluctuate in closed environments.

Temperature is a basic physical property of all matter. Slight variations in temperature can cause dramatic changes in the physical state of a compound. As such, temperature is considered a primary factor affecting the state of matter. It follows from the preceding discussion that temperature is a result of molecular activity. As the temperature of a substance increases, the atoms and molecules vibrate with greater strength, producing pressure. Likewise, as the temperature decreases, the opposite occurs.

Increasing temperature provides thermal energy to convert liquids to gas. In most cases, the environment and the liquid itself provide the energy. As the liquid temperature rises, molecules escape and become a vapor or gas. This process produces an interesting (and problematic) phenomenon. As warm liquids convert to gas, energy (heat) is lost from the liquid. Warm liquids (increased molecular activity) have more energy than do colder liquids. As the molecules become gas, energy is lost, causing the temperature of the liquid to fall, ultimately changing vapor output. Remember, kinetic energy is the average. Some molecules will move faster (and get warmer) than others. As the warmer liquid molecules become gas, they leave the liquid. Vaporization is a cooling process, which is a significant problem for anyone who relies on vaporization to deliver an anesthetic. Alterations in temperature will result in variable gas concentration, in effect, an uncontrolled delivery of gas. To maintain consistent vapor output, modern vaporizers must be calibrated and manufactured to an anesthetic agent's *latent heat of vaporization*. The latent heat of vaporization is the amount of heat required to convert a unit mass of a liquid into vapor *without a change in temperature*. Modern vaporizers allow for predictable vaporization because they are constructed with metals that readily conduct environmental heat, limiting the cooling of the liquid agent as it is vaporized. In addition, modern vaporizers compensate for temperature changes by varying flow through the vaporizer as needed. These characteristics result in a maintained, controlled vapor output.

## Vapor Pressure

Liquids and gases have a tendency to evaporate and condense naturally in the environment depending on ambient conditions. Liquids evaporate to gas when they lack adequate surface tension and escape as vapor to the surroundings. *Vapor pressure* is the pressure at which a vapor is at equilibrium with its liquid (condensed) state. Simply, vapor pressure is the rate at which evaporation equals the rate of condensation. Vapor pressure provides clinicians a glimpse of the volatility of anesthetic agents. Vapor pressure and evaporation are directly proportional. The higher the vapor pressure, the more likely (faster) the substance will evaporate. As such, agents with higher vapor pressure are said to be volatile. The effect of vapor pressure is seen when one considers the difference between desflurane and isoflurane. At 20°C, desflurane has a vapor pressure of 664 mm Hg and boils at room temperature, whereas isoflurane has a vapor pressure of 238 mm Hg and remains stable at standard temperature and pressure. Vapor pressure is a temperature-dependent phenomenon.

## Boiling Point

While evaporation and condensation naturally occur as functions of vapor pressure, the addition of heat alters this equilibrium. The boiling point occurs when energy is applied to a liquid, increasing the molecular activity beyond equilibrium. The amount of energy required to boil the liquid is known as the *heat of vaporization.* The *boiling point* of a substance is the temperature at which the vapor pressure of the liquid equals the environmental pressure surrounding the liquid. As heat rises, the number of molecules becoming a gas exceeds the number condensing. Molecules leaving the liquid cause turbulence and bubbling as they exit. Once the liquid starts to boil, the temperature remains constant until all of the liquid has been converted to a gas. The boiling point is directly related to atmospheric pressure. As pressure increases, the boiling point increases. This factor is clinically significant in mountainous regions. Liquids boil faster and at lower temperatures at higher altitudes (lower atmospheric pressure). Liquids that remain stable at sea level may vaporize earlier at higher altitudes.

## Critical Temperature and Pressure

Medical gases are routinely stored in steel cylinders at high pressures. As we know, gases are unique and offer a variety of characteristics that lend and, in many cases, complicate their safe and economical storage. The behavior of the gas in a cylinder depends on whether it is above or below its critical temperature and pressure. The *critical temperature* is the temperature at or above which a vapor cannot be liquefied no matter how much pressure is applied. However, with enough pressure (*critical pressure*) the vapor can be forced into the solid state.

Nitrous oxide has a boiling point of –88°C and a critical temperature of 36°C. At room temperature (20°C), nitrous oxide is a gas. Because nitrous oxide is below its critical temperature, it can be stored under pressure as a liquid. One may wonder why a gas is stored in its liquid state. While it may complicate clinical use, storage of gases as liquids has significant economic advantages. Such is the case with nitrous oxide.

*Clinical vignette:*

*Gases stored as liquids can present clinical challenges. The pressure gauge on a cylinder of nitrous oxide measures only vapor pressure. As gas is used (say during an anesthetic), the liquid in the cylinder evaporates and maintains the pressure gauge reading. The gauge does not change despite the use of gas and "emptying" the cylinder. Subsequently, a nitrous oxide pressure gauge reads 750 psi until approximately three quarters of the volume of gas has been exhausted. The gauge will rapidly fall as the cylinder contents fall below 400 L. This makes measuring the amount of nitrous oxide remaining in a tank via pressure readings problematic. Nitrous oxide must be weighed. Oxygen, on the other hand, is above its critical temperature at room temperature. Oxygen will remain a gas regardless of the pressure applied. As compressed oxygen is used, the pressure gauge will decrease proportionately until it reaches atmospheric pressure and the cylinder is empty. (Pressure gauges read pressure above atmospheric pressure.)*

# Specific Laws Related to the Properties of Gases

A gas is said to be perfect (or ideal) if the intermolecular forces are very small and the size of the molecules compared to the overall volume of gas is infinitely small. If a perfect (ideal) gas is assumed, a number of laws governing the behavior of gases can be applied. A discussion of these laws with particular relevance to anesthesia follows.

# Boyle's Law

Boyle's law states that at a constant temperature and fixed mass, the pressure and volume of a gas are inversely proportional. Simply stated, as volume decreases, pressure increases, and vice versa. Boyle's law permits the calculation of the volume that a gas will occupy at a given pressure if the original pressure and volume are known (given that temperature is constant). This law is demonstrated in the following formula:

$$\mathbf{P_1 \times V_1 = P_2 \times V_2}$$

where $P_1$ and $V_1$ are the original pressure and volume, and $P_2$ and $V_2$ are the new pressure and volume. To solve Boyle's law, you must know 3 of the 4 variables; they may be represented in any unit of measure as long as the units are continued throughout the equation.

The application of Boyle's law can be seen throughout human physiology and is the basis for the understanding of respiratory physiology. One of the most poignant examples of Boyle's law in anesthesia is controlled ventilation. At end exhalation, the pressure between the lungs and a ventilator bellows is at or near 0 cm $H_2O$. As the bellows ascend (decreased volume), pressure increases within the ventilator, causing the anesthetic gases to flow from high pressure (inside the bellows) through the circuit to the lungs. Once the predetermined volume (or pressure) of gas is delivered to a patient, the bellows descend (volume increases) and gas moves from the patient's lungs back through the anesthesia circuit.

*Clinical vignette:*

*In addition to describing respiratory physiology, Boyle's law explains the importance of compressed gas to anesthesia and medicine. Imagine a quantity of gas in a 5-L cylinder under 2,000 psi of pressure. If we took that same quantity of gas (molecules) and reduced the pressure to 100 psi, how would the volume be affected?*

---

$$2{,}200\ psi \times 5\ L = 100\ psi \times V_2$$

When we solve for $V_2$ the volume of the gas at lower pressure would be 110 L. Since the number of molecules of gas did not change, a cylinder (or container) 22 times larger would be required to have an equivalent amount of gas as with 1 cylinder at 5 L and 2,200 psi.

---

# Charles' Law

Jacques Charles, a French chemist, physicist, and balloonist, observed the relationship of gas volume and temperature in the late 18th century. Charles' observations note that at constant pressure and mass, the volume of a gas increases or decreases in direct proportion to its temperature. Charles' law predicts that as heat is applied to a gas, the gas will expand, and as the gas is cooled, the opposite will occur. The linear relationship of temperature implies that as the temperature approaches 0 kelvin (ie, absolute zero), the volume of a gas will also approach zero. While the relationship of temperature and pressure remains, atoms and molecules of a gas have a finite volume and will occupy some space and will have volume. As such, real gases liquefy as temperature approaches 0 K. Charles' law can be expressed as follows:

$$V_1/T_1 = V_2/T_2 \ or \ V_1T_2 = V_2T_1$$

where V is volume in any unit and T is the temperature in K (273 K = 0°C).

# Gay-Lussac's Temperature/Pressure Law

Jacques Charles made his observations on the effects of temperature and volume on gases in the late 1780s. It was not until 1802 that Joseph Louis Gay-Lussac systematically described how pressure varied–at a constant volume–when a gas was heated. Gay-Lussac's law is a derived corollary of Boyle's and Charles' laws and is exceedingly important when one considers compressed gases. It states that if the volume of a gas is held constant, the pressure varies directly with temperature. The preceding clinical vignette is a classic example of this relationship. Because of the fixed constraints of the volume, heating a cylinder could result in an explosion. Gay-Lussac's Law is defined as follows:

$$P_1/T_1 = P_2/T_2$$

*Clinical vignette:*

*E cylinders are constructed for a maximum pressure of 5,000 psi. Despite this, E cylinders are pressurized far below their maximum fill pressure. One may wonder why cylinders are not maximally filled. Gay-Lussac's law explains the rationale for "underfilling" cylinders. Suppose a cylinder of oxygen is placed in a truck for transport to a hospital. The cylinder is filled at 20°C, 5,000 psi (more than double the typical fill pressure of 2,200 psi). The cylinder volume will not change—it is steel and a fixed size. In transport, the environmental temperature rises to 140°F (60°C) in the trailer. What will the pressure in the cylinder become?*

---

$$5,000 \text{ psi}/293K = x/333K$$

When we solve for x (the change in pressure), we see that the new cylinder pressure will be approximately 5,700 psi. This pressure would likely rupture the cylinder.

---

## The Combined Gas Law

Individually, no single gas law can truly account for the variables that affect a gas in the environment. Boyle's, Charles' and Gay-Lussac's laws evaluate only 2 variables with one another while holding all else constant. As we know from kinetic theory and our experience in the world, pressure, volume, and temperature are often interdependent. The combined gas law allows us to see the influence each has on the others. The combined gas formula is as follows:

$$P_1V_1/T_1 = P_2V_2/T_2$$

## Avogadro's Law

Avogadro believed that at equal temperature and pressure, equal volumes of gas contain the same number of molecules regardless of their chemical nature and physical properties. In other words, the volume of gas is related to the number of molecules. Avogadro's hypothesis provides a means to quantify the *mass* of a gas. The mass of an object is a fundamental property. Mass, measured in grams, provides a measure of the object's inertia (the ability to move an object at rest). Obviously, the measurement of a gas is profoundly more difficult than that of a solid or liquid. Avogadro's law states that 1 mole of gas contains $6.02 \times 1,023$ molecules and occupies approximately 22.4 L of space.

While Avogadro's law may initially seem perplexing given the chemical and physical diversity of gases, Avogadro knew that pressure was the result of molecules of gas striking a container's walls. Furthermore, he knew that the molecules of a gas at a given temperature all have the same velocity. He reasoned that the number of molecules in equal volumes of gas must be the same. It follows that:

$$n_1/v_1 = n_2/v_2$$

where n is the number of moles of the substance. A *mole* (mol) of a substance is the weight of that substance equal to its molecular mass in atomic mass units (from the periodic table). One mole of carbon is 12 g. A mole of any material will contain the Avogadro number of molecules ($6.02 \times 10^{23}$ molecules).

At standard (S) temperature (T) of 0°C (273 K) and standard pressure (P) of 760 mm Hg and in the dry (D) state, ie, at STPD, 1 mole of an ideal gas has a volume of 22.40 L.

The usefulness of Avogadro's law is often lost in clinical practice, yet measurement of mass allows clinicians to quantify the amount of anesthetic agent and to compare the physical properties of a gas. Avogadro's law provides a means to determine the amount of liquefied gas stored in a cylinder and compare the density (mass per unit volume) of one gas with that of another.

### Clinical vignette:

*As previously stated, nitrous oxide is stored in the liquid state. As such, the pressure gauge does not describe how much nitrous oxide is contained in the cylinder. Determine how many liters of nitrous oxide are in an E cylinder of nitrous oxide that weighs 7 kg.* **Facts**: *The weight of an empty E cylinder is 5.9 kg; the molecular weight of nitrous oxide is 44 g.*

---

7 kg total cylinder weight − 5.9 kg empty weight = 1.1 kg of liquid nitrous oxide.
1,100 g (liquid nitrous oxide)/44 g (molecular weight) × 22.4 L =
50.9 L nitrous oxide

---

## Combining Laws to Form the Ideal Gas Law

Boyle, Charles, Gay-Lussac, and Avogadro define the relationship of ideal gases under a defined set of conditions. The previous discussion shows that the interrelationship among pressure, volume, temperature, and number of moles is profound. Yet to this point, the laws function in isolation. We know that the variables acting on gases do not act in utter independence. The *ideal gas law* is a synthesis of the empirical gas laws describing the relationship among pressure (P), volume (V), and temperature (T) as it relates to the mass (n = number of moles) of a gas and how these variables affect gas behavior. The ideal gas law is described as:

$$PV = nRT$$

where R is a constant of proportionality known as the ideal (or universal) gas constant, computed by

$$R = PV/nT$$

For ideal gases, R = 0.082 L • atm/mol • K. The ideal gas law notes that 1 mole of a gas occupies 22.40 L at 0°C and 1 atm of pressure.

### Clinical vignette:

*You are a part of a team to support an austere medical mission. You and your team will be required to provide no more then 20 hours of anesthesia time. You decide to have an additional 10 hours of oxygen for this mission (total 30 hours of anesthesia time). While total gas flow may vary, you anticipate 1 L/minute $O_2$ flow. Since your team will be flying to the destination, weight is a factor. Determine the minimal weight (in kg) of oxygen that you will need to take and how much it will weigh in the cylinder.* **Facts:** *molecular mass $O_2 = 32$ g/mol. Empty B-cylinder weighs 3.3 lbs.*

1. Determine the total amount of $O_2$ needed. 1 L/min x 60 min x 30 hours = 1800 L
2. n = (1 atm) (1800 L) / (0.082) (293) = 75 mol
3. 75 mol = 32 g/mol = 240 g or 2.4 kg of $O_2$
4. 3.3 lbs / 2.2 = 1.5 kg (empty cylinder)
5. 1.5 kg + 2.4 kg = 3.6 kg traveling weight

## Dalton's Law of Partial Pressures

While the previous laws or theorems explain the behavior of an individual gas, Dalton's law provides a framework to describe the mixing of gases and how they behave together. Dalton's law states that in a mixture of gases, the pressure exerted by each gas is the same as the gas would exert if it were alone in a container. Dalton's law of partial pressures shows that the total pressure exerted by a mixture of gases equals the sum of the individual pressures exerted by the constituents in the mixture. Its representative formula is as follows:

$$P_{Total} = P_1 + P_2 + P_3 \dots P_\infty$$

Dalton's work is extremely important in anesthesia, critical care, flight, and dive medicine. Whether evaluating an arterial blood gas result, deciding on an appropriate fresh gas mixture delivered via the anesthesia circuit, or observing vaporization of a liquid anesthetic, Dalton's law is continually applied. Clinicians sometimes refer to this law as the "sum of the partial pressures" law.

### Clinical vignette:

*When we exhale, we eliminate a mixture of gases from our lungs. When measuring this exhalation mixture using infrared or mass spectrometry analysis (as anesthetists routinely do in the care of their patients), it might be noted that the contribution of carbon dioxide to the total pressure of the exhaled gas is approximately 5.0%. Assuming an atmospheric pressure of 760 mm Hg (at sea level), the carbon dioxide exerts a partial pressure of 38 mm Hg (5.0%/100% × 760 mm Hg = 38 mm Hg).*

*A sedated, intubated patient in the intensive care unit is ventilated using pressure-controlled ventilation with an inspired oxygen concentration of 35%. Assuming the patient is at sea level, the $PaO_2$ could be calculated as follows: 35%/100% × 760 mm Hg = 266 mm Hg. One could ideally* *anticipate the patient's arterial blood gas value (PaO₂) to be 266 mm Hg. Obviously, Dalton's law does not account for physiologic variations in perfusion (a more likely PaO₂ ≤200 mm Hg), nor does one routinely sample arterial blood from pulmonary arterioles. These results, however, reflect the clinical usefulness of Dalton's work.*

## Adiabatic Compression and Expansion

From earlier discussion, it can be noted that changes in pressure or volume involve energy transfer and, thus, an expected change in temperature. If a gas is compressed within the walls of its container, the temperature would be expected to rise unless the compression took place very slowly. *Isothermal* means that the change in volume occurred in the absence of a temperature change.

   Adiabatic compression and expansion are changes in the volume of a container, but in which heat is neither lost nor gained from its environment (**Figure 1**). Consider an E cylinder of oxygen pressurized to 2,000 psig connected to an anesthesia machine. When the cylinder valve is opened, the pressurized oxygen moves into a delivery tube between the cylinder valve and the diaphragm of a pressure gauge, experiencing instantaneous recompression (from 2,000 psig to atmospheric pressure to 2,000 psig). There is no time for heat dissipation, and temperatures can rise to extraordinary levels. The presence of flammable materials, such as grease, oil, and dust, within the tubing can result in immediate combustion and fire. This matter is of such concern that it is recommended that cylinder valves be briefly opened before attachment to a machine (to blow out dust particles) and that cylinder valves be opened slowly to minimize recompression heat.

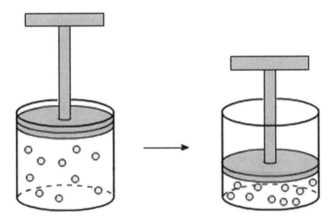

**Figure 1.** *Adiabatic compression of a gas.*

## The Joule-Thomson Effect

The Joule-Thomson effect describes a gas that is housed at a high pressure and is suddenly released into a vacuum. The molecules of the gas pull away from one another into the vacuum, losing substantial kinetic energy and speed; a fall in temperature ensues. This effect is quite pronounced and demonstrable in everyday practice by opening an E-cylinder valve quickly and noting the valve's coldness to the touch. In humid environments, one can observe misting in the path of the released gas as ambient water vapor is condensed. For a common example of this, pop off the lid of a carbonated soft drink, and note the vapor cloud and the demonstration of the Joule-Thomson effect!

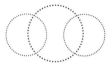

# Section II:

## *Providing Gases to Patients*

The first half of this chapter was spent reviewing kinetic theory and how properties of gases are used to deliver anesthetic gases to patients. Obviously, this is only part of the journey. A general anesthetic is achieved only when the agent reaches the brain. Gases reach their destination by bulk flow and diffusion, traveling through membranes, dissolving into blood, and, ultimately, becoming available to anesthetize a patient. The remainder of this chapter describes the movement of gas through the endotracheal tube, through the lungs, and as it dissolves into the blood.

The journey to anesthetize a patient begins as gas enters the patient's body. Providing the gas can be accomplished by spontaneous or controlled ventilation. In either case, Boyle's law describes that as the thoracic volume increases (spontaneous ventilation) or pressure outside the patient exceeds intrathoracic pressure (controlled ventilation), gas moves from high to low pressure and fills the patient's lungs. In most cases, this gas will travel through a tube. Flow through a tube (eg, a nasal cannula, an anesthetic circuit, or the trachea) is defined as a bulk flow of molecules that are forcibly propelled. The gas flows as a unit, driven by barometric pressure (spontaneous ventilation) or by an external force such as that created by a ventilator.

## The Flow of Gases Through Tubes

In the parlance of physicists, gases *and* liquids are "fluids" in that they lack rigidity, they flow under certain conditions, and their shape depends on the container in which they are housed. Many factors combine to predict and influence flow. One consideration is whether flow occurs through a tube (diameter < length) or an orifice (diameter > length), the latter ideally having negligible length. The nature of the flow may be laminar (in which fluid molecules move in an orderly manner in pathways parallel to the tube's walls) or turbulent (in which flow paths are chaotic and at various angles to the tube's walls; **Figure** 2).

*Laminar flow* is a streamlined movement of fluid that typically occurs at lower velocities. In general, fluid and particles move parallel with one another, avoiding cross-current motion, eddies, and swirls. The Reynolds number, which characterizes laminar flow, is a dimensionless expression derived from the ratio of pressure and shearing force through a tube. Although opinions vary, laminar flow is characterized by a Reynolds number less then 2,100. In contrast with laminar flow, *turbulent flow* is characterized as chaotic movement of fluid that has rapid changes in pressure and velocity. As such, the fluid moves slowly because of congestion. Turbulent flow has a nonlinear relationship between flow and pressure. In other words, the addition of pressure does not result in a proportional increase in flow. There is no exact Reynolds value that denotes turbulent flow (often cited as >4,000). What is clear, however, is that fluids with a Reynolds number greater than 2,100 experience an increase in friction as they move. There is a transitional period in which laminar and turbulent flow converge. As friction increases, fluid movement is worsened and progresses to turbulent flow.

The flow of fluids (as gases or liquid medications) is a mainstay of anesthesia practice. It governs the rate and administration of intravenous (IV) fluids and the ability to adequately ventilate an intubated patient. It is a priority to administer fluids with the greatest control and precision. Anesthetists depend on, manipulate, and advantage themselves of fluid flow in a wide range of situations. A discussion of laws describing flow follows.

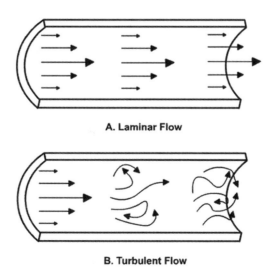

A. Laminar Flow

B. Turbulent Flow

**Figure 2.** *Laminar versus turbulent flow.*

## The Hagen-Poiseuille Equation

The Hagen-Poiseuille equation, commonly referred to as Poiseuille's law, defines laminar flow through a tube (such as an endotracheal tube or IV catheter) and how this flow is affected by the tube's length and radius, the change in pressure, and the viscosity of the fluid. The Hagen Poiseuille's law is derived as follows:

$$Q = \pi r^4/8\eta \times \Delta P/L$$

where Q is flow, $\pi$ is pi or 3.14, r is the radius of the tube, $\eta$ is the viscosity of the fluid, $\Delta P$ is the change in pressure, and L is the length of the tube.

The Hagen-Poiseuille equation demonstrates 3 essential conventions to fluid administration: (1) Flow is directly proportional to a change of pressure and radial size to the fourth power. (2) Flow is inversely proportional to viscosity of the fluid and length of the tube. (3) Denser fluids have a tendency for turbulent flow.

Of these conventions, radial diameter has the greatest influence on flow. Importantly, halving the radius of a tube will increase the resistance by *16* times.

The Hagen-Poiseuille equation explains many clinical scenarios intimately relevant to anesthesia ranging from a patient with asthma who has difficulty moving air to administering fluid (blood vs crystalloid) to a bleeding, hypovolemic patient.

*Clinical vignette:*

*A patient is admitted to the operating room from the emergency department with a grade 4 (severe) splenic injury. The patient arrives with a 20-gauge, 1-inch IV catheter that is infusing lactated Ringer's solution. You promptly insert a 14-gauge, 1-inch IV catheter to assist with the resuscitation. Determine the difference in flow rates between the 2 IV catheters.*

*A 20-gauge IV catheter has a radius of 0.5 mm. When applied to the Hagen-Poiseuille equation, we see that a 20-gauge IV catheter, at standard temperature and pressure, infusing crystalloid (viscosity of 0.01 cm³/s) will infuse 0.13 cm³/s. When we compare that with the 14-gauge IV catheter (radius 1.0 mm) under the same conditions, the flow rate increases to 2.1 cm³/s. This is a 16-fold increase in flow! This scenario considers only the radius of the catheter. Unfortunately, larger bore IV catheters rarely are 1 inch (typically to ensure that rapidly infusing IV catheters stay in place). Let's compare the flow rates of a 20-gauge, 1-inch IV catheter with a 16-gauge (radius 0.75 mm), 1.25-inch catheter, both infusing crystalloid. In this instance, the flow rate of the 16-gauge IV catheter is 0.523 cm³/s. Although the flow rate remains greater for the 16-gauge catheter, it has only 4 times the flow of the 20-gauge catheter. Slight variations in length, 0.25 inches, can produce significant clinical implications.*

## Bernoulli's Theorem

As gas molecules move through an endotracheal tube, they arrive at the trachea, a large tubular structure. Pressure flowing through the trachea will vary according to the cross-sectional diameter. As the gas moves further down the trachea, it branches off to smaller generations of bronchi that constitute the peripheral branches of the lung. In pressure-volume relationships, we understand that liquids flow from high to low pressure. Typically, low pressure exists in a larger volume. Smaller airways seem to contradict this concept. Bernoulli's theorem solves this dilemma and describes the movement of gases through tapering tubes.

As discussed, the trachea bifurcates and splits to become smaller airways. These transitions can be visualized as a tube that narrows at the end. As fluid flows through this tube, the pressure is lowest and the velocity is greatest at the point of greatest narrowing (**Figure 3**). One can think of this concept as the fluid being "squeezed" through the narrowing and rapidly moving through the tube. Imagine you are in a movie theatre with only 1 exit and someone yells "fire." The bulk of moviegoers will rapidly move toward the exit. Movement will be slower in the back of the line and move quickly at the front. The door creates a narrowing. The mass behind the door (near the fire) is congested, slowly moving. Pressure is higher at this end of the evacuation line (for many reasons) because many are cramped in a space. As you reach the exit and point of narrowing (much like a bottleneck), the flow of evacuees will be rapid as others quickly follow, almost pulled through the door.

The same occurs with gas molecules as they move toward the peripheral lung. Because this flow is laminar, energy must remain constant and low. Because energy remains constant through the tube, kinetic energy increases as molecules flow at the narrowing, and potential energy, created by pressure, decreases at the larger section. As such, there is no change in total energy. Bernoulli's theorem does not apply in conditions of considerable turbulence or in the case of high viscosity. This makes sense if we relate it to our movie example. If the crowd begins to panic and push, people will not be able to evacuate quickly. Turbulence (pushing and fighting) will occur at the exit, causing flow to slow.

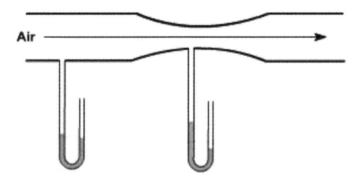

**Figure 3.** *A Venturi tube: As air flows left to right, the diameter of the tube narrows, then widens. As the air flows through the narrow diameter, the flow of air increases. As the air flow increases, the pressure decreases, as shown by the differing heights of liquid in the open U tubes.*

## The Venturi Principle

Venturi built on Bernoulli's observations in designing a model in which a sidearm was placed at a right angle at the point of maximum constriction of the primary tube, thus allowing another fluid to be entrained and mixed with the original fluid traversing the tube (**Figure 4**). Venturi noted that a drop in pressure occurred at the narrowest point, allowing the entrainment of a gas or fluid via a sidearm tube.

Consider the electronic ventilator apparatus used on an anesthesia machine. The drive gas used to power the bellows is a combination of 100% oxygen from the pipeline or cylinder and ambient air. An air injector increases the volume of drive gas acting on the bellows assembly. Ambient air becomes part of the drive gas through an unrestricted port, thus economizing the use of pure oxygen.

As oxygen flows toward the bellows assembly, it is forced through a narrow aperture, causing a significant increase in the velocity of the oxygen flow. The increased velocity causes a pressure drop as oxygen enters the entrainment port (Bernoulli effect). This pressure drop draws room air toward an entrainment port and increases the volume of the drive gas flow. This process illustrates the Venturi principle.

In addition to the previous example, Venturi applications in the field of anesthesia care abound. Consider an air-entrainment mask (known as a Ventimask after its Venturi-based operation) delivering a preselected fraction of inspired oxygen by entraining room air into an oxygen flow directed at a patient. Mechanical aerosol delivery systems also rely on the Venturi principle for their operation.

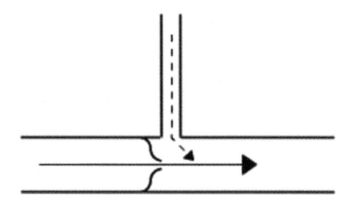

**Figure 4.** *The high velocity primary flow (solid arrow) creates a subatmospheric pressure at the point of narrowing, allowing entrainment of a second stream of flow (dashed arrow).*

## The Flow of Gases to the Blood

Gases move from an area of high pressure or concentration to an area of lower pressure or concentration, a phenomenon termed *differential pressure gradient.* This phenomenon accounts for a gas leaving a pressurized cylinder on its way to a patient's nasal cannula, carbon dioxide moving from the pulmonary capillaries to the alveoli, and oxygen diffusing from the arterial blood on its way to an individual mitochondrion. Gases ultimately seek equilibration or uniform distribution (**Figure 5**).

Inspired gas moves from the endotracheal tube through the airways to the alveoli. The alveoli are the final branching of the respiratory tree and are the primary gas-exchange units of the lung. The alveolar membrane is a gas-blood barrier between the alveolar space and the pulmonary capillaries. The alveolar membrane is extremely thin. Gas traverses the 0.5-µm barrier by passive diffusion down a concentration gradient. To reach the blood, gas must diffuse through the alveolar epithelium, a thin interstitial space, and the capillary endothelium; carbon dioxide and other gases follow the reverse course to reach the alveoli.

*Diffusion* is the movement of molecules from an area of high concentration to one of lower concentration due to the random molecular motion of the molecules. There are several laws related to the movement of molecules through a tube or space. These laws, which have great importance in the field of anesthesia, include Fick's diffusion law, Graham's law of effusion, and Henry's law.

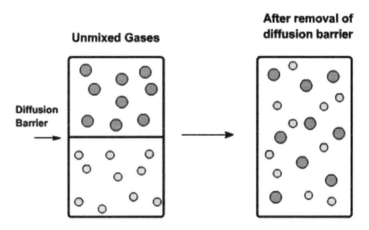

**Figure 5.** *Gases diffuse within a container until a uniform distribution is achieved.*

## Fick's Diffusion Law

Once gas flows to the alveoli, it randomly moves around the space and begins to diffuse. Diffusion is a process in which molecules move through pores and channels within a membrane. Fick's law states that the rate of diffusion across a unit area is greatest where the concentration changes most rapidly with respect to distance. In other words, the rate of diffusion across a membrane is proportional to the following: (1) the partial pressure gradient of substance on either side of the membrane (high concentration moves to low concentration), (2) the solubility of the gas with respect to the membrane, and (3) the inverse of the thickness of the membrane. Diffusion is the primary mechanism for the delivery of oxygen and nutrients into cells and for the elimination of waste products. If we consider the travel of oxygen, we know it flows to the alveolar membrane. Since the amount of oxygen delivered in anesthesia is greater than the amount in room air, the concentration gradient quickly builds in the alveoli. As gas diffuses across the membrane, it is quickly bound to hemoglobin. The bound hemoglobin flows away, in relation to cardiac output, reducing the capillary concentration of oxygen in the vicinity and causing further diffusion from the alveoli.

While concentration gradients are the primary driving force for diffusion, membrane thickness is a rate-limiting factor. For example, patients with acute respiratory distress syndrome have a protein-rich, fluid-filled alveolar membrane. They are hypoxic because their alveolar membrane is edematous and thickened. In this case, gas must diffuse not only through a membrane, but also through fluid. Diffusion does not occur or is limited, despite the substantial concentration gradient on either side of the membrane.

## Graham's Law of Effusion

Although the alveolar membrane is permeable, it provides an obstacle for the gas to overcome. Effusion is related to diffusion. *Effusion* is the process in which individual molecules flow through pores and channels without colliding with other molecules. In 1828, Thomas Graham noted that the rate of effusion of 2 gases varies inversely with the square root of their molecular weight. He noted that smaller molecules effused faster than larger molecules. Graham's law is described as follows:

$$\frac{ER_1}{ER_2} = \sqrt{\frac{MW_2}{MW_1}}$$

where ER is the effusion rate and MW is the molecular weight of the gas. Anesthetists are concerned not only with the diffusion of particles with respect to each other, but also, more specifically, with the effusion of gas particles through a vessel or cellular membrane. As the density or mass of a molecule increases, it tends to effuse more slowly. While this seems rather clear, it is hardly this simple.

Carbon dioxide has a molecular weight of 44 g, and oxygen has a molecular weight of 32 g. Based on Graham's law, oxygen should diffuse faster. Yet, we see the opposite clinically. In fact, carbon dioxide is 20 times more diffusible than oxygen. This discrepancy can be explained when one considers the medium through which the gases are passing. Graham's law describes only a membrane. Oxygen diffuses faster through the alveolar membrane. Yet the membrane is only a small portion of the journey. The interstitial space is a fluid-filled matrix. Graham's law is unidimensional and does not consider the solubility of the gas. While size is a factor, solubility has a far larger role, thus accounting for the faster diffusion of carbon dioxide relative to oxygen.

## Henry's Law

In 1803, William Henry described how the total number of gas molecules dissolved in a liquid varies directly with the partial pressure of a gas overlying the liquid, assuming that temperature remains constant and no chemical interaction occurs between the gas and liquid. A simple way to illustrate Henry's law is that if the partial pressure of a gas is doubled, then on average, twice as many molecules will hit the liquid surface. Therefore, twice as many particles will be captured in the solution. Henry's law helps to predict the amount of gas that will go into the solution. Like Graham's law, however, gas solubility will also affect the rate. Henry's law describes the clinical phenomenon of overpressurizing a vaporizer to rapidly increase anesthetic depth. If the partial pressure of the anesthetic gas is increased (such as 2% or 5% sevoflurane), the solubility of the anesthetic in the blood increases. Henry's law also is fundamental to the efficacy of hyperbaric oxygen therapy.

Henry's law aside, there is no foolproof or simple formula for predicting how soluble a particular gas will be in a liquid except to say that, generally, the more easily liquefied gases tend to be more soluble. As temperature increases (suggesting generalized molecular agitation), there is a tendency for liquids to transition to gas molecules. This is generally true, unless a chemical reaction between the gas and liquid occurs. Clinically, at equivalent, inspired, anesthetic tensions, less gas will dissolve in the blood of a febrile patient than in a patient with normal body temperature. During hypothermic bypass, more anesthetic gas is dissolved in the patient's blood than at normothermia.

## Solubility Coefficients: Cornerstones of Gas Uptake and Distribution

Manipulating the partial pressure tension of a gas in the brain controls the course of an inhalational anesthetic. Anesthetists use sophisticated technology, as well as science and art, in presenting these drugs to the brain via the lungs and bloodstream. The solubility of an agent in the blood and tissues is one of several key factors involved. There are 2 closely allied, yet distinct, measures of solubility that determine how much of a gaseous or vaporized agent is taken up by the body.

The Bunsen ($\alpha$) and Ostwald ($\lambda$) coefficients are useful indexes of gas solubility in fluids. The $\lambda$ coefficient is more commonly used because it is specific to blood/gas (or tissue/gas) coefficients at ambient pressure and physiologic temperature. The $\lambda$ coefficient describes the relative ability of a gas to dissolve into a liquid independent of pressure. It is always given as a blood/gas or tissue/gas ratio, never the reverse. In general, the solubility of a gas is proportional to the tissue uptake.

Of greater clinical importance to anesthetists is the partition coefficients. These coefficients are evaluated in liquid and gas forms (eg, blood-gas partition coefficient) or as liquids (eg, oil-blood partition coefficient). Partition coefficients (clinically described in blood-gas partition coefficients) indicate the behavior of anesthetic gases as they enter and exit the body. These coefficients describe the solubility of an agent and ultimately have substantial influence on the pharmacokinetics of inhaled anesthetic agents. To illustrate, halothane, with a blood/gas coefficient of 2.4, is considerably more soluble than desflurane, which has a blood/gas coefficient of slightly less than that of nitrous oxide.

## Conclusion

Molecular behavior is a result of the stimuli in the environment occupied by the molecules. The variability of temperature, pressure, and volume changes the dynamics of interactions. Gas molecules move from high to low pressure, their flow a function of the structures through which they pass. As gases reach the patient, they must overcome membrane barriers and dissolve into fluids. Only then will they be available to provide anesthesia.

Applications of the physical principles that govern the behavior of gases abound in the care of anesthetized patients. These principles permeate practice from the point the gas enters the anesthesia machine until it reaches the patient. **Figure 6** summarizes how these principles impact practice. This chapter has reviewed the relevant laws that provide a scientific framework for describing and predicting the behavior of gases that anesthetists use daily in clinical practice.

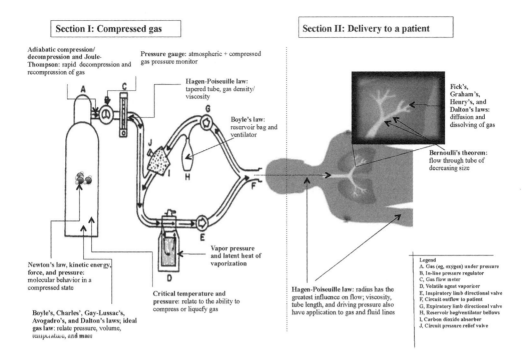

**Figure 6.** *Clinical and practical examples of the gas laws.*

## Suggested Reading

Adriani J. *Chemistry and Physics of Anesthesia.* 2nd ed. Springfield, IL: CC Thomas; 1962.

Davis PD, Parbrook GD, Kenny GNC. *Basic Physics and Measurement in Anaesthesia.* 5th ed. Edinburgh, Scotland: Butterworth-Heinemann; 2003.

Hemmings HC Jr, Hopkins PM, eds. *Foundations of Anesthesia: Basic and Clinical Sciences.* London, England: Mosby Elsevier; 2006

Lumb AB. *Nunn's Applied Respiratory Physiology.* 7th ed. New York, NY: Churchill-Livingston; 2010.

Ohanian HC. *The Principles of Physics.* New York, NY: WW Norton; 1994.

Zajtchuk R, Grande CM, eds. *Anesthesia and Perioperative Care of the Combat Casualty.* Washington, DC: Office of the Surgeon General at TMM; 1995.

## Discussion Topics

1. Describe the behavior of compressed gases as they relate to Newton's laws of motion.

2. Define the latent heat of vaporization and its role in the vaporization of gases.

3. Define and discuss the empirical gas laws (Boyle's, Charles', Gay-Lussac's, and the combined gas law) and how they relate to temperature, pressure, and volume.

4. Discuss the role of gases stored as compressed liquids and how their physical properties affect pressure gauge readings.

5. Compare and contrast laminar and turbulent flow of gases, and describe how this relates to the flow of gases.

6. Discuss how a tube's length and radius, the change in pressure, and the fluid viscosity affect the flow of fluids.

7. Describe Fick's law of diffusion and the relationship of Fick's law to Graham's and Henry's laws.

# Chapter 2

# The Basics of Organic Chemistry
*by Cynthia S. Dowd, PhD, and Lemont B. Kier, PhD*

Nearly all drugs and medicines are organic materials. The term *organic* refers to the nature of the atoms that make up a substance. Organic materials are made predominantly of carbon and hydrogen atoms. Similarly, our bodies and much of our food are made mostly of carbon and hydrogen atoms. We are, in fact, organic (carbon-based) life forms. Metals, such as iron, copper, and magnesium, by contrast, are not made of carbon and hydrogen and are, therefore, not organic. Metals are inorganic. Machines and materials that are made of metals are inorganic as well.

Why does this organic versus inorganic distinction matter? Most of the drugs that nurse anesthetists administer are *compounds*–chemicals containing atoms connected by chemical bonds. The properties of these drugs are determined by the types of atoms and chemical bonds. In organic compounds, the carbon and hydrogen atoms can be bonded to each other, but also can be bonded to other atoms, such as oxygen, nitrogen, or a halogen. These atoms can alter the function of the molecule dramatically and influence its biological activity. Knowing what types of atoms make up a compound and the effect of certain atoms on a particular biological system enables the design of drugs that will have the desired effects.

Most drugs are organic molecules: They have a skeleton composed mainly of carbon atoms and may include other atoms such as oxygen and nitrogen. The carbon skeleton can have many shapes–linear, branched, and cyclic. The carbon skeleton contributes to the overall shape of the molecule. Because the skeleton of an organic molecule is made mostly of carbon atoms, the proper names of these molecules are based on their carbon skeletons. The noncarbon atoms that are part of the molecule are included in the category of functional groups. As the name implies, functional groups are often responsible for much of the behavior of the molecule, as it reacts with other molecules and as it interacts with its target biological system.

Before it is possible to understand how individual drug molecules work in a biological system, it is necessary to understand several basic chemical concepts. The first concept is a description of the types of bonds that are formed between atoms. The types of bonds in a molecule affect the physical properties, as well as the biological activity, of the molecule. The second concept involves functional groups. The functional groups will be described with regard to their chemical properties, as well as their water solubility, nomenclature, and general routes of metabolism by the body. Combinations of functional groups form the basis of different structural classes of drugs. The last concept is the nature and importance of certain physical properties of drug molecules. This concept is important for the understanding of the physical parameters that affect the activity of drugs, including anesthetics, and their potential interactions with other prescribed medicines. General knowledge of particular functional groups also makes it easier to remember certain characteristics of particular drug classes. Later chapters in the text will describe the functional groups and drug properties combined into drug molecules that have specific biological activities.

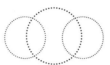

## Structure and Bonding

Several types of bonds can occur between 2 atoms. The different bonds vary in strength and length. Also, not all types of atoms can form all types of bonds. In this text, our discussion on the types of bonds will cover most bonding forms between 2 molecules. Chapter 5 describes noncovalent interactions between molecules, including hydrogen bonds, ionic bonds, and van der Waals forces. The present chapter focuses on covalent bonds.

## Covalent Bonds

A *covalent bond* is a shared pair of electrons between 2 atoms. These electrons can originate from 1 atom, or 1 electron can originate from each of the 2 atoms. The 2 electrons in the bond are attracted to both atomic nuclei and are shared between the 2 atoms. Two atoms share the electrons because atoms (other than hydrogen and helium) are most stable when surrounded by 8 electrons (an octet), which means that an atom with a full octet of electrons has lower energy (is more stable) than one without a full octet. The electrons surrounding the nucleus of an atom are contained in orbitals. An *orbital* is the space around the nucleus of an atom in which an electron orbits. The shape of an orbital is determined by the mathematical probability of the location of that electron around the nucleus. Each orbital contains a maximum of 2 electrons. When 2 electrons are in an orbital, the orbital is considered full, and the electrons are "paired." A covalent bond can also be thought of as the overlap of orbitals surrounding the atomic nuclei.

It is important to understand the following points:

1. Different atoms can support different numbers of covalent bonds.

2. More than 1 covalent bond can be formed between 2 nonhydrogen atoms.

The diversity of atoms and multiplicity of bonds give the tremendous variety of structures available in organic chemistry.

## Covalent Bonds in Different Atoms

The atomic structure of an individual atom determines the number of covalent bonds it can form. The number of covalent bonds formed is equal to the number of valence electrons minus the number of unshared electrons of an atom. *Valence electrons* are the electrons that appear in the outermost shell of electrons surrounding the nucleus of an atom. They include lone pair electrons and unpaired (bonding) electrons. *Lone pair* electrons are 2 electrons in the same orbital. Because an orbital with 2 electrons is full, these electrons participate in covalent bonding much less than do single electrons. From the number of covalent bonds formed by an atom, one can tell how many unpaired valence electrons the atom has in a particular molecule. For example, a halogen (ie, chlorine, bromine, fluorine, iodine) has 1 unpaired electron. Therefore, a halogen atom can form a maximum of 1 covalent bond with another atom. **Table 1** lists the common elements in organic chemistry and the maximum number of covalent bonds that each can form.

## Multiple Covalent Bonds

Table 1 shows that several atoms can form more than 1 covalent bond. Because of the nature of covalent bonding, however, it is possible for an atom to form more than 1 covalent bond with another atom. Carbon will be used as an example.

When 1 unpaired electron from carbon A and 1 unpaired electron from carbon B are shared, a covalent bond is formed. This bond is called a *single bond* and is indicated by a line drawn between the 2 atoms: $C_A-C_B$. Ethane ($CH_3-CH_3$) is an example of a compound having a single bond between 2 carbon atoms. Each carbon atom in ethane forms 4 bonds: 1 to a carbon atom and 3 to each of the attached hydrogen atoms. A single covalent bond containing 2 shared electrons is also called a *sigma* ($\sigma$) *bond*. The simplest form of a $\sigma$ bond is the overlap of two s orbitals.

**Table 1.** *The number of covalent bonds usually formed by common organic atoms.*

| Atom | Number of Covalent Bonds |
|---|---|
| **C** (carbon) | 4 |
| **N** (nitrogen) | 3 or 4 |
| **O** (oxygen) | 2 |
| **H** (hydrogen) | 1 |
| **S** (sulfur) | 2, 4, or 6 |
| **Cl** (chlorine) | 1 |
| **F** (fluorine) | 1 |
| **Br** (bromine) | 1 |
| **I** (iodine) | 1 |

Certain atoms (generally C, N, O, S) may also form double bonds (**Figure 1**). A *double bond* is 4 electrons shared between 2 atoms. In a double bond, 2 of the electrons form a σ bond, and the other 2 electrons form a pi (π) bond. The simplest organic molecule with a double bond is ethylene, $CH_2=CH_2$ (also called ethene). The bond between the 2 carbon atoms in ethylene is a double bond and is indicated by a double line (=) between the 2 carbon atoms.

Two atoms may also form a *triple bond,* which is 6 electrons shared between 2 atoms. In a triple bond, 2 of the electrons form a σ bond, and the other 4 electrons form 2 π bonds. The simplest organic molecule with a triple bond is acetylene, HC≡CH (also called ethyne). The bond between the 2 carbon atoms in acetylene is a triple bond and is indicated by a triple line (≡) between the 2 carbon atoms.

**Covalent bond formation in Cl₂.**  **sigma bond**

**p orbital overlap**    **double bond**    **electron delocalization**

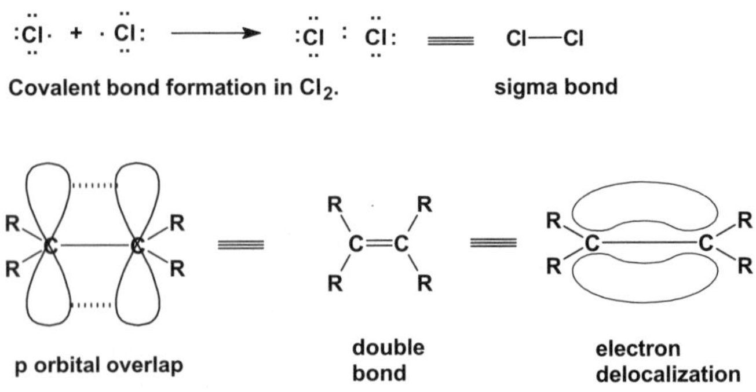

**Figure 1.** *A covalent bond is the sharing of 2 electrons between 2 atoms. Chlorine atoms form a σ bond with each other to make Cl₂. In ethane, a pi (π) bond is formed from the overlap of p orbitals. Note that a π bond can be formed only after a σ bond is already present between 2 atoms. Electrons are free to travel (delocalize) between both atoms of the π bond.*

Double and triple bonds are due to the overlap of p orbitals, which contain π electrons. Other common double and triple bonds include C=O, C=N, C=S, C≡N, and S=O. **Figure 2** shows the bonding patterns of several common molecules.

The strength of a chemical bond is measured by the amount of energy required to break it. Although the exact strength of a bond is dependent on the particular atoms forming it, typical bond energies are useful to know. Breaking a carbon-carbon single bond requires about 70 to 90 kcal/mol of energy (approximately 348 kJ/mol). Breaking a double bond between 2 carbon atoms requires about 145 to 160 kcal/mol (approximately 612 kJ/mol). Breaking a carbon-carbon triple bond requires still more energy: 190 to 230 kcal/mol (approximately 837 kJ/mol).

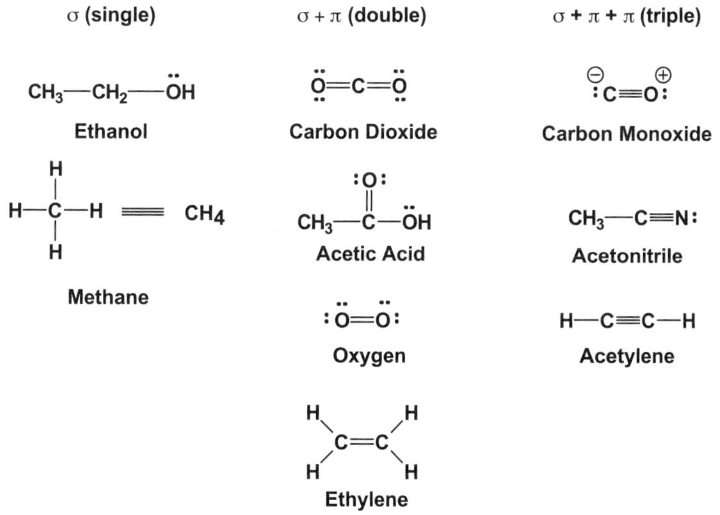

σ (single)          σ + π (double)          σ + π + π (triple)

$CH_3$—$CH_2$—$\ddot{O}H$          $\ddot{O}$=C=$\ddot{O}$          $^{\ominus}\!\!:\!C$≡$O\!:^{\oplus}$

**Ethanol**          **Carbon Dioxide**          **Carbon Monoxide**

$$H—\underset{\underset{H}{|}}{\overset{\overset{H}{|}}{C}}—H \;\equiv\; CH_4$$

$$CH_3—\overset{\overset{:O:}{||}}{C}—\ddot{O}H$$          $CH_3$—C≡N:

**Methane**          **Acetic Acid**          **Acetonitrile**

:Ö=Ö:          H—C≡C—H

**Oxygen**          **Acetylene**

$$\underset{\underset{H}{}}{\overset{\overset{H}{}}{C}}=\underset{H}{\overset{H}{C}}$$

**Ethylene**

**Figure 2.** *Common molecules with single, double, and triple bonds.*

Some useful points to remember are the following:
• A multiple bond is almost always stronger than a single bond.
• A double bond is always stronger than a single bond between the same 2 atoms.
• A triple bond is always stronger than a double bond between the same 2 atoms.

An important detail to note is that the strength of a double bond is less than twice the strength of a single bond. Based on the average strengths, one would expect that it would require 696 kJ/mol ($2 \times 348$) to break a double bond; however, the actual energy required is 612 kJ/mol. This means that the second bond of the double bond (ie, the π bond) is itself not as strong as a single bond. Although the double bond is stronger than a single bond overall, the π bond of the double bond is not as strong as the σ bond of the single bond. Because the π bond is not as strong as the σ bond, the π bond is usually more reactive than the σ bond. This is reflected in the metabolism of certain drugs containing a double bond in which metabolic enzymes functionalize the double bond of the drug but not the single bond.

Even though 2 electrons are shared in a covalent bond, they may not always be shared equally between the 2 atoms. When the 2 electrons in a covalent bond are shared unequally between the 2 atoms, a dipole exists. A *dipole* is a molecule, or part of a molecule, with a polarized, covalent bond, such that the electrons of the bond surround one atomic nucleus more than the other. In this situation, the atom surrounded by increased electron density has a slight negative charge, while the atom with less electron density has a slight positive charge. Dipoles exist when atoms of different electronegativities are bonded to each other. In these cases, the more electronegative atom of the bond has increased electron density surrounding it and has a slightly negative charge. Examples of groups that are dipoles include C=O, C–O, C–F, and C–N.

## Functional Groups

The structures of organic molecules can be very different. Although organic compounds are based on a skeleton made of carbon atoms, the additional atoms attached to the skeleton provide the molecule with different properties, functionality, and, often, biological activity. The additional atoms are called *functional groups,* and their properties influence the overall properties of the molecule on which they are located. Because there are many types of functional groups, the structural variety of organic compounds is endless. The names and properties of the most common functional groups and examples of molecules in which they appear are discussed. The following functional groups are covered in this chapter:

| | | |
|---|---|---|
| Alkanes | Alkenes | Alkynes |
| Aromatics | Alcohols | Phenols |
| Ethers | Thiols/Thioethers | Amines |
| Aldehydes | Ketones | Carboxylic Acids |
| Esters | Amides | Sulfonamides |

An important aspect of the structure of a molecule relates to how the body will degrade the molecule on consumption. The body has specific enzymatic pathways that break down most of the molecules encountered, from food or drugs. There are 2 parts, or phases, of metabolism. Phase 1 reactions are involved in making the foreign molecule more polar. These reactions typically oxidize the atoms already present in the molecule. Phase 2 reactions begin with the polar molecule and conjugate it to other (also polar) molecules. These conjugation reactions give the molecule "tags" that assist the body in excretion. The general metabolism of each functional group is discussed in the following sections.

By knowing and understanding the general metabolism of different functional groups, clinicians can more easily understand the metabolism of particular pharmaceuticals. This knowledge is of particular importance to nurse anesthetists for several reasons, including the following: The rate of onset and duration of action of an anesthetic agent are directly affected by its metabolism. Also, the metabolism of other medicines may affect the activity of the anesthetic agent. As an introduction to the metabolic routes encountered by drug molecules, the most common routes of metabolism (and their products) are included in each functional group description that follows. Understanding these basic reactions will facilitate learning the metabolic fate of a drug once the functional groups are put together.

# Alkanes (C–C)

When a molecule contains only carbon and hydrogen atoms, and the carbon atoms are bonded together by only single (σ) bonds, the molecule is called an *alkane*. In a carbon-carbon σ bond, there is little separation of charge or delocalization of electrons because there is essentially no difference in electronegativity between the carbons and/or hydrogens. Similarly, there is little difference in electronegativity between a carbon and its attached hydrogen. Because an alkane has no delocalized electrons or large electronegativity differences among its atoms, it is a nonpolar molecule. Furthermore, because it cannot bond with water (through hydrogen bonding or dipole-dipole interactions; see Chapter 5), an alkane is not very soluble in water. Alkanes are hydrophobic ("water fearing"). Alkanes are also described as lipophilic ("lipid loving"). The types of alkanes (cyclic, straight chain, and branched) are shown in **Figure 3**.

Alkanes or alkyl groups in a molecule can be metabolized by oxidation of the ω-1 carbon atom. The term ω-1 refers to the penultimate, or next to last, atom in a chain. **Figure 4** shows how a generic alkane would be metabolized by this mechanism. An alternative, minor route of alkane metabolism is ω oxidation, in which the last carbon atom in a chain is oxidized. When an alkane is halogenated, such as in halothane gas, the bond between the carbon and halogen atoms is broken, leading to oxidation of the carbon atom. Metabolism of these molecules is often carried out by the $P_{450}$ enzymes. The $P_{450}$ metabolizing enzymes are responsible for a substantial portion of drug metabolism.

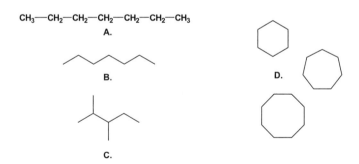

$$CH_3-CH_2-CH_2-CH_2-CH_2-CH_2-CH_3$$
**A.**

**B.**

**C.**

**D.**

**Figure 3.** *Types of alkanes. A, Alkanes can be written by naming each carbon atom, as in this representation of n-heptane. B, A shorter version of n-heptane in which each joint/end point represents a carbon atom. C and D, Alkanes can be branched structures (C), such as in 2,3-dimethyl-pentane, or cyclized (D), such as in cyclohexane (top), cycloheptane (right), and cyclooctane (bottom).*

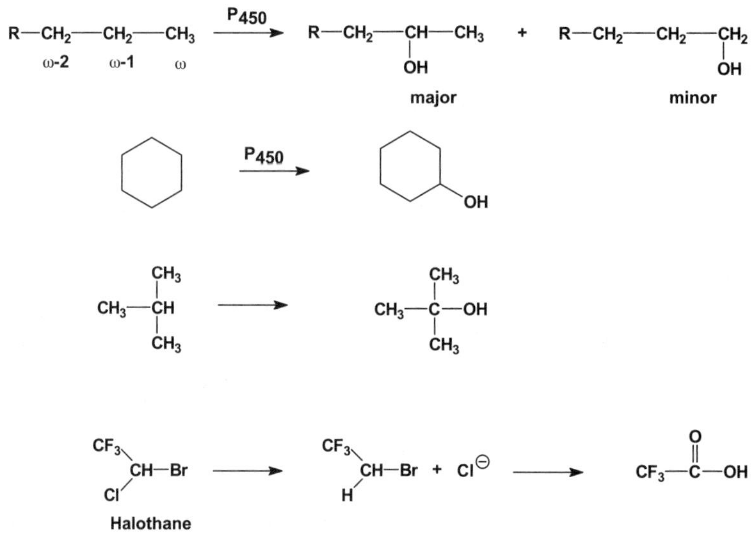

**Figure 4.** *Metabolism of alkanes. The predominant route of metabolism for an alkane is oxidation of the penultimate, or ω-1, carbon atom. Halogenated alkanes, such as halothane, are metabolized by removal of the halogens and oxidation of the remaining carbon atom(s).*

Organic molecules are named by referring to the arrangement of carbon atoms. Alkanes, the simplest organic molecules made from carbon and hydrogen atoms, form the basis for naming organic molecules. The system of correctly naming a molecule is called *nomenclature*. The bonding structure of a molecule can be completely described by its molecular name.

Alkanes are named based on the number of carbon atoms in the molecule. In all organic nomenclature, a prefix indicates the number of carbon atoms and a suffix refers to the class of molecules to which the compound belongs. In the case of alkanes, the compounds belong to the alkane family and, therefore, contain the "-ane" suffix from alkane. **Table 2** gives examples of simple alkanes and their proper names.

In an alkane, each carbon atom makes 4 covalent σ (single) bonds to 4 other atoms. These bonds can be to 4 atoms that are the same, such as in methane ($CH_4$) in which the carbon atom is covalently bonded to 4 hydrogen atoms. Alternatively, the carbon atom of an alkane can be covalently bonded to 4 different atoms. For example, 2-butanol contains a carbon atom (carbon-2) that has 1 covalent bond to each: a hydrogen atom, a hydroxyl group, a methyl group (-$CH_3$), and an ethyl group (-$CH_2CH_3$) (**Figure 5**). Although the methyl and ethyl groups both involve a carbon atom bonded to carbon-2, the groups themselves are different. When a carbon atom is bonded to 4 distinctly different groups of atoms, it is called a *stereogenic center*. A molecule is *chiral* when it is not superimposable onto its mirror image.

**Table 2.** *Common alkanes.*

| Structure | Name | Prefix/ No. of Carbon Atoms |
|---|---|---|
| $CH_3$-$CH_3$ | Ethane | eth/2 |
| $CH_3$-$CH_2$-$CH_3$ | Propane | prop/3 |
| $CH_3$-CH-$CH_3$ <br> $\quad$ $CH_3$ | | 2-Methyl-propane |
| $CH_3$-$CH_2$-$CH_2$-$CH_3$ | n-Butane | but/4 |
| $CH_3$-$CH_2$-$CH_2$-$CH_2$-$CH_3$ | n-Pentane | pent/5 |
| $CH_3$-$CH_2$-$CH_2$-$CH_2$-$CH_2$-$CH_3$ | n-Hexane | hex/6 |
| $CH_3$-$(CH_2)_5$-$CH_3$ | n-Heptane | hept/7 |
| $CH_3$-$(CH_2)_6$-$CH_3$ | n-Octane | oct/8 |
| $CH_3$-$(CH_2)_7$-$CH_3$ | n-Nonane | non/9 |
| $CH_3$-$(CH_2)_8$-$CH_3$ | n-Decane | dec/10 |

Names are formed by combining a prefix (indicating the number of carbon atoms) and the -ane suffix (from the alkane family). An "n" before a name indicates that the structure is a linear straight chain of singly bonded carbon atoms.

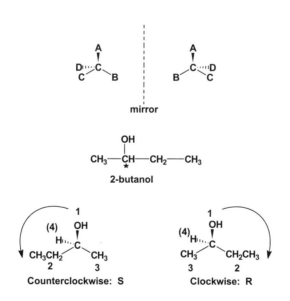

**Figure 5.** *Determining the stereochemistry at a stereogenic center. A molecule is chiral when 4 different substituents are attached to a single carbon atom. 2-Butanol, which has a stereogenic carbon atom at position 2, can be written in the R (clockwise) or the S (counterclockwise) configuration.*

A chiral molecule has a unique geometry defined by the positions of the atoms attached to the stereogenic carbon. Using 2-butanol as an example, each of the 4 groups bonded to carbon-2 points to the 4 corners of a tetrahedron. Depending on which groups are adjacent to each other, the molecule will have different properties. The property most closely associated with chirality is the rotation of plane polarized light. All chiral molecules (ie, with a stereogenic center) will rotate the plane of polarized light. The extent to which this rotation occurs is a unique property of the specific chiral molecule. This property (in addition to melting point, boiling point, etc) is a critical one that is used to determine the identity of an unknown substance and the purity of a known substance. Furthermore, the precise name and structure of a molecule cannot be known without first knowing the configuration of each group around a stereogenic center.

How is the location of the groups around a stereogenic carbon defined? First, there is a way of drawing these molecules that conveys their geometry. Atoms pointed toward the viewer are connected to the stereogenic carbon by a bond that looks like a solid wedge. Conversely, atoms pointed away from the viewer are connected to the carbon by a dashed wedge. These symbols are accepted ways of representing the orientation of groups around a stereogenic carbon. Second, the Cahn-Ingold-Prelog method (named for its inventors) is a system for indicating the exact geometric configuration of the 4 groups surrounding a stereogenic carbon atom (Figure 5). By using this method, naming a molecule can be accomplished in a few easy steps:

1. Identify the 4 unique groups attached to the carbon atom.

2. Rank the atoms immediately attached to the carbon in order of atomic number (ie, S, O, N, C, H). Label the highest-ranking substituent as 1 and the lowest-ranking substituent as 4.

3. Orient the molecule with the lowest substituent (ie, number 4) pointed away, using a dashed wedge.

4. Draw an arrow in the direction of the remaining substituents, from 1 to 2 to 3.

5. If the direction of the substituents is in the clockwise direction, the molecule is designated "R," from the Latin word *rectus* meaning "right." If the direction of the substituents is counterclockwise, the molecule is designated "S," from the Latin word *sinister* meaning evil (ie, the opposite of right).

There are only these 2 ways that the groups can be oriented around the carbon atom. The R and S labels define the orientation of the molecule's substituents accurately and completely. One isomer of a molecule can often have very different biological activities compared with the other isomer. Furthermore, many drug molecules have multiple stereogenic centers. Therefore, naming and drawing these molecules accurately is essential to understanding which molecule is being discussed. The R and S naming method will be used in later chapters of this book to describe commonly used drugs.

## Alkenes (C=C)

An *alkene* is a molecule that contains carbon and hydrogen atoms and at least 1 double bond between 2 carbon atoms. When a carbon-carbon double bond exists in the molecule, it is converted from an alkane to an alkene. The "-ane" suffix in the name is replaced by an "-ene" suffix referring to the alkene family. Examples of alkenes include ethene ($CH_2=CH_2$) and propene ($CH_3-CH=CH_2$). Note that only 1 double bond in a molecule is necessary to convert it from an alkane to an alkene. When naming alkenes, a number is used to indicate the position of the first carbon involved in the double bond. For example, 2-butene indicates that the double bond is between carbons 2 and 3 (ie, $CH_3-CH=CH-CH_3$).

A carbon-carbon double bond is formed by a σ bond plus a π bond. The π bond results from the overlap of 2 p orbitals from the bonded atoms. A result of the double bond is that the 2 atoms of the double bond, along with the atoms bonded directly to them, lie in the same 2-dimensional plane (**Figure 6**). Furthermore, the carbon atoms are unable to rotate around the axis of the double bond. That is, the 3-dimensional configuration of the double bond is fixed.

Because the configuration around the double bond is fixed, alkenes having the same molecular formula and connectivity can have different stereochemical configurations. When this occurs, the molecules are called *double-bond isomers*. For example, 2-butene can have 2 forms. One form is *cis*-2-butene, which is formed when the methyl groups bonded to carbon-2 and carbon-3 are on the same side of the double bond. A *cis* relationship exists when the 2 substituents of highest molecular weight are on the same side of the double bond but not bonded to the same carbon atom. The other form is *trans*-2-butene, which is formed when the methyl groups are on opposite sides of the double bond. A *trans* relationship exists when the 2 substituents of highest molecular weight are on opposite sides of the double bond.

Sometimes, however, it is not easy to determine which of 2 substituents is of lower molecular weight. For this reason, an alternative naming scheme has been developed. In this system, the substituents on each carbon atom are examined. The 2 substituents on each carbon atom of the double bond are ranked in order of molecular mass. These rankings are compared. If the substituents with the highest rankings (ie, highest molecular masses) are on the same side of the double bond, they are considered zusammen (Z) with respect to each other. *Zusammen* is the German word for "together." If the highest-ranking substituents are on opposite sides of the double bond, they are considered entgegen (E) with respect to each other. *Entgegen* is the German word for "opposite." The E/Z system can accurately describe the bonding relationship between complex substituents (Figure 6).

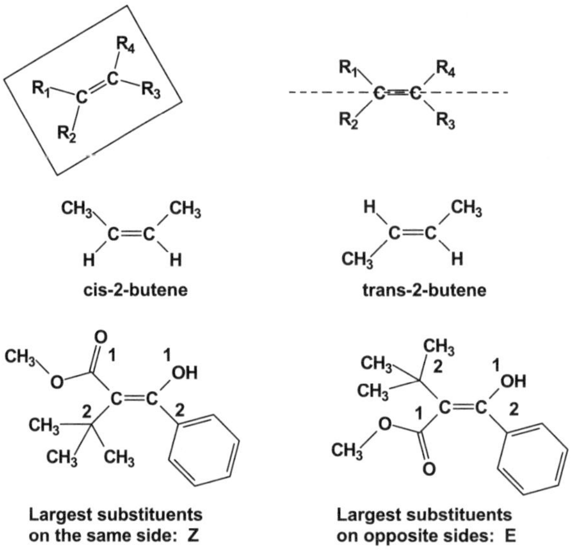

cis-2-butene

trans-2-butene

Largest substituents
on the same side: Z

Largest substituents
on opposite sides: E

**Figure 6.** *Stereochemistry of an alkene. Because there is no rotation around the carbon-carbon double bond, the 2 carbon atoms and their 4 substituents are located in the same plane of space. The pattern of substitution around a double bond determines how the molecule will be named. When the 2 largest substituents are on the same side of the double bond, a cis relationship exists. When these substituents are on opposite sides of the double bond, a trans relationship exists. Often, it is difficult to determine which are the largest substituents. In these cases, the E/Z notation is used, in which E indicates the largest substituents are on opposite sides and Z indicates they are on the same side.*

Many drug molecules contain an alkene functional group. Tamoxifen, naloxone, and vitamin $K_1$ are a few examples of alkenes (**Figure 7**). In tamoxifen, the double bond is a *cis*, or Z, double bond. In vitamin $K_1$, the double bond is a *trans*, or E, double bond. In naloxone, the double bond is a terminal double bond and does not have *cis* or *trans* isomers. A terminal double bond is at the end of a chain. Conversely, an internal double bond, as in tamoxifen and vitamin $K_1$, is within the structure of a molecule.

During metabolism, the double bond of an alkene is normally oxidized to form an epoxide (**Figure 8**). An *epoxide* is a highly strained, 3-membered ring containing an oxygen atom and is, therefore, highly reactive. An epoxide can react with any nucleophile (an atom or molecule that reacts, by donating a pair of electrons, with a molecule that is partially or fully positive) present, including DNA, RNA, or an amino acid residue of a protein. If these reactions occur, the drug is covalently and irreversibly bound to the nucleophilic molecule and disrupts the latter's natural state. This situation can be toxic in a physiological system. If the epoxide reacts with water, a diol is formed. Allylic carbon atoms,

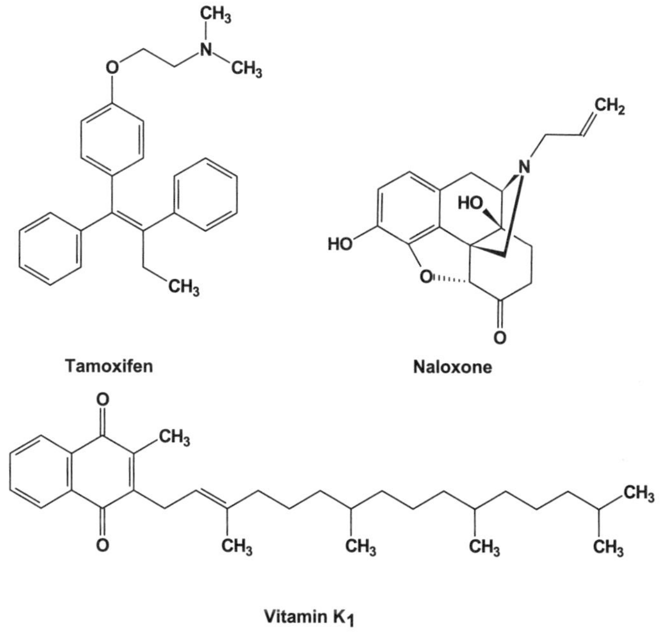

Tamoxifen

Naloxone

Vitamin K₁

**Figure 7.** *Drug molecules with an alkene in their structures.*

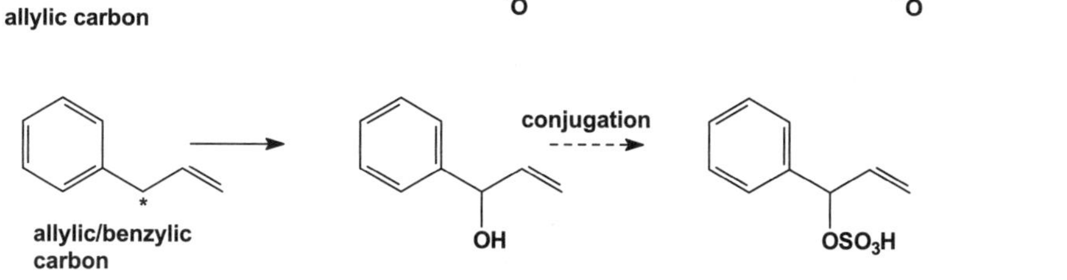

**Figure 8.** *Metabolism of alkenes. The primary route of metabolism of an alkene is epoxidation. Owing to the strain in a 3-membered ring, epoxides are extremely reactive and can be opened by any nucleophile. Oxidation of the alkene can also occur on the carbon atom immediately adjacent to the double bond (the allylic carbon). If this carbon is also adjacent to a benzene ring (benzylic), it is especially prone to oxidation.*

which are adjacent to an alkene, are also metabolized by oxidation. The oxidized products can be conjugated to form sulfates or glucuronides. A carbon atom that is allylic *and* benzylic (adjacent to a benzene ring) is doubly reactive and easily metabolized by these routes.

Because alkenes are made of carbon and hydrogen atoms, their water solubility properties are similar to those of alkanes. Alkenes are not able to form hydrogen bonds or form dipole interactions with water and are, therefore, considered nonpolar and hydrophobic. The presence of a double bond confers a slight increase in water solubility due to the collection of electron density above the π bond. This partially negative charge is somewhat attractive to the hydrogen atoms of the water molecule. A double bond alone, however, is not usually enough to make an alkene water soluble.

## Alkynes (C≡C)

When a carbon skeleton contains a triple bond between 2 carbon atoms, it is a member of the alkyne family of molecules. The suffix "-yne" refers to molecules with a carbon-carbon triple bond. A triple bond, as discussed earlier, is made by 1 σ bond and 2 π bonds. In progression from a single bond to a double bond to a triple bond, a 4-carbon molecule is named: butane, butene, butyne. As with alkenes, a triple bond can be a terminal triple bond or an internal triple bond. Norethindrone, pargyline, and deprenyl (selegiline) are drugs that contain triple bonds (**Figure 9**). The metabolism of alkynes is not extensive and is not thought to have a major role in the metabolic fate of a drug molecule. The water solubility of alkynes is similar to that of alkanes and alkenes.

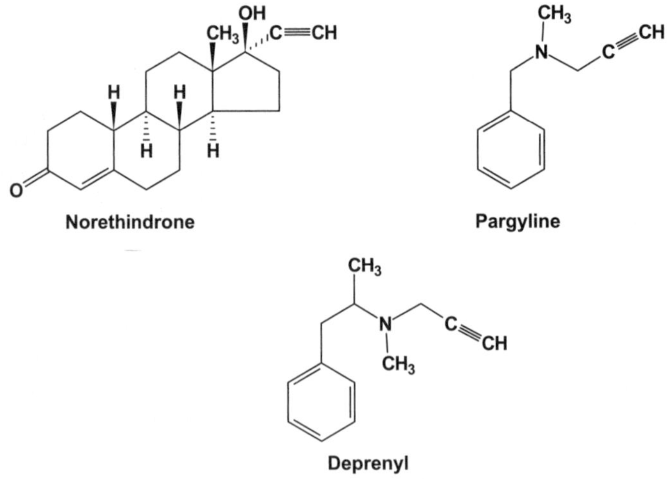

**Figure 9.** *Common drug molecules containing the alkyne functional group.*

# Aromatics (Benzene, Phenyl Groups, Heterocyclic Aromatics)

A class of molecules that is characterized by cyclic structures with specific patterns of double (π) bonds is the aromatics. The most common molecule of this type is benzene (**Figure 10A**). Benzene is composed of 6 carbon atoms and 6 hydrogen atoms. The carbon atoms are joined together in a ring, and each is singly bonded to one other carbon, singly bonded to a hydrogen atom, and doubly bonded to a second carbon atom. In this way, the carbon-carbon bonds of benzene are arranged as follows: single-double-single-double, etc. Because π bonds are the result of 2 overlapping p orbitals, the π electrons of benzene can delocalize throughout the entire structure. This delocalization of electrons gives benzene great stability compared with its hydrocarbon cousin, cyclohexane. Aromatic compounds (named as such because they were first noted for their appealing aromas) can also involve heteroatoms such as nitrogen, sulfur, and oxygen. Examples include pyridine, thiophene, furan, and indole. Aromatic functional groups are often part of larger molecules. A benzene molecule contained in a larger structure is referred to as a *phenyl group*.

For a new cyclic molecule, 2 rules can help determine whether a molecule is aromatic. First, in the string of atoms that comprise the ring, no $CH_2$ (methylene) group can interrupt the pattern of "single bond, double bond, single bond, double bond, etc." The addition of such a group would interrupt this pattern and the ability of the π electrons to delocalize through the entire ring. Second, the cyclic molecule must satisfy the Hückel rule, which states that for a molecule to be aromatic, the number of π electrons in the ring (an integer) must equal $4n + 2$, where n = zero or a positive integer. For example, benzene contains 6 π electrons. Each carbon atom in the ring contributes 1 π electron. If we say $6 = 4n + 2$, n = 1, which is a positive integer, the equation is correct. According to the Hückel rule, only rings of a certain size can be aromatic. For example, in a ring with 8 π electrons, $8 = 4n + 2$, n = 1.5, which is not an integer. Therefore, a molecule with 8 π electrons arranged in an alternating pattern is not aromatic. Based on these 2 rules, one can distinguish aromatic molecules from ones that are not aromatic. Figure 10A lists common aromatic ring systems often found in drug molecules. Aspirin, nicotine, and diazepam are a few of the many drug molecules with aromatic rings contained in their structures (**Figure 10B**).

The metabolism of aromatic compounds resembles that of the alkenes. During metabolism, one of the double bonds in the aromatic ring is oxidized to an epoxide (**Figure 11**). A nucleophile can then react with this epoxide. Glutathione can react with this epoxide to form a normal metabolite. However, if DNA, RNA, or a protein reacts with the epoxide, a covalently modified macromolecule results. It is this potential side reaction that contributes to the high toxicity of aromatic rings.

Because aromatic molecules have π electron systems, their water solubility is increased compared with that of their hydrocarbon cousins. The partial negative

A. Common aromatic ring systems.

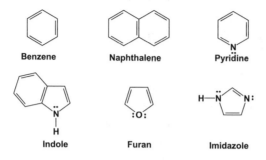

B. Drug molecules containing aromatic rings.

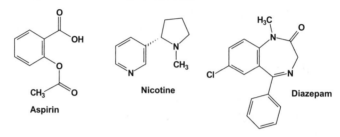

**Figure 10.** *The aromatic ring is a common structural component of many organic molecules. A variety of aromatic rings are found in naturally occurring molecules (A) and in drug molecules (B).*

charge of the π electrons is attractive to the partially positive charge of the hydrogen atoms in water. However, the solubility of aromatics is far less than that of molecules that can form hydrogen bonds with water (ie, amines, alcohols, and thiols).

## Alcohols (-OH)

An *alcohol* is a molecule with a hydroxyl group (-OH) in its structure that is bonded to an alkyl carbon atom. The hydroxyl group (sometimes referred to as hydroxy) consists of an oxygen atom with 2 single σ bonds: one to a hydrogen atom (the "hydroxyl hydrogen") and the other to a carbon atom. The oxygen also has 2 lone pairs of electrons. The 2 bonds and 2 lone pairs of electrons result in the hydroxyl group having a tetrahedral geometry (**Figure 12A**). The oxygen atom of the hydroxyl group is significantly more electronegative than the attached carbon atom and, therefore, has partial negative character. This electronegativity makes the hydroxyl group polar and imparts increased water solubility to the molecule to which it is attached. Furthermore, a hydroxyl group, with a hydrogen atom attached to an oxygen atom and two lone pairs of electrons, can act as a hydrogen bond donor and as a hydrogen bond acceptor. The ability of a hydroxyl group to form a hydrogen bond with water also increases the water solubility of the entire molecule.

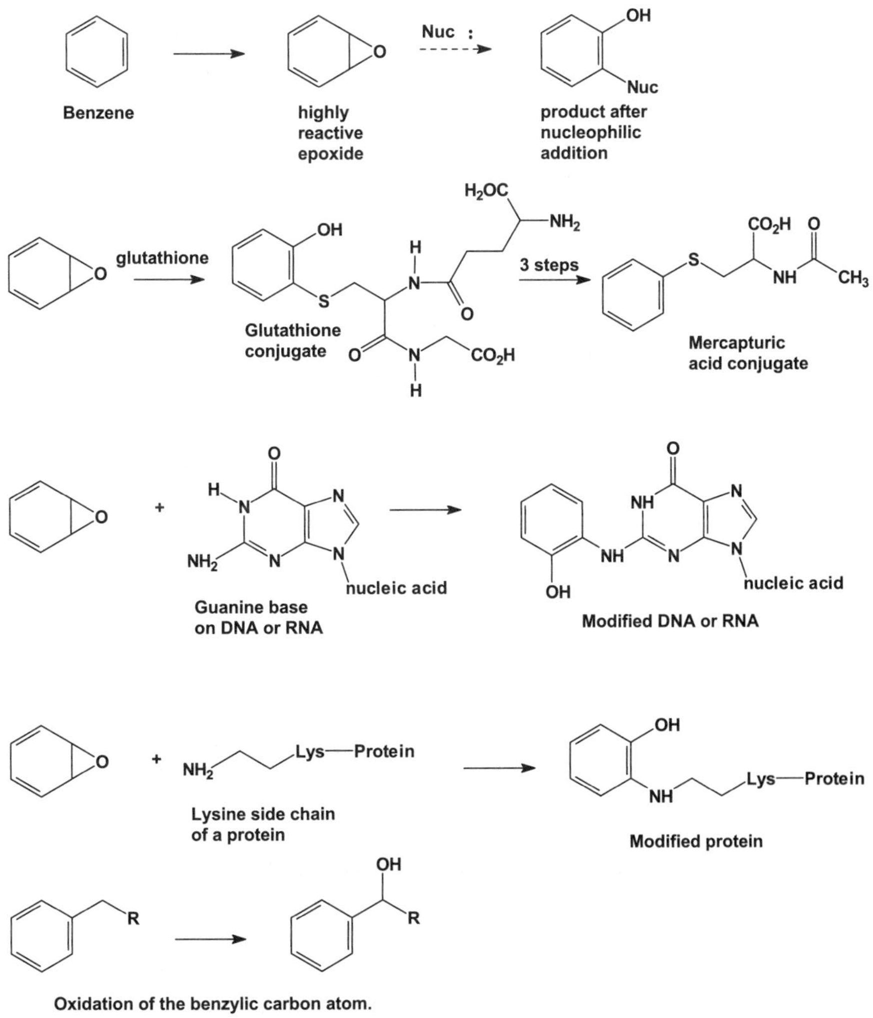

**Figure 11.** *Metabolism of aromatic compounds. The primary route of metabolism of an aromatic ring involves epoxidation of one of the ring double bonds. The reactive epoxide can be opened by any one of several nucleophiles present, including glucuronic acid or glutathione (to form a desired conjugate) or DNA, RNA, or protein (to form an undesired conjugate). Because of their proximity to the benzene ring, benzylic carbon atoms are easily oxidized during metabolism.*

A hydroxyl group can be bonded to differentially bonded carbon atoms. These alcohols are referred to as primary (1°), secondary (2°), or tertiary (3°) depending on the number of carbon-carbon bonds on the attached carbon atom (Figure 12A). When a hydroxyl group is bonded to a carbon atom with a σ bond to only 1 other carbon atom, the molecule is a primary alcohol. Examples of primary alcohols are ethanol ($CH_3CH_2OH$) and methanol ($CH_3OH$). When a hydroxyl group is bonded to a carbon with σ bonds to 2 other carbon atoms, the molecule is a secondary alcohol. An example of a secondary alcohol is isopropanol (($CH_3)_2CHOH$). When a hydroxyl group is bonded to a carbon atom with σ bonds to 3 other carbon atoms, the molecule is a tertiary alcohol. An example of a tertiary alcohol is tert-butanol (($CH_3)_3COH$). There are many examples of alcohols in drug molecules, some of which are propranolol, cholesterol, and albuterol (**Figure 12B**).

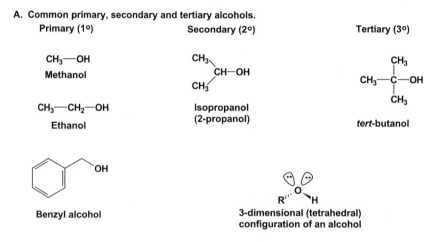

A. Common primary, secondary and tertiary alcohols.

B. Drug molecules with alcohol functional groups in their structures.

**Figure 12.** *Alcohols can exist as primary, secondary, and tertiary molecules (A). The alcohol functional group is found frequently in drug molecules (B).*

Alcohols are metabolized by 2 distinct mechanisms (**Figure 13**). In the first, the alcohol is oxidized to an aldehyde and then can be further oxidized to a carboxylic acid. Ethanol, commonly found in alcoholic beverages, is metabolized in this way. Disulfiram (Antabuse), an inhibitor of the second oxidation reaction, is used as a deterrent from excessive drinking because the accumulation of acetaldehyde makes the person feel nauseous. The second route of metabolism involves conjugation of the alcohol to glucuronic acid or sulfuric acid. Glucuronides and sulfates, the products of these conjugations, are common alcohol metabolites.

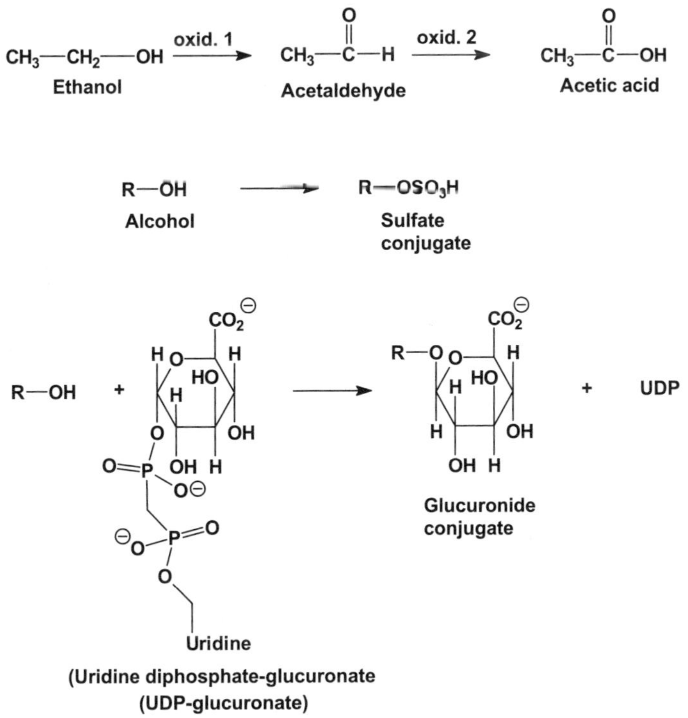

**Figure 13.** *Metabolism of alcohols. There are 2 primary routes of metabolism for alcohols: oxidation and conjugation. Oxidation of an alcohol to the aldehyde is quickly followed by oxidation to the carboxylic acid. This path is characterized by the metabolism of ethanol. Alcohols can also be conjugated to form sulfates or glucuronides.*

## Phenols (Ph-OH)

A *phenol* is a molecule with a hydroxyl group bonded directly to a phenyl ring (**Figure 14**). Phenols are substantially different from other alcohols. The phenolic hydroxyl proton is more acidic ($pK_a$ (phenol) $= 10$) than the hydroxyl proton from a simple alcohol ($pK_a$ ($CH_3OH$) $= 16$). Also, because of the $\pi$ electron system combined with the hydroxyl group, the water solubility of phenols greatly surpasses that of nonaromatic alcohols of the same molecular weight. Molecules that have phenolic groups in their structures include morphine, estradiol, and epinephrine (Figure 14). Phenols are metabolized following the same conjugation reactions as for alcohols (**Figure 15**). Glucuronides and sulfates are the common metabolites of phenols.

## Ethers (-C-O-C-)

An ether is a molecule with 1 oxygen atom connecting 2 carbon atoms. The carbon atoms can be aromatic or aliphatic and have any number or kind of substituents. Ether groups increase the water solubility of a molecule, compared with an alkane, due to the lone pairs of electrons on the oxygen atom. Ethers are named by combining the carbon-unit name with "oxy." For example, an oxygen atom that connects an ethyl group to the remainder of the molecule is called an *ethoxy group* (-$OCH_2CH_3$). One kind of ether linkage that is often seen in drug molecules is the methoxy group. A *methoxy group* is an oxygen atom bonded to a methyl group (-$OCH_3$). Examples of molecules that contain ether linkages are diethyl ether, diphenhydramine, fluoxetine, and doxepin (**Figure 16**).

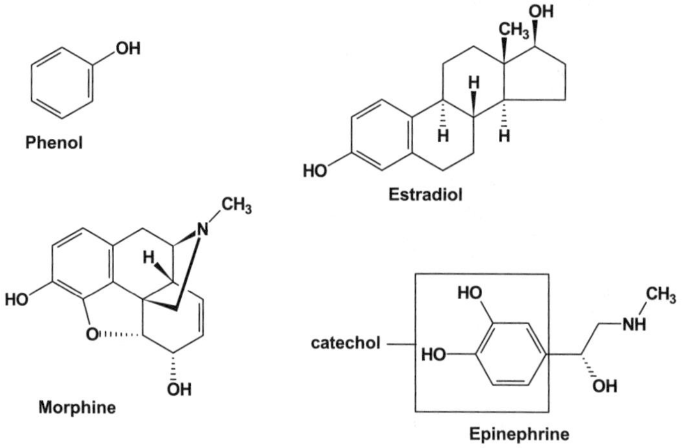

**Figure 14.** *Phenol and drug molecules containing phenolic functional groups. Catechol, a special kind of phenol, has 2 hydroxyl groups on adjacent carbon atoms of the benzene ring.*

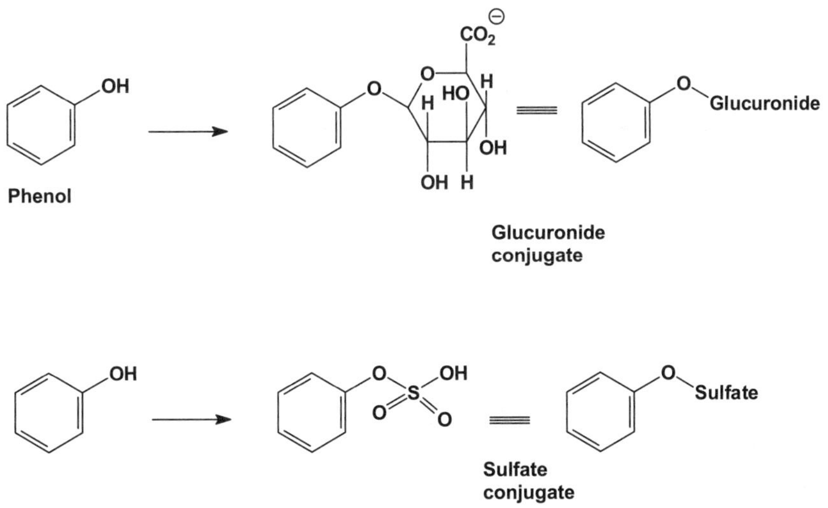

**Phenol**

**Glucuronide**

**Glucuronide conjugate**

**Sulfate**

**Sulfate conjugate**

**Figure 15.** *Metabolism of phenols. Phenolic compounds undergo a single type of metabolism: conjugation. Sulfation and glucuronidation are the principal routes of phenolic conjugation.*

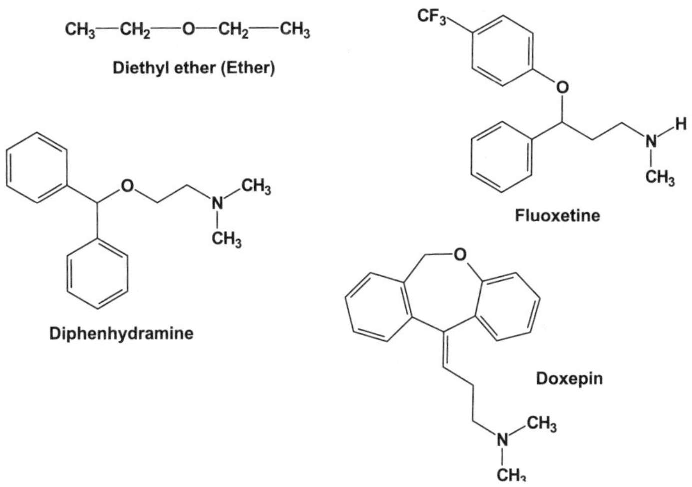

$CH_3$—$CH_2$—O—$CH_2$—$CH_3$

**Diethyl ether (Ether)**

**Fluoxetine**

**Diphenhydramine**

**Doxepin**

**Figure 16.** *Drug molecules with ether linkages.*

Diethyl ether was used as an anesthetic gas for many years. Drawbacks to diethyl ether as a drug include toxic effects and high flammability. These side effects were reduced with the addition of halogen substituents to the molecule. When a chlorine atom is added, for example, the flammability is dramatically reduced. In addition, the lipophilicity of the molecule is enhanced, which increases its absorption in the body. Diethyl ether and related anesthetic gases are the subject of Chapter 9.

Ethers are metabolized by hydroxylation of the carbon atom adjacent to the ether oxygen to give a hemiacetal (**Figure 17**). This reactive intermediate is quickly fragmented by further oxidation of the carbon to give an aldehyde (or ketone). The remaining alcohol is metabolized following the route of other alcohols.

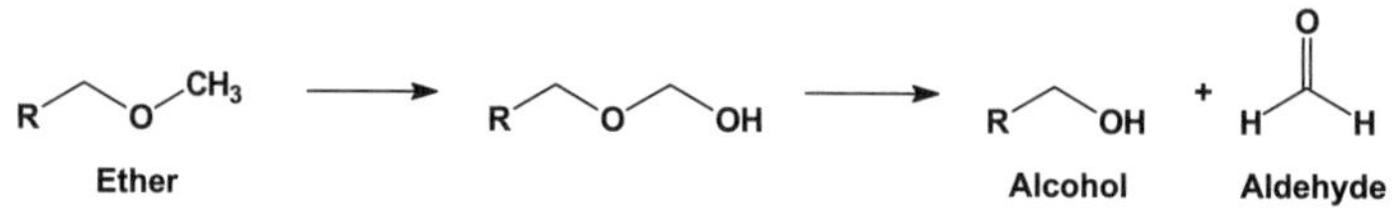

Ether        Alcohol    Aldehyde

**Figure 17.** *Metabolism of ethers. The metabolic route primarily seen with the ether functional group is hydroxylation of the carbon atom adjacent to the ether oxygen atom, followed by fragmentation.*

## Thiols (-SH) and Thioethers (R-S-R)

A *thiol* (also called a mercaptan) consists of a sulfur atom covalently bonded to a carbon atom and a hydrogen atom. When sulfur is covalently bonded to 2 different atoms, the sulfur atom has 2 lone pairs of electrons. In this configuration, thiols and thioethers adopt a tetrahedral conformation. Molecules containing a thiol group have a characteristic, unpleasant, "rotten eggs" smell. The electronegativity of sulfur is not very different from carbon, and, therefore, the polarity and hydrogen bonding potential of the thiol group is less than those of alcohols or amines. Thiols participate in weak hydrogen bonds. Examples of molecules with a thiol group include β-mercaptoethanol and cysteine (**Figure 18A**). Thioethers have very similar physical properties to oxygen-containing ether compounds. Examples of thioethers in drug molecules include nelfinavir and lamivudine (**Figure 18B**).

The metabolism of thiols resembles that of alcohols (**Figure 19A**). Thiols are conjugated to form glucuronides by uridine diphosphate-glucuronosyltranferases. Thioethers can undergo 2 types of metabolism (**Figure 19B**). First, the carbon atom adjacent to the sulfur can be oxidized. Fragmentation of this product results in the formation of a thiol and an aldehyde (or ketone). Second, the thioether can undergo oxidation of the sulfur to form a sulfoxide. A second oxidation reaction forms a sulfone.

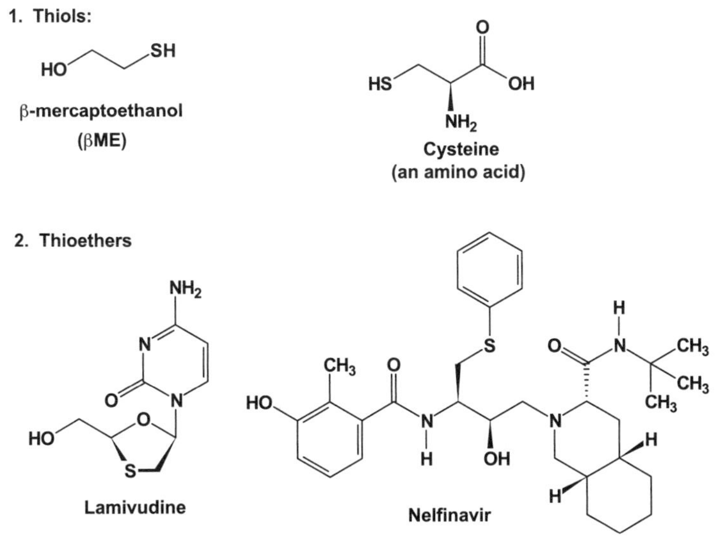

1. Thiols:

β-mercaptoethanol
(βME)

Cysteine
(an amino acid)

2. Thioethers

Lamivudine

Nelfinavir

**Figure 18.** *Common molecules with sulfur atoms.*

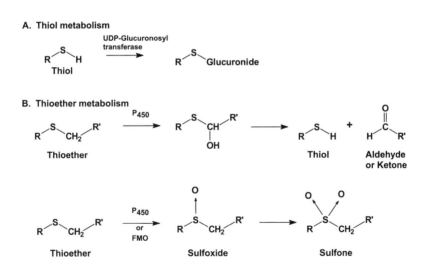

A. Thiol metabolism

Thiol

UDP-Glucuronosyl
transferase

Glucuronide

B. Thioether metabolism

Thioether

P₄₅₀

Thiol + Aldehyde or Ketone

Thioether

P₄₅₀
or
FMO

Sulfoxide

Sulfone

**Figure 19.** *Metabolism of thiols and thioethers. A, Thiols, like alcohols, are metabolized by formation of conjugate molecules, such as glucuronides. B, Thioethers can be oxidized at the adjacent carbon atom or at the sulfur itself. First, oxidation of the thioether sulfur atom results in a sulfoxide. Second, oxidation of the sulfur atom yields a sulfone.*

## Amines (-NH$_2$, -NHR, -NRR', +NRR'R'')

An *amine* contains a nitrogen atom singly bonded to 3 or 4 atoms. These atoms can be hydrogens or carbons (R = carbon). When a nitrogen atom is bonded to 3 hydrogens (ie, NH$_3$), the molecule is called *ammonia*. Ammonia, like many other simple amines, has a characteristic fishlike smell. When a nitrogen atom is bonded to 3 other atoms, it has a remaining lone pair of electrons and adopts a tetrahedral geometry. While slightly less electronegative than oxygen, nitrogen is still more electronegative than carbon. Therefore, amino groups are more polar than alkyl groups. With the lone pair of electrons, an amino group can act as a hydrogen bond acceptor and can form hydrogen bonds with the solvent (eg, water), as well as with other molecules around it.

Amines are distinguished from each other by the number of carbon atoms bonded to the nitrogen (**Table 3**). A nitrogen atom that is singly bonded to 1 carbon (and 2 hydrogens) is a primary (1°) amine. Methylamine (NH$_2$CH$_3$) is an example of a primary amine. A nitrogen atom that is singly bonded to 2 carbons (and 1 hydrogen) is a secondary (2°) amine. Methylethylamine (CH$_3$NHCH$_2$CH$_3$) is an example of a secondary amine. A nitrogen atom that is singly bonded to 3 carbons (and no hydrogens) is a tertiary amine. N,N-dimethylethylamine ((CH$_3$)$_2$NCH$_2$CH$_3$) is an example of a tertiary amine. A group with a nitrogen atom singly bonded to 4 carbon atoms carries a positive charge. The resulting ion is a type of onium ion. If the nitrogen is bonded to 4 hydrogen atoms ($^+$NH$_4$), it is called an ammonium ion. If the nitrogen is bonded to 1 carbon atom and 3 hydrogen atoms, it is called a primary ammonium ion. Likewise, a secondary ammonium ion has 2 carbons and 2 hydrogens bound to the nitrogen, a tertiary ammonium ion has 3 carbons and 1 hydrogen, and a quaternary ammonium ion has 4 carbons. Tetramethylammonium chloride ((CH$_3$)$_4$N$^{+-}$Cl) is an example of a quaternary amine-containing salt. Note that the anion (negative atom) is specified when naming this molecule.

**Table 3.** *Examples of substituted amines.*

| Ammonia | Primary Amines | Secondary Amines | Tertiary Amines | Quaternary Amines |
|---|---|---|---|---|
| NH$_3$ | CH$_3$–NH$_2$ <br> Methylamine | CH$_3$–NH <br> CH$_3$ <br> Dimethylamine | CH$_3$–N–CH$_3$ <br> CH$_3$ <br> Trimethylamine | CH$_3$ <br> CH$_3$–$\overset{\oplus}{N}$–CH$_3$ Cl$^\ominus$ <br> CH$_3$ <br> Tetramethylammonium chloride |
| | CH$_3$–CH$_2$–NH$_2$ <br> Ethylamine | CH$_3$ <br> CH–NH <br> CH$_3$ CH <br> CH$_3$ CH$_3$ <br> Diisopropylamine | CH$_3$ CH$_3$ <br> CH–N–CH <br> CH$_3$ CH CH$_3$ <br> CH$_3$ CH$_3$ <br> Triisopropylamine | $\overset{\oplus}{N}$(⌐⌐⌐⌐)$_4$ <br> Cl$^\ominus$ <br> Tetrabutylammonium chloride |
| | CH$_3$ <br> CH–NH$_2$ <br> CH$_3$ <br> Isopropylamine | CH$_3$–NH <br> CH$_2$ <br> CH$_3$ <br> Ethylmethylamine | CH$_3$–N–CH$_3$ <br> CH$_2$ <br> CH$_3$ <br> Dimethylethylamine | |

The different types of amines have distinct properties that affect the characteristics of the molecule to which they belong. The 2 main properties of amines that are important are lipophilicity and basicity. For amines of approximately the same molecular weight, the lipophilicity of an amine increases with each additional carbon atom or group attached to nitrogen: primary is less than secondary, which is less than tertiary. Tertiary amines have the greatest number of carbon-containing groups attached to the nitrogen. Therefore, tertiary amines are the most lipophilic. Quaternary amines, with 4 carbon-containing groups, would be more lipophilic; however, they have a positive charge, which makes them hydrophilic (water loving).

There are 2 forces that affect the basicity of an amine: (1) the number of attached electron-donating groups and (2) the accessibility of the lone pair of electrons. A molecule can act as a base only if it has a lone pair of electrons to bond to a proton ($H^+$) from another molecule. Quaternary amines do not have a lone pair of electrons. The nitrogen lone pair is used to make the fourth nitrogen-carbon bond. Therefore, quaternary amines cannot act as bases and are not discussed further with respect to basicity.

Most alkyl groups can act as electron donors to the nitrogen. In this sense, electron donation refers to the passage of a negative charge through the carbon-nitrogen bond. A nitrogen atom is more electronegative than a carbon atom, so the nitrogen can effectively pull electron density toward itself through the covalent bond. The added electron density at the nitrogen enables the nitrogen's lone pair of electrons to be shared more easily. Because the number of alkyl groups increases progressively from primary is less than secondary, which is less than tertiary, the basicity of these amines would be expected to proceed in the same order. However, the accessibility of the lone pair of electrons needs to be considered.

If an atom is imagined as a balloon, a molecule would look like a number of balloons tied together. Ammonia, for example, consists of a nitrogen atom (1 medium-sized balloon) covalently bonded to 2 equal hydrogen atoms (3 small balloons). The lone pair of electrons on the nitrogen point to one corner of the molecule, while the 3 hydrogens point to the remaining 3 corners. If 1 hydrogen atom (small balloon) is replaced with 1 carbon atom (medium-sized balloon), the amount of space available for the lone pair of electrons is decreased slightly. As the second and third hydrogens are replaced by carbon atoms, the space for the lone pair of electrons is further limited. For any amine to act as a base, another molecule must be able to get close to the lone pair of electrons. As more carbon atoms are attached to the central nitrogen atom, the lone pair of electrons becomes increasingly hidden from view. In this way, the more crowded (or sterically hindered) a lone pair of electrons, the less the molecule will be able to act as a base. Based on steric hindrance alone, primary amines would be the most basic, and the trend would be: primary>secondary>tertiary (1>2>3).

Clearly, a paradox exists. In terms of electronic effects, tertiary amines should be the most basic. Conversely, in terms of steric hindrance, primary amines should be the most basic. These ways of determining basicity bring exactly opposite conclusions. What kind of amine is most basic? The answer: secondary amines. The reason: Secondary amines have a balance between the number of electron-donating groups and the accessibility of the lone pair of electrons (**Figure 20**).

The polarity and hydrogen-bonding ability of amines give them increased water solubility compared with carbon-based molecules. Another advantage of the amine functional group for drugs is the ability of amines to form acid-base salts. For example, if a simple amine, such as triethylamine, is mixed with an acid such as hydrochloric acid, the result is an acid-base salt: triethylammonium chloride. The acid salts of amines are often more soluble in water than the free amine. For this reason, many drugs that contain amines are usually administered in the form of a salt. Examples of amines include γ-aminobutyric acid (also called GABA), morphine, clozapine, and dopamine (**Figure 21**).

Amine metabolism has been extensively characterized. Amines can be oxidized in several ways, and all paths lead to $N$-dealkylated products (**Figure 22**). $P_{450}$, a group of key metabolic enzymes, catalyzes the oxidation of an amine nitrogen to an $N$-oxide or a hydroxylamine. The molecule fragments and 1 alkyl substituent are removed. Alternatively, amines can be metabolized by oxidation of the carbon atom adjacent to the amine nitrogen atom. Catalyzed by $P_{450}$ or monoamine oxidase, this reaction results in a free amine and an aldehyde or ketone (for primary and secondary amines). A third route of metabolism involves $N$-oxidation and dealkylation, followed by sulfate formation. The sulfate intermediate is unstable and very reactive. This highly reactive species can quickly combine with various nucleophiles in the body.

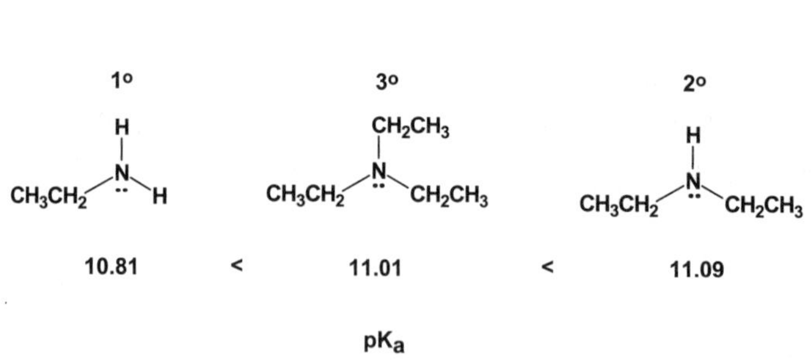

**Figure 20.** *$pK_a$ values for primary (1°), secondary (2°), and tertiary (3°) amines. The $pK_a$ of a molecule will increase as its basicity increases. Secondary amines are more basic than primary or tertiary amines because they have a balance of electron-donating alkyl groups and steric availability of the lone pair electrons on the nitrogen atom.*

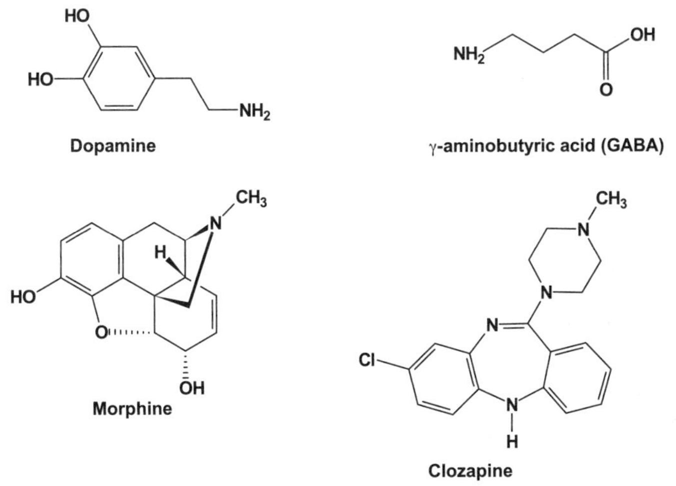

**Figure 21.** *Molecules of biological interest with amine functional groups.*

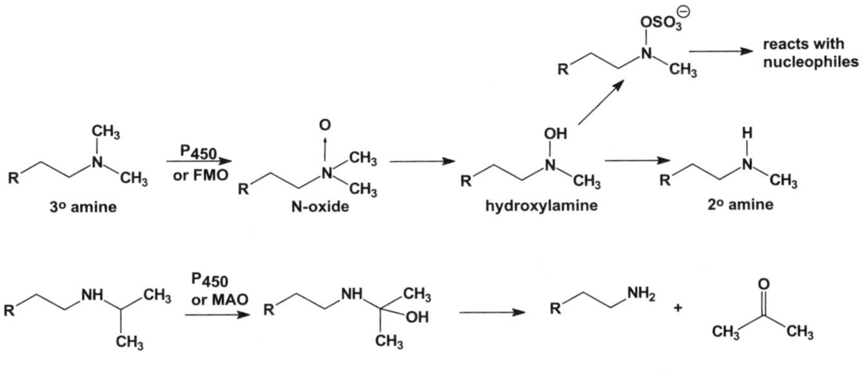

**Figure 22.** *Metabolism of amines. Because so many drug molecules contain amine functional groups, the metabolism of amines has been extensively studied. The primary routes of amine transformation are N-oxidation and oxidation of the adjacent carbon atom. Both of these paths lead to cleavage of a nitrogen-carbon bond and dealkylation.*

## Carbonyls

A number of functional groups contain a carbon (called the *carbonyl carbon*) that has a double bond ($\sigma + \pi$) to an oxygen atom (called the *carbonyl oxygen*) (**Figure 23**). Because of this double bond, the carbon is attached to only 3 atoms and has the form RC(=O)R', where R represents the remainder of the molecule and R' can be a hydrogen atom, a hydroxyl group, an ether, an amine, or another carbon. A carbonyl group has trigonal planar geometry. The electronegativity and 2 lone pairs of electrons on the carbonyl oxygen make the double bond between the carbon and oxygen fairly polar. The carbonyl oxygen is partially negative, while the carbonyl carbon is partially positive.

If the carbonyl carbon is bonded to an atom with a lone pair of electrons, it becomes more stable. This stabilization comes from the delocalization of the lone pair electrons into the carbonyl. In this way, the electrons in the system (the π electrons of the C=O double bond and the lone pair electrons in the adjacent atom) resonate between all 3 atoms (Figure 23). The electrons, all contained in p orbitals, are able to move between the 3 atoms and become delocalized (ie, removed from their atom of origin). For this reason, carbonyl groups with adjacent heteroatoms bearing lone pair electrons are resonance stabilized. All groups that are stabilized due to resonance are planar. This planarity allows the maximum overlap of all p orbitals contributing to the electron delocalization.

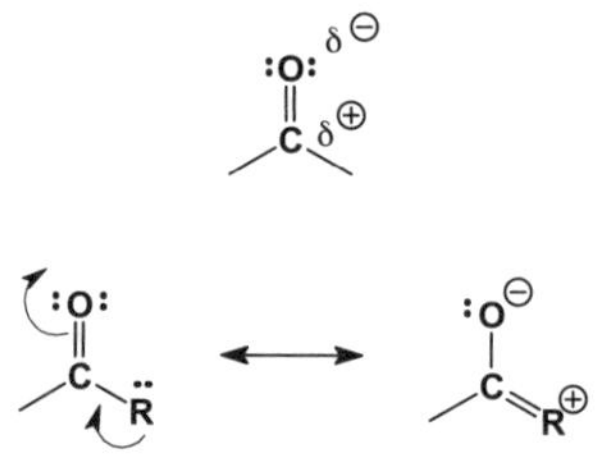

**Figure 23.** *The electronic nature of a carbonyl. The carbon-oxygen double bond is polarized with the oxygen atom bearing a slightly negative charge and the carbon atom bearing a slightly positive charge. If one of the atoms attached to the carbonyl carbon has a lone pair of electrons (ie, nitrogen, oxygen, sulfur), electron delocalization between the 3 bonded atoms is possible. This resonance makes the molecule more stable because no single atom is required to bear a significant charge.*

## Aldehydes (RC(=O)H, RCHO)

An *aldehyde* is formed when a carbon atom is doubly bonded to an oxygen atom, singly bonded to a hydrogen atom, and singly bonded to another carbon atom (**Figure 24**). The aldehyde is the simplest form of a carbonyl group. Formaldehyde (HC(=O)H) is the simplest aldehyde. The lone pairs of electrons on the oxygen enable the aldehyde to form hydrogen bonds with water. As the "R" group on the aldehyde increases in size and hydrophobicity, the water solubility of the molecule decreases. The lone pairs of electrons on the oxygen plus the double bond between the carbon and oxygen atoms make the aldehyde fairly polar. Aldehyde groups on a molecule are referred to as *formyl groups*. Molecules named as aldehydes often have an "-al" ending to indicate the class to which the molecule belongs. Because of their great instability in the body, aldehyde groups are rarely seen in drug molecules. Aldehydes are rapidly metabolized to carboxylic acids (**Figure 25**) by one of several enzymes. The primary enzyme that catalyzes this action in the body is aldehyde dehydrogenase. Once the carboxylic acid is formed, it can undergo conjugation reactions similar to those of all carboxylic acids.

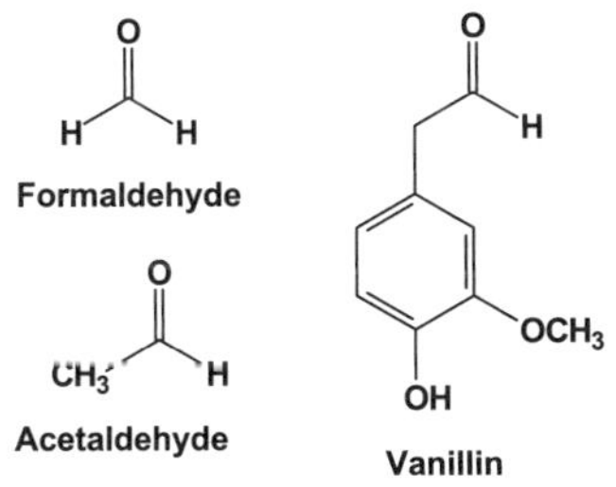

**Figure 24.** *Examples of common aldehydes.*

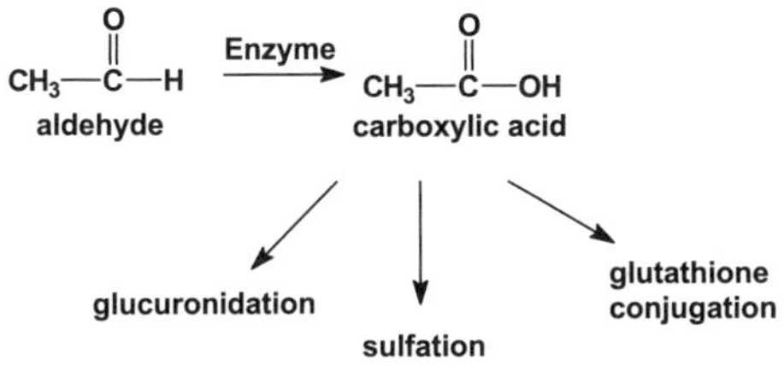

**Figure 25.** *Metabolism of aldehydes. Being highly reactive, aldehydes are quickly oxidized to carboxylic acids. Several enzymes are able to catalyze this reaction, including xanthine oxidase, aldehyde oxidase, and aldehyde dehydrogenase. The latter enzyme is thought to be predominantly responsible for the transformation in the human body. Once the carboxylic acid is formed, it will undergo the same conjugation reactions that are typical of all carboxylic acids.*

## Ketones (RC(=O)R)

A ketone is a carbon atom with 1 double bond to an oxygen atom and 2 single bonds to other carbon atoms. The lone pairs of electrons on the oxygen allow hydrogen bonding to occur between the ketone and water. This bonding results in increased water solubility of ketones compared with related hydrocarbons. Small ketones are very soluble in water, whereas ketones with large substituents are less water soluble. The carbon-oxygen double bond also imparts polarity to the ketone. Because of the additional carbon group attached to the carbonyl carbon, ketones are more stable to oxidative metabolism than are aldehydes. Therefore, ketones are seen more often as part of drug molecules. Some examples of ketones in drug molecules include methadone and corticosterone (**Figure 26**).

Ketones are metabolized by reduction to the corresponding 2° alcohol (**Figure 27**). This reaction is catalyzed by aldo-keto reductase. The alcohol that is produced is then metabolized following the conjugation reactions of other alcohols.

## Carboxylic Acids (RC(=O)OH, -CO₂H)

A carboxylic acid contains a carbonyl carbon bonded to a hydroxyl group. Because of the lone-pair electrons on the hydroxyl oxygen, the carboxylic acid is resonance stabilized. Furthermore, the 2 oxygens of the carboxylic acid are very electronegative. Therefore, the hydrogen on the hydroxyl group is bonded very weakly to its attached oxygen. It is very easy to remove a proton ($H^+$) from the group, and, therefore, the molecule is acidic ($pK_a = 3.5$-$5.5$). For this reason, $CO_2H$ groups are called *carboxylic acids.* Once the proton is removed, there is a negative charge on the carboxylic acid: $CO_2^-$. However, because of the ability of the electrons to resonate, the negative charge can be spread over all 3 atoms (**Figure 28**). This delocalization of charge increases its stability. At physiological pH, carboxylic acids are deprotonated and negatively charged ($CO_2^-$). These negatively charged species are called *carboxylate anions* or *carboxylates.*

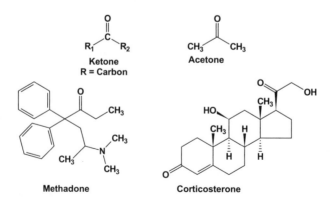

**Figure 26.** *The structure of a ketone and several molecules that contain the ketone functional group.*

**Figure 27.** *Metabolism of ketones. The primary route of metabolism of ketones is reduction to the corresponding secondary alcohol by aldo-keto reductase. Once reduced, the alcohol undergoes the same conjugation reactions as do other alcohols.*

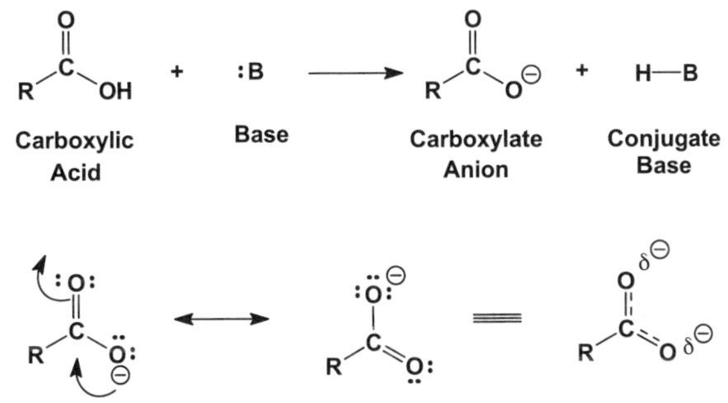

**Figure 28.** *Resonance stabilization of a carboxylate anion. Electrons can move between the 2 oxygen atoms via the central carbon atom of the carboxylic acid. For this reason, the negative charge is delocalized over 3 atoms and imparts stability to the anion.*

When the carboxylic acid proton is in place, the carboxylic acid can act as a hydrogen bond donor and an acceptor. This property increases the solubility of carboxylic acids in solutions made of water and alcohols. When the proton is removed, the polarity of the molecule is greatly increased. The molecule now has a negative change. For this reason, molecules that have a carboxylic acid, which will be negatively charged at physiological pH, are highly water soluble.

Because a molecule containing a carboxylic acid is acidic, it can form an acid-base salt when mixed with a base. A simple acid such as benzoic acid, when mixed with sodium hydroxide (a strong base), forms a salt: sodium benzoate. Sodium benzoate is more soluble in water at pH 7 than is benzoic acid. For this reason, many drugs that contain a carboxylic acid group are administered as their basic salts. For example, naproxen is administered as naproxen sodium.

Carboxylic acids are metabolized by conjugation. The primary product of carboxylic acid metabolism is the glucuronide (**Figure 29**). Several examples of molecules with carboxylic acid functional groups are naproxen (eg, Aleve), aspirin, ibuprofen (eg, Motrin), and glutamate (**Figure 30**).

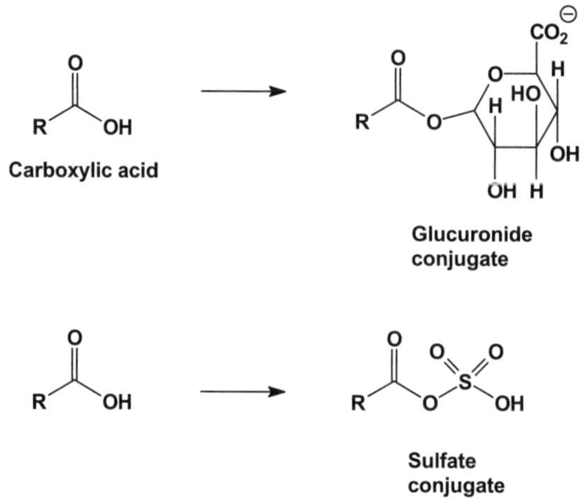

**Figure 29.** *Metabolism of carboxylic acids. Because they are already very polar, carboxylic acids do not undergo Phase I metabolism. Carboxylic acids undergo conjugation reactions to form the corresponding glucuronides and sulfates.*

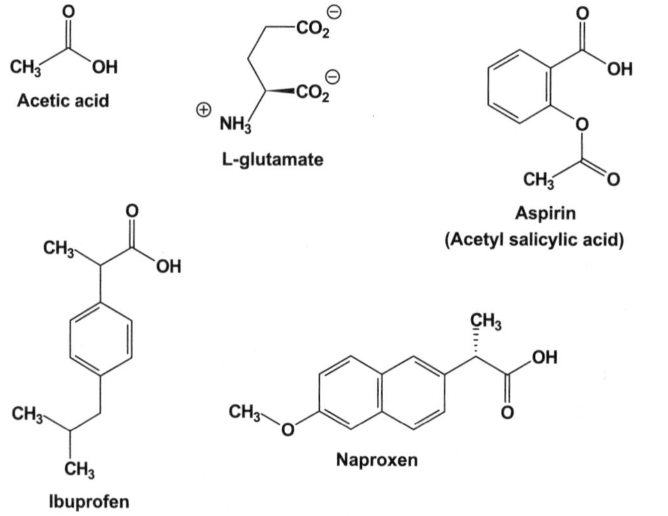

**Figure 30.** *Examples of common molecules and drugs that contain the carboxylic acid functional group.*

# Esters (-C(=O)OR, -CO₂R)

An *ester* is a carbonyl group attached to an aryloxy or alkoxy group. An *alkoxy group* is an alkyl group that has a single bond to an oxygen atom (-OR). An *aryloxy group* is an aromatic (aryl) group attached to an oxygen atom. Esters are formed by replacing the hydroxyl group of a carboxylic acid with an alkoxy (or aryloxy) group (-OR) (**Figure 31**). As with carboxylic acids, an ester benefits from resonance stabilization and electron delocalization. The alkyl group (R), however, cannot be removed from the oxygen atom, as was the case for the carboxylic acid proton. The bond between carbon and oxygen atoms is stronger than the O–H bond. With the carbonyl oxygen and alkoxy oxygen atoms, hydrogen bonding between esters and water occurs readily. This bonding, as seen with other functional groups, increases the water solubility of esters. Molecules that have an ester functional group include cocaine, aspirin, and acetylcholine (**Figure 32**).

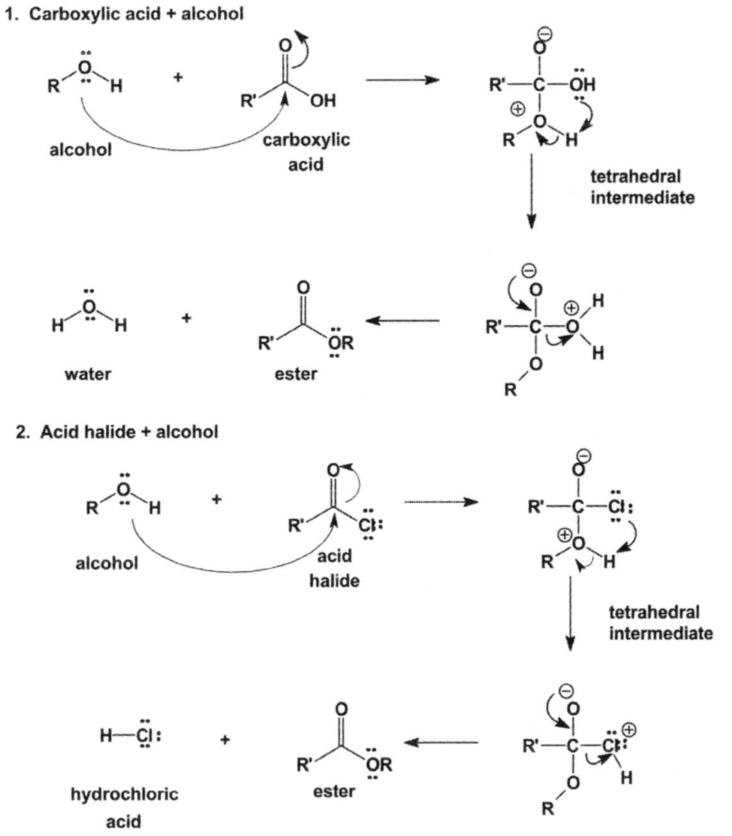

**Figure 31.** *Synthesis of an ester. An ester can be formed via many reactions. Two routes of ester synthesis are (1) attack of an alcohol on a carboxylic acid and (2) attack of an alcohol on an acid halide. Both mechanisms involve the formation of a tetrahedral intermediate.*

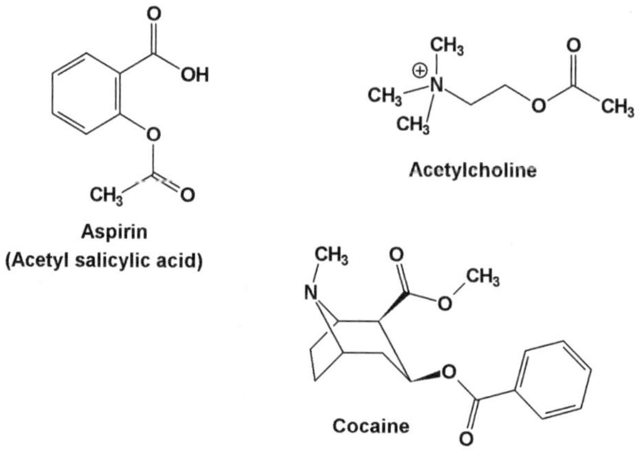

**Figure 32.** *Drug molecules containing the ester functional group.*

Esters can undergo a number of reactions in which the carbonyl carbon is attacked by a nucleophile, which reacts, by donating a pair of electrons, with a molecule that is partially or fully positive. On the other hand, an *electrophile* is an atom or molecule that reacts by accepting a pair of electrons, usually by reacting with a molecule that is partially or fully negative. In an ester, the carbonyl carbon has a partial positive charge. Both oxygen atoms are more electronegative than the carbonyl carbon to which they are bonded. For this reason, the electron density around the carbon is pulled away from it, toward the carbonyl oxygen or the alkoxy oxygen, leaving the carbon with a partial positive charge.

When a nucleophile attacks the carbonyl carbon atom and forms a new single bond, one of the other bonds to the carbonyl carbon must break. The kind of nucleophile that attacks will determine what kind of new product will be formed. In each of these reactions, however, the same bond is broken: the bond between the carbonyl carbon and the alkoxy oxygen atom. This bond is replaced with a new single bond between the carbonyl carbon and the nucleophile.

Common nucleophiles that can attack esters include amines, alcohols, thiols, and carboxylic acids (**Figure 33**). Each of these nucleophiles has a lone pair of electrons that seeks out the partial positive charge of the carbonyl carbon. The lone pair of electrons is responsible for the reaction that occurs on the ester. When an amine attacks an ester, the products are an amide and an alcohol. Alcoholic attack of an ester results in a new ester being formed and the loss of an alcohol. Thiol attack of an ester gives a thioester (RC(=O)SR') and an alcohol as the products. When a carboxylic acid attacks an ester, a large portion of the carboxylic acid replaces the alcoholic piece. The resulting molecule has 2 carbonyl groups and is called an *anhydride* (RC(=O)OC(=O)R'). Nucleophilic attack of an ester by water (ie, hydrolysis) results in the break up of the ester into an alcohol and a carboxylic acid. **Figure 34** shows 2 possible mechanisms for the hydrolysis of an ester.

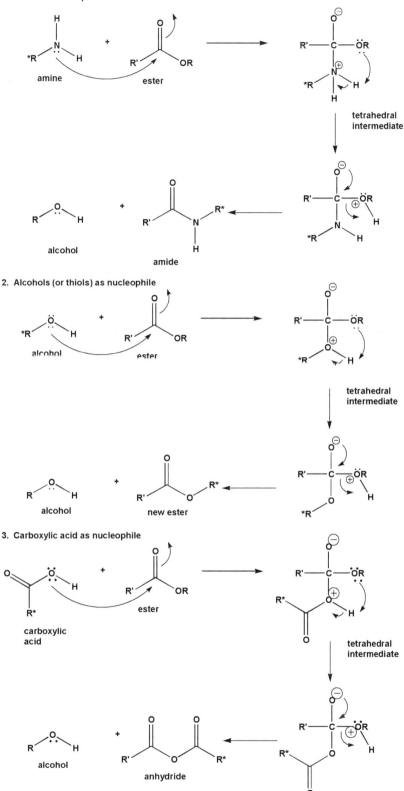

**1. Amine as nucleophile**

**2. Alcohols (or thiols) as nucleophile**

**3. Carboxylic acid as nucleophile**

**Figure 33.** *Esters can be reacted on by many types of nucleophiles. A, Amines react with esters to form amides. B, Alcohols or thiols (when O=S) react with esters to form new esters or thioesters. C, Carboxylic acids combine with esters to form anhydrides.*

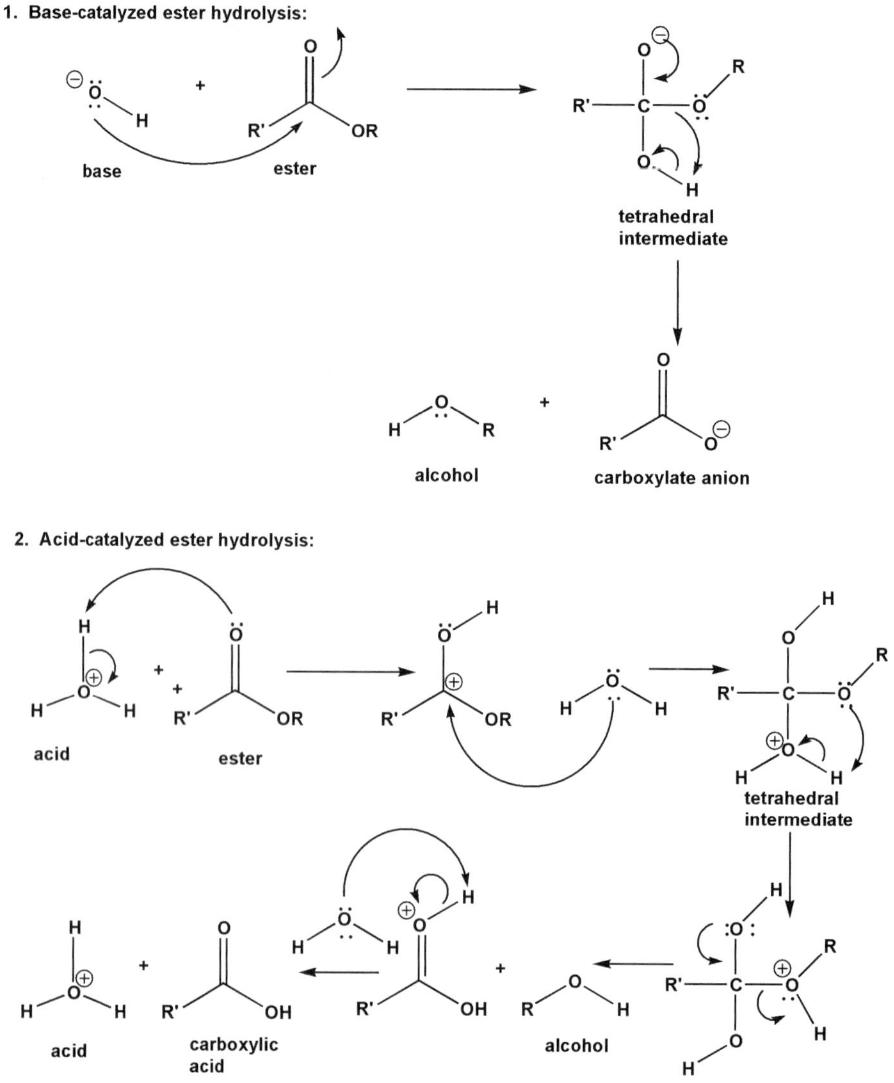

1. Base-catalyzed ester hydrolysis:

2. Acid-catalyzed ester hydrolysis:

**Figure 34.** *Two mechanisms of ester hydrolysis: base-catalyzed and acid-catalyzed.*

Esters are predominantly metabolized by hydrolysis, yielding a carboxylic acid and an alcohol (**Figure 35**). This characteristic has been used in drug development. For example, the active form of a drug that is a carboxylic acid with poor lipid solubility may be inhibited from reaching its site of action because of poor absorption. To overcome this problem, the carboxylic acid can be made into an ester. Esters have increased lipophilicity, which may increase the absorption of the drug. Once this "prodrug" has reached the target, it is hydrolyzed into the active drug molecule.

# Amides (-C(=O)NRR', -CONRR')

Amides are similar to esters. Amides contain a carbonyl carbon atom singly bonded to a nitrogen atom. Because of their similarity with esters, the chemistry of amides is very close to that of esters. The water solubility of amides can be greater than that of esters because the hydrogen atoms on a primary or secondary nitrogen atom allow it to accept and donate a hydrogen bond with water. Esters (with no hydrogen atoms) can act only as hydrogen bond acceptors.

   The amide bond is also referred to as a *peptide bond* when the bond is formed by 2 amino acids. Therefore, every protein is composed of a series of amino acids connected by peptide (amide) bonds. Many drug molecules contain an amide group, including penicillin, lysergic acid diethylamide (LSD), and lidocaine (**Figure 36**).

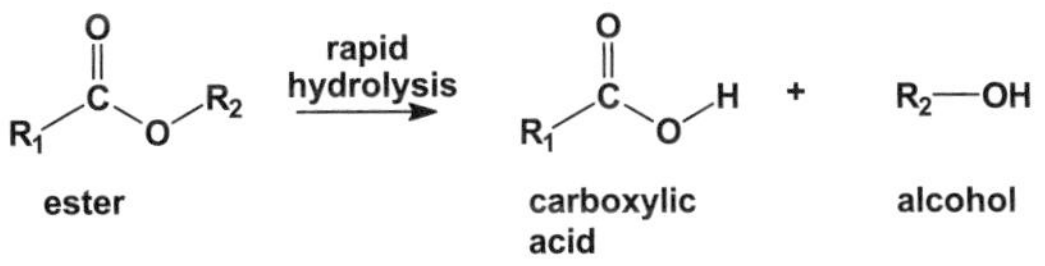

**Figure 35.** *Metabolism of esters. The primary route of ester metabolism is by rapid hydrolysis of the ester bond, yielding a carboxylic acid and an alcohol. This metabolic fate has often been used to our advantage. Prodrugs are often esters that are hydrolyzed to the active form of the drug in the body.*

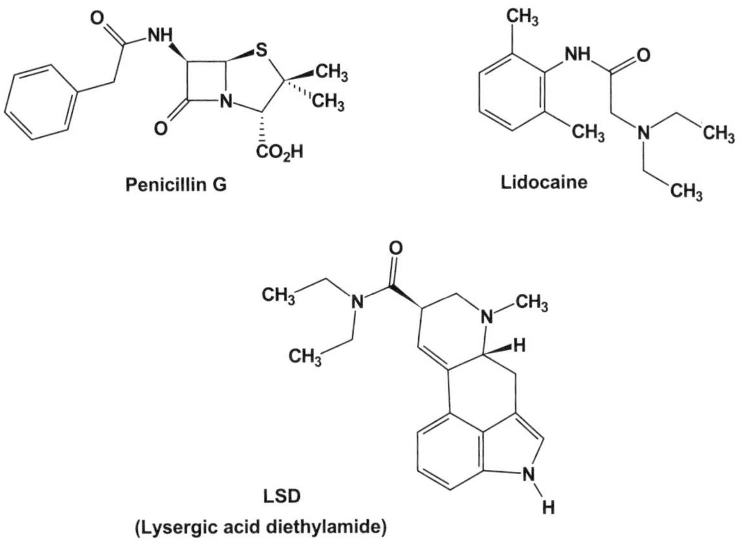

**Figure 36.** *Drug molecules containing the amide functional group.*

There are 2 primary routes of metabolism for amides: hydrolysis and
*N*-oxidation (**Figure 37**). Amide hydrolysis involves the addition of water to
the molecule and results in the formation of a carboxylic acid and an amine.
Hydrolysis of an amide follows the same mechanisms as that of ester hydrolysis
(**Figure 38**). As in the case of esters, amides can also be used as prodrugs. The
second type of amide metabolism involves hydroxylation of the amide nitrogen,
sulfation, and fragmentation to the iminium species. This charged intermediate is
highly reactive and will combine with any nucleophile in the body to result in a
modified macromolecule.

An important difference between esters and amides is their rate of hydrolysis.
Amides, in general, are more stable than esters for 2 reasons. First, the carbonyl
portion of the amide is strongly stabilized by delocalization of the lone pair of
electrons of the nitrogen atom. This stabilization is more pronounced in amides
than in esters. A nitrogen donates its lone pair of electrons more easily than does
an oxygen. Second, hydrolysis of an amide in basic conditions requires formation
of a nitrogen anion (RRN- or RHN-). These negatively charged groups separate
from the molecule with difficulty and are, therefore, poor leaving groups. On
the other hand, when esters are hydrolyzed under basic conditions, an alkoxide
anion (RO-) is initially formed. Alkoxide anions are better leaving groups than
nitrogen anions. Therefore, hydrolysis of an amide is slower than is hydrolysis
of an ester.

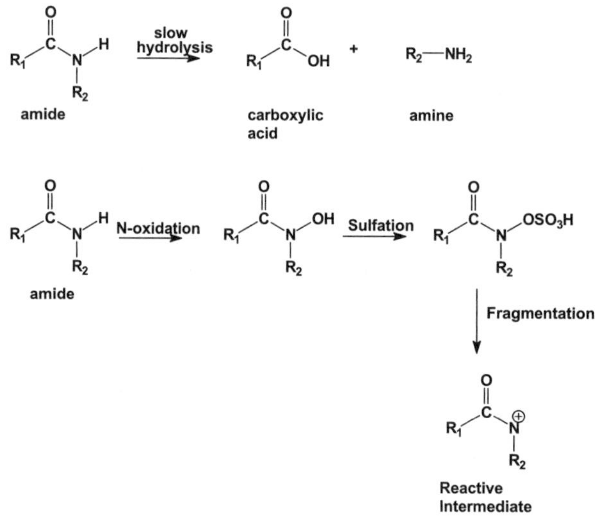

**Figure 37.** *Metabolism of amides. The metabolism of an amide is characterized by slow
hydrolysis of the amide bond, resulting in a carboxylic acid and an amine. A second route
of metabolism involves oxidation of the nitrogen atom, sulfate formation, and fragmentation,
leading to a reactive intermediate.*

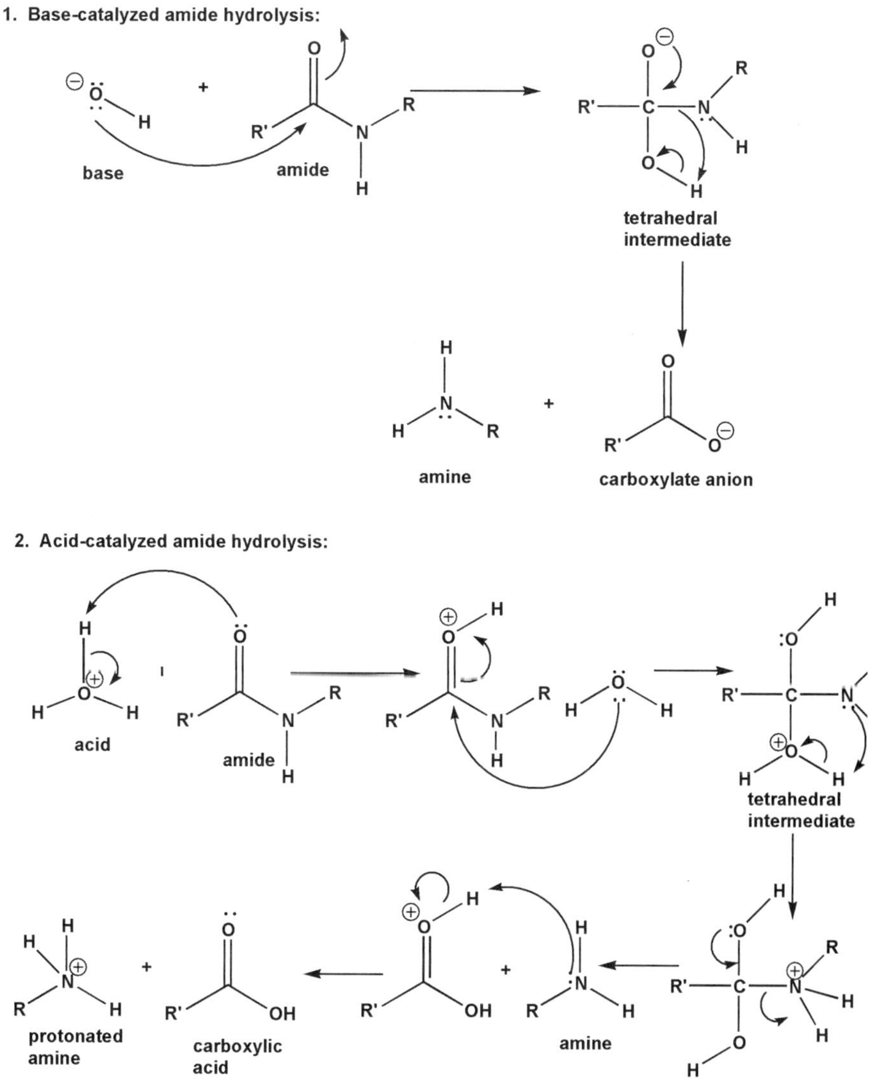

1. Base-catalyzed amide hydrolysis:

2. Acid-catalyzed amide hydrolysis:

**Figure 38.** *Two mechanisms of amide hydrolysis: base-catalyzed and acid-catalyzed.*

Consider 2 anesthetic agents: lidocaine (an amide) and procaine (an ester) (**Figure 39**). Procaine is used topically and has a very short duration of action. Lidocaine, on the other hand, can be administered via injection and has a much longer duration of action. The differing duration of action of these drugs lies in the difference in their molecular structures. The ester of procaine is hydrolyzed more quickly than is the amide of lidocaine. Because both agents become inactivated on hydrolysis, lidocaine has a longer duration of action than that of procaine.

## Sulfonamides (R-NH-SO$_2$-R)

Another functional group that has had a significant role in certain classes of drug molecules is the *sulfonamide* (**Figure 40**). Sulfonamide molecules are similar to amides in that a nitrogen atom is immediately adjacent to an atom (sulfur) multiply bonded to oxygen atoms. In this case, the sulfonyl (SO$_2$) group resembles the carbonyl group of the amide. A primary difference between an amide and a sulfonamide is the acidity of the proton on the nitrogen atom. An amide proton is not very acidic (pK$_a$ = 18-26). A sulfonamide proton, however, is much more acidic (pK$_a$ = 12-18) because of the strong electron-withdrawing nature of the SO$_2$ group. The negative charge produced by removing the proton is delocalized across the nitrogen and sulfur atoms and 2 oxygen atoms.

There is a class of antibiotics referred to as the "sulfonamides," or "sulfa drugs" (see Chapter 13). The acidity of the sulfonamide group contributes to the activity of the sulfa drugs. Some sulfa drugs are shown in Figure 40. Sulfonamides are metabolized primarily by oxidation of the sulfonamide nitrogen atom (**Figure 41**).

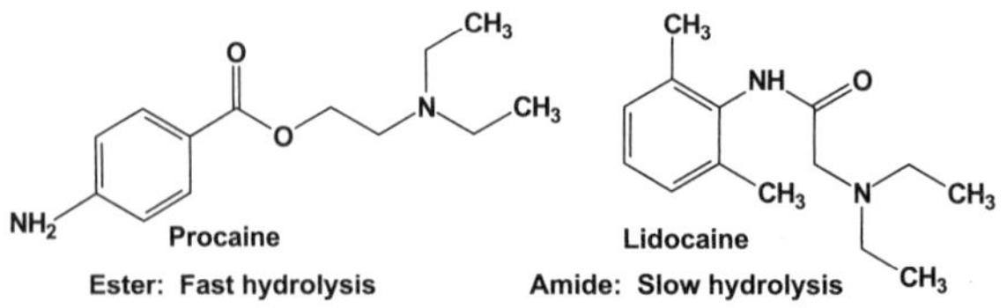

**Figure 39.** *Procaine versus lidocaine. The ester of procaine is hydrolyzed faster than is the amide of lidocaine. This difference in metabolic rate has been used to designate these as short-acting and long-acting medicines, respectively.*

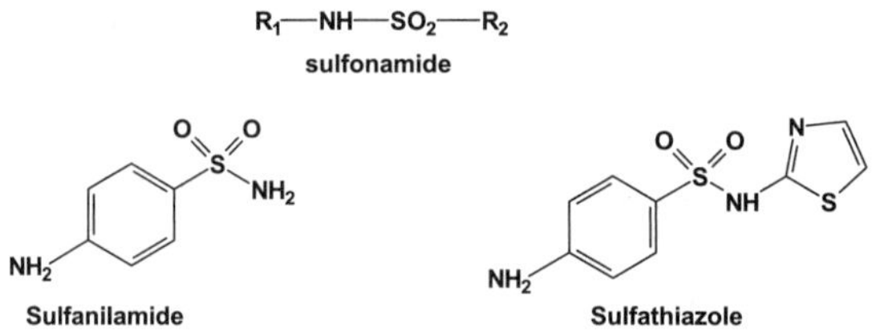

**Figure 40.** *The general structure of a sulfonamide and drugs containing the sulfonamide functional group.*

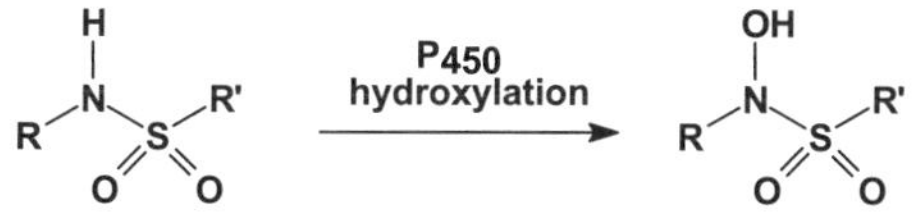

**Figure 41.** *Metabolism of sulfonamides. Sulfonamides are metabolized by $P_{450}$ hydroxylation of the nitrogen atom.*

# Important Physical Properties of Drugs

The hydrogen-bonding ability, lipophilicity, branching structure, and other features of a molecule influence the way that the molecule interacts with itself and its environment. These interactions are unique to the specific molecule and manifest themselves through the physical properties of the molecule. Physical properties are measurable quantities, such as melting point, boiling point, and aqueous solubility, that are directly related to the atomic structure of the molecule. Several of these properties are relevant to the action of a drug. This section of the chapter discusses the importance of these properties and how to predict them from the structure of a drug molecule.

## Acid and Base Characteristics of Molecules

Many biological and drug molecules have acidic and/or basic properties. To a chemist, these properties can be used in a laboratory for specific chemical reactions. In a patient, acidic and basic properties of a drug are important for 2 reasons. The first is that these properties of a molecule contribute to its water solubility. Water solubility is frequently desired so that a drug molecule can be given orally. There is a balance that many drug molecules must maintain between water solubility (to dissolve and enter the bloodstream) and lipid solubility (to pass through gastrointestinal and cellular membranes). The second reason that the acidic or basic properties of a molecule are important is that often these properties have a role in the binding of the molecule to its site of action. Examples are given in later chapters.

   As discussed earlier in this chapter, there are several functional groups found in drug molecules. Some of these functional groups are lipophilic ("lipid loving"), such as alkanes and benzene rings. Other types of functional groups are more polar and more hydrophilic ("water loving"). These include alcohols and amines. Some of these latter functional groups are also acidic or basic.

## Definitions of Acid and Base

Before addressing the functional groups themselves, it is helpful to define clearly what is meant by the terms *acid* and *base* (**Table 4**). A base is generally the opposite of an acid, and vice versa. One commonly accepted definition of these terms, Brønsted-Lowry, is named after the chemists who first proposed them. In this definition, an acid is a molecule that donates a proton (A-H, a proton donor), and a base is a molecule that accepts a proton (B:, a proton acceptor). After an acid donates a proton, it is referred to as a *conjugate base*. After a base accepts a proton, it is called a *conjugate acid*. A simple way of remembering the Brønsted-Lowry definition is this: An acid is the molecule with the extra proton. (Therefore, a base is the molecule without the proton.) The strength of a Brønsted-Lowry acid indicates the tendency for the molecule to give up a proton. Conversely, base strength is the tendency to accept a proton. The Brønsted-Lowry theory of acids and bases is most useful for discussing the acid-base properties of drugs.

A second way of defining acids and bases was proposed by Lewis. In the Lewis definition, an acid is a molecule that can accept a pair of electrons, and a base is a molecule that can donate a lone pair of electrons. Lewis' theory is commonly used when talking about inorganic molecules and metallic compounds.

$$\text{A-H} + \text{B:} \rightleftarrows \text{A:} + \text{B-H}$$

The preceding reaction shows the movement of a proton from one molecule to another. The base (B:) abstracts a proton, becoming the conjugate acid (B-H).

**Table 4.** *Examples of Brønsted-Lowry and Lewis acids and bases.*

| Type | Acid | Base |
|------|------|------|
| **Brønsted-Lowry** | HCl | NaOH |
| | $HNO_3$ | KOH |
| | $H_2SO_4$ | $RNH_2$ (all amines) |
| | $RCO_2H$ | |
| | Phenol | |
| **Lewis** | $AlCl_3$ | |
| | $SnCl_4$ | |
| | $TiCl_4$ | |
| | $FeCl_3$ | |

At the same time, the acid (A-H) gives up the proton, becoming the conjugate base (A:). The amount of the reactants or products will be determined by the strength of the acid or the base.

How can a solution's acidic or basic strength be described? By using the pH scale. The pH value is generally a number between 0 and 14. The pH scale measures the strength of an acid or base relative to water. The pH value is calculated by using the following equation:

$$\text{pH} = \text{-log } [\text{H}^+]$$

where [H⁺] is the hydrogen ion concentration. A neutral solution has a pH of 7. Very acidic solutions have a pH in the range of 0 to 4. Very basic solutions have a pH in the range of 10 to 14. Solutions with a pH in the middle of the scale (6 to 8) are said to be more neutral. Water has a pH of 7. It is useful to know the pH of certain biological systems. Blood has a pH of 7.4. Saliva has a pH of about 6 to 7. The stomach is very acidic and measures approximately 2 on the pH scale. The intestine is more basic and has a pH of approximately 8.

Acids and bases also can be described qualitatively: strong or weak. A *strong acid* is an acid that essentially fully dissociates into H⁺ and its conjugate base, which means that if a drop of a strong acid, such as HCl, is placed in water, all of the HCl molecules become H⁺ and Cl⁻. Other examples of strong acids include phosphoric acid and sulfuric acid. A *weak acid,* on the other hand, does not dissociate fully into H⁺ and its conjugate base: If a drop of a weak acid, such as acetic acid, is placed in water, only a certain percentage of the acid molecules dissociate into H⁺ and its conjugate base, the acetate anion. Almost all of the acidic and basic drug molecules described in this text and used clinically are weak acids or bases.

All weak acids and weak bases are not of equal strength. A quantitative description of a molecule's acidity or basicity is the $pK_a$ of a molecule. To understand $pK_a$, consider the following reaction:

$$HA \rightleftarrows A^- + H^+$$

The reaction describes the dissociation of an acid into H⁺ and its conjugate base, A⁻. How much acid dissociates into H⁺ and A⁻ depends on the particular acid being considered. The concentration of each of the molecular species in the reaction can be measured, and a formula can be written that provides a numerical value called the equilibrium constant. The equilibrium constant $K_a$ is defined as follows:

$$K_a = \frac{[H^+][A^-]}{[HA]}$$

where [H⁺], [A⁻], and [HA] are the concentrations of each of the molecular species at equilibrium. As more of the molecule dissociates, [H⁺] and [A⁻] become larger, and, consequently $K_a$ becomes larger. Therefore, the stronger the acid, the larger the $K_a$. For example, acetic acid ($K_a = 1.8 \times 10^{-5}$) is a stronger acid than phenol ($K_a = 1.3 \times 10^{-10}$).

The $pK_a$ is the negative log of the $K_a$. That is,

$$pK_a = -\log K_a$$

As the $K_a$ increases, the $pK_a$ decreases. The value of $pK_a$ can range from very low (large negative numbers) to very high, depending on the acidity of the molecule. The stronger the acid, the lower the $pK_a$. Continuing with the preceding example, acetic acid has a $pK_a$ of about 4.76, whereas phenol has a $pK_a$ of about 10.

For bases, an equilibrium constant can be calculated as well and is referred to as a $K_b$. For purposes of this discussion, however, it is best to consider the acidity of the conjugate acid of a particular base. Instead of determining how basic a molecule is, the acidity of the base's conjugate acid is determined. For example, it is often said that the $pK_a$ of an amine, such as triethylamine, is about 9 to 11. What is actually being described is not the acidity of triethylamine but the acidity of the triethylammonium ion $(Et_3NH^+)$. Measuring the acidity of the conjugate acid allows for easy comparison with other molecules, particularly acids. For example, it can be concluded that phenol $(pK_a \sim 10)$ and the triethylammonium ion $(pK_a \sim 9\text{-}11)$ are about equally acidic.

## $pK_a$ Values of Important Functional Groups

Many of the functional groups discussed earlier in this chapter have $pK_a$ values associated with them. **Table 5** lists a number of functional groups and their $pK_a$ values. The most acidic proton is highlighted in bold.

As shown in Table 5, many functional groups have a $pK_a$ outside the range of clinically relevant values. The designation "no $pK_a$" does not mean that the molecules cannot, under any circumstances, gain or lose a proton. (In an organic laboratory, it is very easy to remove protons from an anhydride, for example.) This designation simply means that for clinical purposes for nurse anesthetists, these functional groups can be seen as not participating as acids or bases and not being affected by changes in the pH.

**Table 5.** *$pK_a$ values of selected functional groups.[a]*

| Functional Group | Formula | $pK_a$ |
|---|---|---|
| Carboxylic acid | R-COO**H** | 3.5-5.5 |
| Phenol | phenyl-O**H** | ~10 |
| Aliphatic alcohol | R-O**H** | 15-20 (no $pK_a$) |
| Anhydride | -C(=O)OC(=O)C**H**- | ~20 (no $pK_a$) |
| Ketone | -C(=O)C**H**$_3$ | ~20 (no $pK_a$) |
| Amide | -C(=O)N**H**$_2$ | ~25 (no $pK_a$) |
| Alkane | -CH$_2$-**H** | ~40 (no $pK_a$) |
| Alkyne | C≡C-**H** | ~20 (no $pK_a$) |
| Thiol | R-S**H** | 7-8 |
| Sulfonamide | R-N**H**-SO$_2$-R | ~12-18 |
| Amine | R-N**H**$_3{}^+$ | 8-11 |
| Aniline | Phenyl-N**H**$_3{}^+$ | 4-5 |
| Aromatic amine | Pyridine-**H**$^+$ | 4-7 |
| 1 aromatic amine + 1 nonaromatic amine | Imidazole-**H**$^+$ | 4-7 |

[a] For acidic groups, the most acidic proton is highlighted in bold. The term "no $pK_a$" refers to the fact that these $pK_a$'s lie outside the range of clinically relevant values.

# Substituent Effects on Functional Group pK$_a$ Values

The pK$_a$ of a functional group can be affected by other substituents on the molecule. Certain groups of atoms draw electron density toward themselves and away from the rest of the molecule. These groups are called *electron-withdrawing groups* (EWGs). Other groups have the opposite effect and push electron density away from themselves, toward the rest of the molecule. These groups are called *electron-donating groups* (EDGs). The electronic differences of these groups can have important effects on the pK$_a$ of a molecule.

The effects of EDGs and EWGs can be seen clearly in the following series of substituted acetic acids. The pK$_a$ of acetic acid is about 5. Chloro groups are generally EWGs. When 1 chloro group is placed on the methyl group, to form chloroacetic acid, the acidity increases and the pK$_a$ decreases to about 2.9. Adding 1 (dichloroacetic acid) or 2 (trichloroacetic acid) additional chloro groups increases the acidity even further.

| pK$_a$ | 4.76 | 2.86 | 1.29 | 0.65 |

Methyl groups are generally EDGs, so when methyl groups are added to acetic acid, the opposite trend in acidity and pK$_a$ results. Because the electronic effect of a methyl group is smaller than that of a chloro group, the change in pK$_a$ over the series is not as large.

| pK$_a$ | 4.76 | 4.88 | 4.86 | 5.05 |

The effect of EDGs and EWGs can also be transmitted through an aromatic ring, such as a benzene ring. Phenol has a pK$_a$ of about 10. Substituents on the phenyl ring of phenol can strengthen or weaken its acidity (**Table 6**). The addition of a methyl group (EDG) decreases the acidity of the molecule, resulting in a pK$_a$ of approximately 10.3. The addition of a nitro group, however, increases the acidity of the molecule dramatically. A nitro group is a very powerful EWG. Successive additions of nitro groups increase the acidity (and decrease the pK$_a$) of phenol even further.

**Table 6.** *Effect of electron-donating and electron-withdrawing groups on the $pK_a$ of phenol.*

| | EDG | $pK_a$ | EWG | $pK_a$ |
|---|---|---|---|---|
| Phenol | (benzene ring)—OH | 10 | (benzene ring)—OH | 10 |
| | $CH_3$—(benzene ring)—OH | 10.26 | $O_2N$—(benzene ring)—OH | 7.2 |
| | | | $O_2N$—(benzene ring with $NO_2$)—OH | 4 |
| | | | $O_2N$—(benzene ring with $NO_2$, $NO_2$)—OH | 0.4 |

**Table 7** is a list of common EDGs and EWGs. These functional groups will be important when the reactivity of molecules and their mechanisms of action are discussed.

While Table 7 is a formidable list of functional groups, the similarities among these groups make them easier to remember. For the EWGs, in most cases the attached atom (C or N) has a multiple bond to another atom. For example, the nitro group has a multiple bond between the nitrogen (the attached atom) and the oxygen. For the EDGs, in most cases each attached atom has a lone pair of electrons. For example, the oxygen of an alcohol and the nitrogen of an amine both have lone pairs of electrons.

As discussed in the next section, whether a molecule is charged or uncharged can affect the water solubility of a drug. Consideration of other substituents on the molecule around the functional group can assist in the comparison of the acidity or basicity of 2 molecules.

**Table 7.** *Common electron-withdrawing (EWGs) and electron-donating groups (EDGs).*

| EWGs | EDGs |
|---|---|
| -$NO_2$ (nitro) | -OH (alcohol) |
| -COOH (carboxylic acid) | -SH (thiol) |
| -C(=O)H (aldehyde) | -NHR (amine) |
| -C(=O)R (ketone) | -alkyl |
| -C(=O)OR (ester) | |
| -C(=O)NHR (amide) | |
| -$CF_3$ (trifluoromethyl) | |
| -halogens | |

# Effect of pK$_a$ on Ionization

How can one tell if a drug molecule will be charged in water or in a patient's body? Although not always an easy determination, there is a quick way of estimating the relative solubility of a drug molecule. Most body fluids, such as blood, saliva, and stomach fluid, are mainly water. Therefore, the water solubility of a drug molecule is very important when determining whether a drug will dissolve in a certain body fluid. The presence of polar functional groups on the molecule increases water solubility.

The pH of the particular fluid may also be important. The pH of blood is about 7.4, but the pH of other fluids differs. The stomach and intestine, 2 main areas of oral drug absorption, have pH values of about 2 and 8, respectively. The pH of the fluid affects whether any acidic or basic functional groups will be ionized, or charged. If the functional group is charged, water solubility increases. Knowing the pH of the particular fluid and the pK$_a$ of the particular functional group can help determine whether the functional group will be ionized, or charged, in that particular fluid.

In many cases, it can easily be determined that a particular functional group is charged or uncharged at a particular pH. For example, if a drug containing a basic amine, such as a secondary amine, is ingested, the amine will become protonated and charged once it enters the stomach, where the pH is about 2. In other cases, it may not be as clear. In addition, the precise ratio of charged to uncharged drug may be of interest. To make these determinations, the *Henderson-Hasselbalch equation* must be used:

$$pH = pK_a + \log \frac{[A^-]}{[HA]}$$

where pH is the pH of the solution containing the drug, pK$_a$ is the negative log of K$_a$ (of the functional groups present in the drug) as described earlier, [A$^-$] is the concentration of the base form (conjugate base) of the drug, and [HA] is the concentration of the acid form of the drug. Think of the base form of the drug as that without the acidic proton. The acid form of the drug contains the acidic proton. For example, in an amine, R-NH$_2$ is the base form (A$^-$) and R-NH$_3^+$ is the acid form (HA). Note that the acid form of the amine has a positive charge. Conversely, consider the carboxylic acid RCOO$^-$ is the base form (with the proton removed) and R-COOH is the acid form (with the proton). Here, the base form of the carboxylic acid is charged.

Will an amine, eg, ketamine (an anesthetic agent), be charged at pH 2? If so, what is the ratio of charged to uncharged molecules? The Henderson-Hasselbalch equation can be used to obtain the answer. The pK$_a$ of ketamine is about 7.5.

Input the values of pH and $pK_a$ into the equation ([Ket] is the concentration of the base form, and $[KetH^+]$ is the concentration of the acid form):

$$2 = 7.5 + \log \frac{[Ket]}{[KetH^+]}$$

$$-5.5 = \log \frac{[Ket]}{[KetH^+]} \quad \text{--Take inverse log of both sides}$$

$$3 \times 10^{-6} = \frac{[Ket]}{[KetH^+]}$$

Thus, the ratio of the base form (Ket) to the acid, or protonated, form $(KetH^+)$ is about $3 \times 10^{-6}$–very small. In other words, at pH 2, there are about $3 \times 10^6$ (3 million!) protonated ketamine molecules for every 1 nonprotonated molecule. Most of the molecules will be in the protonated (acid) form. Therefore, at pH 2, ketamine will be charged, making it highly water soluble.

A drug molecule often contains several functional groups. In some cases, there are multiple acidic groups or multiple basic groups with differing strengths. Depending on the pH of the solution, all, some, or none of the basic and/or acidic groups can be charged. To determine the ionization state of the molecule, the Henderson-Hasselbalch equation must be used for each group separately.

## Water Solubility

If a substance can be dissolved in water, it is said to be water soluble. Dissolving is the process of separating individual molecules of one substance, the solute, by another, the solvent. For most drugs, its potential to be water soluble is important for its administration. Increased water solubility will allow a drug to be more easily transported from its administered form (eg, pill, intravenous solution, or oral suspension) to the bloodstream. The bloodstream is typically responsible for distributing the drug to its site of action.

What makes a drug water soluble? While the presence or absence of charged functional groups can have a substantial effect on water solubility, other factors affect the water solubility of a drug.

A drug will more likely be water soluble if it can make intermolecular, noncovalent bonds with water. A molecule that can form hydrogen bonds, dipole-dipole interactions, or ion-dipole interactions with water will be more water soluble compared with a molecule that cannot participate in these interactions. Certain functional groups can form intermolecular bonds with water and will, therefore, exhibit increased water solubility compared with those that cannot.

For example, amines, alcohols, carboxylic acids, and other carbonyl-containing compounds can form hydrogen bonds with water. Molecules with these functional groups will most likely have higher water solubility compared with alkanes and alkenes, which cannot form hydrogen bonds with water.

In the body, there must be a combination of water-solubility properties of a molecule (to allow it to dissolve) and lipid-solubility properties (to allow it to cross tissue and cellular membranes). Often, these properties are delicately balanced to ensure that the proper amount of drug gets to the appropriate tissue destination to treat the patient's condition. Although the scope of this book does not permit a detailed discussion of this process, it is important that practitioners have an understanding of the principles at work.

## Diffusion

*Diffusion* means that any gaseous or liquid mixture, at a constant temperature, will become uniform over time with an equal distribution of particles throughout. The process of diffusion depends on the natural motion that exists in all molecules. The *diffusion rate* is the speed at which a certain molecule is able to travel over a given distance through a given medium. For example, if a powdered drink mix is poured into a gallon of water, the mix will eventually spread throughout the liquid until the solution is homogeneous. However, if a volume of syrup, which is thick and viscous, is added instead, diffusion into the gallon of water will still occur, but at a rate that is much slower than that of the drink mix.

A variety of factors influence the diffusion rate of a molecule. Some of these have nothing to do with the molecule, but instead involve the environment into which the molecule was added. For example, the density and particle size of the medium, as well as the temperature, will all change the diffusion rate of a molecule. The size, polarity, and solubility of the molecule will also greatly affect its diffusion rate. A large molecule will have more difficulty moving through a solution than will a smaller molecule. Likewise, a polar molecule more easily diffuses through a polar solution than does a nonpolar one. For example, ethanol, which is polar and forms hydrogen bonds, diffuses very quickly through a gallon of water. Ethanol would diffuse more slowly through a gallon of a nonpolar solution, such as gasoline.

## Suggested Reading

Atkins P, Jones L. *Chemical Principles: The Quest for Insight.* 5th ed. New York, NY: WH Freeman & Co; 2010.

Karty J. *Get Ready for Organic Chemistry.* 2nd ed. Boston, MA: Pearson; 2012.

Lemke TL. *Review of Organic Functional Groups: Introduction to Medicinal Organic Chemistry.* 5th ed. Baltimore, MD: Lippincott Williams & Wilkins; 2012.

March J, Smith MB. *March's Advanced Organic Chemistry: Reactions, Mechanisms, and Structure.* 7th ed. Hoboken, NJ: Wiley; 2012.

Wade LG Jr. *Organic Chemistry.* 7th ed. Upper Saddle River, NJ: Prentice Hall; 2009.

## Discussion Topics

1. The difference in activity between procaine and lidocaine is described in the chapter. Draw the hydrolysis mechanism for each compound, highlighting the differences.

2. Figure 36 shows the structure of LSD. The molecule contains 2 stereogenic centers. By using the Cahn-Ingold-Prelog method, describe the stereochemistry of these centers.

3. Physiological pH is generally considered to be around 7.2, whereas the pH of the stomach is very acidic (approximately pH 2). Describe the ionization state of a carboxylic acid versus an amine under these different conditions. If a molecule must be neutral (have no charge) to cross biological membranes, which type(s) of functional groups would be able to cross in the stomach?

4. Ionic compounds (salts) are typically thought to have increased water solubility. Many salts are ingredients in common food items and over-the-counter medications. Discuss common examples of these compounds, and describe their possible structures.

5. Complex organic molecules are composed of many functional groups. As we will see in the following chapters, the pattern of functional groups determines the biological activity of these molecules. Devise a hypothetical organic molecule with at least 3 different functional groups. Think about its characteristics with respect to ionization, hydrogen bonding, polarity, shape, and water solubility.

# Chapter 3

# Biological Macromolecules
*by Cynthia S. Dowd, PhD, and Lemont B. Kier, PhD*

Although most of this book focuses on small molecules, an understanding of larger biological molecules is necessary to fully comprehend the mechanisms of anesthetics and other medicinal agents. Unwanted side effects of a drug are often due to the drug interacting with one or more biological molecules other than the intended target. The pharmacokinetic and pharmacodynamic properties of anesthetic agents can also be affected by biological macromolecules of the cell.

The 4 main groups of biological macromolecules are: (1) nucleic acids and polynucleotides, (2) amino acids and proteins, (3) lipids, and (4) carbohydrates. This chapter introduces each of these groups with respect to their structure, function in the body, and clinical relevance in terms of drug action.

## Nucleic Acids and Polynucleotides
The first group of biological macromolecules is the nucleic acids. Called such because they are found in the nucleus of every cell in the body, nucleic acids (DNA and RNA) are the building blocks from which every organism is built. These large molecules contain the information, in the form of genes, for all other components of an organism. DNA and RNA can also act as receptors for drug molecules.

### Deoxyribonucleic Acid
DNA is often depicted as 2 ribbons that curve together in the shape of a double helix (**Figure 1**). The strands are held together by hydrogen bonds and are complementary to each other, that is, they have structures that form hydrogen bonds with, and only with, each other. DNA is usually double stranded.

Each strand of DNA is made of a linear chain of nucleotides. A *nucleotide* is the combination of 1 phosphate, 1 deoxyribose unit, and 1 DNA base. The nucleotides of DNA are adenosine monophosphate (AMP), guanosine monophosphate (GMP), cytosine monophosphate (CMP), and thymidine monophosphate (TMP). Nucleotides are made from nucleosides. A *nucleoside* is the combination of 1 deoxyribose unit and 1 DNA base. The nucleosides of DNA are adenosine, guanosine, cytosine, and thymidine. A phosphodiester bond connects the 3'-ribose carbon atom of one nucleotide and the 5'-ribose carbon atom of the next nucleotide, forming the linear strand of DNA. This pattern aligns the phosphate groups on the outside of the DNA molecule and the bases on the inside.

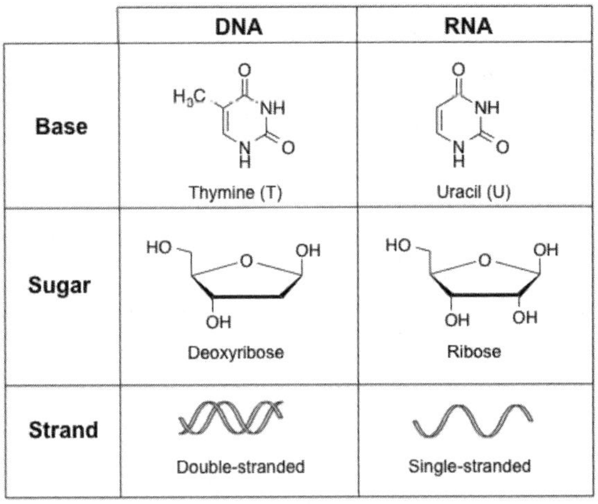

| | DNA | RNA |
|---|---|---|
| **Base** | Thymine (T) | Uracil (U) |
| **Sugar** | Deoxyribose | Ribose |
| **Strand** | Double-stranded | Single-stranded |

**Figure 1.** *Comparison of DNA and RNA. The 3 primary differences between DNA and RNA are the sugar, the base, and the strand structure.*

There are 4 DNA bases: adenine (A), guanine (G), cytosine (C), and thymine (T). The 2 strands of DNA that create the double helix are held together by hydrophobic forces between the stacked bases and hydrogen bonds between the bases from each strand. Adenine forms 2 hydrogen bonds with thymine. Cytosine forms 3 hydrogen bonds with guanine (**Figure 2**). When these bases come in contact with their hydrogen-bonding partner, the bases are *paired*. The DNA bases can be divided into the purines and pyrimidines. The purines are adenine (A) and guanine (G) and have 1 six-membered ring fused to 1 five-membered ring (Figure 2). The pyrimidines are cytosine (C) and thymine (T). Pyrimidines have only 1 six-membered ring.

The genetic information for all living things is contained in the linear strand structure of DNA. The pattern of bases determines the sequence of a specific protein that a cell will make. Herein lies the central dogma of most biological systems: DNA encodes RNA, which, in turn, encodes protein. The process of synthesizing RNA from DNA is called *transcription*. The process of synthesizing protein from RNA is called *translation*. A sequence of 3 DNA bases is called a *codon*. Each codon is translated into 1 amino acid. Linear combinations of amino acids form proteins. In this way, a pattern of thousands of DNA bases is converted into 1 protein. The set of cellular components required for the cell is encoded by the complete set of DNA bases. The entire set of genes for an organism is called the *genome*.

Several drug classes have mechanisms of action that involve various types of interruption of DNA synthesis and transcription. The primary classes of drugs are antineoplastic agents, used in cancer chemotherapy, and antiviral agents. Several antineoplastic agents work through a DNA-based mechanism. Methotrexate halts the production of tetrahydrofolic acid by inhibition of dihydrofolate reductase. Tetrahydrofolic acid is an essential cofactor for DNA synthesis. Anthracyclines, namely doxorubicin, intercalate into DNA and prevent transcription. Bleomycin has been shown to cause fragmentation of DNA and the inhibition of transcription. Anthramycin binds covalently to the amino group of guanine. This covalent modification of DNA prevents transcription.

The human immunodeficiency virus (HIV)/AIDS epidemic has renewed interest in antiviral medications. Zidovudine (Retrovir), also called AZT, is a mimic of thymidine. Zidovudine fools the viral machinery and is incorporated by viral reverse transcriptase into viral DNA. The azido group of zidovudine prevents DNA elongation from occurring, and HIV replication is halted. Acyclovir and ganciclovir selectively inhibit viral DNA polymerase, the primary enzyme for viral DNA synthesis.

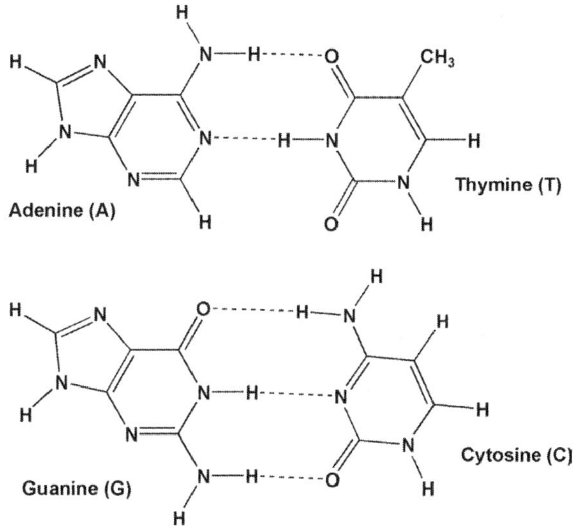

**Figure 2.** *Watson-Crick hydrogen-bonding pattern between adenine and thymine (2 hydrogen bonds) and guanine and cytosine (3 hydrogen bonds). Hydrogen bonds are indicated by the dashed lines.*

## Ribonucleic Acid

While DNA contains the genetic code, or information necessary to create all proteins in a cell, RNA is necessary for the conversion of this code into proteins. RNA is a linear chain of nucleotides, containing bases, sugars, and phosphates, similar to DNA. There are 3 important differences, however, between the structures of RNA and DNA (Figure 1). First, the sugar in RNA is ribose, not deoxyribose, as in DNA. Second, the bases in RNA are adenine, guanine, cytosine, and uracil. There is no thymine in RNA. Third, RNA generally exists as a single-stranded molecule, while DNA is in a double-stranded form. Because RNA is normally single stranded, any secondary structure that may occur usually does so because of base pairing in the strand.

There are 4 types of RNA. Each is necessary for a cell to properly convert the information in DNA into protein. Messenger RNA (mRNA) transfers genetic information directly transcribed from DNA to ribosomes. Ribosomal RNA (rRNA) molecules, together with various enzymatic proteins, form ribosomes, the site of protein synthesis. Transfer RNA (tRNA) recognizes a 3-base codon presented by mRNA and brings the amino acid that corresponds to that codon to the ribosome for addition to the growing protein chain. Mitochondrial RNA (mtRNA) encodes proteins that are made and used only in the mitochondria and pertain mainly to synthesis of adenosine triphosphate (ATP) and energy flow in the organelle.

In the same way that some drugs act through interruption of DNA synthesis and transcription, some drugs disrupt RNA synthesis and/or translation. Mithramycin binds to RNA and was originally found to be an effective antibiotic. However, its usefulness has also been extended to the treatment of certain cancers. The macrolide antibiotics, such as erythromycin, inhibit protein synthesis by interrupting the action of tRNA at the ribosome. Rifampin, another antibiotic, inhibits RNA polymerase. An antineoplastic agent, 5-fluorouracil, mimics uracil and becomes incorporated into RNA. In this way, 5-fluorouracil inhibits the synthesis of mRNA, tRNA, and therefore, proteins.

## Amino Acids and Proteins

Just as DNA and RNA are made of repeated units or building blocks, so are proteins. The building blocks that comprise proteins are the *amino acids* (**Figure 3**). As their name implies, each amino acid has an amine group and a carboxylic acid group. In α amino acids, both of these groups are attached to a central carbon atom, called the α carbon atom. Also bonded to this central carbon atom is a *side chain,* which is the only part of the molecule that varies among all amino acids. In all but 1 of the 20 common α-amino acids, the central carbon atom of the amino acid is covalently bonded to 4 different substituents, ie, the central carbon is stereogenic. Therefore, each of these amino acids is chiral. The 2 stereoisomers are usually referred to as the D and L isomers. In most proteins, the amino acids have the L configuration. (Glycine is the remaining amino acid that does not have a stereogenic center. The central carbon atom of glycine is bonded to 2 hydrogen atoms.)

The 20 common amino acids are divided into groups based on the character-istics of their side chains. The nonpolar amino acids are glycine (Gly), alanine (Ala), valine (Val), leucine (Leu), isoleucine (Ile), phenylalanine (Phe), proline (Pro), tryptophan (Trp), and methionine (Met). The polar amino acids are tyrosine (Tyr), serine (Ser), threonine (Thr), cysteine (Cys), asparagine (Asn), glutamine (Gln), aspartic acid (Asp), glutamic acid (Glu), lysine (Lys), arginine (Arg), and histidine (His). Among the polar amino acids, some molecules have side chains that may be ionized at pH levels found in the body. The basic residues are Lys, Arg, and His. The acidic residues are Asp and Glu. Figure 3 summarizes the amino acids and their structures.

The joining of amino acids to create a protein occurs at the ribosome. The order of amino acids joined together is determined by the DNA sequence of codons. In making a protein, 2 amino acids are joined together by a peptide bond (**Figure 4**). This bond is formed between the carboxylic acid of one residue and the amino group of the next residue. The condensation that occurs between the 2 molecules results in the formation of an amide linkage, known as the peptide bond. The joining of many amino acids in this way leads to the synthesis of a protein. The linear sequence of amino acids that is used to make a protein is its *primary structure.*

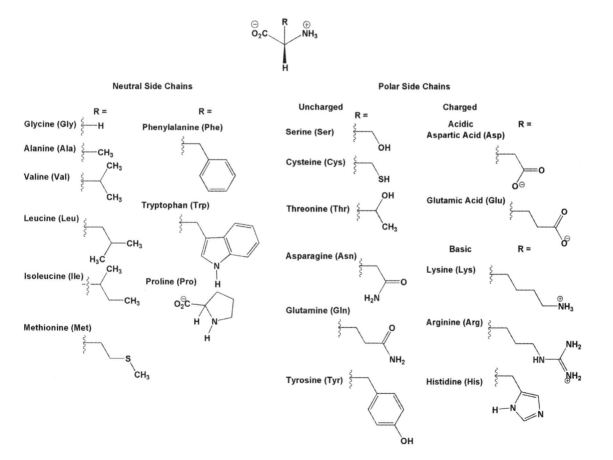

**Figure 3.** *Structures of the 20 common amino acids.*

As in all amides, the lone pair electrons on the nitrogen atom can resonate through the carbon-oxygen double bond. There is partial double-bond character in the carbon-nitrogen linkage (Figure 4). The resonance stabilization of the peptide bond leads to structural planarity in the molecule. Thus, the amide carbon, the oxygen, the α carbon of the first amino acid and the nitrogen, the attached hydrogen, and the α carbon of the second amino acid all lie in the same plane (Figure 4). This planarity of the peptide bond adds rigidity to the structure of the rest of the protein.

Linear strands of amino acid residues can quickly adopt a conformation that is a result of noncovalent forces, including hydrogen bonds, within the protein. This type of organization is called the *secondary structure* of the protein. The 2 most common forms of secondary structure are the α helix and the β pleated sheet. An α helix is formed when the amino acid residues of a protein form a hydrogen bond with each other in a coiled manner so that each residue interacts with residues above and below it. In a typical α helix, a complete turn occurs every 3.6 residues. The second type of secondary structural element is the β pleated sheet. In the sheet, 2 linear strands of amino acid residues lie against each other. Hydrogen bonds are formed between the 2 strands. In α helices and β pleated sheets, hydrogen bonds are formed between the hydrogen of one amide nitrogen and the lone pair electrons of the carbonyl oxygen from a different residue. The residue side chains are not normally involved in creating the secondary structure of a protein.

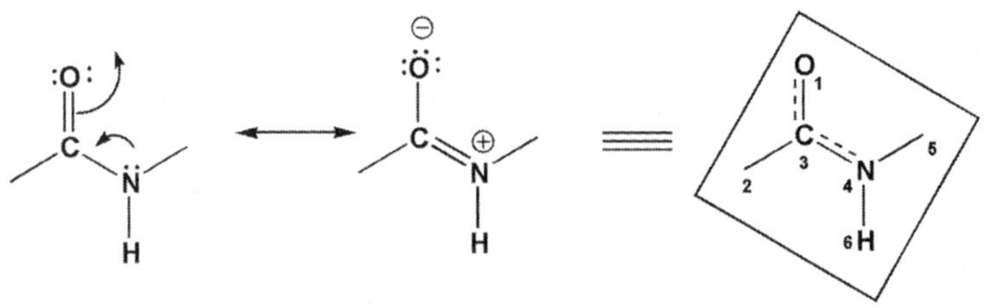

**Figure 4.** *The peptide bond has a planar structure because of the delocalization of electrons between the carbonyl carbon and oxygen and the amide nitrogen atoms. This delocalization gives the carbon-nitrogen bond slight double-bond character. Because of this characteristic, the 6 atoms surrounding the peptide bond share the same plane of geometry.*

Proteins can vary in size from only a few amino acid residues to several hundred or several thousand amino acid residues. Small proteins are often called peptides or oligopeptides. Larger proteins are sometimes called polypeptides. Certain strands in a protein adopt α-helical conformations, while other strands form β sheets. The combination of α helices and β sheets and the way they pack together define the *tertiary structure* of a protein. Often a large protein, such as hemoglobin, is actually several discrete polypeptide chains that are closely associated. Hemoglobin is composed of 4 polypeptides, or subunits, each of which folds into a discrete region, called a domain. After the domains fold into their respective secondary and tertiary structures, the domains come together to form the fully functional protein. The arrangement of separate protein domains with respect to each other in space determines the *quaternary structure* of the protein.

## Protein Functions

Proteins perform a wide range of functions. They provide structure, perform chemical reactions to create new molecules, transport molecules from one place to another, and send and receive chemical signals within a cell and between cells. Because proteins serve so many varied and vital roles, they have been the most popular and successful drug targets. The following section describes classes of proteins categorized by function. These types of proteins are often seen as receptor targets for clinically useful medicines.

## Regulatory Proteins

A *regulatory protein* transmits a message from a chemical signal to another portion of the cell. The distribution of regulatory proteins determines where the effect of that receptor will be experienced. Tissues containing a specific protein respond to certain chemical stimuli in a specific way, whereas tissues without that protein do not respond. Similarly, the effects of drugs used selectively to alter the behavior of certain proteins are seen only in tissues where that protein is present. For example, one family of regulatory proteins is the serotonin receptors. The natural ligand for serotonin receptors is 5-hydroxytryptamine (serotonin). Serotonin receptors are found predominantly on nerve cells in the central nervous system (CNS). The major physiological effects of serotonin receptors are, therefore, experienced in the CNS. Regulatory proteins can have a variety of shapes and sizes and can be located within a membrane or float freely in the cytosol. Several families of regulatory proteins are discussed herein.

An important class of regulatory proteins is the *G protein coupled receptor* (GPCR) family, which are transmembrane receptors. In general, in transmembrane proteins, at least one portion of the protein crosses a cell membrane that separates 2 cellular compartments. This transmembrane region connects protein domains that are on either side of the membrane. It is through this portion of the protein that a signal is passed from one side of the membrane to the other. The GPCRs have 7 transmembrane regions and are typically found in the exterior membrane of nerve cells (**Figure 5**). The actions of GPCRs affect a variety of organ systems in the body. The endogenous chemical substance that binds to a GPCR is called a *ligand*. If the GPCR and ligand are associated with the nervous system, the ligand is called a *neurotransmitter*. Neurotransmitters are chemical signals that pass between nerve cells in the nervous system. Examples of neurotransmitters are serotonin, dopamine, epinephrine, norepinephrine, acetylcholine, and γ-aminobutyric acid (GABA). The GPCRs get their name because, on the interior portion of the receptor, they bind to G proteins. G proteins mediate the signals that are received by the GPCR and catalyze changes in the cell.

*Ion channels* are located in the cell membrane and regulate the entry or exit of ions from one side of the membrane to the other (**Figure 6**). Potassium, sodium, and calcium are examples of cations that pass through ion channels. Chloride anions are also transported via ion channels. Ion channels are particularly important in nervous signal transmission. Some neurotransmitters act on ion channels. When the neurotransmitter binds to an ion channel on a nerve cell, the ion channel opens, allowing the passage of ions into or out of the cell. Binding of a neurotransmitter to an ion channel can result in transmission of the nerve signal (in an excitable cell) or delay of the signal (in an inhibitory cell).

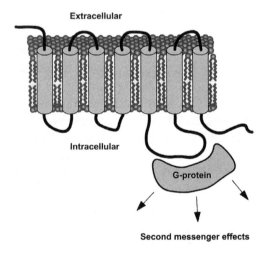

**Figure 5.** *The G protein coupled receptors (GPCRs) have 7 transmembrane regions and are coupled to a G protein on the intracellular membrane surface. The G protein mediates the signal between the GPCR and the second messenger systems of the cell.*

*Nuclear hormone receptors* are a second family of regulatory proteins (**Figure 7**). All nuclear hormone receptors have a binding site for ligands and a separate binding site for DNA. By directly binding to DNA, the nuclear hormone receptor can modulate transcription of DNA into RNA. Thus, binding of a ligand to a nuclear hormone receptor triggers direct effects on gene expression of that particular cell. Hormones and vitamin D exert their effects by binding to nuclear receptors. Hormones are molecules that are released from a gland or organ in one part of the body, move through the circulatory system, and have their effects on another part of the body. Nuclear receptors are not membrane-bound.

*Tyrosine kinases* are a family of proteins that mediate the activity of intracellular proteins. Tyrosine kinases influence the activities of secondary proteins by *phosphorylation,* which is the addition of a phosphate group to a molecule. Tyrosine kinases transfer a phosphate group from ATP to a tyrosine residue of the secondary protein. Phosphorylation of the secondary protein acts as a switch that turns the activity of the secondary protein on or off. Tyrosine kinases are important because many of these proteins have been implicated in tumor growth. Epidermal growth factor receptors, platelet-derived growth factor receptors, and vascular endothelial growth factor receptors have all been shown to be upregulated in malignant tissues. Overabundance of these types of receptors is thought to have a role in tumor growth. For this reason, tyrosine kinases are considered an important family of target receptors for cancer drug development.

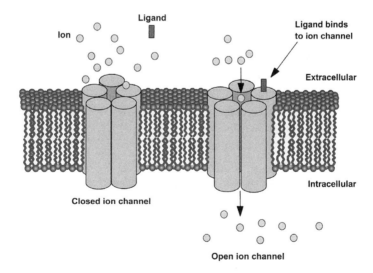

**Figure 6.** *A ligand-gated ion channel. Ion channels are composed of several transmembrane subunits. On ligand binding outside the cell, the ion channel opens, allowing a specific ion to enter the cell.*

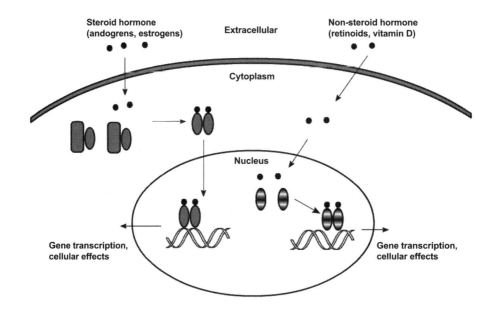

**Figure 7.** *Nuclear hormone receptors. Ligand binding to a nuclear hormone receptor causes receptor dimerization, followed by binding to genetic material in the nucleus.*

## Transport Proteins

*Transport proteins,* often called transporters or pumps, move a chemical substance from one place in the cell to another. Transporters can be located in a cell membrane or floating in the cell. Examples of transport proteins include neurotransmitter reuptake pumps, amino acid transporters, efflux pumps, and chaperone proteins.

*Neurotransmitter reuptake pumps* are usually located on the presynaptic side of a synapse and are responsible for removing excess neurotransmitter from the synapse. In this way, neurotransmitters are recycled back into the presynaptic cell and can be stored for later release. The action of reuptake pumps is one of the primary ways that neurotransmitters are removed from the synapse. An example of a reuptake pump is the serotonin reuptake transporter. Specifically designed for serotonin, this reuptake pump removes serotonin from the synapse after it has been released from the presynaptic cell and acts on the serotonergic receptor of the postsynaptic cell. Removal of serotonin from the synapse by the reuptake pump stops stimulation of the postsynaptic cell. A group of antidepressants, called selective serotonin reuptake inhibitors (SSRIs), exert their pharmacological effect by binding to the serotonin reuptake pump and blocking the reuptake of serotonin. In this way, SSRIs result in an increased concentration of serotonin in the synapse and, consequently, continued transmission of the nervous signal. Examples of SSRIs are fluoxetine and paroxetine.

Because they are used in protein synthesis and, sometimes, as chemical signals themselves, amino acids are valuable to a cell. To recycle amino acids as much as possible, the cell has *amino acid transporters,* located in membranes, that move amino acids from one compartment to another. In the design of new drugs, understanding amino acid transporters can be useful. If a drug molecule resembles a certain amino acid, the transporter can be fooled into moving the molecule across the membrane. In this way, the drug uses cellular machinery to pass through the exterior membrane and into the cell.

*Efflux pumps* exist in cellular membranes to discard molecules that are unwanted by the cell. Efflux pumps have been implicated in the removal of specific drug molecules from the interior of the cell. The presence of efflux pumps can have an important influence on the duration of action of a drug. If a drug is removed from the cellular site of action by an efflux pump, its duration of activity will be decreased.

## Structural Proteins

Certain proteins in the body function to hold components of the cell together or in place. *Structural proteins,* as they are called, provide stability in the cell, much like the walls of a building provide support to hold it up. An example of a structural protein is tubulin. Tubulin forms fibers during cell division to assist in pulling the chromosomes apart between the 2 (forming) daughter cells. Paclitaxel (Taxol), a cancer drug, works by inhibiting tubulin polymerization, thereby decreasing the rate at which cells can divide. Similarly, colchicine is used to treat gout and works by binding to tubulin. Colchicine binding to tubulin prevents its polymerization, which decreases phagocytosis of uric acid and movement of leukocytes to a site of inflammation.

## Enzymes

A protein that catalyzes a specific chemical reaction is called an *enzyme.* These reactions can involve the breakdown of a molecule, as in metabolism, or the joining of 2 molecules, as in protein biosynthesis. In all cases, an enzyme accelerates a chemical reaction to several hundred times the rate at which the reaction would occur without the enzyme. Enzymes can speed up these reactions because they bring the substrates required for the reaction in proximity to one another, in the proper alignment, so that the chemical reaction can easily take place. This process works so well that often a single molecule of an enzyme can repeat a reaction several thousand times per second.

The number of enzymes contained in the human body is immense. A few examples, however, can illustrate the breadth of function within this class of proteins. Acetylcholinesterase (AchE), an enzyme found in the synapse between nerve cells, binds a molecule of acetylcholine, which is a neurotransmitter, and hydrolyzes its ester functionality, rendering the molecule inactive. This action removes acetylcholine from the synapse and prevents continuation of the nervous cell stimulation. DNA polymerase I, as its name implies, forms strands of DNA that are complementary to a DNA template and repair damaged or incorrect DNA sequences. A final example of an enzyme is dopa decarboxylase. Dopa decarboxylase catalyzes the removal of the carboxylate group from dopa to give dopamine as the product. This is an important enzymatic reaction in the biosynthesis of dopamine, a neurotransmitter in the CNS.

Many different drugs target enzymatic proteins. These drugs act as inhibitors to slow or stop the normal function of the enzyme. For example, inhibitors of AchE bind to the enzyme and result in decreased degradation of acetylcholine. Tacrine (Cognex) is an inhibitor of AchE and is approved for the treatment of Alzheimer disease. HIV protease inhibitors bind to HIV protease, an essential enzyme in the HIV life cycle, and prevent the enzyme from completing its function. The loss of HIV protease activity results in the death of the virus. Amprenavir (Agenerase) and indinavir (Crixivan) are examples of protease inhibitors used to treat HIV. Throughout the chapters of this text, many drugs will be discussed that mediate their effects through enzymes.

## Antibodies

*Antibodies* are a key component of the humoral immune system. The immune system uses antibodies to identify foreign substances in the body. When an antibody binds to a foreign substance, the substance is engulfed and destroyed by the immune system. In this way, the body can eliminate foreign substances. Because the body can remember these foreign substances, via production of antibodies, it can mount an immune response quickly should the foreign substance be encountered again.

The natural production of antibodies by the body has been relied on for the development and use of some types of vaccines. A person is given a dose of a substance representing the foreign substance (eg, killed form of a virus or a related, but nonlethal, virus or bacterium). In response to this dose, the body produces antibodies that will recognize a subsequent attack by the infectious agent. Antibodies can also be used as drugs. Trastuzumab (Herceptin) is an antibody that is used to treat breast cancer. The antibody binds to the HER2 receptor, a protein that is overexpressed in some breast cancers.

## Signaling Proteins

*Signaling proteins* act as molecular messengers that carry signals between cells. Some hormones and cytokines are examples of signaling proteins. As described earlier, hormones are molecules that are synthesized and released in one area of the body, to have their effect on a different part of the body. Examples of hormones that are proteins include growth hormone and insulin. Hormones are usually associated with the endocrine system. *Cytokines* typically are molecules involved in the immune system that are secreted in response to a stimulus. Examples of cytokines are tumor necrosis factor $\alpha$, the interleukins (eg, IL-5, IL-8, IL-12), and the interferons, such as interferon-$\gamma$.

## *Lipids*

*Lipids* are nonpolar, hydrophobic molecules that are soluble in nonpolar, organic solvents such as chloroform and ether and much less soluble in polar solvents such as water. In the body, lipids fulfill vital roles because of their nonpolar nature. Lipid macromolecules serve several functions within the cell: They form the basic structure of membranes within an organism, provide a means of storing energy for the cell, and serve as the building blocks of many hormones, vitamins, and cellular receptors. This section focuses on the classes of lipids, their structures, and how these structures are influential in the roles of lipids in biological systems.

## Fatty Acids

The basic building block of many lipids is the *fatty acid*. In simple terms, a fatty acid is an alkyl chain with a carboxylic acid on one end. The alkyl chain can vary between short and long, straight chain and branched, and saturated and unsaturated. The structures of several fatty acids are shown in **Figure 8**. The most common fatty acids in humans have 16, 18, or 20 carbon atoms and are identified by commonly accepted names rather than their systematic (International Union of Pure and Applied Chemistry) names. Most fatty acids are composed of an even number of carbon units because they are biosynthesized by the sequential addition of 2 carbon units. Many fatty acids have double bonds and are referred to as *unsaturated*. These double bonds usually have *cis* geometry.

The alkyl chain of a fatty acid is what gives it its nonpolar, hydrophobic character and allows it to be a successful barrier against water. As with other alkanes and alkenes, fatty acids can stack against one another by hydrophobic bonding, eliminating water between the fatty acid molecules. This behavior forms the basis for membrane structure. Fatty acids are obtained through the diet and by biosynthesis. So, a certain amount of fatty acids in the diet is required for normal lipid development. However, an overly high intake of fatty acids in the diet can lead to obesity and related health concerns.

## Eicosanoids

Fatty acids containing 20 carbons have unique roles in biochemistry. These molecules, called *eicosanoids,* make up the prostaglandin, thromboxane, and leukotriene classes of molecules. The synthetic precursor for each of these classes of compounds is *arachidonic acid* (Figure 8). The prostaglandins have a 5-membered ring in their structure (Figure 8). The 3 major types of prostaglandins are PGA, PGE, and PGF, which are characterized by the degree of oxidation at carbon atoms 9 through 11. Prostaglandins are involved in the inflammatory response. Agents that decrease the production of prostaglandins, such as nonsteroidal anti-inflammatory drugs (NSAIDs; Chapter 11), and decrease prostaglandin release, such as steroids, have been shown to be effective in reducing the discomfort and physical manifestations of inflammation due to prostaglandins. Prostaglandins PGE, PGA, and $PGI_2$ function as vasodilators. $PGI_2$ also inhibits platelet aggregation.

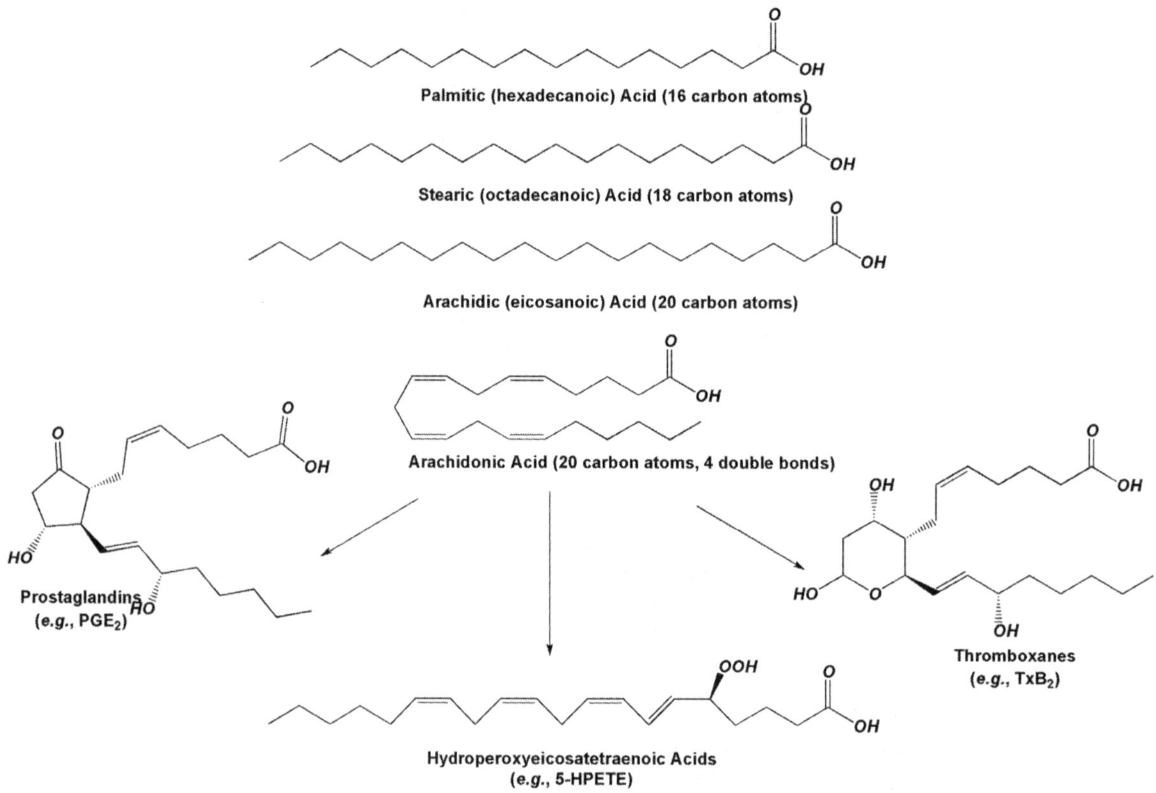

**Figure 8.** *Examples of fatty acids and selected metabolic products. Fatty acids can be named by referring to the number of carbon atoms in the linear chain (in parentheses) or by a common name. Arachidonic acid (20 carbons) leads to a variety of important macromolecules in the body, including prostaglandins, 5-hydroperoxyeicosatetraenoic acids (5-HPETEs), and thromboxanes.*

The second major class of eicosanoids is the *thromboxanes* (Figure 8). Thromboxanes are the 6-membered-ring cousins and direct metabolites of prostaglandins. The 6-membered ring of this class is made by the incorporation of an oxygen atom into the 5-membered ring of the prostaglandin precursor. The main role of thromboxane $TXA_2$ is to promote clotting and platelet aggregation, a process vital to wound healing.

The final groups of eicosanoids are the *leukotrienes* and the *5-hydroperoxyeicosa-tetraenoic acids* (HPETEs). These linear molecules have different double-bond and oxidation patterns compared with the prostaglandins and thromboxanes (Figure 8), while still being metabolites of arachidonic acid. The list of physiological roles for these molecules is extensive. Among other functions, leukotrienes and HPETEs are involved in contraction of smooth muscle, constriction of the trachea, and modulation of the immune response.

Several prostaglandin analogs are currently approved drugs. Misoprostol (Cytotec) is used to treat or prevent NSAID-induced damage to the stomach. Misoprostol and related prostaglandin analogs have been used as abortifacients; therefore, misoprostol is contraindicated for pregnant women. Latanoprost (Xalatan), travoprost (Travatan), and bimatoprost (Lumigan) are prostaglandin analogs used to treat glaucoma or intraocular hypertension.

## Triacylglycerols

In plants and animals, fatty acids often exist as triesters of glycerol, or *triacylglycerols* (**Figure 9**). Fatty acids are stored in this form until the cell is ready to use them for energy. Each molecule of glycerol can form 3 esters, each to the carboxylic acid of a different fatty acid molecule. If the 3 fatty acids are identical, the triacylglycerol is called a *simple triglyceride*. For example, glycerol esterified to 3 molecules of oleic acid is called trioleoylglycerol. If the 3 fatty acid molecules are not identical, the resulting triester is called a *mixed triglyceride* and each fatty acid is named according to the carbon of glycerol to which it is esterified.

Triacylglycerols are made and stored in special cells called *adipocytes*. When the body needs energy, triacylglycerols are hydrolyzed in the adipose tissue, yielding 1 molecule of glycerol and the original 3 fatty acids. The fatty acids are transported through the bloodstream to the mitochondria of energy-needing cells, where the fatty acids undergo a series of oxidation and cleavage reactions. These steps break down the fatty acids to form 2-carbon units, which will be used in the future, and several molecules of reduced cofactors ($FADH_2$ and NADH [the reduced forms of flavin adenine dinucleotide and nicotinamide adenine dinucleotide, respectively]) that can be directly used in the synthesis of ATP.

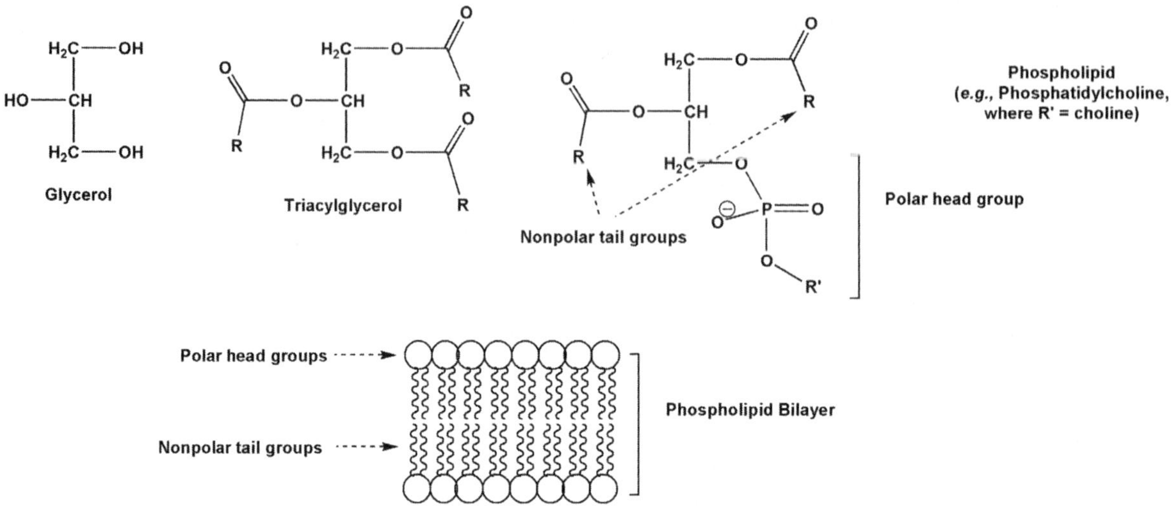

**Figure 9.** *Triacylglycerols and phospholipids. Fatty acids are stored by the body in triacylglycerol molecules. A triacylglycerol is a molecule of glycerol esterified to 3 fatty acid molecules (R). Triacylglycerols that contain a phosphate ester are called phospholipids. Phospholipids typically have 2 fatty acid esters (R) and 1 phosphatidyl group (R'). The fatty acids are the nonpolar (tail) portions of the molecule, while the polar phosphate ester is the head group. Phospholipids align with polar groups together to form bilayers, the primary structural component of cellular membranes.*

## Phospholipids

Related structurally to triacylglycerols, *phospholipids* are based around a molecule of glycerol. As shown in Figure 9, a phospholipid contains a molecule of glycerol that is esterified to 2 fatty acids and 1 phosphate group. At physiological pH (~7.4), the phosphate group will be in its ionized (anionic) form. The phosphate is esterified to an additional polar group, which is usually basic. Typically, the fatty acids of a phospholipid are esterified to carbons 1 and 2 of the glycerol molecule. This piece of the molecule is called a 1,2-diacylglycerol. The phosphate ester is linked to carbon 3. The phosphate can link several different groups to the 1,2-diacylglycerol. The most common phospholipids found in human cells are phosphatidylcholine, phosphatidylserine, and phosphatidylethanolamine. Phosphatidylinositol, also commonly found in humans, contains an inositol group that is esterified to the phosphate.

Phospholipids have dual polarity. The phosphate part of the molecule is ionized and, therefore, highly polar. This portion of the molecule is often referred to as the "head" group. The polar head group is hydrophilic and water soluble. The fatty acid chains are very nonpolar and are referred to as the "tail" group of the molecule. The fatty acid chains are hydrophobic and are not water soluble.

Because of the dual polarity of phospholipids, they are found most abundantly in the membranes of cells and tissues. In an aqueous environment, phospholipids quickly organize themselves so that the polar groups are positioned near one another. Similarly, the tail groups align with each other through strong hydrophobic interactions. In this way, a cellular (or organelle) membrane consists of 2 layers of phospholipids, with the head groups pointing outward and the tail groups pointing inward. This structure is called a phospholipid bilayer (Figure 9). The outer layers of the bilayer, composed of the phosphate head groups, interact freely with water. The core of the bilayer, composed of the nonpolar tail groups, forms a barrier through which water, and other polar molecules or ions, cannot readily penetrate. It is because of the phospholipid bilayer that organelles, cells, and tissues are able to compartmentalize their substructures and vital components away from the rest of the organism.

Phospholipids also have detergentlike properties. Dipalmitoyl lecithin, or surfactant, acts in the lungs to decrease surface tension. The surface tension of the lungs needs to be lowered to prevent lung collapse at the end of expiration.

## Sphingolipids

A large class of lipids is grouped under the general category *sphingolipid* because each member of this class is structured around a molecule of *sphingosine* (**Figure 10**). Sphingosine is an amino alcohol with 18 carbons and 1 double bond. It cannot be obtained from the diet and must be made by the body. Sphingosine is synthesized from palmitoyl CoA (coenzyme A) and L-serine. The final form of sphingosine that is used by the body is *N*-acylsphingosine, or ceramide (Figure 10).

Subclasses of sphingolipids include sphingomyelins and glycosphingolipids (including the cerebrosides and globosides). Although the details of each subclass are beyond the scope of this text, it is important to note their relevance in biological systems. Sphingolipids are found in nervous tissue and often serve as recognition markers between cells. The structural diversity in this family of molecules enables varied and specific contacts between cells.

## Cholesterol

Structurally very different from triacylglycerols and phospholipids, cholesterol is an aliphatic, pentacyclic structure with a hydroxyl group attached to one side of the molecule (the A ring) and an alkane attached to the opposite side (the D ring) (Figure 10). Cholesterol, which is obtained through the diet or by biosynthesis, is a vital component of cellular membranes, especially in the brain and nervous tissue. Cholesterol is also the precursor of bile acids, which help dissolve triacylglycerides and nonpolar vitamins obtained in the diet, and serves as the precursor to several biologically important molecules. The hormones that are associated with gender, testosterone and estradiol, are derived from cholesterol. Vitamin D, when not obtained from dietary sources, is derived from cholesterol. Steroid hormones originating from the adrenal gland, cortisone and corticosterone, among others, are derived from cholesterol as well.

Despite its many uses in the body, elevated levels of cholesterol are unhealthy. Consequences of too much cholesterol include atherosclerosis and increased risk of heart disease. Modified dietary habits and medications have been aimed at lowering a person's blood cholesterol level. Cholesterol-lowering agents include lovastatin (Mevacor), which inhibits a key enzyme in the biosynthesis of cholesterol, and cholestyramine, which increases the excretion of bile salts from the liver.

## Carbohydrates

*Carbohydrates* are a class of molecules most often associated with sugars. For example, sucrose, a common carbohydrate, is more commonly known as table sugar. Lactose is a carbohydrate found in dairy products and can often cause digestive problems. Carbohydrates include other compounds as well, such as starch, dextrose, and cellulose. In general, carbohydrates have a number of functions, including acting as a source of energy, being involved in cellular recognition, and providing structural support to cells and organelles. Carbohydrates are also commonly found attached to proteins, such as glycoproteins, or attached to lipids, as in glycolipids.

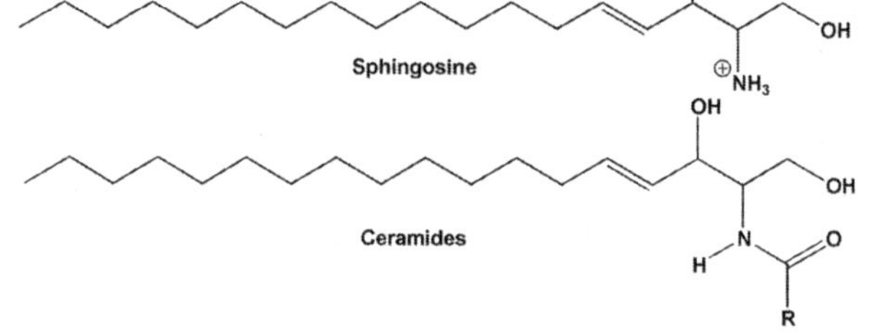

**Figure 10.** *The structures of cholesterol, sphingosine, and the family of ceramides. Ceramides are formed by the acylation of sphingosine at the nitrogen atom. R = any fatty acid chain.*

The term "carbohydrate" literally means "hydrated carbon." This phrase refers to the general molecular formula of the most common, simple carbohydrates–$C_nH_{2n}O_n$. For every carbon atom in the molecule, there are 2 hydrogen atoms and 1 oxygen atom, or 1 molecule of water. For example, the molecular formula of glucose is $C_6H_{12}O_6$, or, written another way, $6C + 6(H_2O)$. The names of most carbohydrates end with "ose." Common examples include fructose, glucose, lactose, and cellulose.

To recognize fully the variability of carbohydrates, it is important to have an understanding of their basic structures. For this section, the carbohydrate molecules are divided into 3 major groups: monosaccharides, oligosaccharides, and polysaccharides. Monosaccharides are carbohydrates that are 1 molecule of a simple carbohydrate. Oligosaccharides, on the other hand, are larger molecules, usually made of 2 to 10 monosaccharides covalently linked to each other. Polysaccharides are still larger molecules, usually made of 10 or more monosaccharides covalently linked to each other.

## Monosaccharides

Monosaccharides are compounds that are 1 molecule of a carbohydrate having the general formula $C_nH_{2n}O_n$. Monosaccharides can be thought of as compounds that are derived from glyceraldehydes. Glyceraldehyde is a 3-carbon molecule with the molecular formula $C_3H_6O_3$ (**Figure 11**).

Glyceraldehyde and related derivatives are important molecules involved in glycolysis, the process of converting glucose into ATP or energy. Because the central carbon on glyceraldehyde is stereogenic, there are 2 chiral forms of the molecule: D-glyceraldehyde and L-glyceraldehyde. Most carbohydrates have a D form and an L form. In the body, the D form of carbohydrates is most prevalent.

Monosaccharides are further classified based on 2 features: (1) the number of carbons in the molecule and (2) whether the molecule has a ketone group or an aldehyde group. The 2 main classes of monosaccharides, based on the number of carbons, are the pentoses and the hexoses. The pentoses contain 5 carbons, and the hexoses contain 6. The 2 main classes of monosaccharides, based on the functional group, are the ketoses and the aldoses. The ketoses contain a ketone group, and the aldoses contain an aldehyde group. These 2 sets of names can be combined: A carbohydrate that contains 5 carbons and a ketone group is a ketopentose. A number of common monosaccharides and their classifications are shown in Figure 11.

The structure of a monosaccharide can be represented in a linear conformation or a cyclic conformation. There is an equilibrium between the 2 forms, the position of which depends on the particular environment and the identity of the monosaccharide. Glucose, for example, can be drawn as a linear molecule or a cyclic molecule, as shown in Figure 11. In solution, the glucose molecule converts back and forth between these 2 conformations.

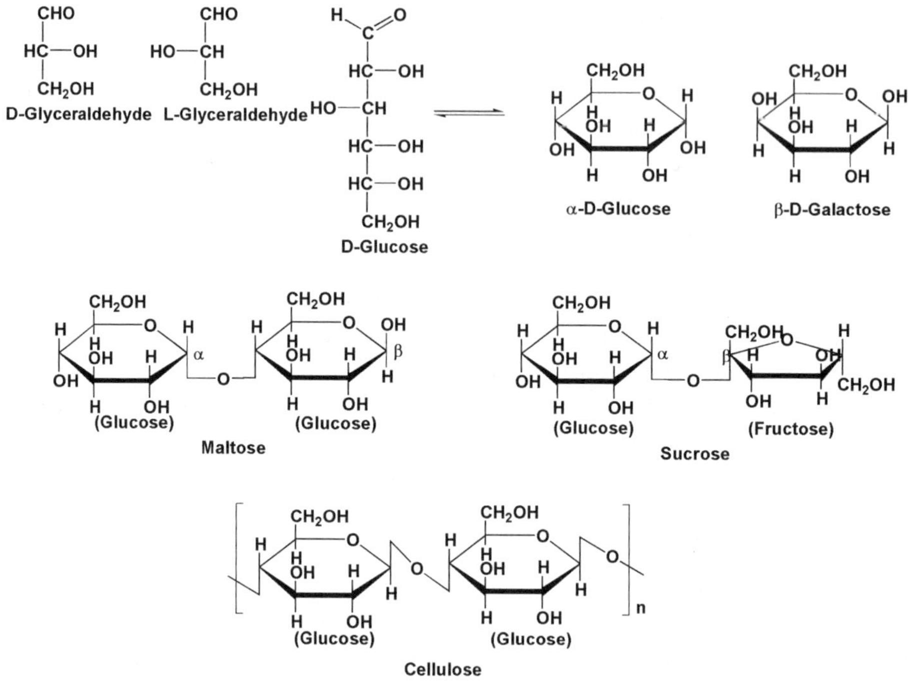

**Figure 11.** *Monosaccharides, disaccharides, and polysaccharides. The stereochemistry of all monosaccharides is based on that of glyceraldehyde. D-sugars are found throughout nature. Glucose and galactose are examples of monosaccharides, whereas maltose and sucrose are examples of disaccharides. Cellulose is an example of a polysaccharide. It is made of repeating glucose units (n = thousands).*

Two important monosaccharides that were introduced earlier in the chapter are ribose and deoxyribose. Both are pentoses because each has 5 carbon atoms. The more precise name for deoxyribose is 2-deoxyribose because it does not contain a hydroxyl group at the 2 position. Ribose and deoxyribose are the sugars contained in the nucleotides of RNA and DNA, respectively.

## Oligosaccharides and Polysaccharides

A saccharide that contains 2 to 10 monosaccharide residues is called an *oligosaccharide* ("oligo" means few). Other common terms are often used to refer to certain oligosaccharides. For example, a disaccharide contains 2 monosaccharide units; a trisaccharide contains 3 monosaccharide units. The term *polysaccharide* usually refers to larger saccharides containing 10 or more monosaccharides. Examples of a disaccharide and a polysaccharide are shown in Figure 11.

# Biological Functions of Carbohydrates

Carbohydrates have a number of biological functions, including acting as a source of energy, being involved in cellular recognition, and providing structural support to cells and organelles. Some of the functions of carbohydrates are discussed herein.

*Energy.* The primary role for glucose is as an energy source for plants and animals. Glycolysis is the pathway by which glucose is converted to pyruvate ($CH_3COCO_2^-$). This enzymatic process results in the production of 2 molecules of ATP. A second enzymatic pathway that produces ATP from glucose is oxidative phosphorylation. By this mechanism, 1 molecule of glucose is oxidized to 6 molecules of carbon dioxide plus 6 molecules of water. Oxidative phosphorylation results in the synthesis of 38 molecules of ATP per molecule of glucose.

Glycogen is a highly branched polymer of glucose. It is a storage form of glucose and can be degraded when glucose is scarce. Glucose and glycogen are degraded more quickly than fat and, thus, are ready sources of energy for the cell.

*Cellular recognition.* The surface of cell membranes often contains a variety of macromolecules. The main structural component of a cell membrane is the phospholipid bilayer. Interspersed in the phospholipid bilayer are proteins. Carbohydrates are linked to the surfaces of many proteins in the phospholipid bilayer. A protein that contains carbohydrates is called a *glycoprotein*. Many proteins, such as the GABA and serotonin receptors, are glycoproteins. The carbohydrate portion of a glycoprotein is usually bonded to a serine, threonine, or lysine amino acid of the protein. The main function of the carbohydrate portion of a glycoprotein is thought to be cellular recognition.

*Structural support.* Carbohydrates can be indispensable macromolecules in the structural integrity of cells, especially in bacterial and plant cells. Carbohydrates assist in the support of the bacterial cell wall. The bacterial cell wall is an example of a proteoglycan. A *proteoglycan* is a macromolecule that consists of a core protein surrounded by carbohydrate units, predominantly aminoglycans. Chapter 13 describes the mechanism of action of several classes of antibiotics, including those that work by inhibiting the synthesis of the bacterial cell wall.

Cellulose and chitin are carbohydrate polymers that form strong matrices. Cellulose is a polymer made of thousands of (1-4 linked) D-glucose units and is the primary component of plant walls. Cellulose gives a plant cell structural integrity and protection from osmotic differences between the cell and its environment. Cellulose is held together by layers of hydrogen bonds, which give it immense strength. Despite so many hydrogen bonds, cellulose is water insoluble and resistant to hydrolysis. Trees (ie, tall plants) are able to sway in the wind without breaking because of the strength of the cellulose fibers holding the cells intact. Chitin is a polymer of *N*-acetylglucosamine residues. Chitin forms the exterior shells, or exoskeletons, of insects and other invertebrates. Like cellulose, chitin has an extensive network of hydrogen bonds that give the polymer its strength.

## Drugs Related to Carbohydrates

For a number of reasons, there are not many drugs currently used that are based on carbohydrates. First, the chemical synthesis of carbohydrates is expensive and difficult. Second, the importance of carbohydrates in cellular recognition, disease, and infection has not been fully recognized until relatively recently. With advances in carbohydrate chemistry and a deeper understanding of the biology of carbohydrates, the development of carbohydrate-based pharmaceuticals has progressed.

One of the most well-known carbohydrate-based drugs is heparin. Heparin is a polysaccharide that contains several acidic functional groups (see Chapter 8). Heparin, an anticoagulant, works by binding to antithrombin. Antithrombin is a natural inhibitor of thrombin and factor Xa, agents that assist in the blood-clotting process. By binding to antithrombin, heparin increases the inhibitory action of antithrombin and, thus, results in increased anticoagulation effects. The carbohydrate residues that make up the structure of heparin are vital to its binding to antithrombin and to its mechanism of action.

A number of antibiotics contain carbohydrate residues in their structures. Streptomycin, neomycin, paromomycin, gentamicin, and kanamycin are carbohydrate-based compounds with chemical modifications (see Chapter 13). Streptomycin, for example, is an aminoglycoside. The term *aminoglycoside* refers to a class of molecules based on carbohydrates and having 1 or more amino groups. The structure of streptomycin has a carbohydrate skeleton that resembles a trisaccharide with several chemical modifications, including an amino group, a carboxylate group, and 2 guanidinium groups.

Zanamivir (Relenza) and oseltamivir phosphate (Tamiflu) are newer pharmaceuticals that are approved for the treatment of the influenza virus. These drugs inhibit an enzyme called *neuraminidase*. Neuraminidase is a viral enzyme that cleaves the bond between neuraminic acid (a sugar) and a glycoprotein. In the case of viruses, the enzyme is thought to be responsible for releasing a new viral particle, which will infect additional cells. Drugs that inhibit neuraminidase prevent influenza viruses from being released from their parent viral particle and, thus, prevent the infection of additional cells.

One class of antidiabetic agents includes compounds based on carbohydrates. Acarbose (Precose) and miglitol (Glyset) are used for the management of type 2 diabetes mellitus. Miglitol inhibits α-glucosidase enzymes in the endoplasmic reticulum, thereby delaying the digestion of ingested carbohydrates. Blood glucose levels increase to a smaller degree after a meal. Acarbose is an oligosaccharide analog containing 4 carbohydrate units. Miglitol is similar in structure to glucose.

Certain antiviral agents contain carbohydrates or carbohydratelike groups. Zidovudine (Retrovir) and acyclovir (Zovirax) are analogs of nucleotides (see Chapter 13). As discussed earlier in this chapter, a nucleotide comprises a base (A, C, G, T, or U), a phosphate group, and a sugar (ribose for RNA or deoxyribose for DNA). Zidovudine and acyclovir are nucleotide analogs in which the sugar, or carbohydrate, portion has been modified. In zidovudine, the deoxyribose group has an azido group at the 4' position instead of the hydroxyl group of a nucleotide. In acyclovir, the deoxyribose has been replaced by an acyclic hydroxyethyl ether. Both analogs cause termination of DNA synthesis.

## Suggested Reading

Garrett RH, Grisham CM. *Biochemistry*. 5th ed. Hoboken, NJ: Brooks Cole; 2013.

Haluska P, Adjei AA. Receptor tyrosine kinase receptors. *Curr Opin Investig Drugs*. 2001;2(2):280-286.

Rochette-Egly C. Nuclear receptors: integration of multiple signaling pathways through phosphorylation. *Cell Signal*. 2003;15(4):355-366.

## Discussion Topics

1. In this chapter, many macromolecules are discussed. These molecules have different polar and lipophilic properties. In the next chapter, we will learn about interactions between drugs and different kinds of receptors. Based on what you have learned so far, discuss the types of attractive interactions you might encounter. What atoms are important for these interactions and why?

2. Prepare a 3-dimensional model of a DNA double helix using simple materials. Describe the forces holding the structure together.

3. By using folded paper, prepare a simple model of an α helix and a β sheet. How are these structures the same? How are they different? Where are the side chains?

4. Biological macromolecules are often described as polymers–repeating chains of similar subunits. Describe the following in terms of their subunits and how the subunits are connected: protein, carbohydrate, nucleic acid.

5. The biological properties of macromolecules are complex. Describe what structural features of proteins, for example, are important for a biological activity. How could the structural features be varied? Provide the same descriptions with respect to sugars and nucleic acids.

# Chapter 4

## The Biochemistry of Fundamental Metabolic Processes
*by Cynthia S. Dowd, PhD*

Before we dive into the chemistry of different drug classes, it is important to have an understanding of several fundamental metabolic processes. This understanding will give context to how certain drug families work and how their functions are detrimental or advantageous for the cell. In a book of this size, it is not practical to cover all of the relevant biochemical pathways. Certainly, many biochemistry textbooks explain the details of these processes beautifully. The topics covered are those deemed most relevant to the nurse anesthesia audience. The 6 topics covered in this chapter are as follows:

1. Glycolysis

2. The tricarboxylic acid (TCA) cycle

3. Electron transport and oxidative phosphorylation

4. Cholesterol biosynthesis

5. Transcription

6. Translation

To understand these processes, it is necessary to become familiar with some important cellular small molecules. These could be molecules that work with an enzyme and its substrate to make a chemical reaction occur. These molecules are often called "cofactors," which are small molecule helpers that are necessary for a reaction or pathway to proceed. Often, these molecules are quite complex, so rather than using their chemical name, an abbreviation is used. Alternatively, important small molecules could be important products of a reaction or process that are needed for the cell.

**Figure 1** shows the most common small molecules and cofactors found in biochemical processes. Adenosine triphosphate (ATP) is the "energy carrier" for the cell. When the phosphate bonds are hydrolyzed, energy is released. The cell uses the energy to drive important chemical reactions. The product from this hydrolysis can be inorganic monophosphate ($P_i$) when 1 phosphate group is removed (eg, ATP to adenosine diphosphate [ADP]), or the product can be pyrophosphate ($PP_i$) when 2 phosphate groups are removed.

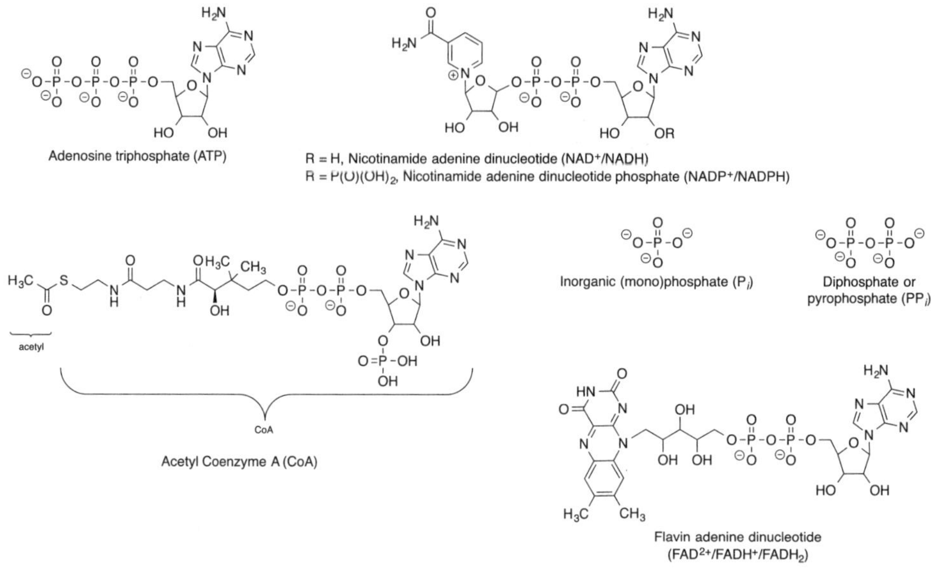

**Figure 1.** *Structures of important small molecules and cofactors required for many metabolic processes.*

Many of the larger molecules shown in Figure 1 contain the adenosine part of ATP. Nicotinamide adenine dinucleotide ($NAD^+$/NADH) and flavin adenine dinucleotide ($FAD^{2+}$/$FADH^+$/$FADH_2$) are cofactors that are often needed in enzymatic reactions. These molecules can be reduced or oxidized depending on the needs of the enzyme. As such, they act as a cellular "general acid" or "general base." Coupled with that function, the molecules can donate and accept electrons. Nature uses these cofactors repeatedly in cell biochemistry, and, as such, the cofactors are great examples of nature's efficiency in completing chemical reactions. Similarly, nature often uses acetyl coenzyme A (CoA) to move 2-carbon building blocks throughout the cell. The CoA portion is merely a handle to hang onto the 2-carbon acetyl group. Once the acetyl portion is used in a reaction, the cell recycles CoA for use in a subsequent acetylation or acylation reaction. Several of the fundamental processes discussed in the chapter use acetyl CoA as a key building unit.

The first 3 cellular processes discussed in this chapter are glycolysis, the TCA cycle, and electron transport/oxidative phosphorylation. These processes are coupled, and the products from one process directly feed into the next process (**Figure 2**). Glycolysis converts glucose to pyruvate. The TCA cycle first converts pyruvate to acetyl CoA and then converts acetyl CoA to carbon dioxide. During the TCA cycle, important cellular cofactors, NADH and $FADH_2$, are formed. These cofactors carry protons and electrons from the TCA cycle to electron transport. The electron transport process uses oxidation and reduction to set up a proton gradient across the membrane. This proton gradient drives the production of ATP, the primary energy carrier for the cell. The goal of the 3 processes, working together, is to produce energy in the form the cell can use.

A second set of processes work together to transform genetic information into proteins, functional units of work in the cell. These processes are transcription and translation, and, like the aforementioned routes, they work together in a tightly coupled manner (**Figure 3**). Transcription is the process by which the DNA code is converted to RNA. The reaction is catalyzed by RNA polymerase. The product of transcription (RNA) is the necessary starting material for translation–translating the genetic code into protein. The cell uses proteins for many tasks needed for survival. Translation occurs at the ribosome.

Cholesterol biosynthesis is included as part of this chapter for 2 reasons: First, several clinically useful drugs work through inhibition of this pathway. Knowledge of these drugs and the pathway is therefore important for all healthcare professionals. Second, the pathway is a great example of how nature begins with very simple building blocks of 2 carbon atoms and, through a long series of enzymatic steps, elaborates these 2 carbons atoms into a complex, polycyclic steroid structure. Nature has many examples of this elaborative process. While including all of those pathways is beyond the scope of this book, the cholesterol pathway is an elegant example.

Clinically useful drugs inhibit many of the metabolic processes discussed in this chapter. These drugs are mentioned in each section as appropriate.

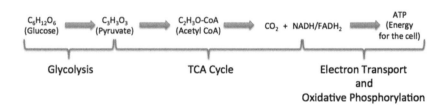

**Figure 2.** *Relationships between glycolysis, the tricarboxylic acid (TCA) cycle and electron transport/oxidative phosphorylation. Glycolysis breaks down glucose to form two 3-carbon pyruvate molecules. The TCA cycle first converts pyruvate to acetyl coenzyme A (CoA) and then oxidizes acetyl CoA to carbon dioxide. During this process, cofactors NADH (the reduced form of nicotinamide adenine dinucleotide) and FADH$_2$ (the reduced form of flavin adenine dinucleotide) are formed. Electron transport uses the electrons and protons in NADH and FADH$_2$ to reduce oxygen to water and to set up a proton gradient across the membrane. The proton gradient drives the production of adenosine triphosphate (ATP) during oxidative phosphorylation.*

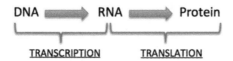

**Figure 3.** *The overall process of making protein from DNA. Through transcription, the genetic information in DNA is converted to RNA. Through translation, the RNA message is converted into proteins the cell needs to function.*

## Glycolysis

Glycolysis (or sugar breaking) is the process of breaking down glucose (a sugar) to store energy in the form of ATP. One glucose molecule ($C_6H_{12}O_6$) is converted to 2 pyruvate molecules ($C_3H_3O_3$) through a series of 10 reactions. The process uses glucose as a fuel to gain energy. This fundamental pathway happens in all cells and is vital to every living thing. Because of its fundamental nature, disruption of glycolysis can easily result in cell death. Although a few anticancer drugs work by inhibiting the glycolytic pathway (see "Drugs Interfering With Glycolysis"), the essentiality of this pathway prevents it from being extensively used therapeutically. This limitation is reasonable given that few human cells would survive if subjected to drugs that stopped glycolysis.

Glycolysis is the basis for many other metabolic functions in the cell, so it makes sense to start the discussion of metabolism here. Cells survive by consuming fuel to make energy. At the molecular level, the main fuel is glucose and the energy is ATP. The pyruvate generated by glycolysis can be further metabolized as shown in **Figure 4**. In the presence of oxygen (aerobic conditions), pyruvate is oxidized to carbon dioxide and water through the TCA cycle. In the absence of oxygen (anaerobic conditions), pyruvate is converted to lactic acid (or lactate), which can occur in muscle under extreme exertion, for example.

Glucose is a very high-energy molecule. Glycolysis converts the energy into ATP, which serves as the general energy "currency" of the cell. Many downstream processes rely on ATP, so production of this important molecule is vital to the survival of the cell.

The overall glycolytic process is shown in **Figure 5**. One molecule of glucose, 2 molecules of ADP, 2 inorganic phosphates ($P_i$), and 2 $NAD^+$ cofactors react to form 2 pyruvate molecules, 2 ATP molecules, 2 NADH molecules, 2 water molecules, and 4 protons. The 6 carbons of glucose are equally split into 2 pyruvate molecules, each having 3 carbons. During this conversion, 2 $NAD^+$ cofactors are reduced to give 2 NADH molecules. The chemical energy of glucose is contained in the new phosphodiester bond created when 1 ADP molecule combines with 1 phosphate ($P_i$) molecule to form ATP.

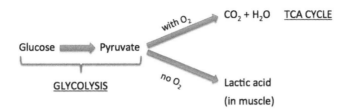

**Figure 4.** *The cellular fate of glucose and pyruvate. Most glucose is converted to pyruvate via glycolysis. In the presence of oxygen, pyruvate is converted to carbon dioxide and water through the tricarboxylic acid (TCA) cycle. In the absence of oxygen, pyruvate is converted to lactic acid.*

$$C_6H_{12}O_6 + 2\,ADP + 2\,P_i + 2\,NAD^+ \longrightarrow$$
(Glucose)

$$2\,C_3H_3O_3 + 2\,ATP + 2\,NADH + 2\,H_2O + 4\,H^+$$
(Pyruvate)

**Figure 5.** *Glycolysis. For each molecule of glucose, 2 molecules of pyruvate, 2 of adenosine triphosphate (ATP), and 2 of NADH (the reduced form of nicotinamide adenine dinucleotide) are formed.*

The 10 reactions of the glycolysis pathway are shown in **Figure 6**. The first reaction converts glucose to glucose-6-phosphate. The enzyme performing this task is called hexokinase. "Hexo" means 6 and refers to the 6-membered ring of the substrate glucose. Kinase refers to the action of the enzyme in which a phosphate group is added to the substrate. The reaction consumes 1 molecule of ATP per molecule of glucose that is reacted. The energy gained when ATP is converted to ADP is the driving force behind the reaction. The phosphate group is added to the sixth carbon of glucose, giving rise to glucose-6-phosphate.

Step 2 of the glycolysis pathway is an isomerization reaction. This type of reaction merely rearranges the atoms of the substrate so that they are attached to each other differently. The substrate and product are isomers. Phosphoglucose isomerase converts glucose-6-phosphate, having a 6-membered ring, to fructose-6-phosphate, having a 5-membered ring. Because there is little energy difference between the substrate and product, the reaction can go in either direction and is written in equilibrium (double arrow). The isomerization is important because it allows eventual splitting of the molecule in two (step 4).

The third step of the pathway is a second kinase reaction, catalyzed by phosphofructokinase. Also using 1 molecule of ATP for each molecule of substrate, the enzyme adds a phosphate to the 1-carbon of fructose-6-phosphate.

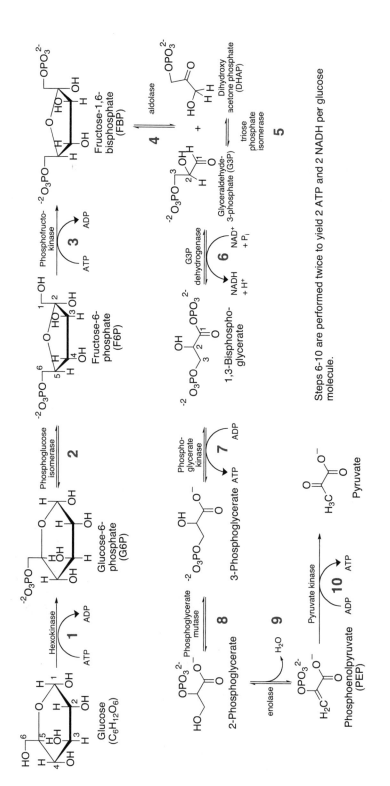

**Figure 6.** *The enzymatic transformations of the glycolysis pathway.*

The product is fructose-1,6-bisphosphate. (Bis is a way to refer to 2 of the same type of group.) At this stage in the pathway, 2 molecules of ATP have been consumed for each molecule of glucose. From this point forward, energy is stored in the form of ATP.

In the fourth step of the pathway, the cyclic substrate is split into two pieces. The substrate fructose-1,6-bisphosphate is divided into glyceraldehyde-3-phosphate and dihydroxy acetone phosphate. The reaction is catalyzed by aldolase. The 2 products of the reaction can be interconverted by triose-phosphate isomerase (step 5). This enzyme is important because the subsequent enzymes in the pathway can use only glyceraldehyde-3-phosphate as a substrate, and not dihydroxyacetone phosphate. *Triose* means a sugar with 3 carbon atoms. The isomerase in step 5 then isomerizes 3-carbon sugars.

Step 6 converts glyceraldehye-3-phosphate to the first high-energy intermediate of the pathway, 1,3-bisphosphoglycerate. The aldehyde of the substrate is oxidized and phosphorylated to give an acyl phosphate. The acyl phosphate is the high-energy portion of the molecule and will give rise to ATP in the next step. The reaction also yields a molecule of NADH, a necessary cofactor for other biochemical processes such as electron transport and oxidative phosphorylation.

The energy contained in the acyl phosphate group in 1,3-bisphosphoglycerate is converted to a phosphodiester bond in step 7. This reaction moves the phosphate group from the substrate to the ADP, creating a new molecule of ATP. The product is called 3-phosphoglycerate. The reaction that catalyzes this reaction is called phosphoglycerate kinase, named for the reverse transformation.

Step 8 moves the phosphate group from the 3-position to the 2-position of the substrate. Catalyzed by phosphoglycerate mutase, 3-phosphoglycerate is converted to 2-phosphoglycerate. This reaction is necessary to prepare a second high-energy acyl phosphate intermediate. Step 9 is a dehydration reaction that removes water from 2-phosphoglycerate to form phosphoenolpyruvate (PEP). The reaction is catalyzed by enolase. PEP is among the highest energy metabolites known. The energy contained in PEP is quickly converted to ATP by the action of pyruvate kinase (step 10). ADP is converted to ATP, yielding a molecule of pyruvate. Steps 6 through 10 are repeated to carry the "other half" of glucose through the pathway. Overall, 1 molecule of glucose yields 2 molecules of ATP and 2 molecules of NADH. The pyruvate product is used as the starting substrate in the TCA cycle.

## Drugs Interfering With Glycolysis

Because of its central importance in cellular metabolism, interference with the glycolysis pathway has not been used extensively. However, a handful of agents are known to work by inhibiting 1 or more of the glycolytic enzymes (**Figure 7**). These have been examined primarily as anticancer agents, and their clinical usefulness is being examined.

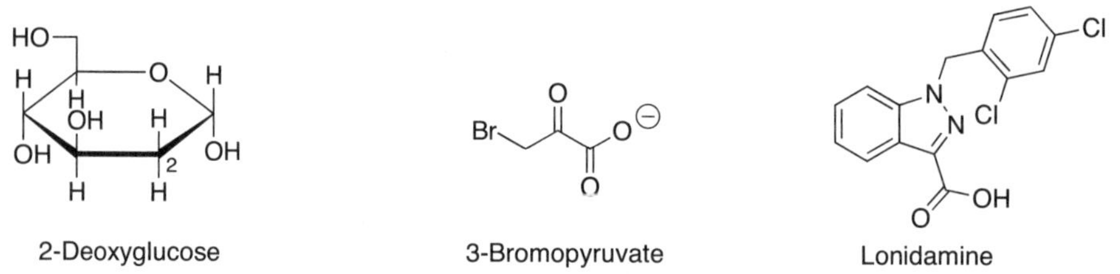

2-Deoxyglucose          3-Bromopyruvate          Lonidamine

**Figure 7.** *Molecules working through inhibition of the glycolysis pathway.*

2-Deoxyglucose is taken up into cells and phosphorylated by hexokinase just like glucose. Once phosphorylated, however, the inhibitor cannot leave the cell and also cannot proceed through the rest of the pathway. In this way, 2-deoxyglucose keeps natural glucose from being phosphorylated and broken down, interrupting the oxidative cycle. The cell is depleted of ATP and dies. More potent than 2-deoxyglucose, 3-bromopyruvate inhibits hexokinase and depletes cellular ATP levels. This drug can also act as an alkylating agent, indicating that its effect may be through additional enzymes. Lonidamine decreases oxygen consumption by cells and suppresses glycolysis in cancer cells. This effect is likely through inhibition of mitochondrial-bound hexokinase.

## The TCA Cycle

The previous section described how the cell uses glycolysis to gain chemical energy in the form of ATP molecules. Additional high-energy metabolites, sometimes called *cofactors,* are needed by the cell. The TCA cycle is a mechanism by which the cell creates several high-energy cofactors, namely NADH, $FADH_2$, and guanosine triphosphate (GTP) (**Figure 8**). It is also called the citric acid cycle or the Krebs cycle, for Hans Krebs who was the first to elucidate it in 1937. The TCA cycle effectively uses the product of glycolysis to create the cofactors required by the cell.

The product of glycolysis is pyruvate. In preparation for the TCA cycle, pyruvate is converted to thioester acetyl CoA by pyruvate dehydrogenase (**Figure 9**). This step creates a molecule of NADH for each molecule of pyruvate esterified. In the first step of the TCA cycle, acetyl CoA, a 2-carbon molecule, is combined with oxaloacetate, a 4-carbon molecule. The product is 6-carbon citrate, and the reaction is catalyzed by citrate synthase. This first step of the cycle gives rise to one of the names of the pathway, the citric acid cycle. During this step, CoA is reduced to yield CoASH.

Acetyl CoA  +  3 NAD⁺  +  FAD  +  GDP  +  P$_i$  ⟶

$$3\ NADH\ +\ FADH_2\ +\ GTP\ +\ CoA\ +\ 2\ CO_2$$

**Figure 8.** *The overall reaction of the tricarboxylic acid (TCA) cycle.*

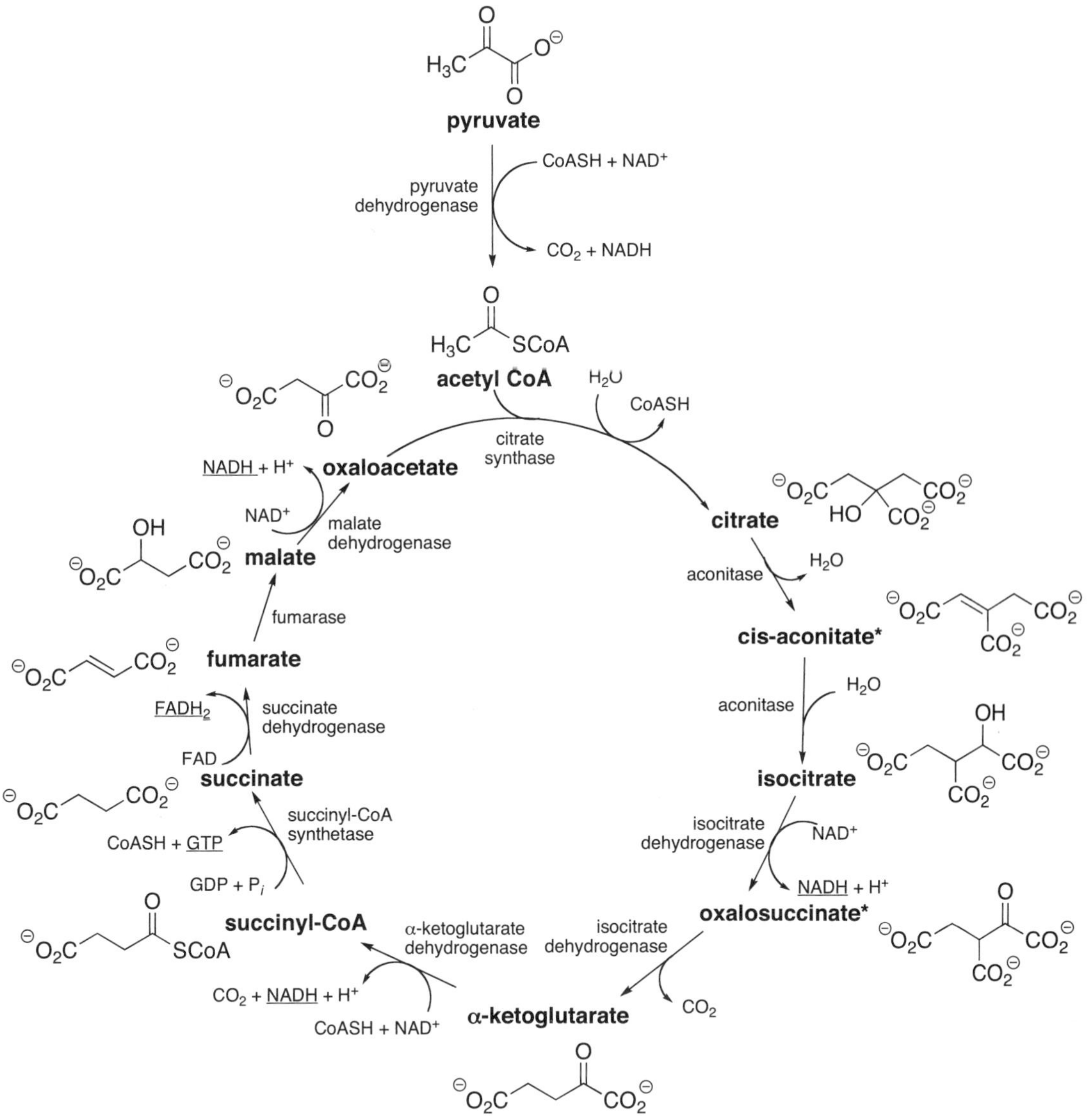

**Figure 9.** *The enzymatic steps of the tricarboxylic acid (TCA) cycle. *These intermediates are unstable and react quickly in the subsequent step.*

Citrate is a tertiary alcohol. The next transformations occur to make an alcohol that is more easily oxidized. Aconitase first dehydrates citrate to form *cis*-aconitate having a double bond between the second and third carbon atoms. *cis*-Aconitate is not isolated. Taking advantage of the symmetry of the 5-carbon backbone, the second reaction of aconitase is to hydrate across the double bond, giving the secondary alcohol of isocitrate. Overall, the action of aconitase is to isomerize citrate to isocitrate, moving the hydroxyl group from the third to the fourth carbon atom. The secondary alcohol of isocitrate is easily oxidized to the corresponding ketone of oxalosuccinate by isocitrate dehydrogenase. One equivalent of NADH is produced during this reaction.

Oxalosuccinate is a 1,3-diketo system and is easily decarboxylated. Because of this feature, oxalosuccinate is not isolated, but the reaction easily proceeds to give 5-carbon α-ketoglutarate.

The fourth enzyme of the pathway is α-ketoglutarate dehydrogenase, which converts the dicarboxylic acid α-ketoglutarate to thioester succinyl CoA. This is an oxidative decarboxylation reaction in which 1 equivalent of NADH is made. Succinyl CoA is then reduced by succinyl-CoA synthetase. The ketone is reduced to a methylene group. (Note the name of this enzyme comes from the reverse reaction.) As seen earlier, the thioester is a high-energy bond. When this bond is cleaved by succinyl-CoA synthetase, the energy is captured by creating a new phosphodiester bond in GTP.

Succinate, a 4-carbon molecule, is dehydrogenated to give fumarate. The transformation is catalyzed by succinate dehydrogenase and yields a molecule of $FADH_2$. Fumarase then hydrates across the double bond of fumarate to create malate. The secondary alcohol of malate is oxidized to a ketone by malate dehydrogenase, also producing another equivalent of the reduced cofactor NADH. The product of the reaction is oxaloacetate, a highly oxidized 4-carbon molecule. Note that the last 3 steps of the cycle (steps 6-8) function to oxidize succinate "up" to oxaloacetate so that the cycle can start again. A single oxaloacetate can be used to oxidize an infinite number of 2-carbon acetyl groups to 2 carbon dioxide molecules. The valuable product of this oxidation is the reduction of 4 cofactor equivalents and the capture of energy in the form of GTP.

Despite known inhibitors of several TCA cycle reactions, none are currently considered therapeutically useful. The centrality of the TCA cycle to all cellular metabolism likely prohibits its interruption for therapeutic purposes.

## *The Electron Transport Chain and Oxidative Phosphorylation*

The glycolysis pathway and TCA cycle work together to convert glucose to carbon dioxide (**Figure 10**). Glucose, a 6-carbon sugar, is broken down to 2 molecules of pyruvate, each with 3 carbon atoms, during glycolysis. Pyruvate is converted to acetyl CoA by pyruvate dehydrogenase. The 2 -carbon unit of acetyl CoA is further broken down to carbon dioxide in the TCA cycle. Figure 10 shows the overall breakdown process and how carbon-carbon bonds are successively broken to ultimately yield carbon dioxide (with no carbon-carbon bonds remaining).

At the molecular level, each molecule of glucose is combined with 6 molecules of oxygen to give 6 molecules of carbon dioxide and 6 molecules of water (**Figure 11**). This is the overall chemical reaction for these 2 very large enzymatic processes. When looked at from this view, however, key elements of the pathways get lost.

Breakdown of glucose to carbon dioxide is essential for all cells and organisms because this conversion facilitates the production of energy and reduced cofactors for the cell. The energy comes in the form of ATP and GTP, and the reduced cofactors are NADH and $FADH_2$. Splitting the overall glycolysis/TCA cycle chemical reaction into 2 half reactions (Figure 11) shows that glucose is oxidized to carbon dioxide and oxygen is reduced to water. In addition, 24 protons ($H^+$) and 24 electrons ($e^-$) are "produced" through the process.

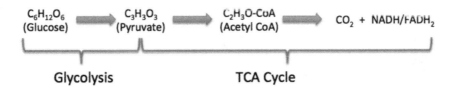

**Figure 10.** *Coupled relationship between glycolysis and the tricarboxylic acid (TCA) cycle. Abbreviations: CoA, coenzyme A; NAD, nicotinamide adenine dinucleotide; and NADH, the reduced form of NAD.*

Overall reaction:

$$C_6H_{12}O_6 \text{ (Glucose)} + 6\,O_2 \longrightarrow 6\,CO_2 + 6\,H_2O$$

Two ½ reactions:

$$C_6H_{12}O_6 \text{ (Glucose)} + 6\,H_2O \longrightarrow 6\,CO_2 + 24\,H^+ + 24\,e^-$$

$$6\,O_2 + 24\,H^+ + 24\,e^- \longrightarrow 12\,H_2O$$

**Figure 11.** *Half reactions showing how conversion of glucose to carbon dioxide occurs with the reduction of oxygen to water.*

It is important to note that electrons are not added to oxygen directly to form water. Instead, they are used to reduce the cofactors $NAD^+$ and FAD to give NADH and $FADH_2$. These reduced cofactors then shuttle the electrons to the electron transport chain. There, as the cofactors are oxidized, oxygen is reduced. The electron transport chain is the coupling of the 2 reactions: oxidation of NADH (or $FADH_2$) and reduction of oxygen. As 1 molecule is oxidized, another is reduced. Therefore, reduced cofactors are necessary for the cell to reduce oxygen to water.

The second half of the process involves capture of the energy from glucose. The energy is captured in the form of ATP in a process called *oxidative phosphory-lation*. Oxidative phosphorylation is closely coupled to electron transport, and the two are dependent on one another. For this reason, they are often described (and taught) together.

NADH and $FADH_2$ act as electron shuttles, carrying electrons to the site where oxygen will be reduced. The reduction takes place within the cellular mitochondria. The *mitochondrion* is a cellular organelle containing an inner membrane with many, many folds. Because of its twists and turns, the surface area of the inner membrane is 15-fold greater than that of the outer membrane. The electron transport chain and oxidative phosphorylation meet at the inner membrane of the mitochondrion.

The mitochondrion is the site of several important processes. First, the TCA cycle enzymes are housed in this organelle. The TCA cycle provides NADH and oxidized carbon small molecules (succinate, etc) that feed into the electron transport chain. Second, pyruvate dehydrogenase, the enzyme converting pyruvate (the product of glycolysis) to acetyl CoA (the starting material for the TCA cycle) is housed in the mitochondria. Colocation of this enzyme with the TCA cycle enzymes ensures that the latter will be able to function. Third, the complexes of the electron transport chain and oxidative phosphorylation are housed in the mitochondrion. Their coupled relationship (see the next paragraph) ensures that energy is produced for the cell. Finally, the mitochondria hosts the enzymes involved in fatty acid oxidation, which makes additional ATP molecules. The colocation of these pathways gives the mitochon-drion the role of the "power plant" of the cell.

The electron transport chain and oxidative phosphorylation are coupled through a proton (or pH) gradient across the inner membrane of the mitochondrion (**Figure 12**). The electron transport chain carries electrons (via NADH) to a large enzyme complex where oxygen is reduced to water and NADH is oxidized to $NAD^+$. The reaction is coupled to a proton pump that pushes protons outside the membrane. This reaction establishes a pH gradient in which the outside of the membrane has a high proton ($H^+$) concentration (low pH) and the inside has low proton concentration (high pH). Because of this difference, protons naturally cross from the outside to the inside to establish the same concentration on both sides. Energy is required to maintain this difference in proton concentration. Conversely, energy is released when protons are allowed to cross the membrane. The energy stored in the proton gradient is used to produce ATP from ADP plus $P_i$ by ATP synthase in a process called oxidative phosphorylation.

Although examination of the many enzyme complexes required for electron transport is beyond the scope of this chapter, it is important to understand how these processes are coupled and the role of each in capturing energy for the cell from nutrients like glucose. Figure 12 shows the colocation of the TCA cycle, electron transport, and oxidative phosphorylation within the inner membrane of the mitochondria. NADH is one of the products of the TCA cycle. NADH is oxidized to $NAD^+$ at the cytochrome complex. The electrons travel through the complex, where they are ultimately used to reduce oxygen to water. At the same time, as NADH oxidation occurs, protons are pumped across the membrane. This action creates a proton gradient: low proton concentration on the inside of the cell and high proton concentration on the outside.

The proton gradient is used at another part of the mitochondrial membrane to drive ATP synthesis. A proton transporter (ATP synthase) selectively allows protons to enter the space only when coupled to synthesis of an ATP molecule from ADP. The colocation of these 3 functions is essential to create the proton gradient that then drives energy production.

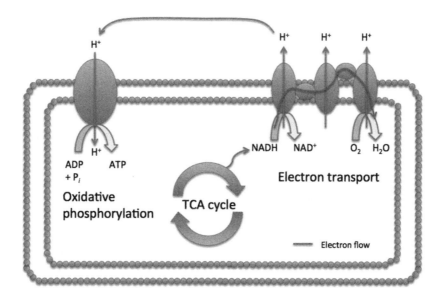

**Figure 12.** *Electron transport and oxidative phosphorylation occur at the mitochondrial membrane. NADH (the reduced form of nicotinamide adenine dinucleotide [NAD]) from the tricarboxylic acid (TCA) cycle feeds into the electron transport process. Electrons flow through the complex reducing oxygen to water and oxidizing NADH to NAD$^+$. Protons are pumped out of the mitochondrion to the site of oxidative phosphorylation. This proton gradient drives the production of adenosine triphosphate (ATP) from adenosine diphosphate (ADP) and $P_i$ (inorganic monophosphate).*

## Cholesterol Synthesis

The human body contains a number of important steroid molecules. Steroids are organic small molecules containing a characteristic 4-ring structure as seen in cholesterol. The basic ring structure is conserved among all steroids, and the synthesis of these molecules is related as well. Cholesterol (**Figure 13**) is the most important steroid and is found in all mammals and bacteria. It is interesting that cholesterol is not found in plants, but other structurally related steroids are. In the cell, cholesterol serves as a biosynthetic precursor for many other steroids.

The synthesis of cholesterol begins in the cell cytoplasm and ends in the endoplasmic reticulum. The overall synthetic scheme is shown in **Figure 14**. From here, all of the carbon atoms of cholesterol originate in 2 carbon units (acetyl CoA). Chains of acetyl CoA are linked together, first to make mevalonate and then to make squalene. After oxidation, squalene undergoes a rapid chain reaction that forms the 4-ring steroidal structure in 1 step. Further transformation of this carbon skeleton yields cholesterol.

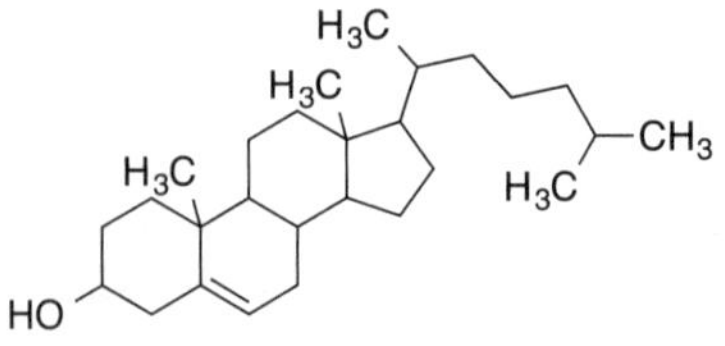

**Figure 13.** *The structure of cholesterol.*

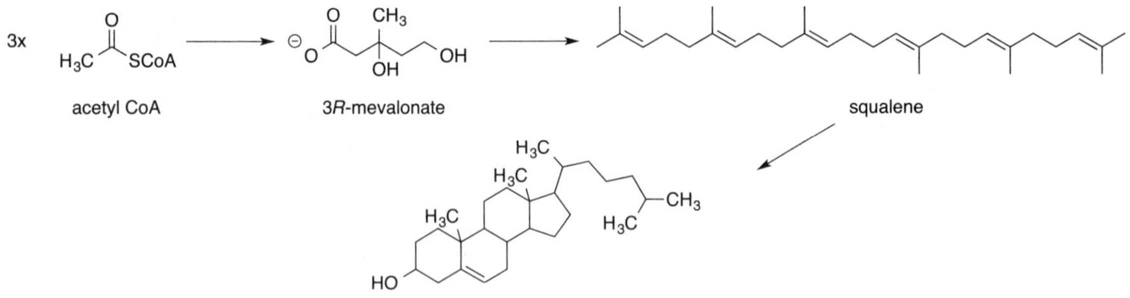

**Figure 14.** *The overall synthesis of cholesterol starting with 3 molecules of acetyl coenzyme A (CoA).*

## Acetyl CoA to Mevalonate

The synthesis of cholesterol makes substantial use of CoA, a small molecule that merely serves as a shuttle to carry the intermediates through the reaction series (Figure 1). The presence of CoA ensures that the small molecules remain part of the synthetic scheme progress through the route. CoA does not itself participate in the chemistry of the reactions.

In the first set of reactions (**Figure 15**), the 2-carbon-unit acetyl CoA is elaborated to yield the 6-carbon molecule: mevalonate. In the first step, β-ketothiolase promotes a Claisen condensation of 2 acetyl CoA molecules, yielding acetoacetyl CoA. The second step of the process adds a third molecule of acetyl CoA to the growing chain. Acetoacetyl CoA is combined with acetyl CoA via a second Claisen condensation, yielding 3-hydroxy-4-methyl-glutaryl CoA, or HMG-CoA. The reaction is catalyzed by HMG-CoA synthase.

The third step of this set is the conversion of HMG-CoA to (3$R$)-mevalonate, mediated by HMG-CoA reductase and 2 molecules of cofactor NADPH. HMG-CoA is reduced twice. The first reaction reduces the carbonyl at C-5 to an alcohol. The second reduction replaces the CoA at C-5 with a hydride. The hydrides originate from NADPH. This step, HMG-CoA reductase, is the most important step in cholesterol biosynthesis because it is the rate-limiting step. The main points of regulating cholesterol biosynthesis occur here. As is described subsequently, the statin drugs also work by inhibition of this enzyme.

## Mevalonic Acid to Squalene

The next set of reactions elaborates mevalonic acid (6 carbon atoms) to squalene (30 carbon atoms) (**Figure 16**). The first 2 steps of this sequence use 2 molecules of ATP; the energy is used to drive the process forward. The reactions are back-to-back kinases that each add a phosphate group to mevalonate. First, mevalonate kinase adds a phosphate to C-5 of mevalonate, yielding phosphomevalonate. The first molecule of ATP is consumed, and ADP is given off as a side product.

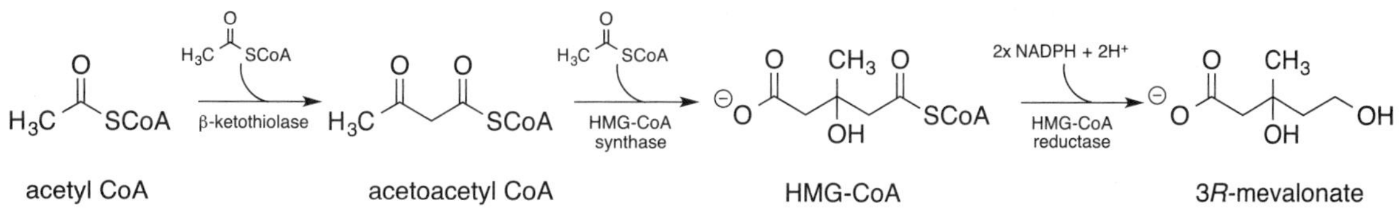

**Figure 15.** *The initial steps of cholesterol biosynthesis: production of 3R-mevalonate from acetyl coenzyme A (CoA).*

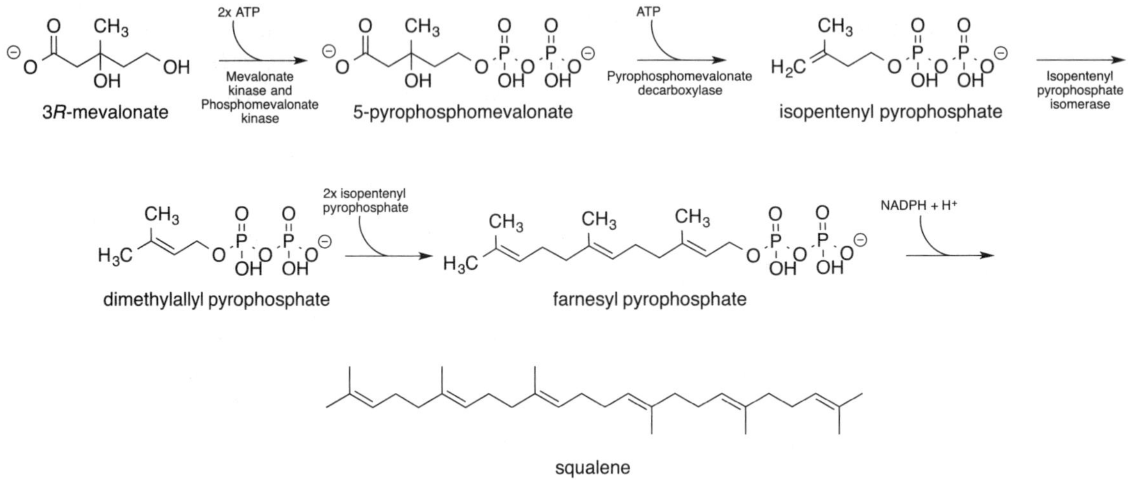

**Figure 16.** *The second set of reactions in the biosynthesis of cholesterol: production of squalene from 3R-mevalonate.*

Second, phosphomevalonate kinase adds a second phosphate group, yielding 5-pyrophosphomevalonate. Again, ATP is consumed, and ADP is given off. The purpose of these reactions is to raise the energy (and, thus, the reactivity) of the growing molecule. The downstream release of this energy drives the process forward. The third step in this part of the synthesis is a decarboxylation and an elimination reaction. This step requires the third molecule of ATP. 5-Pyrophosphomevalonate is converted to isopentenyl pyrophosphate by pyrophosphomevalonate decarboxylase. Initially, a phosphate group is added to the C-3 position from ATP. This highly energetic molecule then undergoes trans elimination to release the C-3 phosphate and the C-1 carboxylate (as carbon dioxide). The reaction yields isopentenyl pyrophosphate, with a terminal double bond between the new C-1 and C-2. The next reaction is an isomerization of isopentenyl pyrophosphate to dimethylallyl pyrophosphate (DMAPP). The reaction is catalyzed by isopentenyl pyrophosphate isomerase. The reaction moves the double bond from the terminal (end) position of the starting material to an internal (C-2 to C-3) position. These 2 five-carbon units are used by the cell to synthesize several larger compounds that are important for cell survival.

The final steps of this portion of the pathway convert DMAPP to squalene. DMAPP is elongated with 2 isopentyl units to yield 15-carbon farnesyl pyrophosphate. This is an energy-releasing reaction in which the 2 pyrophosphate groups lost in the reaction yield valuable energy for the cell—helping to drive the process forward. The reaction proceeds with head-to-tail addition of the isopentene units. Finally, 2 farnesyl pyrophosphate molecules are joined together in a tail-to-tail manner to yield squalene. This unique tail-to-tail coupling results in the symmetry of squalene. This step also releases valuable pyrophosphate. Squalene has 30 carbons, sufficient to form the carbon skeleton of cholesterol and related steroids.

## Squalene to Cholesterol

In this last sequence of reactions, the linear arrangement of bonds in squalene is folded and reacted to yield the classic 4-ring arrangement found in steroid molecules (**Figure 17**). To do this, the squalene hydrocarbon must first be activated–or be made more reactive. The cell carries out this function by oxidizing squalene. Specifically, one of the terminal double bonds in squalene is oxidized to an epoxide. Because squalene is symmetrical, it makes no difference which end of the molecule is epoxidized. The enzyme carrying out the epoxidation is squalene-monooxygenase. The enzyme uses cofactors FAD and NADPH, with oxygen as the oxidant. An oxygen atom is inserted across the carbon-carbon double bond, creating a 3-member epoxide ring. An epoxide is a highly reactive intermediate, increasing the reactivity of squalene so that it can undergo the next reaction. The product of this reaction is squalene-2,3-epoxide.

  The next reaction occurring in the sequence is a marvel chemically and biosynthetically. In a single step, squalene-2,3-epoxide reacts intramolecularly (with itself) to gain all 4 bonds required for the steroid skeleton (Figure 17). These are carbon-carbon bonds that form sequentially, in a "domino" manner because of the reactivity of the epoxide. It is interesting that the 4 bonds form with the correct regiochemistry (correct carbon pairs) and correct stereochemistry (R vs S) at 5 new stereogenic centers. The product of this reaction is lanosterol, which serves as the precursor for many steroids in the cell. Conversion of lanosterol to cholesterol is largely manipulation of only a handful of carbon atoms. Perhaps surprisingly, this part of the process takes an additional 20 enzymatic steps.

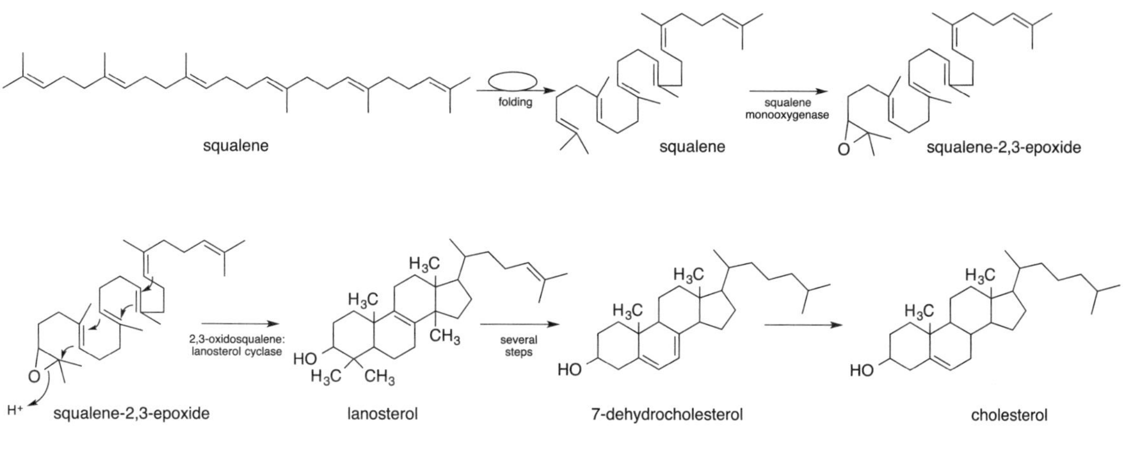

**Figure 17.** *The final set of reactions in the biosynthesis of cholesterol: production of cholesterol from squalene.*

## Drugs That Interrupt Cholesterol Biosynthesis or Alter Cholesterol Levels

Because of the connection between cholesterol and heart disease, many drugs have emerged in an effort to limit the amount of cholesterol in the circulatory system. The most important of these are the statins (**Figure 18**). In general, the statins act as inhibitors of HMG-CoA reductase. Lovastatin is found in certain fungi. The lactone is hydrolyzed in the body to form the β-hydroxy acid, which is the active metabolite. Simvastatin is structurally related and also requires hydrolysis to form the active metabolite. Ezetimibe acts as a cholesterol-lowering agent by blocking absorption of dietary cholesterol from the intestine into the bloodstream.

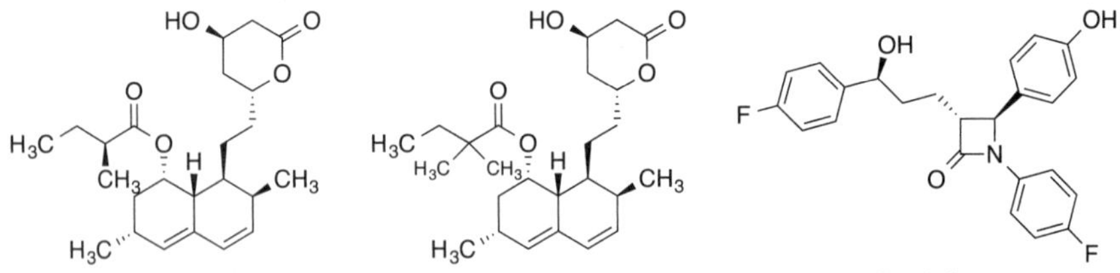

**Figure 18.** *Inhibitors of cholesterol biosynthesis (lovastatin and simvastatin) and cholesterol absorption (ezetimibe).*

## *Transcription*

The conversion of DNA to RNA to protein is often referred to as the "central dogma" of biology (**Figure 19**). *Transcription* is the process by which DNA is converted to RNA. *Translation* is the process by which RNA is converted to protein. As described in Chapter 3, proteins come in many varieties and are the workhorses of the cell.

Transcription is an essential piece of this process because DNA cannot be converted to protein directly. It is the mechanism by which DNA is converted to RNA. RNA is later converted to protein. DNA and RNA use combinations of the 4 nitrogenous bases to form codons. The DNA bases are adenine (A), guanine (G), thymine (T), and cytosine (C). In RNA, the bases are A, G, C, and U (uracil). Uracil replaces thymine in RNA. In RNA and DNA, codons are made of 3 bases.

The enzyme RNA polymerase carries out translation and catalyzes the synthesis of messenger RNA (mRNA) from DNA. The mRNA is complementary to and made directly from DNA (**Figure 20**). The role of mRNA is to carry the genetic sequence to the ribosome where it will be translated into protein. At the beginning of transcription, the double helix of DNA unwinds slightly so that the enzyme RNA polymerase can bind to it. The enzyme binds to 1 strand of DNA. The trinucleotides ATP, GTP, CTP (cytosine triphosphate), and UTP (uracil triphosphate) are added to the growing chain of RNA in a manner complementary with the DNA template (**Figure 21**). The driving force of the reaction is the production and hydrolysis of diphosphate ($PP_i$). The nucleotides are incorporated by the polymerase at a rate of 20 to 50 nucleotides per second. Transcription stops when the RNA polymerase falls off the DNA, encounters a "stop" sequence, or in guanosine and cytosine (G:C)–rich regions.

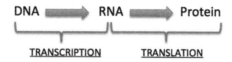

**Figure 19.** *The overall process of making protein from DNA: transcription and translation.*

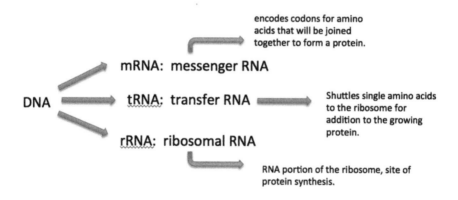

**Figure 20.** *DNA is transcribed into 3 forms of RNA. These RNA molecules have important and different roles in the cell.*

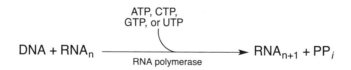

**Figure 21.** *DNA is converted to RNA by RNA polymerase and the 4 trinucleotides. Energy release from hydrolysis of inorganic diphosphate ($PP_i$) drives the reaction.*

## Drugs That Interrupt Transcription

Several drugs inhibit transcription (**Figure 22**). One of the most common of these is actinomycin D, a naturally occurring product found in certain species of *Streptomyces*. It binds to duplex (ie, double-stranded) DNA and inhibits transcription and DNA replication. Actinomycin D is used as an anticancer agent. Rifampin is also a transcription inhibitor, being structurally similar to the *Streptomyces*-derived natural product rifamycin. Rifampin is used as an antibiotic and is one of the first-line treatments for tuberculosis. α-Amanitin also works by stopping transcription. It is a cyclic peptide made of 8 amino acids and was originally isolated from *Amanita* mushrooms. It is a toxin that works by binding to RNA polymerase, thereby preventing the enzyme from binding to DNA.

## *Translation (Protein Biosynthesis)*

DNA is housed in the nucleus of each cell and contains all of our genetic information. RNA is located in the cytosol of the cell and is responsible for synthesizing protein from our genetic information. The process of converting genetic information into protein is called *translation*. Translation converts mRNA codons into amino acids. A set of 3 bases is called a codon. Each codon encodes for a specific amino acid. The genetic code matching codons and amino acids is shown in **Figure 23**.

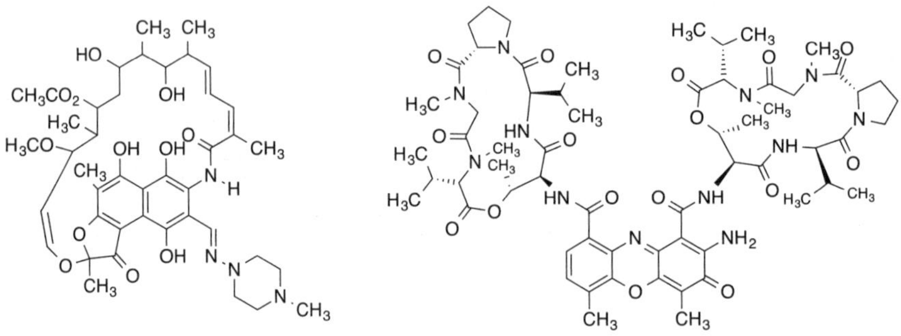

Rifampin

Actinomycin D

**Figure 22.** *Transcription inhibitors.*

| First Position (5' end) | Second Position | | | | Third Position (3' end) |
|---|---|---|---|---|---|
| | U | C | A | G | |
| U | UUU Phe<br>UUC Phe<br>UUA Leu<br>UUG Leu | UCU<br>UCC<br>UCA Ser<br>UCG | UAU Tyr<br>UAC Tyr<br>UAA Stop<br>UAG Stop | UGU Cys<br>UGC Cys<br>UGA Stop<br>UGG Trp | U<br>C<br>A<br>G |
| C | CUU<br>CUC<br>CUA Leu<br>CUG | CCU<br>CCC<br>CCA Pro<br>CCG | CAU His<br>CAC His<br>CAA Gln<br>CAG Gln | CGU<br>CGC<br>CGA Arg<br>CGG | U<br>C<br>A<br>G |
| A | AUU<br>AUC Ile<br>AUA<br>AUG Met | ACU<br>ACC<br>ACA Thr<br>ACG | AAU Asn<br>AAC Asn<br>AAA Lys<br>AAG Lys | AGU Ser<br>AGC Ser<br>AGA Arg<br>AGG Arg | U<br>C<br>A<br>G |
| G | GUU<br>GUC<br>GUA Val<br>GUG | GCU<br>GCC<br>GCA Ala<br>GCG | GAU Asp<br>GAC Asp<br>GAA Glu<br>GAG Glu | GGU<br>GGC<br>GGA Gly<br>GGG | U<br>C<br>A<br>G |

**Figure 23.** *The genetic code.*

Translation occurs at the ribosome, a huge complex made of RNA and proteins. The function of the ribosome is to bring together mRNA, the required amino acids, and the enzymes needed for their coupling. Most relevant biochemically, there are 3 kinds of RNA most relevant to this discussion:

1. Messenger RNA (mRNA) is complementary to and made directly from DNA. The role of mRNA is to carry the genetic sequence to the ribosome where it will be translated into protein. The mRNA recognizes transfer RNA.

2. Transfer RNA (tRNA) is a family of cloverleaf-shaped molecules that carries a 3-base anticodon and the corresponding amino acid. The tRNA molecules go to the ribosome for protein synthesis.

3. Ribosomal RNA (rRNA) is the RNA component of the ribosome.

The mRNA is the code that is translated into protein (the polymer of amino acids). It is important to note that mRNA does not recognize amino acids directly. The mRNA recognizes tRNA. A tRNA molecule carries 2 things: a 3-base anticodon and an amino acid. The 3-base anticodon is complementary to the mRNA codon and corresponds to the bound amino acid (**Figure 24**). Once recognition between the complementary mRNA codon and tRNA occurs, the amino acid is transferred to the growing polypeptide chain (**Figure 25**). The process continues, growing the peptide chain, until a stop codon appears.

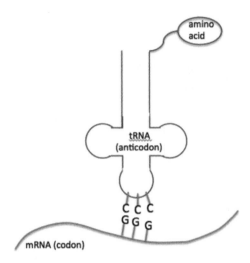

**Figure 24.** *The first steps of translation occur when a messenger RNA (mRNA) codon binds to a transfer RNA (tRNA) molecule bearing a complementary anticodon and the encoded amino acid. This process occurs at the ribosome.*

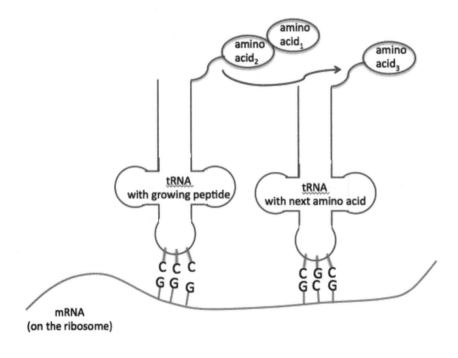

**Figure 25.** *Translation proceeds when the growing peptide chain from one transfer RNA (tRNA) molecule is transferred to the next tRNA molecule in the sequence. Recognition by the complementary messenger RNA (mRNA) drives the process.*

Because genetic information is passed on using 3-base codons, small disruptions in the code can produce substantial genetic errors. Four such errors are the most common:

1. Deletion mutation: Skipping 1 base results in frameshifting the sequence. The sequence downstream of this deletion is incorrect. For example, a 3-codon sequence might read UUU-AGG-CAG, which translates to Phe-Arg-Gln. Deletion of 1 base (eg, UU*-AGG-CAG) would result in codons UUA-GGC-AG…, giving a peptide that is Leu-Gly-…. The new protein will have a mutated sequence because of the deletion.

2. Exchange mutation: Exchange of 1 base for another results in an incorrect amino acid in the polypeptide. For example, UUU encodes for the Phe amino acid. UUA encodes for Leu. Exchange of A for U causes the occurrence of this error in translation.

3. Insertion mutation: This mutation is the opposite of a deletion mutation, in which an extra base is added to the sequence. For example, UUU-AGG-CAG translates to the Phe-Arg-Gln protein sequence. Addition of an A in the first codon gives UUA-UAG-GCA, which translates to Leu-Stop-Ala.

4. Sections of the code ($>$ 1 base) can be inserted or deleted.

All of these errors can have huge consequences in protein sequence. The range of impact can be very small (or negligible) to fatal for the person. For example, sickle cell anemia is caused by the single exchange of a glutamic acid residue for a valine. Cystic fibrosis is caused by the deletion of 3 bases and the corresponding amino acid (phenylalanine) from a required protein. Many diseases and disorders have been linked to seemingly simple errors in transcription and translation. The importance of translation is why a host of drugs, largely targeting bacteria, have been developed.

## Drugs That Interrupt Translation

Many drugs have been discovered and developed for the inhibition of protein synthesis. Most such translation inhibitors have found clinical use as antibiotics. Because of the complexity of translation, small molecules are found to inhibit at many points in the mechanism. The diversity of structures that inhibit translation is quite significant. Although the exact details of each mechanism are beyond the scope of this book, it is important to recognize the primary structural families that function as translation inhibitors (**Figure 26**). Many of these compounds, their analogs, and clinical details are discussed in more depth in Chapter 13. Streptomycin is one of the oldest known antibiotics. Developed in the early 1940s, streptomycin is still used as an antibiotic and remains an important drug against tuberculosis. Streptomycin and the more recently described spectinomycin represent the family of aminoglycosides. Tetracycline, with 4 rings bound together, is an inhibitor of aminoacyl tRNA binding. Erythromycin, a prototypical macrolide antibiotic, binds rRNA. Chloramphenicol is an older drug and a broad-spectrum antibiotic. Important globally as an inexpensive drug, chloramphenicol inhibits protein elongation.

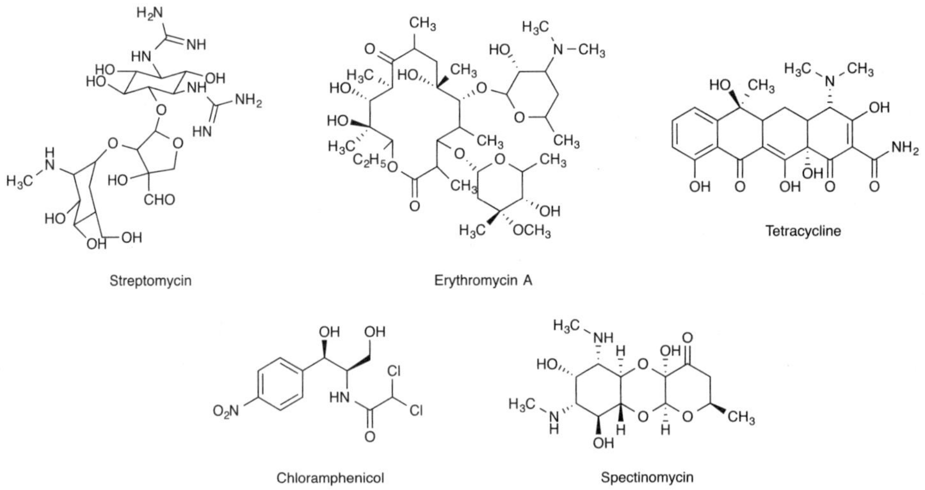

Streptomycin     Erythromycin A     Tetracycline

Chloramphenicol     Spectinomycin

**Figure 26.** *Translation inhibitors.*

# Suggested Reading

Garrett RH, Grisham CM. *Biochemistry*. 5th ed. Belmont, CA: Brooks/Cole, Cengage Learning; 2013.

Lv PC, Zhu HL. Aminoacyl-tRNA synthetase inhibitors as potent antibacterials. *Curr Med Chem*. 2012;19(21):3550-3563.

Pelicano H, Martin DS, Xu R-H, Huang P. Glycolysis inhibition for anticancer treatment. *Oncogene*. 2006;25(34):4633-4646.

Sanyal G, Doig P. Bacterial DNA replication enzymes as targets for antibacterial drug discovery. *Expert Opin Drug Discov*. 2012 Apr;7(4):327-39.

Taylor F, Huffman MD, Macedo AF, et al. Statins for the primary prevention of cardiovascular disease. *Cochrane Database Syst Rev*. 2013;1:CD004816.

Voet D, Voet JG. *Biochemistry*. 4th ed. Hoboken, NJ: John Wiley & Sons; 2011.

## Discussion Topics

1. In the cell, glycolysis, the TCA cycle, and electron transport are linked. Describe how this takes place.

2. The subcellular location of a metabolic process is often important. Discuss where the processes described in this chapter are located and why their location may or may not be important.

3. There is wide variety in the structures of translation inhibitors. Discuss why this is important given their clinical use.

4. Using structures, follow the path of a single carbon atom from glucose to carbon dioxide.

5. Using structures, follow the path of a single oxygen atom from glucose to water.

6. In cholesterol biosynthesis, conversion of squalene-2,3-epoxide to lanosterol resembles a chemical domino reaction. Draw the mechanism of this process, and prove how such a reaction can happen so quickly with high fidelity.

7. In some ways, it is surprising to find clinically useful drugs that inhibit such fundamental biochemical processes. Discuss some reasons why these types of inhibition might be detrimental.

# Chapter 5

# Drug-Receptor Interactions
*by Lemont B. Kier, PhD, and Cynthia S. Dowd, PhD*

The responsibilities and skills of nurse anesthetists require an excellent understanding of all drugs, not just anesthetic drugs. Remembering all drugs, along with their potential side effects and interactions, can be a Herculean task, which becomes even more daunting without an understanding of the mechanisms of the drugs. However, before delving into the ways different classes of drugs work, it is important to be familiar with the basics of how a drug can interact with other molecules.

Medicinal chemists define a *drug* as any substance used for treating, curing, or preventing disease in human beings or animals. A drug may also be used for making a medical diagnosis or for restoring, correcting, or modifying physiological functions (eg, oral contraceptives). To exert its effect, a drug usually encounters another molecule residing in the living system. This other molecule is referred to as a *receptor*. A receptor is a molecule or a polymeric structure (such as DNA) in or on a cell that specifically recognizes and binds a compound (such as a drug) acting as a molecular messenger. The particular location on the receptor to which the drug binds is referred to as the *binding site*.

When a drug encounters or binds to a receptor, a physical change occurs that alters the normal function of the living system. The drug does not produce a new function in the system; it only alters the rate of an existing process or the concentration of an existing biological molecule. The end result of this change is of clinical value, ie, an improvement in the state of the living system that we call health.

Whether a particular drug is likely to encounter a particular type of receptor is governed by the basic forces that control the interactions of all molecules. For a drug to bind to a receptor, the attractive forces between the molecule and the receptor must be stronger than the repulsive forces. These forces–essentially forces of physics–can be described by mathematical equations. It is not necessary to describe these equations mathematically to understand the forces involved in drug-receptor binding. The following section qualitatively describes the physical forces in binding and provides examples in which these forces come into play. The second section of the chapter describes events that occur when a drug binds to a receptor. These 2 sections lay the groundwork for understanding specific mechanisms of action of drugs that will be discussed in the text.

## *Molecular Forces in Drug-Receptor Binding*
Several types of forces can be at work when 2 molecules are attracted to one another. These forces can be relatively strong, such as in a covalent bond,

or relatively weak, such as in a hydrogen bond. More often than not, many interactions, both weak and strong, are responsible for holding together 2 molecules. This section of the chapter discusses the covalent and noncovalent forces that hold molecules together.

## Covalent Interactions

Most interactions between a drug and a receptor involve noncovalent forces. However, some drugs form covalent bonds with their target receptors. In general, a covalent bond is stronger than a noncovalent bond, which means that a drug that binds to a receptor and forms a covalent bond will remain bound to the receptor for a much longer time than if it were bound by noncovalent forces. In addition, it is usually difficult for a covalently bound drug to become unattached from the receptor. A drug that binds to its receptor through 1 or more covalent bonds is called an *irreversible drug*. Because the drug binds to the receptor irreversibly, the effect of the drug usually lasts a long time. This longer duration of action is not always warranted in therapy. Irreversible inhibitors can also lead to undesirable effects such as allergenicity and mutagenicity. However, several notable examples of approved drugs work by irreversibly binding to their target receptor. For example, physostigmine forms a covalent bond with its target receptor, acetylcholinesterase, prohibiting function of the enzyme.

As discussed in Chapter 3, the strength of a covalent bond varies. Generally, a covalent bond ranges in strength from 40 to 150 kcal/mol. The strength of a covalent bond will change depending on the chemical nature of the atoms that make up the bond. In drug-receptor systems, the most influential forces are noncovalent. The next section focuses on the most important noncovalent forces between a drug and its receptor.

## Noncovalent Interactions

Interactions between drug and receptor molecules mostly, and often only, involve noncovalent forces. *Noncovalent forces* are forces between 2 or more atoms based on differences in electronic character. The basis for noncovalent forces is the physical law that states that a positive charge and a negative charge will, depending on the distance between the charges, be attracted to one another. The contrary is true as well–2 positive charges or 2 negative charges will repel one another. However, because the main focus of this book is drugs that bind to a receptor, the emphasis is on the noncovalent interactions that produce attractive forces. Noncovalent interactions of an attractive nature are usually referred to as *noncovalent bonds*.

Noncovalent bonds are usually classified based on the types of groups interacting. The classes of noncovalent forces discussed include ionic, ion-dipole, dipole-dipole, and nonpolar binding forces. One of the most important noncovalent bonds in living systems is the *hydrogen bond* (see Dipole-Dipole Bonds), which is a type of dipole-dipole interaction and is the key attractive force in biological systems.

## Ionic Bonds

An *ionic bond* is a bond between 2 charged atoms, one of which has a positive charge and the other a negative charge (**Figure 1**). The force of the ion-ion interaction extends over several angstroms and decreases with the square of the separating distance. An angstrom is $1 \times 10^{-10}$ meters. If the distance between the atoms is doubled, the resulting force is one-fourth the original magnitude. The strength of an ionic bond is typically 4 to 8 kcal/mol.

An ionic bond that frequently occurs in biological systems is the interaction between a negatively charged carboxylate group $(CO_2^-)$ and a positively charged onium group $(R_4N^+)$. These functional groups are seen in proteins as part of amino acids and are often seen in the structures of neurotransmitters. Attractive forces in drug-receptor binding are frequently attributed to ionic bonds. Other functional groups that can form ionic bonds include the phosphate group, sulfate group, and alkoxide anions.

## Ion-Dipole Bonds

An *ion-dipole bond* occurs between a charged molecule and a nonionic, polar functional group called a *dipole*. The dipole is a polar fragment rich in lone pair electrons or labile hydrogen atoms. Examples of polar groups include carbonyl, cyano, amino, ether, hydroxyl, and halogen atoms such as chlorine and fluorine (**Figure 2**). These groups usually have 2 atoms that differ in electronegativity. The heteroatom typically has lone pair electrons and represents the negative portion of the dipole.

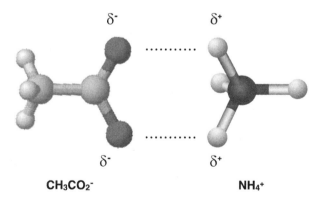

$\delta^-$       $\delta^+$

$\delta^-$       $\delta^+$

$CH_3CO_2^-$       $NH_4^+$

**Figure 1.** *Example of ion-ion interactions. In an ionic bond, the negative charge of one ion, such as a carboxylate anion, is attracted to the positive charge of another ion, such as an onium cation.*

The ion-dipole force is similar to the ionic bond in that it extends over several angstroms. The force of the ion-dipole bond, however, diminishes with the cube of the distance of separation ($1/r^3$). That is, if the distance between the ion and dipole is doubled, the resulting force is only one-eighth ($1/2^3$) the strength of the original force. Ion-dipole bonds have energies in the range of 1 to 7 kcal/mol.

An example of the ion-dipole bond is the force of attraction between a negatively charged ion ($CH_3CO_2^-$) and the partially positive hydrogen atoms (positive dipole) of a water molecule (**Figure 3**). A major difference between an ion-dipole bond and an ionic bond is that in an ion-dipole bond, the strength of the bond is affected by the direction of the dipole relative to the ion.

## Dipole-Dipole Bonds

A *dipole-dipole bond* forms between 2 neutral but polar molecules. Each molecule has structural fragments that are rich in lone pair electrons or labile hydrogen atoms (dipoles). A dipole-dipole bond is generally weaker than an ionic bond or ion-dipole bond. Also, the force of the dipole-dipole bond diminishes with the distance of separation to the fourth power ($1/r^4$). That is, if the distance between the 2 dipoles is doubled, the resulting force is only one-sixteenth ($1/2^4$) the original force. Like ion-dipole bonds, the strength of dipole-dipole bonds is affected by the relative orientation of the 2 dipoles. Dipole-dipole bonds have energies in the range of 2 to 6 kcal/mol.

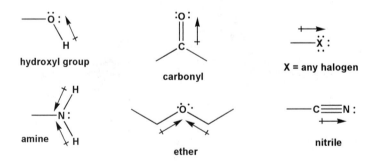

**Figure 2.** *Examples of functional groups that have dipole moments and are dipoles. Arrows indicate movement of electrons toward the heteroatom.*

The most important dipole-dipole attraction in biological systems is the hydrogen bond. The term *hydrogen bond* is familiar to most students who have studied biology and chemistry. Hydrogen bonding is responsible for the high boiling point of water and is the reason ice floats. Hydrogen bonding gives DNA its characteristic double helix shape and holds proteins in their functional forms.

A hydrogen bond is a noncovalent, attractive interaction between the lone pair electrons of an electronegative atom and a nearby hydrogen atom attached to a second, relatively electronegative atom (**Figure 4**). Because the hydrogen atom is covalently bonded to a more electronegative atom, it is essentially a bare proton and, therefore, has considerable positive character. The strength of this positive charge increases the electrostatic interaction between the hydrogen atom and the lone pair electrons of a second electronegative atom. The lone pair of electrons usually lies on an oxygen, a sulfur, or a nitrogen atom. Because of the lone pair of electrons and their electronegative character relative to hydrogen, there is considerable negative charge around these atoms. This negative charge forms the basis for the negative side of the hydrogen bonding attraction.

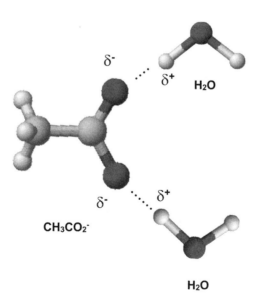

**Figure 3.** *Ion-dipole interaction between a carboxylate anion and water. The negative ion is attracted to the partially positively charged hydrogen atoms of the water molecule.*

An example of hydrogen bonding occurs in ethanol (Figure 4). Ethanol contains a hydroxyl group that has a hydrogen atom covalently bonded to an oxygen atom. Because of the electronegative nature of the oxygen, the 2 electrons in the O-H bond are pulled toward the oxygen, leaving the hydrogen with a partially positive charge due to the loss of electron density. The oxygen is surrounded by the bulk of the electron density contained in the O-H bond, in addition to its 2 lone pairs of electrons. If 2 molecules of ethanol are in proximity, a hydrogen-bonding situation develops. Here, the partially positive hydrogen atom of one molecule is attracted to the partially negative oxygen atom of another molecule. The hydrogen atom is effectively shared between the 2 molecules. Any molecule that has a hydrogen atom covalently bound to an electronegative atom can serve as a hydrogen bond donor (eg, -OH, -NH$_2$, -SH, -COOH). Hydrogen bond donors provide the hydrogen atom to a hydrogen bond. Any molecule that has an atom with a lone pair of electrons can serve as a hydrogen bond acceptor (eg, -O-, -N-, -S-, -Cl, -F, and =O). The lone pair of electrons accepts the hydrogen atom.

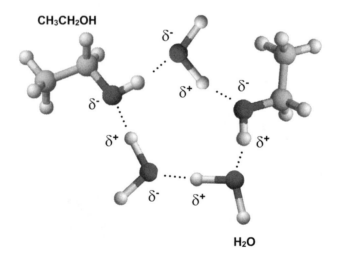

**Figure 4.** *Dipole-dipole interactions between ethanol and water. Hydrogen bonding is the most important type of dipole-dipole interaction. In a hydrogen bond, the lone pair electrons of one atom, such as the oxygen atom of ethanol, are attracted to the hydrogen atom of a neighboring molecule, such as those in water.*

The importance of the hydrogen bonding activity of water cannot be understated. With a hydroxyl group (-OH), water can act as a hydrogen bond donor and a hydrogen bond acceptor. A water molecule can share both hydrogen atoms and can receive 2 hydrogen atoms at each lone pair of electrons. Thus, a water molecule can form hydrogen bonds with up to 4 other water molecules or other suitable donor or acceptor molecules. Furthermore, there is nothing else within the structure of water to take away from its hydrogen bonding potential.

The strength of 1 hydrogen bond is not large (2-6 kcal/mol). However, the strength of multiple hydrogen bonds is tremendous. This strength gives water a number of special properties that would not be expected from its structure. These properties include high boiling point, high specific heat capacity, great power as a solvent, lower density of ice than liquid water, and the ability of water to stick to itself as reflected by its surface tension. All of these properties are due to the preference of water molecules to associate with one another (due to the attractive hydrogen bonds) rather than with nonwater molecules.

When considering molecules that vary in size, shape, and molecular structure, it is important to note whether these molecules are able to participate in hydrogen bonding. Most biologically active molecules are able to act as hydrogen bond donors or acceptors. This flexibility greatly influences their activity in biological systems.

## Nonpolar Bonding Forces

Weak forces between atoms in different molecules arise from small changes in the probable positions of electrons in their orbitals. These transient changes in position produce temporary dipoles in molecules that otherwise do not have a dipole moment. A *dipole moment* is a description of the overall polarity of a molecule, taking into account the polarity of each individual bond. In this temporary state, dipoles are induced in atoms of adjacent molecules. The 2 temporary dipoles are attractive, leading to a weak bonding force. Examples of these induced forces are shown in **Figure 5**.

Nonpolar bonding forces are called by several names, including dispersion, London, van der Waals, and charge fluctuation forces. They depend on the close interaction between 2 molecules. The forces are weak and measure approximately 0.2 to 0.6 kcal/mol. These forces accumulate, however, from the contributions of several polarizable bonds. As a consequence, this type of bonding often provides a sizeable contribution to the intermolecular strength of a drug-receptor encounter.

The term *hydrophobic bonding* is sometimes used to define the attraction of 2 nonpolar molecules in water. In this case, a weak bond forms between the nonpolar molecules, as described earlier. Water molecules surrounding the nonpolar molecules bond to each other through hydrogen bonds, preferring this bond to a water-nonpolar bond, which would be less attractive. The hydrophobic bond maximizes the attractive interactions between nonpolar molecules and the attractive interactions between water molecules.

Nonpolar bonds, by any name, are important in molecules engaged in drug-receptor encounters. They provide attractive reinforcement that adds to the stronger and more selective polar types of bonds. Each type of attractive force is important in defining how a drug molecule interacts with its target receptor.

## The Drug-Receptor Concept

Around the beginning of the 20th century, it was noted that some drugs had pharmacological effects on certain tissues, whereas other drugs produced no effect in these tissues. This tissue selectivity was the early basis for the *drug-receptor theory,* a concept known to be true today. This theory states that a drug will exert its effect on a biological system through a specific receptor. Biological systems have a vast array of receptor types. It is because of this variety of receptors that healthcare providers are able to modulate physiology with medication.

As described in later chapters, different receptor types appear in humans, bacteria, viruses, and other organisms. Therefore, medication can often be tailored to fit the cause of a disease. In addition, side effects can result from a drug acting nonselectively between receptor types. In general, the more selective a drug is for a certain receptor, the fewer the side effects that will result. Understanding how a drug interacts with a receptor and the pharmacological result from that interaction provides insight into how to make a drug more selective for its receptor type.

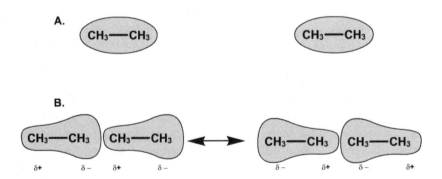

**Figure 5.** *Mechanism of the induced dipole-induced dipole interaction. A, Molecules that do not have a permanent dipole, such as ethane, have electron density distributed evenly around them. B, When these molecules come near each other, however, slight fluctuations in the electron density occur. These fluctuations are transient, but represent small forces of attraction between molecules.*

This section of the chapter is divided into 3 parts. The first part discusses receptors and the types of receptors encountered in treating disease. The second part describes the effects a drug can have once it has bound to the receptor. These effects are changes that occur within the cell that result in a pharmacological change. The final part discusses what can be learned from drug-receptor interactions and how this information is useful in creating new drugs.

## Receptors

In general, a *receptor* is the biological macromolecule through which a drug (or natural substance) exerts its effect. The terms *target* and *target molecule* are also used to refer to receptors. A biological receptor can be composed of many kinds of atoms and functional units, each of which can be a receptor, as described subsequently. All receptors, however, have structural features that are complementary to the structural features found in the molecules that bind to them. In other words, a receptor has the structural elements necessary to attract its binding partner. These elements are related to the physical forces described earlier in this chapter and can be hydrogen bond donors or acceptors, anions or cations to participate in ionic bonds, hydrophobic surfaces, etc. The pattern of structural elements on the receptor defines which molecule (or molecules) will bind to it.

A molecule that binds to a receptor is called a *ligand*. The ligand can be a natural substance found in the body, such as a neurotransmitter or hormone, or it can be a substance not normally found in the body, such as a drug. Most receptors have endogenous substances in the body that are their natural ligands. Endogenous ligands bind to their receptors at a specific location. If the receptor catalyzes a chemical reaction, such as in the case of an enzyme, the site at which the ligand binds is called the *active site*. For all other receptors, the ligand interacts with the receptor at the binding site. The natural ligand that binds to the active site of an enzyme is called the *substrate*.

The strength of the interaction between a receptor and its ligand (a natural ligand or a drug) is compared in terms of affinity. Molecules with higher affinity to a receptor have a tighter interaction with the receptor compared with molecules with lower affinity. The activity of a drug is highly dependent on its affinity for the target receptor. In general, molecules with higher affinity to a certain receptor will be more pharmacologically active than molecules with lower affinity to the receptor.

Occasionally, a macromolecule that serves as a receptor for a drug has no unique natural ligand. In these cases, the drug inhibits the normal function of the macromolecule. Examples are the structural protein tubulin found in mammalian cells and the penicillin-binding proteins found in bacterial cells. In the cell, these proteins act to maintain the structural integrity of a specific cellular component. Drugs that inhibit these proteins, such as the inhibition of colchicine on tubulin and of β-lactam antibiotics on penicillin-binding proteins, prevent the proteins from serving their normal function.

Many types of biological macromolecules can act as receptors. The variety of receptor types allows for great diversity in terms of drug design and pharmacological effect. Several families of biological macromolecules are described in Chapter 3. Each of these can be viewed as a receptor. While not all receptors have clinical importance, some examples of receptors that are encountered in clinical treatment are listed in **Table 1**.

## Drug Actions

Once a natural ligand or drug binds to a receptor, a myriad of cellular events can occur. The events due to drug binding are called *pharmacological effects*. The pharmacological effects are a direct consequence of the specific receptor system involved. Drug binding alters the components of an existing receptor system.

Some receptors can be turned on or off by the binding of a ligand. Thus, ligands can often be classified as agonists or antagonists. An *agonist* generally mimics the action of the natural ligand of the receptor. The clinical objective when administering an agonist is to reproduce the effect of the natural ligand at the receptor. The neurotransmitters serotonin and dopamine are agonists. Binding of these ligands to the serotonergic and dopaminergic receptors, respectively, results in activation of these receptors.

Agonists can be further classified as full or partial. When a full agonist binds to the receptor, the maximal pharmacological response results. Comparatively, when a partial agonist binds to the receptor, only a portion of the maximal pharmacological response results. No additional amount of the partial agonist will result in maximal activation.

An *antagonist* is a molecule that binds to a receptor and prevents the receptor from functioning normally. Antagonists often block the binding of an agonist. In this way, an antagonist can prevent the activation of the receptor. One type of antagonist is called an *inhibitor*. Inhibitors prevent natural ligands from binding to their corresponding receptors. In general, the clinical objective of an antagonist is to diminish the effect of the natural ligand at a receptor.

Several kinds of inhibition of a receptor by a small molecule are possible. It is important to distinguish between *competitive inhibition* and *allosteric inhibition*. If the drug binds to the active site of the receptor and prevents the natural ligand from binding in the same place, competitive inhibition has occurred. Conversely, a drug can bind to a site on the receptor that is removed from the active site, called an allosteric site. If this binding changes the receptor so that it can no longer bind to the natural ligand, allosteric inhibition has occurred.

Most drugs that are used in clinical medicine are pharmacological antagonists. For example, phenothiazine neuroleptics bind to dopaminergic receptors and block the action of dopamine. Dopamine is the natural ligand of the dopaminergic receptors and acts as an agonist. Because phenothiazines block the binding of dopamine, they prevent activation of the dopaminergic receptor and, thus, are classified as antagonists.

**Table 1.** *Examples of receptors, ligands, and their actions.*

| Receptor Type | Receptor Subtype | Receptor Name | Natural Ligand | Effect When Natural Ligand Is Present | Agonist Drug | Antagonist Drug |
|---|---|---|---|---|---|---|
| **Regulatory protein** | GPCR | $D_2$ dopamine receptor | Dopamine | Decreases cAMP; open $K^+$ and $Ca^{2+}$ channels | Bromo-criptine | Haloperidol |
| | Nuclear hormone receptor | Estrogen receptor | Estradiol | Activates transcription and protein synthesis | Diethyl-stilbestrol | Clomiphene (weak partial agonist) |
| | Ion channel | nAchR | Acetylcholine | Influx of $Na^+$ ions into the cell | Nicotine | — |
| **Enzyme** | — | MAO | Amine NTs | Degradation of NT by oxidative deamination | — | Tranylcypromine |
| | — | DNA gyrase | DNA | DNA translation | — | Ciprofloxacin |
| **Transporter** | Reuptake transporter | Serotonin reuptake transporter | Serotonin | Transport of serotonin from synapse into presynaptic cell | — | Fluoxetine |
| **Structural protein** | — | Tubulin | — | No ligand; normal cell structure and mitosis | — | Colchicine, paclitaxel |
| | — | Penicillin-binding proteins | — | No ligand, maintains bacterial cell wall strength | — | β-lactam antibiotics (eg, penicillin and cephalosporin) |
| **Polynucleotide** | — | RNA | — | No ligand; normal RNA synthesis and translation | — | Aminoglycosides (eg, gentamycin and kanamycin) |
| | — | DNA | — | No ligand; normal DNA synthesis and transcription | — | Cisplatin, anthracyclines (eg, doxorubicin) |

Abbreviation: NT, neurotransmitter.

## Drug Effects on Signal Transduction

Cells communicate with other cells and tissues in the body using a variety of mechanisms. The process of a cell receiving a chemical signal from its environment and producing a response is called *signal transduction*. In general, there are 4 mechanisms of signal transduction: (1) a ligand binding to an intracellular receptor; (2) a ligand binding to a membrane-bound protein that alters the intracellular enzymatic activity of the protein; (3) a ligand binding to a membrane-bound, ligand-gated ion channel that results in opening or closing of the channel; and (4) a ligand binding to a membrane-bound receptor that is coupled to a GTP-binding protein on the intracellular surface. A drug that alters one of these events can have a profound effect on the overall pharmacological system.

One family of regulatory proteins that has been extensively studied is the G protein coupled receptor (GPCR) family (see Chapter 3, Figure 5). This family of receptors participates in signal transduction between cells. The extracellular domain of the GPCR binds the ligand or drug. The intracellular domain of the GPCR is linked to a GTP-binding protein (ie, G protein). The G protein is responsible for linking the changes in the GPCR to downstream signaling events in the cell. The downstream signaling events are called *second-messenger events*. A second messenger is an intracellular chemical signal that carries out the action of the agonist bound to the GPCR. (The first messenger is the extracellular ligand that imitates the response.) Several types of second messengers are known and include cyclic adenosine-3',5'-monophosphate (cAMP), inositol-1,4,5-triphosphate (IP$_3$), and calcium. These second messengers trigger further events within the cell such as protein activation, protein synthesis, glucose metabolism, and the production and/or release of additional second messengers. Among other events, an agonist binding to a GPCR can stimulate the synthesis or degradation of cyclic adenosine-3',5'-monophosphate or inositol-1,4,5-triphosphate and mediate release of intracellular calcium stores. Through the production of second messengers, the chemical signal from one cell is received and acted on by a second cell. In this way, cells communicate and can act in concert.

An example of GPCRs and second-messenger signal transduction occurs in nerve cell communication. Two nerve cells meet at a junction called a synapse (**Figure 6**). The *synapse* is the space between 2 nerve cells through which a neurotransmitter travels. A *neurotransmitter* is the chemical signal released from a (presynaptic) neuron to carry a message. The message is received by the postsynaptic cell when the neurotransmitter binds to its complementary receptor. After the neurotransmitter (the ligand) binds to the receptor, the corresponding second-messenger signaling events occur. If the neurotransmitter were dopamine, for example, the second-messenger signaling events specific for dopaminergic receptors would result. Examples of neurotransmitters include serotonin, dopamine, and γ-aminobutyric acid. Figure 6 shows the many events that occur at a synapse.

From this discussion, it can be seen how a natural ligand or a drug will result in intracellular changes. These changes are due to chemical signals moving from one location to another, creating a network of communication between the cell and its environment. The response of a cell to a stimulus can also lead to communication between one cell and another. Cellular communication governs how a tissue will respond to natural or pharmaceutical alteration. Groups of tissues act in concert to express the outward response of the system. In this way, a chemical signal is transmitted from the receptor to the whole system, where clinical changes in physiology and disease can be seen.

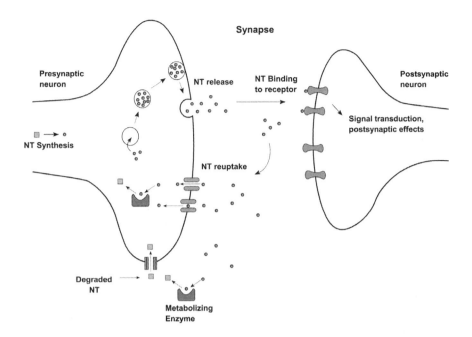

**Figure 6.** *General events that occur at a synapse. There are many events that occur at a synapse. In a presynaptic cell, the neurotransmitter (NT) is synthesized and stored in vesicles. After release from the presynaptic vesicle, the NT travels across the synapse to the postsynaptic cell. Binding of the NT can occur at a postsynaptic receptor. Metabolizing enzymes in the synapse degrade the NT. The products of this reaction diffuse away from the synapse or can be taken up by the presynaptic cell. Unmetabolized NTs are taken up by the presynaptic cell by reuptake transporters.*

## Structural Requirements for Drug Binding

As described, a drug exerts its clinical effect by binding to a receptor. This binding causes changes in the receptor that lead to intracellular effects and, possibly, effects on the system further downstream. The portion of the receptor to which the drug binds is called the *binding site.* Just like drugs have very different chemical structures, the sites to which they bind also have very different structures. Understanding the structural relationship between a drug and its binding site is the focus of this section.

## The Pharmacophore

For a drug to bind to a receptor, the binding site of the receptor should have structural features that are complementary to those found in the drug. In other words, the affinity that exists between a drug and a receptor comes from the attractive forces between key structural features of the drug and key structural features of the receptor's binding site. These structural features of the drug (or receptor) can be, for example, groups that can participate in ionic bonds, groups that can accept or donate hydrogen bonds, or groups that are more lipophilic and form hydrophobic interactions.

When a drug and receptor come in proximity to one another, the measure of the attractive forces between them will determine whether binding will occur. If the binding site of the receptor has a hydrogen bond donor near the hydrogen bond acceptor of the drug, an attractive hydrogen bond is created. Similarly, if the binding site of the receptor has a cationic site near the anionic site of the drug, an attractive ionic bond is created. When the structural features of the receptor pair with the structural features of the drug, the two are said to be *complementary*.

The analogy of a "lock and key" relationship is often used to describe the process of a drug binding to a receptor. Just as one key will only open a certain lock, a drug molecule will bind only to a certain receptor. Each key is made to fit one lock. Each drug is made to fit one type of receptor.

The pattern of essential structural features of the drug molecule is called the *pharmacophore* of the drug. A pharmacophore is a pattern of 3 or more atoms and/or functional groups on a drug that are arranged so that attractive forces between the drug and receptor are maximized. The stronger the attractive forces between the drug and the receptor, the tighter the binding between the pair will be. The structural features in the pharmacophore must be present in the drug for it to have pharmacological activity.

**Figure 7** shows the pharmacophore of acetylcholine and how this pattern of functional groups is thought to interact with specific sites within the acetylcholinesterase enzyme active site. Each structural feature has a certain polarity, electronic structure, and steric arrangement that matches with a complementary part of the receptor. It is this matching of structural features that gives the ligand its activity.

By understanding the structural features of a natural ligand or a drug that are important for receptor binding, it is possible to design a new molecule that contains the same features. This process, called *drug design,* is used by research scientists to develop new and/or better medicines for receptors thought to be involved in certain disease states. An added advantage of drug design is that in the process of developing new ligands, it is possible to infer information about the structural features of the binding site of a receptor. This structural information helps explain how ligand binding results in intracellular pharmacological change. As described earlier, these intracellular changes are what ultimately lead to physiological changes in the entire system and a desired clinical outcome.

This chapter has described some of the smallest attractive forces that can occur between 2 molecules. Patterns of hydrogen bonding, ionic interactions, and hydrophobic forces, when combined, can provide a strong enough force to hold 2 molecules temporarily together. When these forces lie in the proper geometrical arrangement on a drug and receptor, binding can occur. It is this binding that leads to cellular changes and, further downstream, desirable clinical effects in the patient.

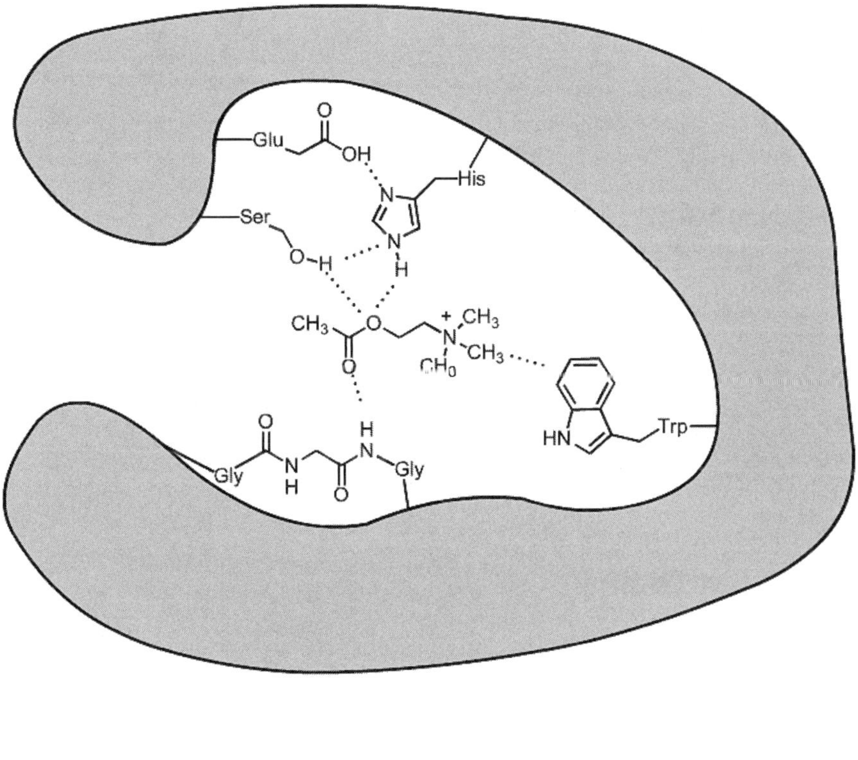

**Figure 7.** *Acetylcholine binding to acetylcholinesterase. The active site of acetylcholinesterase has several amino acid residues that are important for binding acetylcholine. The residues of the active site are positioned so that the interacting functional groups of acetylcholine lie in proximity. The positive charge of the onium ion is attracted to the negative charge of the electron cloud surrounding the indole ring of the tryptophan (Trp) residue. This interaction is called a cation-pi attractive force. The ester oxygen atom participates in a series of hydrogen bonds with nearby serine (Ser) and histidine (His) residues. The carbonyl oxygen atom forms a hydrogen bond with an amide proton from a neighboring glycine (Gly) residue. These interactions are necessary for the binding of acetylcholine to the enzyme. Acetylcholine's pharmacophore is composed of the onium group, the ester oxygen atom a certain distance removed from the onium, and a carbonyl oxygen atom. Abbreviation: Glu, glucose.*

## Suggested Reading

Bennett MR. The concept of transmitter receptors: 100 years on. *Neuropharmacology*. 2000;39(4):523-546.

Brady ST, Siegel GJ, Albers RW, Price DL. *Basic Neurochemistry: Principles of Molecular, Cellular, and Medicinal Biology*. 8th ed. Waltham, MA: Elsevier Academic Press; 2012.

Foye WO, Williams DA, Lemke TL, Roche VF, Zito SW. *Principles of Medicinal Chemistry*. 6th ed. Philadelphia, Pa: Lippincott Williams & Wilkins; 2012.

Isaacs NS. *Physical Organic Chemistry*. 2nd ed. Essex, England: Longman Scientific and Technical; 1995.

Katzung BG, Masters SB, Trevor AJ. *Basic and Clinical Pharmacology*. 12th ed. New York, NY: McGraw-Hill; 2012.

Masson J, Sagné C, Hamon M, El Mestikawy S. Neurotransmitter transporters in the central nervous system. *Pharmacol Rev*. 1999;51(3):439-464.

Smith HJ, Williams H. *Smith and Williams' Introduction to the Principles of Drug Design and Action*. 4th ed. Amsterdam, The Netherlands: CRC Press; 2005.

## Discussion Topics

1. What forces are involved in drug-receptor interactions?

2. In chemical terms, what is a receptor?

3. In chemical terms, what is a ligand?

4. What are some of the categories of consequences of a drug-receptor encounter?

5. What is a pharmacophore?

# Chapter 6

# Pharmacokinetics and Pharmacodynamics

*by Jürgen Venitz, MD, PhD*

*Pharmacokinetics* (PK) describe the relationship between the administered dose of a drug and its (observed) plasma and/or tissue concentrations (what the body does to the drug) (**Figure 1**). On the other hand, *pharmacodynamics* (PD) describe the relationship between (observed) plasma concentrations of the parent drug and/or its active metabolite(s) and the pharmacological effect (what the drug does to the body). These pharmacological or PD effects are responsible for desired and undesired clinical outcomes, ie, therapeutic efficacy and clinical toxicity. Both PK and PD are sources of variability in drug response among different patients (interpatient variability).

Information about PK parameters, such as volume of distribution (Vd) and total body clearance ($CL_{tot}$), allows the physiological interpretation of the PK behavior of a drug and, more importantly, the identification of important patient factors (covariates, eg, age, concurrent illness, and concomitant medications). These covariates can affect the PK and introduce interpatient variability. Knowledge of patient-specific PK parameters permits the prediction of plasma (and possibly tissue) concentrations following different dosing regimens and the determination of dosing regimens intended to achieve specific target plasma concentrations, ie, dose individualization.

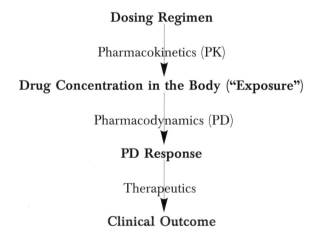

**Dosing Regimen**

Pharmacokinetics (PK)

↓

**Drug Concentration in the Body ("Exposure")**

Pharmacodynamics (PD)

↓

**PD Response**

Therapeutics

↓

**Clinical Outcome**

**Figure 1.** *Definition of PK and PD in drug treatment.*

The PK of a drug includes the processes of absorption, distribution, metabolism, and excretion of the drug and/or its metabolite(s). The PK can be assessed by using compartmental PK or physiologically based PK.

*Compartmental PK* describes the body as a system of hypothetical compartments that are linked by transfer rate processes (**Figures 2** and **3**). These PK

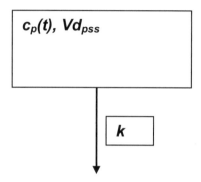

**Figure 2.** *Scheme of a one-compartment body model with first-order elimination; $Vd_{pss}$: volume of distribution at pseudo-steady-state, k: first-order elimination rate constant.*

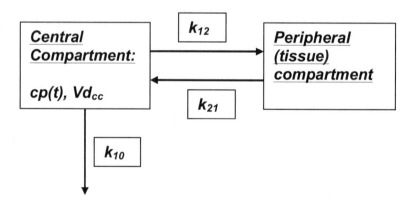

**Figure 3.** *Scheme of an open two-compartment body model with first-order elimination and first-order distribution ($Vd_{cc}$: volume of distribution of the central compartment; $k_{12}$: distribution rate constant, $k_{21}$: redistribution rate constant, $k_{10}$: elimination rate constant).*

compartments group together several physiological compartments (tissues) that have similar kinetic properties. Each compartment is characterized by its size (volume), and concentrations in each compartment are assumed to be homogeneous and instantaneously mixed. In most cases, these connecting transfer processes are assumed to be first order, ie, proportional to the concentrations in their initiating compartment, which leads to linear or dose-proportional PK, ie, the drug concentrations in the body are proportional to the dose administered.

Physiologically based PK describes the body as a system of tissues and organs into and out of which the drug distributes or from which it is eliminated. Tissue and organ blood flows, blood-to-tissue ratios, and drug extraction by eliminating organs, therefore, determine the rate and extent (how fast and how much) of drug distribution and elimination (**Figure 4**). Understanding these parameters helps with the assessment of the effect of physiological or pathophysiological changes in organ function on the PK behavior of a drug.

Drug distribution into various organs and elimination from the body depend on certain physicochemical properties of the drug, such as lipophilicity and ionization (to cross-biological membranes), and the molecular weight and mechanisms for plasma protein and tissue binding and specific uptake. In general, small (molecular weight, 300-700 Da), lipophilic drug molecules cross lipid barriers easily, distribute extensively throughout the body, and are more likely to be hepatically metabolized than renally eliminated. On the other hand, small, polar drug molecules are likely to remain in plasma and to be eliminated renally. Large (molecular weight $> 1,000$ Da) drug molecules are likely to remain in plasma and need to be metabolized and or taken up by tissues before their elimination.

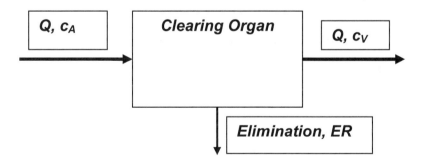

**Figure 4.** *Schematic representation of a clearing organ; Q: organ blood flow, $c_A$: arterial drug concentration, $c_V$: venous drug concentration; ER: organ extraction ratio.*

In addition to the physicochemical drug characteristics, organ perfusion is responsible for delivery of most drugs to organs and determines their distribution into and elimination from organs. This principle applies particularly to small, lipophilic drug molecules that can diffuse quickly across the biological membranes, eg, short-acting benzodiazepines and opioids used for induction of anesthesia. **Table 1** shows the relative volume of several human organs and their blood flow and perfusion rates. It is apparent that the brain, heart, and kidneys are highly perfused organs, and most small, lipophilic drugs will distribute quickly and extensively in these organs, whereas adipose tissue is poorly perfused, and lipophilic drugs may accumulate only very slowly here. The liver is also a highly perfused organ and contributes extensively to the elimination of lipophilic drugs, but it receives blood supply from the gastrointestinal (GI) tract via the portal vein (important for oral administration and first-pass metabolism) and the hepatic artery (important for intravenous [IV] administration). Note that any reduction in cardiac output (eg, during anesthesia) and/or redirection of blood flow to specific organs (due to autoregulation in brain, heart, and kidney vascular beds) can change drug distribution and elimination patterns. Finally, the lungs receive the entire cardiac output and may contribute to drug distribution and elimination, but their actual contribution is mostly unknown.

In contrast with PK, PD describes the plasma concentration–pharmacological effect relationship for the parent drug and/or active metabolite(s). The assessment of PK/PD, therefore, allows the prediction of the onset, magnitude, and duration of the PD effect(s) following different dosing regimens. It also helps in understanding the impact of changes in PK/PD parameters (drug/patient) on the pharmacological response vs. the time profile.

**Table 1.** *Relative volume and blood flow of PK significant organs in a 70-kg man.*

| Organ | Percent Body Volume | Blood Flow (mL/min) | Percent Cardiac Output | Tissue Perfusion Rate (mL/min/mL tissue) |
|---|---|---|---|---|
| Blood | 7 | 5000 | 100 | - |
| Bone | 16 | 250 | 5 | 0.2 |
| Brain | 2 | 700 | 14 | 0.5 |
| Fat | 10 | 200 | 4 | 0.03 |
| Heart | 0.5 | 200 | 4 | 0.6 |
| Kidneys | 0.4 | 1100 | 22 | 4 |
| Liver | 2.3 | 1350 | 27 | 0.8 |
| Portal | | 1050 | 21 | |
| Arterial | | 300 | 6 | |

## Drug Absorption

Pharmacokinetically, *drug absorption* is defined as the rate and extent of drug appearance in the systemic circulation (as measured by plasma concentrations of usually venous, sometimes arterial, blood) after nonsystemic administration, eg, oral or intramuscular. The "gold standard" is IV bolus administration of the drug, resulting in complete and instantaneous absorption into the systemic circulation. Drug absorption is characterized by the following PK parameters: bioavailability, the peak plasma concentration, the time of the peak plasma concentration, and the area under the plasma concentration–time curve.

- Bioavailability (F) is the fraction of the dose that is absorbed, relative to IV administration; F measures the extent of drug absorption and can range from 0 (no absorption) to 1 (complete absorption). Reduced bioavailability results in reduced systemic drug concentrations.
- Peak plasma concentration ($c_{max}$) is the highest observed plasma concentration following administration of the drug (**Figure 5**). The value of $c_{max}$ depends on the rate and extent of absorption. An increased *extent* of absorption (F) increases the $c_{max}$; an increased *rate* of absorption also increases $c_{max}$ (**Figure 6**). Peak plasma levels may be clinically important because drug toxicity may be related to them.
- Time of $c_{max}$ ($t_{max}$) is the time point when $c_{max}$ is observed. The value of $t_{max}$ depends only on the rate of absorption, but not on the extent of absorption. An increase in absorption rate shortens $t_{max}$ (Figure 5).

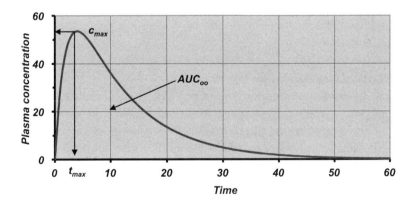

**Figure 5.** *Example of a plasma-concentration versus time ($c_p(t)$) profile; definition of $c_{max}$, $t_{max}$ and $AUC_\infty$.*

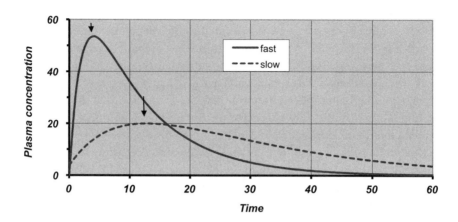

**Figure 6.** *Effect of changing the rate of absorption on the $c_p(t)$-profile, $c_{max}$ and $t_{max}$; the insert denotes the absorption rate constant.*

- The area under the plasma concentration–time curve ($AUC_\infty$) can be estimated by integration of the surface area under the curve from time zero to infinity (Figure 5). It measures the extent of absorption. Accordingly, an increase in F increases the $AUC_\infty$. The $AUC_\infty$ is not affected by changes in the rate of absorption. In Figure 6, the $AUC_\infty$ values for both curves are identical. The $AUC_\infty$ is sometimes referred to as *systemic exposure*; it depends on the bioavailability and the total clearance, $CL_{tot}$.

Drug absorption depends on the following factors, which may help healthcare providers to design clinical dosing regimens to achieve optimal plasma concentration–time profiles: dose and dosage form, rate of administration, and route of administration.

## Dose and Dosage Form

In general, an increase in the dose results in an increase in the $AUC_\infty$. If the absorption process follows first-order kinetics, the $AUC_\infty$ is proportional to the dose. Particularly for oral drugs, the dosage form, eg, solution, capsule, tablet, and extended release, can substantially affect drug absorption. Usually, oral solutions are absorbed rather quickly (because the drug does not need to be dissolved in the GI lumen), whereas extended-release formulations slowly release drug from the dosage form, resulting in slow absorption into the systemic circulation.

## Rate of Administration

A drug can be given as an IV bolus, IV infusion, intermittent infusion, or in multiple doses. Administration of an IV bolus achieves high $c_{max}$ and short $t_{max}$

values, whereas an IV infusion yields delayed $t_{max}$ and reduced $c_{max}$ values. **Figures 7 and 8** illustrate the different plasma concentration–time profiles for IV bolus and IV infusion regimens into a 1-compartment body model (as shown in Figure 2). In both cases, the same dose was given, resulting in identical $AUC_\infty$ values; however, there are dramatic differences in $c_{max}$ and $t_{max}$. Note that the IV infusion resulted in plasma concentrations approaching steady state. Figure 8 demonstrates that the plasma concentration of the drug declines at the same rate after IV bolus administration as after the IV infusion. Multiple or repeated doses may result in slowly increasing $c_{max}$ values because of drug accumulation (**Figure 9**).

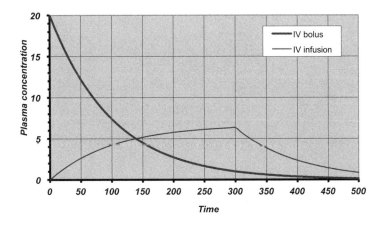

**Figure 7.** *Plasma-concentration versus time profile of a one-compartment body model after IV bolus (thick line) and constant rate IV infusion (thin line).*

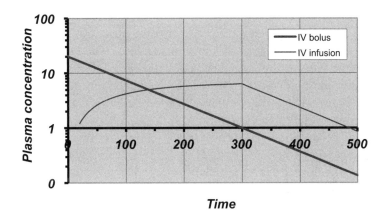

**Figure 8.** *Same as Figure 7 on a logarithmic concentration scale.*

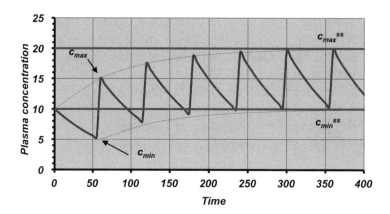

**Figure 9.** *The $c_p(t)$ profile demonstrating drug accumulation in plasma following repeated IV bolus dosing in a one-compartment body model with first-order elimination; definition of peak ($c_{max}$) and trough ($c_{min}$) plasma concentration and illustration of fluctuating steady-state concentrations.*

## Route of Administration

The most common routes of drug administration are IV, intramuscular (IM), subcutaneous, transdermal, rectal, and oral. The IV route allows best control of plasma concentrations because the absorption is instantaneous and complete. The IM route results in slower, incomplete, and more erratic absorption. The rate and extent of IM absorption may depend on the injection site, muscle mass, and blood perfusion. The subcutaneous route is even more erratic and slow relative to IM because the skin is poorly perfused. Absorption through the transdermal route depends on the skin permeability of the drug and can be quite efficient (eg, fentanyl transdermal system). Most transdermal systems release the drug slowly into the skin, intentionally slowing drug absorption into the systemic circulation to achieve a sustained plasma concentration. The rectal route (eg, suppositories) circumvents hepatic first-pass metabolism but can be quite erratic and incomplete and is affected by the rectal content and emptying.

The oral absorption of a drug depends on several physicochemical properties such as aqueous solubility, ionization state, and lipophilicity, as well as stability in the GI tract, absorption through the GI wall (from the stomach at pH 1-2 to duodenum at pH 4-6 and ileum at pH 7-8), and GI motility (eg, stomach emptying). In addition, drugs (especially with high hepatic extraction ratios [ERs]; can be metabolized presystemically by the liver because of first-pass metabolism. First-pass metabolism can also occur in the gut wall and reduce oral bioavailability. Note that oral first-pass metabolism may result in the formation of metabolite(s) that can contribute to the overall pharmacological effect. Finally, drug transporters in the intestinal cells (eg, P-glycoproteins and P-glycoprotein transporters) can secrete the drug back into the GI lumen and reduce oral bioavailability.

## Drug Distribution

*Drug distribution* is defined as the rate and extent of drug distribution from the central (plasma) compartment to peripheral (tissue) compartment(s) and redistribution from tissue back into plasma. The plasma (central) compartment serves as a reference because drug concentrations in plasma can be measured easily and the blood/plasma perfuses all body organs leading to drug distribution.

A 1-compartment body model assumes instantaneous and homogeneous distribution of drug such that the plasma concentrations represent all other tissue concentrations (Figure 2). Under these circumstances, drug disposition after IV bolus administration or at the end of an IV infusion follows a monoexponential decline in the plasma concentration–time profile (Figure 7). On a logarithmic scale, this process results in a monophasic log-linear decline (Figure 8). The slope of this line is characterized by k, the overall elimination rate constant.

A 2-compartment body model assumes that drug distribution to and from the peripheral compartment follows first-order processes characterized by the distribution rate constant $k_{12}$ and redistribution rate constant $k_{21}$ (Figure 3). The values for these rate constants depend on the physicochemical properties of the drug and perfusion rates of the organ and tissue. Furthermore, this model assumes that drug elimination occurs from the central compartment. This assumption is reasonable because the 2 main eliminating organs, the kidney and liver, are highly perfused and in rapid equilibrium with plasma.

Following IV bolus administration, the 2-compartment body model shows a biphasic drug disposition pattern (**Figure 10;** note the logarithmic scale). Initially, the plasma concentration declines quickly (referred to as the α phase), followed by a slower terminal (β) phase. The latter phase is usually determined by drug elimination, whereas the former phase is determined by drug distribution. The terms α and β designate the corresponding slopes on the semilogarithmic plasma concentration–time plot. During the α phase, drug distributes from plasma to the peripheral compartment, and tissue concentrations of the drug increase. During the β phase, drug returns from tissue to plasma (redistribution) to be eliminated. It is noteworthy that during the β phase, drug concentrations in plasma and peripheral compartment(s), while not equal, are declining at the same rate. This condition is referred to as *distribution equilibrium* or *pseudo-steady state* because it appears that the 2-compartment body model has collapsed to a 1-compartment body model as shown in Figure 2. Note that if a drug follows a 3-compartment body model, ie, has 2 peripheral compartments attached to the central compartment, a third phase (γ) appears as the terminal (elimination) phase.

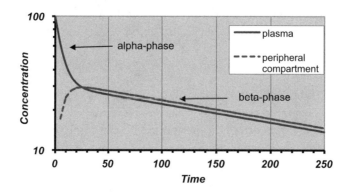

**Figure 10.** *Example of a concentration-time profile for a two-compartment body model following IV bolus administration; both plasma and tissue (peripheral compartment) concentrations are plotted on a logarithmic scale to show both the initial (α) and terminal (β) phase of drug disposition.*

**Figure 11** compares a 2-compartment model with a shallow peripheral compartment (where the distribution rate constant, $k_{21}$, is faster than the drug elimination rate constant, $k_{10}$) with a deep peripheral compartment. In the latter case, the drug-redistribution rate constant from tissue to plasma ($k_{21}$) is slower, ie, rate-limiting, than the drug-elimination rate constant from the central compartment ($k_{10}$). As a result, drug concentrations in the peripheral compartment increase very slowly and decline more slowly than concentrations in plasma, and the pseudo–steady state may never be achieved. If the peripheral compartment is responsible for the PD effect (biophase), the effect will be delayed and prolonged relative to the plasma concentration of the drug.

Drug distribution is characterized by the following PK parameters: volume of distribution, volume of distribution of the central compartment, volume of distribution at steady state, and volume of distribution at pseudo-steady state.

The *volume of distribution* (Vd) relates (observed) plasma concentrations ($c_p$) to the unknown amount of drug in the body ($A_b$):

$$A_b = c_p \times Vd$$

Because $c_p$ and $A_b$ change over time, different Vd values can be estimated. The Vd values assess the extent of distribution, ie, large values for Vd indicate extensive tissue distribution. Physiologically, they may be interpreted as the space in the body that the drug occupies (**Tables 2 and 3**). However, it should be kept in mind that Vd values are hypothetical volume terms that allow conversion of a measured plasma concentration into the amount of drug in the body. The following Vd values are typically reported in the literature:

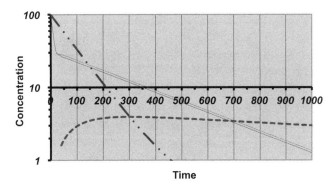

**Figure 11.** *Example of a concentration-time profile for a two compartment body model with a shallow ($k_{21}>k_{10}$, thin lines, same as in Figure 10) and deep peripheral compartment ($k_{21}<k_{10}$, thick lines); both plasma and tissue concentrations are plotted on a logarithmic scale; note the different scale of both abscissa and ordinate compared to Figure 10.*

**Table 2.** *Reference volumes and organ flow rates of various organs responsible for drug distribution and elimination (75 kg man).*

| Volumes (l) | |
| --- | --- |
| Plasma volume | 3 |
| Blood volume | 6 |
| Extracellular space (ECS) | 14 |
| Intracellular space (ICS) | 28 |
| Total body water (TBW) | 42 |
| Body weight (BW) | 75 |
| **Organ Flow Rates (l/min)** | |
| Cardiac output | 6 |
| Pulmonary blood flow | 6 |
| Renal blood flow (RBF) | 1.2 |
| Renal plasma flow (RPF) | 0.6 |
| Glomerular filtration rate (GFR) | 0.12 |
| Hepatic blood flow (HBF) | 1.5 |
| Portal vein | 1 |
| Hepatic artery | 5 |

**Table 3.** *Volumes of distribution of various drugs for a 70-kg man.*

| Drug | Volume of Distribution (l) |
|------|---------------------------|
| Digoxin | 700 |
| Meperidine | 350 |
| Propranolol | 200 |
| Procainamide | 140 |
| Lidocaine | 110 |
| Phenobarbital | 50 |
| Ethanol | 42 |
| Theophylline | 30 |
| Gentamycin | 22 |
| Salicylic Acid | 10 |
| Warfarin | 8 |

The *volume of distribution of the central compartment* ($Vd_{cc}$) is the volume that a drug occupies immediately after an IV bolus dose before any tissue distribution or elimination has occurred (Figure 3). The Vd is also referred to as $Vd_0$ or $V_0$. Physiologically, this volume is close to the plasma volume for most drugs (Table 2). The $Vd_{cc}$ can be calculated as follows:

$$Vd_{cc} = Dose\ (IV\ Bolus)/c_p^{\ 0}$$

where $c_p^{\ 0}$ is the initial plasma concentration at time 0 (ie, the y-intercept in Figure 10). The $Vd_{cc}$ determines peak plasma concentrations and can be used to calculate loading doses.

The *volume of distribution at steady state* ($Vd_{ss}$) estimates the volume a drug occupies at steady state, ie, when the amount of drug input into the body equals the amount of drug lost from the body, and the free drug concentrations in all body compartments are identical. Steady state can be achieved after a long-term IV infusion (Figure 7) or after repeated doses (Figure 9). For a 2-compartment body model, $Vd_{ss}$ is the sum of $Vd_{cc}$ and the volume of the peripheral compartment (Figure 3):

$$Vd_{ss} = Vd_{cc} + k_{12}/k_{21} \times Vd_{cc}$$

The $Vd_{ss}$ is larger than the $Vd_{cc}$ because it includes all peripheral compartments. Physiologically, it is typically larger than the blood volume and can exceed the total body water volume, indicating extensive tissue distribution.

The *volume of distribution at pseudo-steady state* ($Vd_{pss}$) is the volume that the drug occupies during pseudo-steady state, ie, during the β phase in Figure 10. The $Vd_{pss}$ estimates the volume of the apparent 1-compartment body model into which the 2-compartment model has collapsed (Figure 2). The $Vd_{pss}$, also referred to as $Vd_{area}$ or $Vd_β$, can be calculated as:

$$Vd_{pss} = CL_{tot}/β$$

where $CL_{tot}$ is the total body clearance. The $Vd_{pss}$ is larger than the $Vd_{ss}$ and should be interpreted with care; however, it is easily calculated and is widely reported in the literature. Note that if a drug follows a 1-compartment body model as shown in Figure 2, all 3 volumes of distribution are identical.

Table 3 lists several drugs with widely varying Vd values. Digoxin has a large Vd because it is highly bound to proteins ($Na^+/K^+ATPase$) at the surface membrane of skeletal and heart muscle. The polar drug ethanol distributes with the total body water. Gentamicin is a large polar molecule resulting in a small Vd, whereas warfarin is highly plasma protein bound (fraction of drug unbound to plasma proteins [$f_u$] < 1%), leading to a small value for Vd.

## Distribution Half-life

The *distribution half-life* ($t_{1/2}{}^α$) is the time it takes for the drug concentration in plasma to decline by 50% during the distribution phase. This does not mean that 50% of the dose has been distributed. The value of $t_{1/2}{}^α$ depends on the physicochemical drug properties along with tissue perfusion and uptake and determines the rate of distribution. The distribution half-life can be calculated as:

$$t_{1/2}{}^α = ln(2)/α$$

## Fraction Unbound in Plasma

The *fraction unbound in plasma* ($f_u$) indicates the fraction of the drug in plasma that is not bound (reversibly) to plasma proteins and is, therefore, available for distribution, elimination, and interaction with the drug receptors in the biophase. Plasma protein binding can be measured *in vitro* and affects the interpretation of volumes of distribution and body clearances, especially renal clearance ($CL_{ren}$). Highly plasma protein-bound drugs, eg, $f_u$ < 5%, have small volumes of distribution and clearance values because most of the drug in plasma is not available for distribution and elimination (eg, warfarin in Table 3). In general, acidic drugs are more likely to be bound to plasma albumin, particularly if they are lipophilic, whereas basic drugs are more likely to bind to $α_1$-acid glycoprotein, which is present in much smaller concentrations than albumin.

Depending on the drug plasma concentrations, these protein binding sites may be saturated, leading to nonlinear PK. Furthermore, concurrent diseases, eg, chronic renal or hepatic failure, can reduce the extent of plasma protein binding and increase the $f_u$ by decreasing albumin levels or displacing drugs from their binding sites, which may have major long-lasting PK consequences. Concentrations of $\alpha_1$-acid glycoprotein can be elevated by acute trauma and infections. In addition, concurrent medications may displace drugs from their plasma protein binding sites, which can lead to temporary changes in PK.

**Table 4** lists the extent of plasma protein binding for various drugs used in anesthesia practice. It is apparent that plasma protein binding can vary dramatically among drugs. For example, while neuromuscular blockers are polar molecules that do not show a large degree of plasma protein binding, the more lipophilic opioids are substantially bound to plasma proteins.

## Red Blood Cell Binding

Red blood cell (RBC) binding is typically measured as the blood-to-plasma (B/P) ratio and assesses the fraction of drug in the blood that is (reversibly) bound to RBCs and other cellular components of blood. It can be measured *in vitro* but is affected by plasma protein binding as well. In general, lipophilic drugs are more likely to partition into the RBC membrane. RBC binding may affect hepatic drug clearance.

## *Drug Metabolism and Excretion*

## Metabolism

*Metabolism* describes the conversion of the parent drug into secondary molecules (metabolites) that will ultimately be excreted from the body. Metabolism can occur in most body tissues, including plasma (eg, ester hydrolysis of propofol or chemical degradation of atracurium). However, the liver has the largest metabolic capacity and, therefore, is the main contributor to drug metabolism. Metabolism can change the structure of the parent drug to form pharmacologically active or inactive metabolites. For a large number of drugs, the metabolites are more polar, which makes them more suitable for renal and biliary excretion. Individual metabolic pathways may be inhibited specifically by other drugs, leading to drug accumulation, or induced by enzyme inducers, leading to decreased drug concentrations and, possibly, to increased metabolite concentrations. These are examples of drug-drug interactions. Individual pathways may also show genetic polymorphism, which occurs in a subset of the patient population with fewer or less active metabolic isoenzymes.

**Table 4.** *Plasma protein binding (fraction unbound in plasma, $f_u$)
for various drugs used in anesthesia.*

| Drug | Percent Unbound, $f_u$ |
|---|---|
| **Antiarrythmics and Beta-blockers** | |
| Digoxin | 75 |
| Propranolol | 45 |
| Esmolol | 11 |
| **Benzodiazepines** | |
| Diazepam | 1-3 |
| Lorazepam | 8-12 |
| Midazolam | 4 |
| **IV Anesthetics** | |
| Methohexital | 27 |
| Thiopental | 15 |
| **Local Anesthetics** | |
| Bupivicaine | 5 |
| Etidocaine | 5 |
| Lidocaine | 30 |
| Mepivicaine | 20 |
| **Narcotics** | |
| Alfentanil | 8 |
| Fentanyl | 16 |
| Meperidine | 37-47 |
| Morphine | 65 |
| Sulfentanil | 8 |
| **Neuromuscular Blockers** | |
| d-Tubocurarine | 44-51 |
| Metocurine | 35 |
| Pancuronium | 71-89 |
| Vecuronium | 70 |

# Phase I and Phase II Metabolism

Metabolism is subdivided into phase I and phase II processes. Phase I
metabolism involves oxidation, hydroxylation, demethylation, and other
changes to functional groups of the drug molecule that result in relatively
small changes in the molecular structure. Some of these changes may yield
an active metabolite. A large number of these reactions are catalyzed by
cytochrome $P_{450}$-dependent enzymes (**Table 5**). CYP3A4 is the most prevalent
isoenzyme. It is found not only in the liver, but also in the GI wall. The $P_{450}$
enzymes have substrate specificity and inhibitor specificity. Induction of
these enzymes is, however, much less specific and more variable. In addition,

CYP2C9, CYP2C19, and CYP2D6 show genetic polymorphisms. For example, approximately 10% of Caucasians have a defective gene for CYP2D6 that results in a poor metabolizer phenotype, while the remaining 90% have an extensive metabolizer phenotype.

Phase II metabolism involves conjugation reactions, ie, addition of glucuronic acid (glucuronidation by UDP-glucuronosyl transferases), sulfonic acid (sulfonation by sulfotransferases), or acetylation (*N*-acetyltransferase, NAT). Phase II metabolism results in larger molecular weight molecules that are usually

**Table 5.** *CYP450-dependent metabolic pathways for various drugs, designated as substrates, inhibitors and inducers; drugs of particular interest in anesthesia are highlighted.*

### Substrates

| 1A2 | 2C19 | 2C9 | 2D6 | 2E1 | 3A4,5,7 |
|---|---|---|---|---|---|
| clozapine | omeprazole | diclofenac | **codeine** | acetaminophen | clarithromycin |
| imipramine | lansoprazole | ibuprofen | **metoprolol** | chlorzoxazone | erythromycin |
| **mexilitine** | pantoprazole | losaran | **propafenone** | ethanol | quinidine |
| naproxen | **diazepam** | naproxen | timolol | odansetron | alprazolam |
| riluzole | **phenytoin** | **phenytoin** | amitryptiline | **halothane** | diazepam |
| tacrine | amitryptiline | piroxicam | clomipramine | **enflurane** | **midazolam** |
| theophylline | clomipramine | sulfamethoxazole | desipramine | **sevoflurane** | triazolam |
| yclophosphamide | tamoxifen | imipramine | **methoxyflurane** | **soflurane** | cyclosporine |
| | progesterone | tolbutamide | haloperidol | | tacrolimus |
| | | **torsemide** | risperidone | | indinavir |
| | | warfarin | thioridazine | | ritonavir |
| | | | dextromethorphan | | saquinavir |
| | | | flecanainide | | cisapride |
| | | | odansetron | | astemizole |
| | | | **tramadol** | | chlorpheniramine |
| | | | | | diltiazem |
| | | | | | felodipine |
| | | | | | nifedipein |
| | | | | | nisoldipine |
| | | | | | nirendipine |
| | | | | | verapamil |
| | | | | | atorvastatin |
| | | | | | ceriverstatin |
| | | | | | lovastatin |
| | | | | | simvastatin |
| | | | | | buspirone |
| | | | | | trazodone |

### Inhibitors

| 1A2 | 2C19 | 2C9 | 2D6 | 2E1 | 3A4,5,7 |
|---|---|---|---|---|---|
| cimetidine | fluoxetine | **amiodarone** | **amiodarone** | disulfiram | **amiodarone** |
| fluoroquinolones | fluvoxamine | fluconazole | chlorpheniramine | | cimetidine |
| fluvoxamine | ketoconazole | isoniazid | lomipramine | | clarithromycin |
| ticlopidine | lansoprazole | ticlopidine | fluoxetine | | erythromycin |
| omeprazole | ticlopidine I | fluoxetine | indinavir | | grapefruit juice |
| | | | methadone | | itraconazole |
| | | | mibefradil | | ketoconazole |
| | | | paroxetine | | mibefradil |
| | | | quinidine | | troleandomycin |
| | | | | | ritonavir |

### Inducers

| 1A2 | 2C19 | 2C9 | 2D6 | 2E1 | 3A4,5,7 |
|---|---|---|---|---|---|
| **tobacco** | rifampicin | rifampicin | | **ethanol** | carbamazepine |
| | prednisone | secobarbital | | isoniazid | phenobarbital |
| | norethindrone | | | | **phenytoin** |
| | | | | | rifabutin |
| | | | | | rifampicin |
| | | | | | **glucocorticoids** |

more polar and inactive. These metabolites are generally easily eliminated by the kidney or by biliary excretion. A notable exception is morphine-6-glucuronide, a phase II metabolite of morphine. Morphine-6-glucuronide is pharmacologically active, can cross the blood-brain barrier, and binds to μ receptors in the brain, leading to analgesia and respiratory depression. The phase II enzyme system NAT shows genetic polymorphisms. A large number of patients (about 50%) have a defective NAT enzyme and are incapable of metabolizing drugs such as procainamide.

In addition to hepatic and GI metabolism, the plasma shows enzymatic activity as well, particularly to facilitate the hydrolysis of esters. Plasma, therefore, contributes to the metabolic degradation of drugs such as propofol, physostigmine, and certain local anesthetics.

# Excretion

*Biliary excretion* is responsible for the removal of drugs or their metabolites from the liver into the bile. The bile is subsequently released into the GI tract, and the drug or metabolite can be excreted by incorporation into the feces. Some drugs or metabolites can be reabsorbed from the GI tract and undergo enterohepatic cycling after deconjugation by the bacterial flora in the colon. Enterohepatic cycling can substantially prolong the persistence of drug in the body. Administration of activated charcoal disrupts enterohepatic cycling.

*Renal excretion* of drugs and their metabolites can occur by three mechanisms: Glomerular filtration is a passive filtration process that removes the unbound $(f_u)$ drug from plasma and is described in terms of the glomerular filtration rate (GFR). Tubular secretion is an active, ie, potentially saturable, process in the renal tubules that involves specific tubular transporters for acidic and basic drugs. Tubular reabsorption involves the passive or active uptake of drug or metabolite from the primary urine in the renal tubules and placement of the drug or metabolite back into plasma. Tubular reabsorption reduces overall renal elimination and depends on the flow and pH of urine, and the ionization state and lipophilicity of the drug.

Renal excretion can be impaired by acute changes in renal perfusion and by chronic changes in renal function, eg, because of factors such as age or chronic renal failure. Note that the renal function (eg, creatinine clearance) of a 60-year-old healthy person is only about 50% of that of a younger adult.

Drug elimination is characterized by the following PK parameters: clearance (total, renal, and nonrenal) and the elimination half-life.

*Clearance* (CL) is defined as the hypothetical volume of plasma or blood that is completely cleared of the drug per unit of time. It is typically measured in milliliters per minute, ie, flow rate, and relates drug excretion rates to drug plasma concentrations (Table 2). Clearance terms are extremely useful because they can be compared with organ perfusion rates. The following individual PK clearances are typically reported in the literature:

- *Total body clearance* ($CL_{tot}$) measures the sum of all individual elimination pathways. It can be calculated from the $AUC_\infty$ as follows:

$$CL_{tot} = F \times Dose/AUC_\infty$$

The drug exposure ($AUC_\infty$) following IV administration (ie, $F = 1$) is inversely related to $CL_{tot}$. That is, a reduced $CL_{tot}$ leads to higher drug exposure.

The $CL_{tot}$ determines the steady-state plasma concentration ($c_p^{ss}$) for a maintenance dose and allows calculation of the maintenance dose (MD) needed to achieve a target plasma concentration. As long as the drug follows linear (dose-proportional) PK, in which the $CL_{tot}$ does not change with dose, the $c_p^{ss}$ increases as the $CL_{tot}$ decreases, while the MD is proportional to the $CL_{tot}$. The $CL_{tot}$ is difficult to interpret physiologically unless elimination organs and/or mechanisms have been identified. However, the $CL_{tot}$ cannot exceed the cardiac output (Table 2) unless there is chemical or enzymatic degradation of the drug in plasma that is not dependent on any organ perfusion.

- *Renal clearance* ($CL_{ren}$) measures the contribution of renal elimination to the overall elimination of a drug. The $CL_{ren}$ can be calculated as follows:

$$CL_{ren} = CL_{tot} \times f_e$$

where $f_e$ is the fraction of the IV dose administered that is ultimately excreted unchanged by the kidney. Values of $f_e$ can range from 0 (ie, no renal elimination at all, only metabolism) to 1 (ie, the drug is exclusively eliminated by the kidney). The $CL_{ren}$ depends on plasma protein binding because only the unbound drug can be removed by the kidney. It can be interpreted as follows:

$CL_{ren} < GFR$      Drug is reabsorbed in the renal tubules or is plasma protein bound

$CL_{ren} = GFR$      Drug is only filtered, or tubular secretion and reabsorption offset each other

$CL_{ren} > GFR$      Drug undergoes tubular secretion

The $CL_{ren}$ cannot exceed the renal plasma flow. If the $CL_{ren}$ approaches the renal plasma flow, the drug is completely eliminated during a single pass through the kidney (ie, renal ER is 1).

- *Nonrenal clearance* ($CL_{nonren}$) measures the contribution of all pathways (other than renal) to the overall elimination of a drug. The $CL_{nonren}$ can be calculated as follows:

$$CL_{nonren} = CL_{tot} - CL_{ren}$$

The $CL_{nonren}$ is usually attributed to the liver and is assumed to be due to hepatic metabolism and/or biliary excretion. However, other tissue, eg, plasma, may contribute to the $CL_{nonren}$. If the $CL_{nonren}$ exceeds hepatic blood flow (Table 2), there is evidence of extrahepatic elimination.

*Elimination half-life* ($t_{1/2}^{\beta}$) is the time for the plasma concentration to decline by 50% in the terminal $\beta$ phase (Figure 10). This does not mean that the amount of drug in the body is decreased by 50% because a large fraction of the drug in the body may not be in the plasma but in the peripheral compartment(s). The $t_{1/2}^{\beta}$ refers only to the fraction of drug in the plasma. The value for $t_{1/2}^{\beta}$ is inversely related to the elimination rate constant and can be calculated as follows:

$t_{1/2}^{\beta} = \ln(2)/k$ for a 1-compartment body model (Figure 2)

$t_{1/2}^{\beta} = \ln(2)/\beta$ for a 2-compartment body model (Figure 3)

Note that the rate constant k (or $\beta$) is a function of $CL_{tot}$ and $Vd_{pss}$:

$$\mathbf{k = CL_{tot}/Vd_{pss}}$$

Therefore, a long elimination half-life (small k value) can be due to a small value for $CL_{tot}$ or a large value for $Vd_{pss}$.

The elimination half-life determines the following PK properties:

- *Rate of loss*: The elimination half-life measures the rate and degree of loss of drug from the body. However, in a multicompartment body model, the change in plasma concentrations does not necessarily reflect proportional changes in the amount of drug in the body.

- *Time to reach steady state*: The time that it takes for a given dose rate to achieve steady-state concentrations depends only on the elimination half-life. In practice, it takes about 4 to 5 times the $t_{1/2}^{\beta}$ to reach steady state using repeated dosing unless a loading dose is used (Figure 9).

- *Dosing interval* ($\tau$): The dosing interval is determined by the elimination half-life. More frequent dosing will result in increased accumulation and decreased fluctuation but does not change the time to reach steady state. The number of doses required to achieve steady state will change depending on the dosing interval.

- *Drug accumulation* (R): Drug accumulation is the increase in drug concentration on repeated dosing (Figure 9). Drug accumulation increases as the elimination half-life becomes longer, eg, due to a reduction in $CL_{tot}$.

- *Fluctuation*: Fluctuation is the ratio of peak over trough concentration, $c_{max}/c_{min}$, during a dosing interval (Figure 9). Fluctuation decreases as the elimination half-life increases.

## Physiological Interpretation of Clearance Values

Clearances can be interpreted as organ clearances using the following simple physiological model (Figure 4): A clearing organ receives arterial blood with an arterial drug concentration of $c_A$, extracts and eliminates a fraction of the drug, and returns some of the drug with the venous drug concentration of $c_V$. The organ blood flow on the arterial and venous sides is Q. The intrinsic ability of the organ to extract the drug from blood is characterized by the organ extraction ratio (ER), which, in turn, can be assessed as follows:

$$ER = (c_A - c_V)/c_A$$

The ER can vary from 0 (ie, no drug is removed, $c_V = c_A$, for a noneliminating organ) to 1 ($c_V = 0$, when the entire drug is removed during 1 pass through the organ). The total organ clearance ($CL_{organ}$) then becomes a function of blood supply and ER:

$$CL_{organ} = ER \times Q$$

Therefore, the organ clearance depends on the organ perfusion, ie, delivery to the organ, and ER, ie, uptake of the drug into the organ parenchyma and subsequent removal. Drugs can be classified as having a low (ER < 20%), intermediate (20%-80%), or high (ER > 80%) ER (**Table 6**).

**Table 6.** *Classification of drugs used in anesthesia according to their hepatic extraction ratio, ERhep.*

| | |
|---|---|
| **Low Extraction** | Diazepam |
| | Lorazepam |
| | Phenytoin |
| | Theophylline |
| | Thiopental |
| | Warfarin |
| **Intermediate Extraction** | Alfentanil |
| | Methohexital |
| | Midazolam |
| | Vecuronium |
| **High Extraction** | Bupivicaine |
| | Fentanyl |
| | Ketamine |
| | Lidocaine |
| | Meperidine |
| | Metoprolol |
| | Morphine |
| | Naloxone |
| | Propranolol |
| | Sufentanil |

This simple model has been applied quite successfully to drug elimination by the liver, and the following variables have been found to determine the hepatic ER ($ER_{hep}$):

$Q_{hep}$:    If hepatic blood flow, $Q_{hep}$, is increased, the $ER_{hep}$ is reduced because the transit time of the drug through the liver is shortened and hepatic uptake is reduced. Liver perfusion can be affected by changes in cardiac output and by chronic hepatic cirrhosis.

$f_u$:    Plasma protein and RBC binding reduce the hepatic uptake of drugs because only the unbound drug in plasma ($f_u$) can be taken up into hepatocytes. Plasma protein binding can be affected by chronic renal and hepatic diseases and by concurrent medications.

$CL_{int}$:    The intrinsic hepatic clearance ($CL_{int}$) is a measure of the intrinsic ability of the liver to remove a drug (ie, metabolize or excrete into the bile) in the absence of any flow limitations. The $CL_{int}$ may be determined by the metabolizing capacity, ie, the amount and activity of drug-metabolizing enzymes. Therefore, the $CL_{int}$ can be decreased by metabolic inhibitors or in people with a poor metabolizer genotype, or the $CL_{int}$ can be increased by enzyme inducers (Table 5).

The total hepatic clearance, $CL_{hep}$, depends on the aforementioned variables as follows (Wilkinson-Shand equation):

$$CL_{hep} = \frac{f_u \times CL_{int} \times Q_{hep}}{f_u \times CL_{int} + Q_{hep}}$$

**For high-$ER_{hep}$ drugs ($CL_{int} \gg Q_{hep}$):**

$$CL_{hep} = Q_{hep}$$

High-$ER_{hep}$ drugs depend on the perfusion rate only, ie, the rate-limiting step in their hepatic clearance is delivery to the liver. **Figures 12 and 13** illustrate that the $CL_{hep}$ for these drugs is proportional to the hepatic blood flow but is virtually unaffected by changes in plasma protein binding and intrinsic clearance. The $Q_{hep}$ may range from 500 to 2,000 mL/min.

**For low-$ER_{hep}$ drugs ($CL_{int} \ll Q_{hep}$):**

$$CL_{hep} = f_u \times CL_{int}$$

Low-$ER_{hep}$ drugs do not depend on hepatic perfusion, but rather depend on plasma protein binding and the $CL_{int}$, ie, hepatic uptake and metabolism. **Figures 14 and 15** illustrate that the $Q_{hep}$ is not important, whereas increases in $f_u$ and decreases in $CL_{int}$ reduce the $CL_{hep}$ substantially.

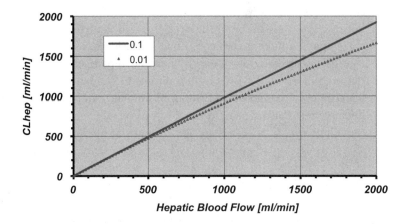

**Figure 12.** *Hepatic clearance for a high hepatic extraction ratio ($ER_{hep}$) drug as a function of hepatic blood flow and plasma protein binding; the insert shows the fraction unbound in plasma, $f_u$.*

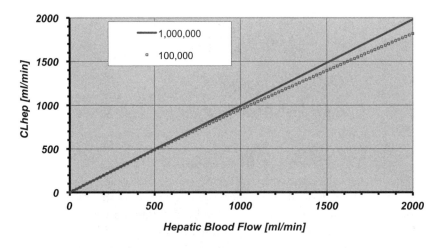

**Figure 13.** *Hepatic clearance for a high $ER_{hep}$ drug as a function of hepatic blood flow and intrinsic hepatic clearance; the insert shows the intrinsic clearance, $CL_{int}$.*

The hepatic ERs of several drugs used in anesthesia are listed in Table 6. It is apparent that quite a few of the lipophilic opioids are high-$ER_{hep}$ drugs whose hepatic clearances depend on hepatic perfusion only.

**Table 7** summarizes how changes in the hepatic variables affect systemic exposure ($AUC_\infty$) and elimination half-life ($t_{1/2}$) after IV administration, as well as oral bioavailability ($F_{oral}$). The latter is included because the liver can be a major first-pass organ, particularly for high-$ER_{hep}$ drugs after oral administration.

It can be seen that low-$ER_{hep}$ drugs have low values of $CL_{hep}$, and their systemic exposures depend only on $f_u$ and $CL_{int,}$ whereas their $F_{oral}$ is high (small first-pass effect) and not affected by any of the 3 variables. In contrast, high-$ER_{hep}$ drugs have high values for $CL_{hep}$ (approaching $Q_{hep}$). Their systemic exposure depends only on $Q_{hep}$, whereas their $F_{oral}$ is low (because of a high hepatic first-pass effect) and dependent on all 3 variables: $Q_{hep}$, $f_u$, and $CL_{int}$.

Several drugs that are eliminated from plasma primarily by renal extraction are listed in **Table 8**. Most of these drugs are polar and basic compounds.

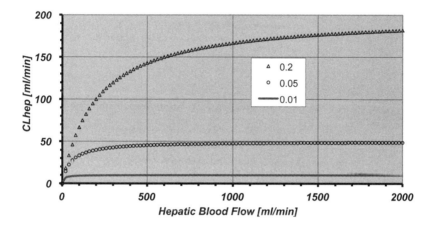

**Figure 14.** *Hepatic clearance for a low $ER_{hep}$ drug as a function of hepatic blood flow and plasma protein binding; the insert shows the fraction unbound in plasma, fu.*

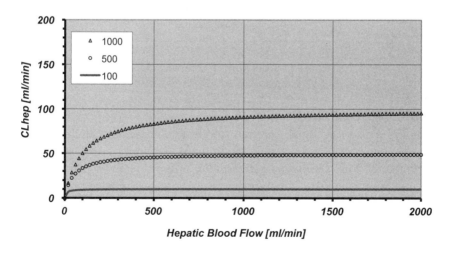

**Figure 15.** *Hepatic clearance for a low $ER_{hep}$ drug as a function of hepatic blood flow and intrinsic hepatic clearance; the insert shows the intrinsic clearance, $CL_{int}$.*

**Table 7.** *Overview of changes in physiological parameters on PK parameters for high and low hepatic ER drugs\*.*

| Physiological Change | | High ER Drug $AUC_\infty$ | Half-life | $F_{oral}$ | Low ER Drug $AUC_\infty$ | Half-life | $F_{oral}$ |
|---|---|---|---|---|---|---|---|
| Hepatic Blood Flow | + | - | - | - | nc | nc | nc |
| $(Q_{hep})$ | - | + | + | + | nc | nc | nc |
| Plasma protein binding | + | nc | - | + | + | nc | nc |
| $(1-f_u)$ | - | nc | + | - | - | nc | nc |
| Intrinsic Clearance | + | nc | nc | - | - | - | nc |
| $(CL_{int})$ | - | nc | nc | + | + | + | nc |

\* $Q_{hep}$=hepatic blood flow, $f_u$=plasma protein binding, $CL_{int}$=intrinsic hepatic clearance, $AUC_\infty$= systemic exposure, half-life is after IV administration, $F_{oral}$=oral bioavailability, "+" denotes increase, "-" denotes decrease, and "nc" denotes no change

**Table 8.** *Drugs used in anesthesia with significant renal elimination.*

Aminoglycosides
Atenolol
Cephalosporins
Metocurine
Cimetidine
Digoxin
d-Tubocurarine
Edrophonium
Nadolol
Pancuronium
Penicillins
Procainamide
Pyridostigmine

## Saturable Pharmacokinetics

Metabolizing enzymes, renal secretion, and drug transporters can be saturated at high plasma concentrations of drugs. In these situations, the PK are nonlinear, and the rate of drug elimination increases nonproportionally to plasma concentrations. Therefore, the clearances are no longer constant but become dependent on plasma concentrations and doses. As a consequence, clearances may decrease with increasing doses, whereas elimination half-life may increase; and systemic exposure increases more than is expected with increasing doses. Fortunately, only a few drugs have nonlinear PK at clinical doses. Examples are phenytoin and ethanol.

# Pharmacodynamics

Pharmacodynamics relate pharmacological effects to plasma concentrations to predict the effect-time profile, ie, onset, duration, peak and magnitude of the effect. This information helps understand when to monitor and/or redose a patient after the initial dose to obtain and maintain the desired effect.

## Effect-Concentration Relationship

Most drugs used in clinical practice interact with specific receptors (eg, $\mu$ opioid receptors, $\gamma$-aminobutyric acid receptors, postsynaptic nicotinic acetylcholine receptors, and acetylcholinesterase). These receptors exist only in certain body compartments, termed *biophases*. The total number of receptors is limited, leading to saturation of the effect at high biophase concentrations of the drug. By using basic principles of mass action between the drug molecule and the receptor, the following model has been developed to describe the relationship between the effect (E) and the biophase concentration ($c_B$):

$$E = \frac{E_{max} \times c_B{}^n}{EC_{50}{}^n + c_B{}^n}$$

This model is referred to as the sigmoidal $E_{max}$ model and is characterized by the following PD parameters (**Figures 16 and 17**):

- $E_{max}$ represents the maximum pharmacological efficacy for the system and marks the plateau phase of the effect-biophase concentration relationship. $E_{max}$ is determined by the total receptor available for drug binding and the intrinsic activity of the drug, ie, its ability to induce receptor changes to cause pharmacological effects. Drugs without intrinsic activity that bind to the same receptor sites are called *antagonists,* which have no pharmacological effects on their own. Antagonists, however, can displace endogenous or exogenous agonists from the receptor and reduce the pharmacological effects of these agents.
- $EC_{50}$ is the concentration responsible for 50% of the maximal pharmacological effect of the drug and represents the potency of the drug. Low $EC_{50}$ values indicate high potency and vice versa. The value for $EC_{50}$ is determined primarily by the affinity of the receptor for the drug. The presence of antagonists can decrease the effects of an agonist and shift the effect-concentration profile to the right.
- The Hill coefficient (n) is a measure of the steepness of the curve at the midpoint. If $n = 1$, the curve becomes hyperbolic (yielding a hyperbolic $E_{max}$ model), similar to the Michaelis-Menten model of enzyme kinetics. Note that on a logarithmic scale (Figure 17), all $E_{max}$ models appear sigmoidal, and the curves are log-linear in their midportions (log-linear effect–concentration relationship). The slope of this midportion reflects n. A larger n value, ie, a steeper curve, means that small changes in concentrations result in large changes in the pharmacological effect.

Overall, the $E_{max}$ model is a nonlinear relationship asserting that the pharmacological effect increases with drug concentration until the point of diminishing returns is reached. At this point, further increases in drug concentration result in only marginal increases in pharmacological effect.

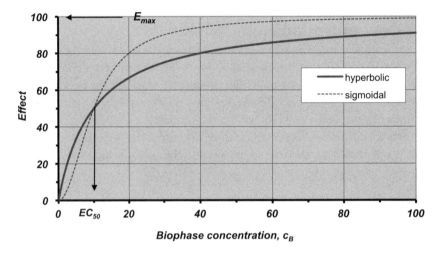

**Figure 16.** $E_{max}$-model of the effect (E) versus biophase ($c_B$) concentration; definition of potency ($EC_{50}$) and efficacy ($E_{max}$); the hyperbolic $E_{max}$-model is plotted by a thick line, a sigmoidal $E_{max}$-model (n=2) by a thin line.

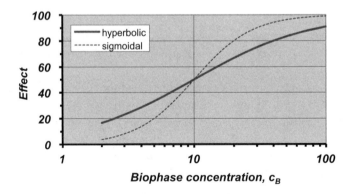

**Figure 17.** Same as Figure 16 on a logarithmic concentration scale; note the differences in slope of the mid-portions of the curves.

# Effect-Time Profile

The effect-time profile following dose administration (assumed IV bolus in the examples) characterizes the onset, duration, and magnitude of the pharmacological response. Its profile is the result of the PK of the drug, as well as the effect-concentration relationship (see previous section) and the rate-limiting steps in the mechanism of action of the drug. In general, there are 3 factors that can result in a delay between the peak pharmacological effect and peak plasma concentration of a drug: slow equilibration of the drug between the plasma and the biophase (biophase-link model), the formation of active metabolites, and a mechanism of action that relies on an indirect action of the drug on the physiological system.

The biophase-link model is illustrated in **Figure 18**. The model assumes that the rate-limiting step in the initiation of the drug effect is the distribution of drug from the plasma compartment into the biophase (disequilibrium between biophase and plasma). Therefore, the onset and duration of response are determined by how fast the drug enters and leaves the biophase compartment. The biophase is assumed to accept only a very small fraction of the total amount of drug in the body (ie, $k_{1e}$ is small, and therefore does not affect the PK of the drug in plasma). The rate of disequilibrium is characterized by the rate constant $k_{e0}$ (the first-order equilibration rate constant between plasma and biophase). The value of this rate constant depends on drug characteristics, eg, lipophilicity and tissue uptake, and tissue perfusion rates.

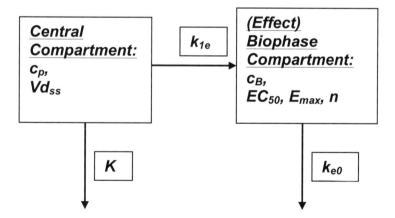

**Figure 18.** *Scheme of the biophase model linked to a one-compartment body model; symbols are explained in the text.*

**Figure 19** shows what happens after IV bolus administration. The biophase concentrations increase initially (because drug distributes from plasma into the biophase), then peak and fall in parallel with the plasma concentration (because drug redistributes from the biophase back into the plasma). Note the similarity with Figure 10. Slowing the equilibration between plasma and biophase delays the peak in biophase concentration. **Figure 20** shows the resulting effect-time profiles. Because the pharmacological effect is driven by biophase rather than

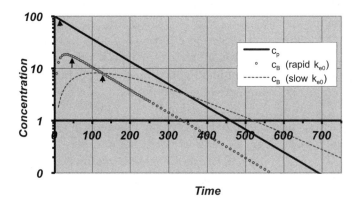

**Figure 19.** *Plasma and biophase concentration-time profile following IV bolus for a shallow (rapid $k_{e0}$, thick line) and deep biophase compartment (slow $k_{e0}$, thin line); the arrows indicate peak biophase concentration.*

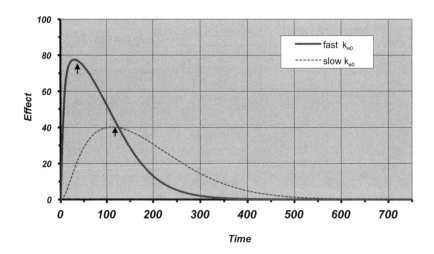

**Figure 20.** *Effect-time profile following IV bolus for a shallow (rapid $k_{e0}$, thick line) and deep biophase compartment (slow $k_{e0}$, thin line); the arrows indicate peak effect.*

by plasma concentration, the effect peaks at the same time as the biophase concentration peaks. This peak in effect lags behind the peak in plasma concentration. This delay in effect relative to plasma concentration is caused by the time that it takes for the drug to equilibrate with the receptor sites.

Slowing the equilibration ($k_{e0}$) delays the onset in response, reduces and delays the peak effect, and prolongs the duration of the effect. This delay in PD effect is shown on the effect versus plasma concentration plot as a "counterclockwise hysteresis" loop (**Figure 21**). The hysteresis indicates that initially during the ascending plasma concentrations, the effect is smaller (because the biophase concentrations are smaller) than it is later during the descending limb when biophase and plasma concentration decline in parallel (and biophase concentrations are higher for given plasma concentrations).

**Figure 22** illustrates a dose-response curve in which with increasing doses, the magnitude of the effect increases until the receptors are saturated. At this point, increases in dose result in a prolongation of the effect rather than an increase in magnitude.

Formation of active metabolite(s) can cause a lag between the plasma concentration of the parent drug and the pharmacological effect. In this case, metabolite formation may become rate limiting (as is $k_{e0}$ for the biophase-link model). If the metabolite is formed and eliminated quickly, there will be a short delay between effect and parent drug plasma concentration. If the metabolite is formed and eliminated slowly, the lag time will be quite long and the effect may be prolonged. Formation of active metabolite(s) can give rise to a counterclockwise hysteresis in the effect-plasma concentration profile.

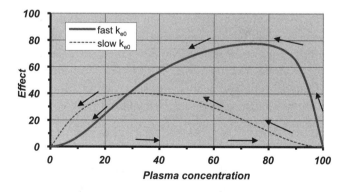

**Figure 21.** *Counterclockwise hysteresis on the effect versus plasma concentration plot for a shallow (rapid $k_{e0}$, thick line) and deep biophase compartment (slow $k_{e0}$, thin line); arrows indicate the progression of time.*

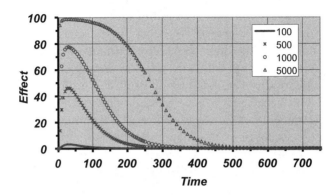

**Figure 22.** *Effect-time profiles following IV bolus administration of escalating doses.*

An alternative mechanism to explain an effect delay and counterclockwise hysteresis may be the fact that the drug affects the synthesis or elimination of an endogenous substance whose kinetics will then determine the effect-time profile. This effect is called the *indirect effect.* An example is with warfarin, which blocks the hepatic synthesis of clotting factors. The anticoagulatory effect is quite delayed relative to the warfarin plasma concentrations because the existing circulating clotting factors have to be depleted for the anticoagulatory effect to occur. In this case, the elimination of the clotting factors from the body is the rate-limiting step for the effect-time profile.

Finally, the effect-plasma concentration profile may demonstrate a clockwise hysteresis suggesting that the effect declines more rapidly than plasma concentrations. This result is called *PD tolerance.* Pharmacodynamic tolerance may occur after repeated or long-term exposure to the drug. Tolerance can be caused by downregulation of the receptors because of long-term drug exposure, activation of physiological negative feedback systems that counteract the initial drug effect, or depletion of endogenous cosubstrates leading to receptor desensitization.

The Biophase-Link Model has been used extensively in anesthesia for neuromuscular blockers, induction agents, and short-acting opioids, where access to the receptor is the rate-limiting step in the effect-time profile.

## Examples

**Table 9** shows the PK characteristics of several induction agents. Because of their lipophilicity, all of these drugs have similar large values for $Vd_{ss}$ that are in excess of body weight, which suggests extensive tissue distribution of these drugs. Diazepam has the smallest $Vd_{ss}$ because it is highly plasma protein bound compared with the other agents. With the exception of diazepam, all agents have moderate to high $CL_{tot}$ values because of hepatic metabolism. Diazepam is a low-$ER_{hep}$ drug with a high degree of plasma protein binding leading to a small

$CL_{tot}$ value. The elimination of diazepam will be affected by changes in the $f_u$ and $CL_{int}$ but not in the $Q_{hep}$. On the other hand, the large value of $CL_{tot}$ for propofol, despite its high degree of plasma protein binding, exceeds the $Q_{hep}$, indicating extrahepatic metabolism, notably in plasma. Its elimination, therefore, is not likely to be affected by any changes in hepatic variables. Ketamine and etomidate are high-$ER_{hep}$ drugs whose elimination depends primarily on the $Q_{hep}$, but not on the $f_u$ or $CL_{int}$. Overall, diazepam has the longest β half-life $(t_{1/2}{}^{\beta})$ because of its low clearance, whereas propofol has the shortest $t_{1/2}{}^{\beta}$ because of its very high clearance value.

**Table 10** summarizes the PK characteristics for several opioids used in anesthesia. Because of their large degree of lipophilicity, all agents are extensively distributed as indicated by their large $Vd_{ss}$ values. Alfentanil is highly plasma protein bound and, therefore, has the smallest $Vd_{ss}$. These agents have very similar distribution half-lives $(t_{1/2}{}^{\alpha}$ and $t_{1/2}{}^{\beta})$ because they follow a 3-compartment body model (with the exception of meperidine). Their terminal elimination half-lives $(t_{1/2}{}^{\gamma})$ are somewhat similar. The half-life $(t_{1/2}{}^{\gamma})$ of alfentanil is slightly shorter than that of the other agents because it has a small $Vd_{ss}$. All agents show $CL_{tot}$ values approaching hepatic blood flow, indicating that they are high $ER_{hep}$ drugs whose elimination is affected primarily by $Q_{hep}$. Alfentanil seems to be an intermediate $ER_{hep}$ drug, possibly because of its high degree of plasma protein binding.

**Table 9.** *PK/PD properties of IV anesthesia induction drugs.*

| Drug | $Vd_{cc}$ [l/kg] | $Vd_{ss}$ [l/kg] | $CL_{tot}$ [mL/min] | $t_{1/2}{}^{\beta}$ [hrs] | $ER_{hep}$ [%] | $f_u$ [%] | $c_p{}^{eff}$ [mcg/mL] |
|---|---|---|---|---|---|---|---|
| Thiopental | 0.53 | 2.34 | 247 | 12 | 15 | 17 | 19.2 |
| Methohexital | 0.35 | 2.20 | 835 | 3.9 | 50 | 27 | 10 |
| Etomidate | 0.15 | 2.52 | 1210 | 2.9 | 90 | 23 | 0.31 |
| Propofol | 0.63 | 2.83 | 3454 | 0.9 | 99 | 2 | 1.05 |
| Ketamine | 1.70 | 3.10 | 1439 | 3.1 | 99 | 88 | 0.64 |
| Diazepam | 0.30 | 1.13 | 27 | 46.6 | 3 | 2 | n/a |

**Table 10.** *PK properties of opioids.*

| Drug | $Vd_{ss}$ [l/kg] | $CL_{tot}$ [mL/min] | $t_{1/2}{}^{\alpha}$ [min] | $t_{1/2}{}^{\beta}$ [min] | $t_{1/2}{}^{\gamma}$ [hrs] | $f_u$ [%] |
|---|---|---|---|---|---|---|
| Morphine | 3.2-3.4 | 1150-1700 | 1.2-2.5 | 9-13.3 | 1.7-2.2 | 64-74 |
| Meperidine | 2.8-4.2 | 750-1300 | 4-17 | n/a | 3.2-4.1 | 18-36 |
| Fentanyl | 3.2-5.9 | 800-1600 | 1.4-1.7 | 13-28 | 3.1-4.4 | 13-21 |
| Sufentanil | 2.86 | 975 | 1.4 | 17.7 | 2.7 | 7.7 |
| Alfentanil | 0.5-1 | 375-600 | 1-3.5 | 8.2-16.8 | 1.2-1.7 | 8-11 |

Not listed in Tables 9 and 10 are additional PD parameters that are important to assess the effect-time profile of a drug. The $EC_{50}$ values for alfentanil and fentanyl have been reported as 520 ng/mL and 6.9 ng/mL, respectively, suggesting that fentanyl is a more potent μ agonist. However, the $k_{e0}$ values for alfentanil and fentanyl are reportedly 0.63 $min^{-1}$ and 0.11 $min^{-1}$, respectively, which suggests that alfentanil has easier access to the receptors in the brain and its onset of action is more rapid, whereas the duration of action is shorter than that of fentanyl.

**Table 11** lists the PK parameters of several neuromuscular blockers. In contrast with the aforementioned drugs active in the central nervous system, these agents, because of their polarity, have small values for $Vd_{ss}$ ranging from blood volume to total body water (see also Table 2). These values suggest that neuromuscular blockers do not distribute extensively. The $CL_{tot}$ values approach GFR for d-tubocurarine, metocurine, gallamine, and pancuronium, suggesting primary elimination by the kidney with low $CL_{nonren}$ values. Therefore, the elimination of these 4 older agents will depend on renal function, and older patients will have reduced drug clearance. The two newer agents, atracurium and vecuronium, have clearance values in excess of GFR, and their major route of elimination is nonrenal, ie, plasma metabolism. Therefore, atracurium and vecuronium will be much less affected by changes in renal function. Metabolites may accumulate in patients with decreased renal function that could change pharmacological effects. Because of their large $CL_{tot}$ values, the latter 2 agents also show the shortest elimination half-lives ($t_{1/2}\beta$), which results in a shorter duration of action and easier dose titration.

## Simple Dosing Calculations

The objective of most dosing regimens is to achieve a target plasma concentration ($c_p^{ss*}$) as rapidly as possible and maintain it for a desired period. Loading doses (LDs) allow rapid achievement of the $c_p^{ss*}$, whereas MDs maintain the $c_p^{ss*}$. Only the half-life determines the time to achieve steady state, and only the $CL_{tot}$ and the $F_{oral}$ for oral administration determine the $c_p^{ss*}$.

**Table 11.** *PK/PD properties of neuromuscular blockers.*

| Drug | $Vd_{ss}$ [l/kg] | $CL_{tot}$ [mL/min] | $t_{1/2}^{\alpha}$ [min] | $t_{1/2}^{\beta}$ [min] | $c_p^{eff}$ [mcg/mL] |
|---|---|---|---|---|---|
| d-Tubocurarine | 0.30-0.60 | 70-210 | 6.2-23.8 | 120-348 | 0.22-0.60 |
| Metocurine | 0.42-0.57 | 90-135 | 16.5-28.6 | 216-348 | 0.25-0.31 |
| Gallamine | 0.21 | 90 | 6-35 | 138-144 | 5.8 |
| Pancuronium | 0.13-0.38 | 75-150 | 5.2-13.2 | 102-144 | 0.14-0.30 |
| Atracurium | 0.13-0.19 | 330-490 | 1.3-3.4 | 18-25 | 0.65 |
| Vecuronium | 0.19-0.27 | 225-400 | 7.4-13 | 58-80 | 0.09-0.25 |

Maintenance infusion rates or MDs can be calculated as follows:

| At steady state | Input rate | = | Output rate |
|---|---|---|---|
| ie, | Infusion Rate | = | $CL_{tot} \times c_p^{ss*}$ |
| or | $F_{oral} \times MD/\tau$ | = | $CL_{tot} \times c_p^{ss*}$ |

where $c_p^{ss*}$ is the (average) steady-state concentration that is targeted based on the therapeutic effect and $\tau$ is the dosing interval. This is a very useful equation whose major assumption is linear, nonsaturable PK. For oral administration, rapid absorption is assumed as well.

The LDs can be calculated as follows:

| For the initial dose: | Amount administered | = | Amount in the body |
|---|---|---|---|
| | $F_{oral} \times LD$ | = | $Vd_{cc} \times c_p^{ss*}$ |

Note that the use of $Vd_{ss}$ rather than $Vd_{cc}$ can lead to higher-than-expected peak concentrations. Depending on the half-life of the drug, the LD may be fractionated into 2 to 4 individual doses. For IV drugs, it is assumed that the drug follows a 1-compartment body model, ie, drug distribution is rapid. For oral drugs, this equation also assumes rapid absorption.

## Simple Concentration Predictions

The following equations allow prediction of plasma concentrations following specified dosing regimens. They assume linear, dose-proportional PK, rapid distribution and rapid absorption (if the drug is given orally).

## Average Steady-State Concentration

The average plasma concentration during a dosing interval is applied for fluctuating plasma concentrations (Figure 9) between the trough concentration at steady state ($c_{pmin}^{ss}$) and the peak concentration at steady state ($c_{pmax}^{ss}$). After repeated equal doses (MD, $\tau$) or constant rate infusion, it can be calculated as follows:

$$c_p^{ss} = F_{oral} \times MD/(CL_{tot} \times \tau)$$

or

$$c_p^{ss} = Infusion\ Rate/CL_{tot}$$

## Peak Concentration

The maximal concentration following an IV bolus or an orally administered drug with fast absorption (eg, LD) is termed $c_{pmax}$ and can be calculated as follows:

$$c_{pmax} = LD/Vd_{cc} \text{ (for a short IV bolus dose)}$$

or

$$c_{pmax} = F_{oral} \times LD/Vd_{cc}$$

## Trough Concentration

The minimal concentration after a single dose achieved at the end of the dosing interval ($\tau$) before the next dose is termed $c_{pmin}$ and can be calculated as follows:

$$c_{pmin} = c_{pmax} \times e^{-k\tau}$$

where k is the overall elimination rate constant.

## Accumulation Factor

The accumulation factor (R) predicts repeated-dose ($c_p{}^n$) or steady-state concentrations ($c_p{}^{ss}$) from single dose (SD) concentrations ($c_p{}^{SD}$):

$$c_p{}^n = c_p{}^{SD} \times R^n \text{ (after n doses)}$$

$$cc_p{}^{ss} = c_p{}^{SD} \times R^{ss} \text{ (at steady state)}$$

The respective factors are calculated as follows:

$$R^n = \frac{1 - e^{-nk\tau}}{1 - e^{-k\tau}} \text{ after n doses}$$

$$R^{ss} = \frac{1}{1 - e^{-k\tau}} \text{ at steady state}$$

For example, the steady-state $c_{pmin}{}^{ss}$ (Figures 7 and 9) can be calculated as follows:

$$c_{pmin}{}^{ss} = c_{pmin}{}^{SD} \times R^{ss}$$

# PK/PD Abbreviations and Symbols

| | |
|---|---|
| $A_b$ | Amount of drug in the body |
| $AUC_\infty$ | Total area under the plasma concentration time profile |
| $c_B$ | Biophase concentration |
| $CL_{int}$ | Intrinsic hepatic clearance |
| $CL_{nonren}$ | Nonrenal clearance |
| $CL_{ren}$ | Renal clearance |
| $CL_{organ}$ | Organ clearance (physiological) |
| $CL_{tot}$ | Total body clearance |
| $c_p$ | Plasma concentration |
| $c_p^{\,0}$ | Initial plasma concentration after IV bolus administration |
| $c_p^{\,eff}$ | Minimum effective plasma concentration |
| $c_{pmax}$ | Peak plasma concentration (after single dose) |
| $c_{pmax}^{\,ss}$ | Peak plasma concentration at steady state |
| $c_{pmin}$ | Trough plasma concentration (after single dose) |
| $c_{pmin}^{\,ss}$ | Trough plasma concentration at steady state |
| $c_p^{\,ss}$ | Plasma concentration (average) at steady state |
| $c_p^{\,ss*}$ | Target steady-state plasma concentration |
| $EC_{50}$ | Concentration of a drug that gives 50% of the maximal pharmacological effect |
| $E_{max}$ | Maximal achievable pharmacological effect |
| ER | Organ extraction ratio |
| $ER_{hep}$ | Hepatic extraction ratio |
| $f_b, f_u$ | Fraction of plasma concentration that is bound or unbound, respectively, to plasma proteins |
| $f_e$ | Fraction of dose that is excreted unchanged in urine |
| F | Absolute bioavailability (fraction absorbed) from a nonsystemic route |
| $F_{oral}$ | Oral bioavailability |
| GFR | Glomerular filtration rate |
| k | (overall) first-order elimination rate constant in a 1-compartment body model |
| $k_{e0}$ | First-order equilibration rate constant between plasma and biophase |
| $k_{12}$ | First-order distribution rate constant from plasma (central compartment) to tissue (peripheral compartment in a 2-compartment body model) |
| $k_{10}$ | Overall first-order elimination rate constant from the plasma (central compartment) in a 2-compartment body model |
| $k_{21}$ | First-order redistribution rate constant from tissue (peripheral compartment to plasma (central compartment) in a 2-compartment body model |
| LD | Loading dose |
| MD | Maintenance dose |
| n | Hill coefficient |

| | |
|---|---|
| Q | Organ blood flow |
| $Q_{hep}$ | Hepatic blood flow |
| $R^n$ | Accumulation factor after n repeated, equal doses/at steady state |
| $R_{ss}$ | Accumulation factor at steady rate |
| $t_{max}$ | Time of peak plasma concentration |
| $t_{1/2}{}^{\alpha}$ | Initial (distribution) half-life |
| $t_{1/2}{}^{\beta}$ | Terminal (elimination) half-life for a 2-compartment body model) |
| $t_{1/2}{}^{\gamma}$ | (Second) distribution half-life for a 3-compartment body model |
| $\tau$ | Dosing interval |
| Vd | Volume of distribution |
| $Vd_{cc}$ | Volume of distribution for central compartment |
| $Vd_{pss}$ | Volume of distribution at pseudo-steady state (distribution equilibrium) |
| $Vd_{ss}$ | Volume of distribution at steady state |

# Suggested Reading

Ebling WF, Lee EN, Stanski DR. Understanding pharmacokinetics and pharmacodynamics through computer simulation, I: the comparative clinical profiles of fentanyl and alfentanil. *Anesthesiology.* 1990;72(4):650-658.

Rowland M, Tozer TN. *Clinical Pharmacokinetics: Concepts and Applications.* 4th ed. Philadelphia, PA: Lippincott Williams & Wilkins; 2010.

Stoelting RK. *Pharmacology & Physiology in Anesthetic Practice.* 4th ed. Philadelphia, PA: Lippincott Williams & Wilkins; 2005.

Venitz J. Pharmacokinetic-pharmacodynamic modeling of reversible drug effects. In: Derendorf H, Hochhaus G, eds. *Handbook of Pharmacokinetic/ Pharmacodynamic Correlations.* Boca Raton, FL: CRC Press; 1995:1-34.

# Chapter 7

# Autonomic Agents:
# Cholinergics and Adrenergics
*by Cynthia S. Dowd, PhD, and Lemont B. Kier, PhD*

The autonomic nervous system is composed of the parasympathetic and sympathetic nervous systems. In most cases, the actions of these systems oppose one another. For example, if the parasympathetic action were to constrict smooth muscle, the sympathetic response would be to relax smooth muscle. Disorders that arise involving these systems are thought to result from an imbalance between the sympathetic and parasympathetic nervous systems. Therapy aimed at treating these disorders strives to regain the balance between these 2 systems.

There are different neurotransmitters that function in the parasympathetic and sympathetic systems (**Figure 1**). *Cholinergic receptors* are found in the parasympathetic system and are responsive to the neurotransmitter acetylcholine (ACh). The sympathetic system contains *adrenergic receptors* using the neurotransmitters epinephrine and norepinephrine. This chapter describes the actions of these neurotransmitters at specific receptor sites and the drugs used to modify the actions of the parasympathetic and sympathetic systems.

**Figure 1.** *Neurotransmitters that function in the parasympathetic and sympathetic systems.*

## The Cholinergic Receptors

The parasympathetic nervous system is controlled by cholinergic receptors. There are 2 types of cholinergic receptors: nicotinic and muscarinic (**Figure 2**). Acetylcholine binds to and activates both types of receptors. Nicotinic receptors are named after nicotine, a compound found in plants (ie, tobacco) that binds to these receptors and not to the muscarinic receptors. Nicotinic receptors are found in autonomic ganglia and neuromuscular junctions and are often referred to as nicotinic ACh receptors (nAChRs). Nicotinic receptors are ion channels made of 5 protein subunits within a cell membrane (see Chapter 3, Figure 6). When ACh binds to the nAChR, at the α-type subunit, the ion channel opens and allows sodium ions to enter the cell.

Muscarinic receptors are named after muscarine, a plant compound that binds selectively to these types of cholinergic receptors and does not bind to the nicotinic receptors. Muscarinic receptors are found in the heart, gastrointestinal (GI) tract, ureters, secretory glands, and pupils. Muscarinic receptors belong to a much larger structural family of receptors called G protein coupled receptors (GPCRs), which have 7 helical regions, passing through the cellular membrane (see Chapter 3, Figure 5). Acetylcholine binds to the extracellular side of the muscarinic receptor. Then, a conformational change in the receptor occurs, which mediates an associated change on the intracellular side of the cell membrane.

Acetylcholine binds to the nicotinic and muscarinic receptors on the outside of the cell membrane, causing a change in each receptor that is transmitted to the interior of the cell. This section of the chapter focuses on the mechanisms of action of cholinergic drugs, uses for cholinergic drugs, and examples of clinically useful agents.

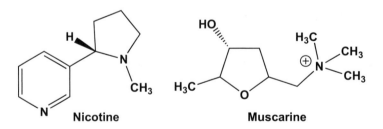

**Figure 2.** *Cholinergic receptor ligands.*

# Cholinergic Mechanisms of Action

Drugs that alter the action of cholinergic receptors (nicotinic and muscarinic) actually increase or decrease the action of ACh at the receptors. Changing the action of ACh will produce physiological effects, eg, decreasing the heart rate and relaxing the pupils. Understanding how ACh modulates a physiological system helps determine how to change the effect of ACh for a beneficial clinical outcome.

It is important to first understand how ACh functions in the synapse. **Figure 3** describes how this neurotransmitter functions in the synapse and the points at which drug intervention can occur. A drug can alter a cholinergic response by 4 mechanisms: ACh synthesis and release, ACh metabolism, modulation of ACh binding to nicotinic receptors, and modulation of ACh binding to muscarinic receptors.

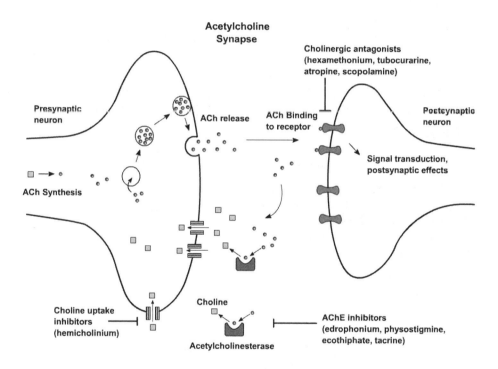

**Figure 3.** *Action of acetylcholine (ACh) at the synapse. ACh is synthesized in the pre-synaptic cell from choline (squares) and acetate. Once made, ACh is stored in pre-synaptic vesicles. Upon ACh release, the NT travels across the synapse to the post-synaptic cell where binding occurs. Acetylcholinesterase (AChE), an enzyme that degrades ACh, is present in the synapse. AChE metabolizes ACh into choline and acetate. Choline is transported back into the pre-synaptic cell via a choline transporter. Many drugs inhibit the action of Ach by interrupting specific portions of this process. Several drugs, and their sites of action, are indicated.*

## Acetylcholine Synthesis and Release

Choline acetyltransferase catalyzes the formation of ACh from choline and acetyl coenzyme A. Acetate (which is used to make acetyl coenzyme A) and choline are transported into the nerve cell by specific transporters. Once it is made, ACh is stored in vesicles until its release into the synapse. One way of decreasing the amount of ACh in the cell is to block the choline transporter. If the cell does not have enough choline, ACh synthesis does not proceed.

The structure of hemicholinium (**Figure 4**) is similar to that of choline. Because of this structural resemblance, hemicholinium is able to bind to the choline transporter. This action blocks choline from entering the cell, interrupting the synthesis of ACh and resulting in less neurotransmitters available. (Quaternary amines are positively charged and are formulated with 1 or more anions to form salts.)

Blocking its release from the presynaptic neuron can also block ACh from entering the synapse. Botulism toxin, for example, inhibits the release of ACh into the synapse. Decreased levels of ACh in the synapse will lead to a diminished ACh response.

## Acetylcholine Metabolism (Acetylcholinesterase Inhibition)

Once ACh is in the synapse, it is quickly metabolized by acetylcholinesterase (AChE) to choline and acetate (**Figure 5**). These products can be transported back into the presynaptic cell to be used again for ACh synthesis. If AChE is inhibited, an increased amount of ACh will accumulate in the synapse and be available to bind to the cholinergic receptors on the postsynaptic cell. In this case, the postsynaptic cell will stay stimulated longer, and the nerve signal will continue.

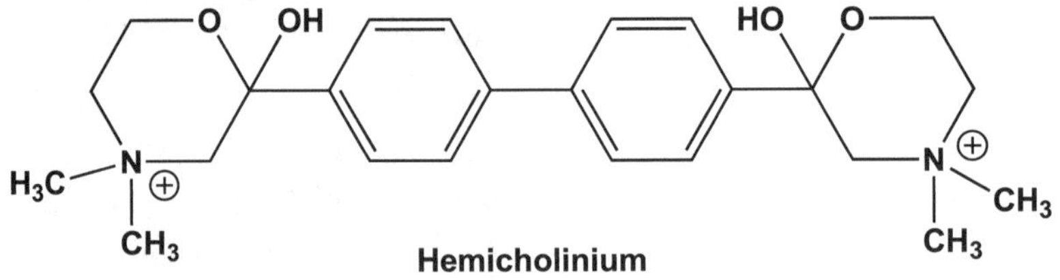

Figure 4. *Structure of hemicholinium.*

The first way to inhibit AChE is by blocking the binding site of ACh on the enzyme with another molecule, which is an example of competitive inhibition. Edrophonium and ambenonium (**Figure 6**) are 2 molecules that compete with ACh for binding to AChE. The second method of inhibiting AChE is to use a molecule that will form a covalent bond with the enzyme (**Figure 7**). In this way, the molecule will stay bound to the binding site (also called the active site), which prevents binding and metabolism of ACh. Several molecules inhibit AChE in this way. Molecules that make a covalent bond with the active site, so that the natural action of the enzyme is disrupted, are called irreversible inhibitors.

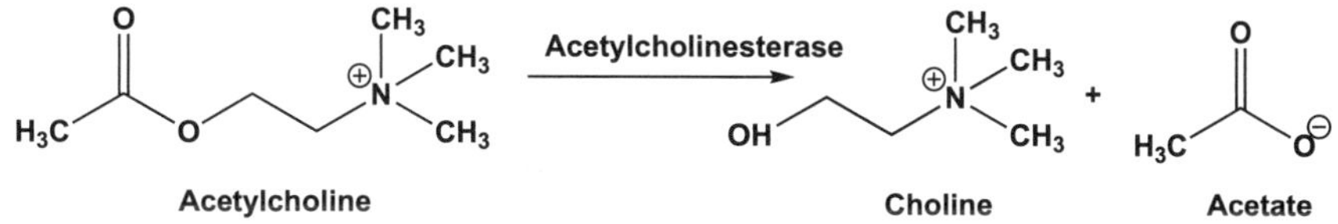

**Figure 5.** *Action of acetylcholinesterase (AChE) to metabolize acetylcholine. The enzyme cleaves the ester of ACh to produce choline and acetate.*

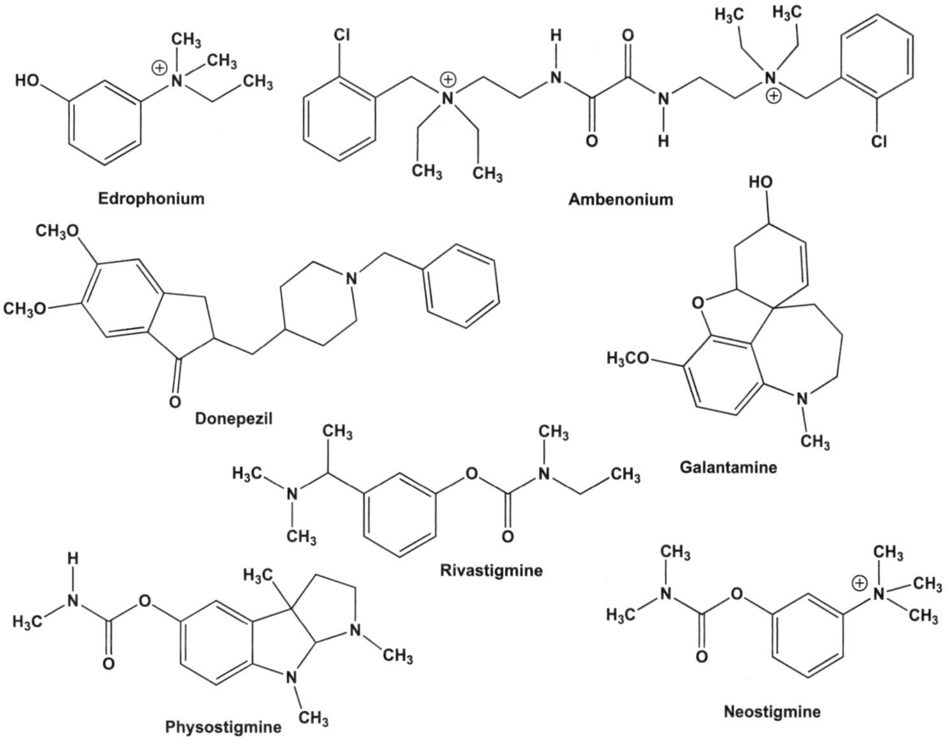

**Figure 6.** *Structures of molecules that inhibit AChE.*

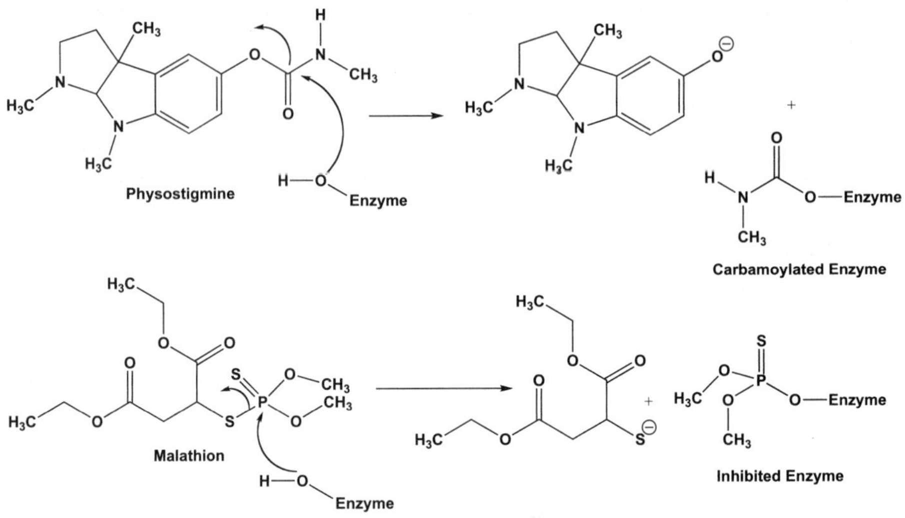

**Figure 7.** *Mechanism of irreversible inhibition of acetylcholinesterase. Physostigmine carbamoylate AChE, while malthion phosphorylates the enzyme. Physostigmine inhibition is slowly reversed by hydrolysis with water.*

Physostigmine and neostigmine (Figure 6) are the most common examples of reversible inhibitors of AChE. These molecules result in carbamoylation of the active site of AChE. Carbamates are hydrolyzed by water relatively quickly, which restores the activity of the enzyme. Therefore, because carbamates are hydrolyzed to give a restored enzyme, inhibition by these molecules is ultimately reversible. Physostigmine and echothiophate are used for glaucoma to reduce intraocular pressure and contract the pupil. The US Food and Drug Administration has approved donepezil, rivastigmine, and galantamine (Figure 6) for symptom management in Alzheimer disease.

Phosphate groups appear in diisopropyl fluorophosphate and echothiophate (**Figure 8**). Malathion, an insecticide, and soman, a chemical warfare agent, are also AChE inhibitors. These agents, like physostigmine and neostigmine, work by binding to the active site of AChE. However, these agents result in the formation of phosphate esters, which are more slowly hydrolyzed by water than are the carbamates of physostigmine and neostigmine (Figure 6). Therefore, the inhibitory action of these phosphate-based agents is much greater than that of the carbamate-forming agents, physostigmine and neostigmine, and they are considered irreversible inhibitors of the enzyme.

Because all of these agents can be very harmful (eg, used in chemical warfare), it is important to have an effective antidote. Pralidoxime acts to remove the inhibiting phosphate group from the serine of AChE, restoring the enzyme to its functional state. The mechanism of action of pralidoxime is shown in **Figure 9**.

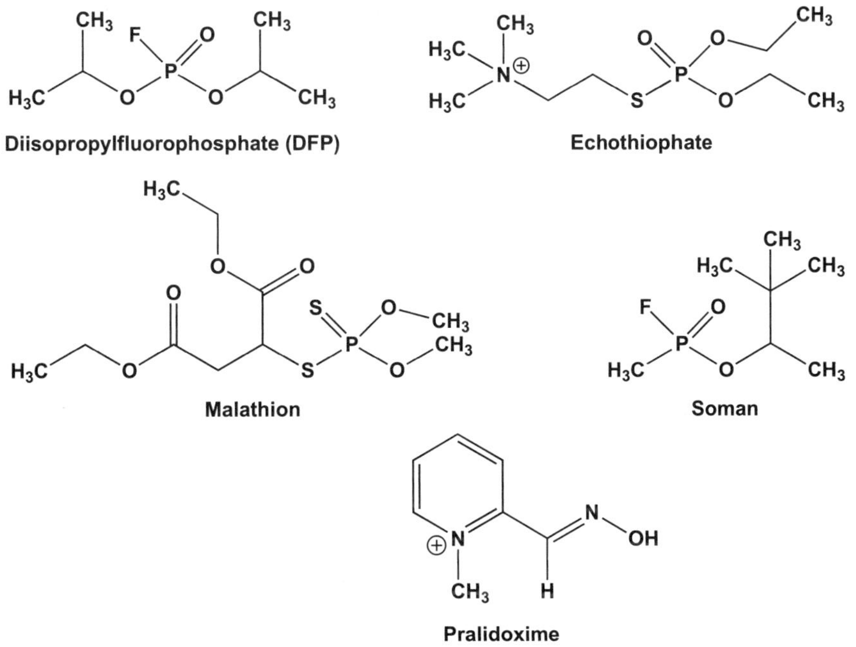

**Figure 8.** *Structures of AChE inhibitors.*

Inhibitors of AChE have clinical usefulness. Myasthenia gravis is an autoimmune disease in which the body attacks its own cholinergic receptors. Increased ACh in the synapse can lessen the symptoms of this disease. The AChE inhibitors lead to increased levels of ACh in the synapse and have, therefore, been shown to be clinically beneficial in the treatment of myasthenia gravis. The AChE inhibitors are potent antidotes for curare-type overdoses (see Neuromuscular Junction Blockers section). The increased ACh present due to AChE inhibition can displace the curare-like molecule from the cholinergic receptor and decrease its effect.

## Nicotinic Receptors

Nicotinic ACh receptors were first isolated from the electric eel and the torpedo ray. These animals have large amounts of nAChRs in their bodies. Nicotinic receptors are ion channels that pass through a cellular membrane. When the channel is opened, positively charged ions are able to pass through the channel and into the cell. Binding of ACh and other agonists (molecules that stimulate the receptor) will open the channel.

Other than ACh, there are few agonists known to stimulate nicotinic receptors. Several antagonists, however, are known. Nicotinic receptor antagonists fall into 2 classes: ganglionic blockers and neuromuscular blockers. These names refer to the location and type of nicotinic receptor that the molecules act on.

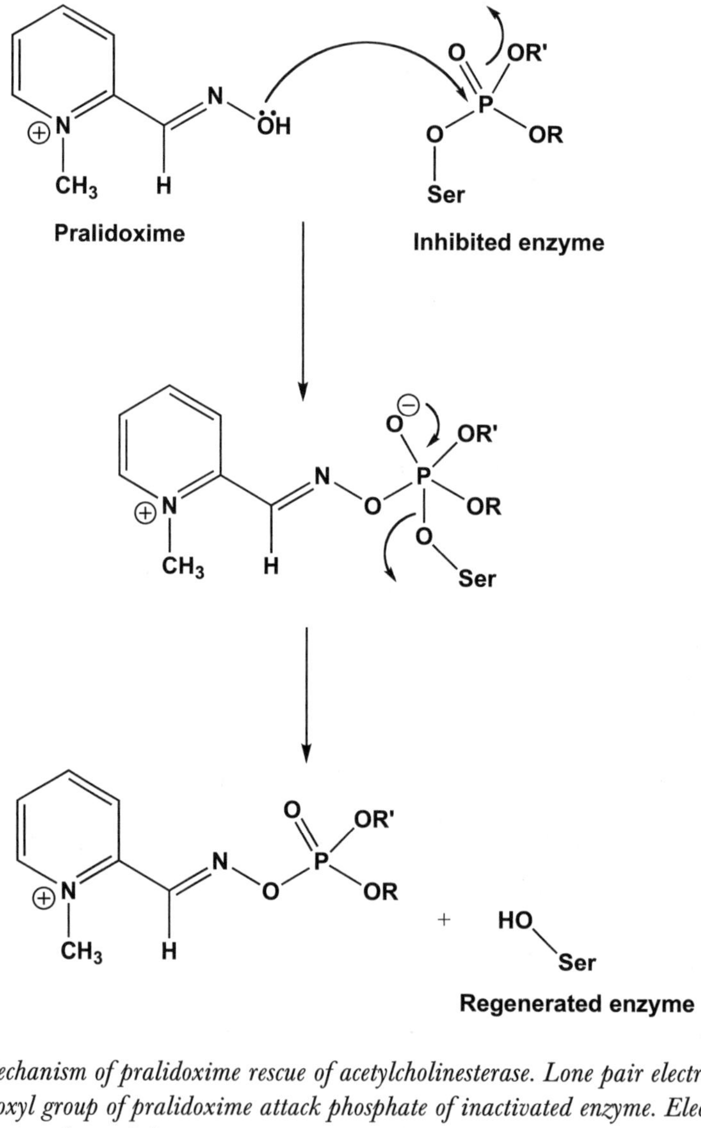

**Figure 9.** *Mechanism of pralidoxime rescue of acetylcholinesterase. Lone pair electrons from the hydroxyl group of pralidoxime attack phosphate of inactivated enzyme. Electron transfer results in release of the enzyme.*

## Ganglionic Blockers

Hexamethonium, pentolinium, trimethaphan, and, when ionized, mecamylamine (**Figure 10**) have positive charges that resemble the positively charged onium groups of ACh and nicotine. These charged regions of the molecules are thought to bind to a similar location on the nicotinic receptor. Historically, mecamylamine was used to decrease vasoconstriction. Since the introduction of β-adrenergic antagonists (β-blockers, see beta adrenergic receptors), the use of mecamylamine has ceased.

## Neuromuscular Junction Blockers

Nicotinic receptor antagonists that block receptors found at neuromuscular junctions are used primarily to relax abdominal muscles during surgery. There are 2 types of inhibitory agents: agents that compete with ACh for binding to the receptor and depolarizing agents. Curare, a plant extract used by South American Indians as a poison, contains compounds belonging to the first class of agents, those that compete directly with ACh for binding. The major component of curare is tubocurarine. Pancuronium, although multicyclic in structure, resembles 2 ACh molecules tethered together and acts as a competitive neuromuscular blocker. Vecuronium and atracurium belong to the same structural class and behave in a similar manner (**Figure 11**).

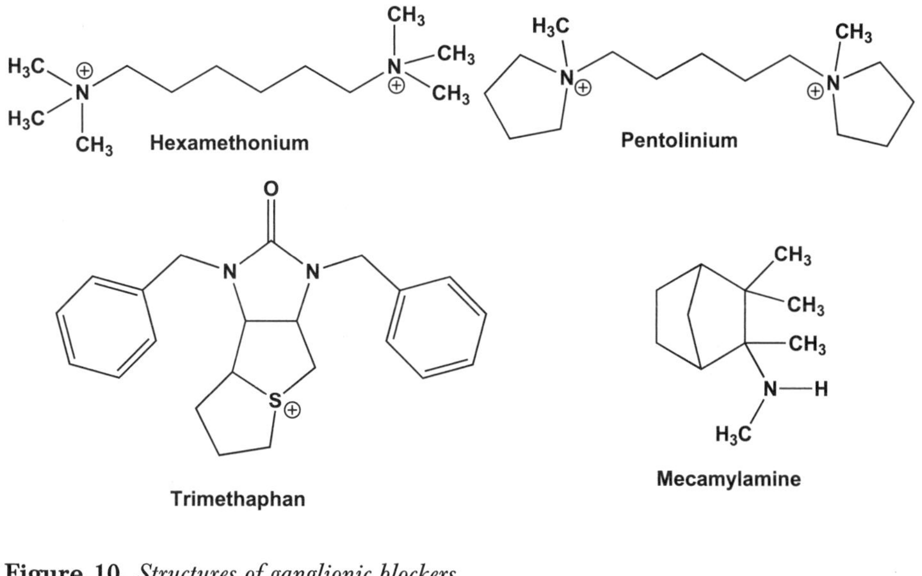

**Figure 10.** *Structures of ganglionic blockers.*

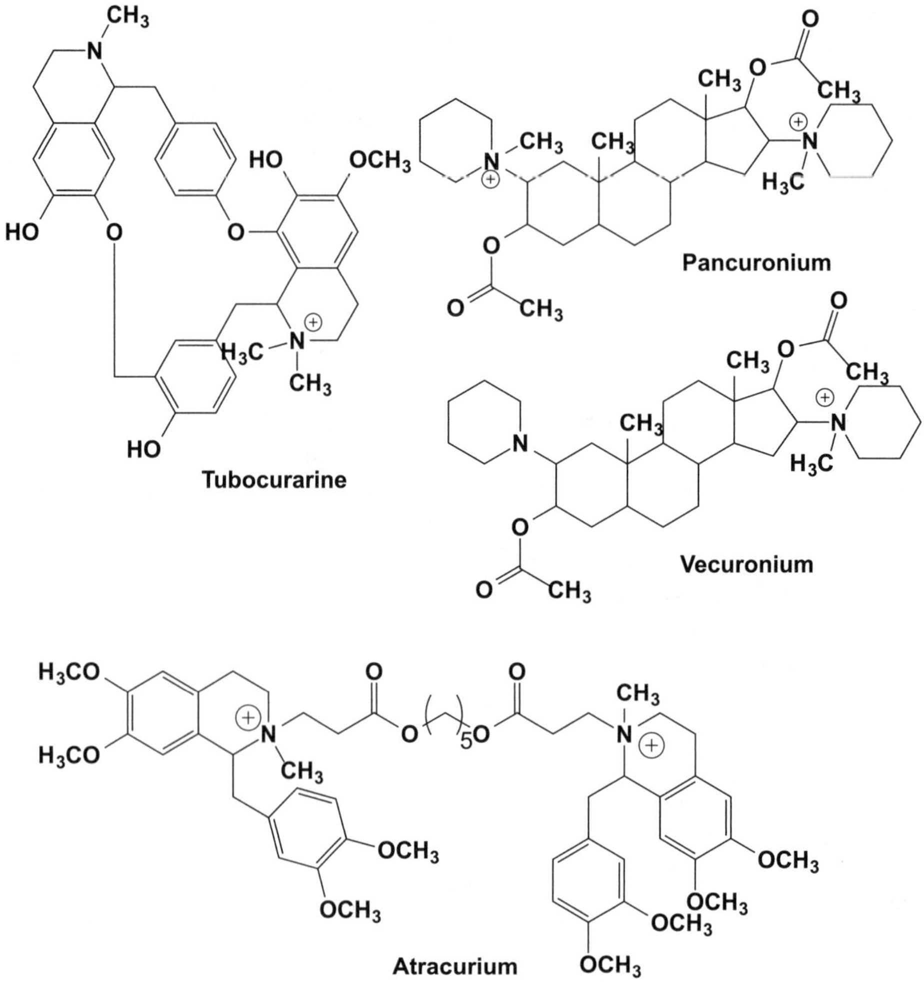

**Figure 11.** *Structures of neuromuscular junction blockers.*

Neuromuscular junction blockers that act as depolarizing agents mimic ACh binding to the neuromuscular nicotinic receptor, thereby producing stimulation. However, these agents remain bound to the receptor for a long period, allowing a large amount of positive ions to flood the cell. Soon after binding, the cell becomes depolarized and cannot respond to another applied stimulus. This action stops nervous signal propagation. α-Bungarotoxin, the deadly toxin from Indian cobra venom, works by binding to this type of nicotinic receptor and causing this depolarizing effect. Decamethonium and succinylcholine, as well as tetraethylammonium chloride, follow the same mechanism of action (**Figure 12**).

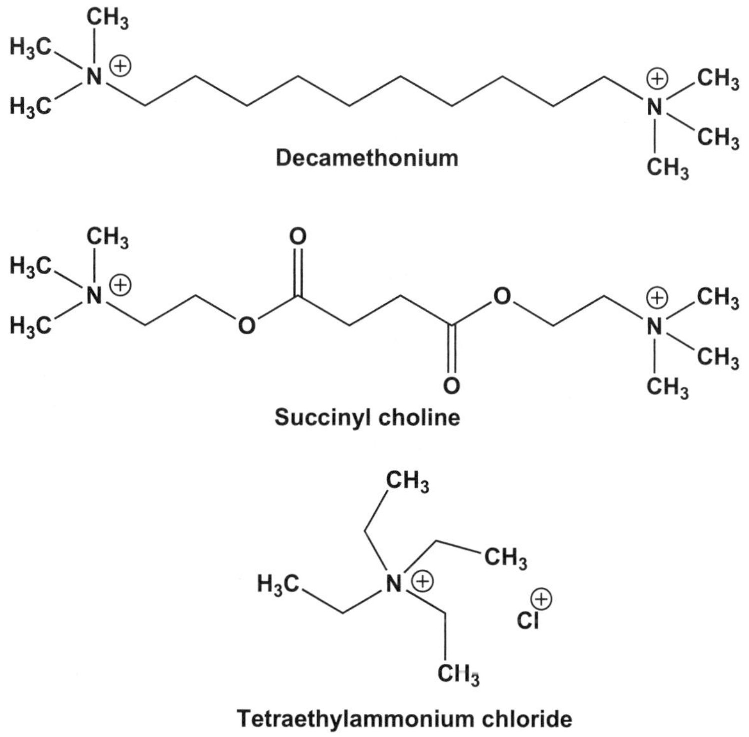

**Figure 12.** *Structures of neuromuscular junction blockers that act as depolarizing agents.*

## Muscarinic Receptors

While able to bind ACh as nicotinic receptors do, muscarinic receptors are members of the GPCR class of proteins and have 7 transmembrane helices that span a cellular membrane. These features make muscarinic receptors very different structurally and functionally from the nAChRs. Whereas nAChRs are ion channels, muscarinic receptors mediate signals across the cellular membrane without translocation of a chemical substance. Muscarinic receptors get their name from muscarine, a plant compound that binds to these receptors and not to nAChRs.

### Muscarinic Receptor Agonists

Molecules that bind to muscarinic receptors and invoke the same response as ACh binding are called *muscarinic agonists*. Muscarine, methacholine, and carbachol are muscarinic receptor agonists. Carbachol has been used for the treatment of glaucoma and has a longer half-life than does ACh. The longer half-life of carbachol is due to the slower hydrolysis of its carbamate versus the ester of ACh. Bethanechol is a muscarinic agonist that stimulates muscarinic receptors in the GI tract and bladder. Other muscarinic agonists are muscarone, pilocarpine, arecoline, oxotremorine, and dioxolane (**Figure 13**).

By measuring the affinity of several compounds, the following structure-activity relationships (SARs) have been formulated for the binding of agonists to muscarinic receptors:

- Large groups substituted on the positively charged nitrogen result in weak agonist activity. It is thought that these larger substituents cannot fit into a hydrophobic pocket on the receptor and, therefore, binding is decreased.
- There can be no more than 5 atoms in the chain connecting the charged nitrogen to the terminal methyl group. For this reason, an ethylene linkage between the nitrogen and the ester, or a group similar in size, has been found to be ideal. The receptor contacts (aspartic acid and histidine residues) limit the distance between the charged nitrogen and the carboxyl oxygen atoms.
- Only a methyl branch is allowed on the linking chain between the nitrogen and the carboxyl oxygen atoms. Larger groups on the branch decrease the interaction of the molecule with the receptor.
- Small substituents on the ester portion of the molecule, such as methyl, are ideal. Larger substituents, such as phenyl rings, convert agonists into antagonists.
- The ester function itself can be replaced by an ether or a ketone; however, the activity is decreased. Cyclic esters, such as that in muscarine, are fully functional.

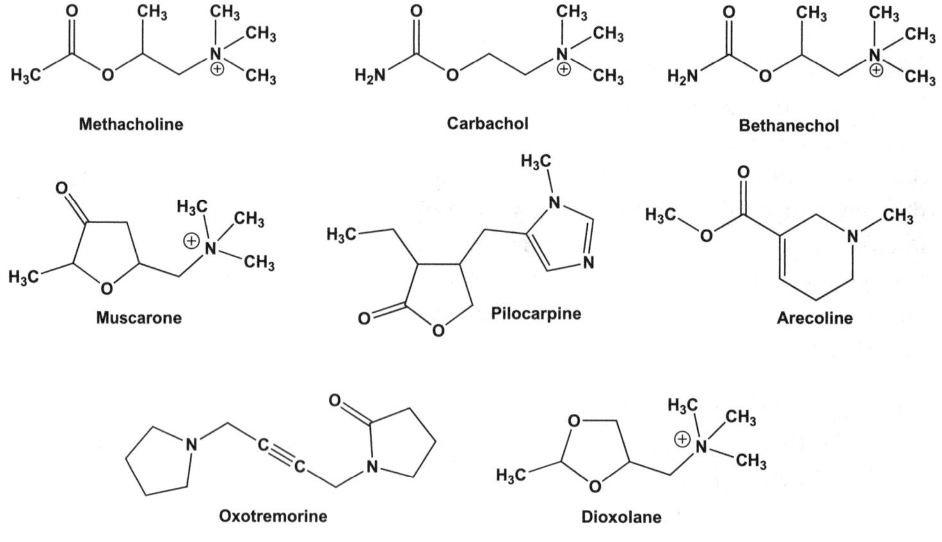

**Figure 13.** *Structures of muscarinic receptor agonists.*

*Muscarinic Receptor Antagonists (Cholinergic Blockers)*

The most well-known muscarinic antagonist is atropine. Isolated from the belladonna plant, atropine was once used to dilate women's pupils. The effect was seen as very attractive, even though it impaired the user's eyesight quite substantially. In general, muscarinic antagonists dilate pupils, decrease salivary and gastric secretions, and decrease GI and urinary tract peristalsis. They are typically used in the treatment of peptic ulcers, in ophthalmology, and to treat Parkinson disease.

Antagonists that result in effects similar to those of atropine include scopolamine, which is currently used to treat glaucoma; homatropine; and hyoscyamine, the pure (–) isomer of atropine. Pirenzepine selectively binds to the $M_1$ type of muscarinic receptor and is used to treat peptic ulcers. Molecules with larger substituents include tridihexethyl bromide, propantheline bromide, and oxyphencyclimine. Other antagonists include adiphenine, oxyphenonium, clidinium, and trihexyphenidyl. These examples show that a molecule that resembles ACh but has ester substituents larger than the methyl groups of ACh will behave as a muscarinic antagonist (**Figure 14**).

# The Adrenergic Receptors

In the autonomic nervous system, actions at the cholinergic receptors (ie, in the parasympathetic system) are balanced by actions that occur at adrenergic receptors in the sympathetic system. The major sympathetic neurotransmitters are the catecholamines norepinephrine and epinephrine. Norepinephrine and epinephrine act on the α and β types of adrenergic receptors.

Norepinephrine and epinephrine are produced through the synthetic scheme shown in **Figure 15**. Before their release into the synapse, catecholamines are stored in vesicles in presynaptic nerve cells. After release from a presynaptic nerve, catecholamines bind to receptors on postsynaptic cells where their effect is propagated. Similar to ACh and the cholinergic receptors, modulation of the effects of the adrenergic catecholamines occurs by altering their presence in the synapse (via synthesis, metabolism, storage, or reuptake) or by altering their binding to the postsynaptic receptors. Each of these effects can have desirable pharmacological effects downstream and, therefore, has resulted in useful clinical agents.

## Adrenergic Mechanisms of Action

There are several ways to interfere with catecholamine action, including inhibiting synthetic, metabolic, storage, release, and reuptake pathways. These pathways will affect the α and β adrenergic responses because the catecholamine will be removed from both types of synapses. Molecules that act at either the α or the β receptor will give responses only through that type of receptor. These latter agents are, therefore, more selective modulators of the adrenergic system. The following sections discuss inhibitors of catecholamine synthesis, metabolism, reuptake, and storage and release.

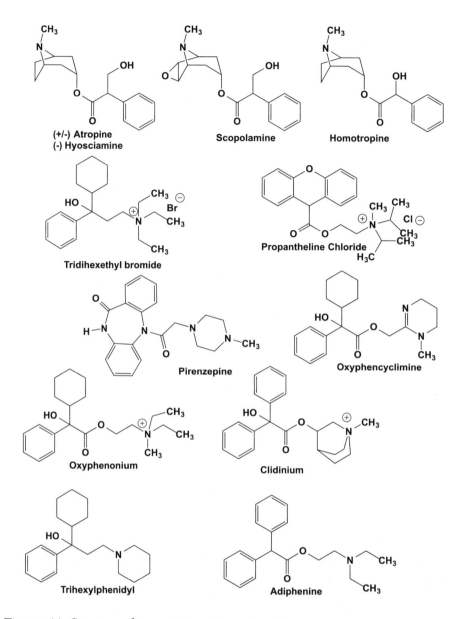

**Figure 14.** *Structures of muscarinic receptor antagonists.*

## Catecholamine Synthesis

Early efforts to combat catatonia and related disorders involved the inhibition of dopa decarboxylase, a key enzyme in catecholamine synthesis (Figure 15). As expected, this inhibition led to a nonselective decrease of many catecholamines. Because such a pervasive decrease of the endogenous neurotransmitter was experienced, dopa decarboxylase inhibition is no longer an accepted method of treatment.

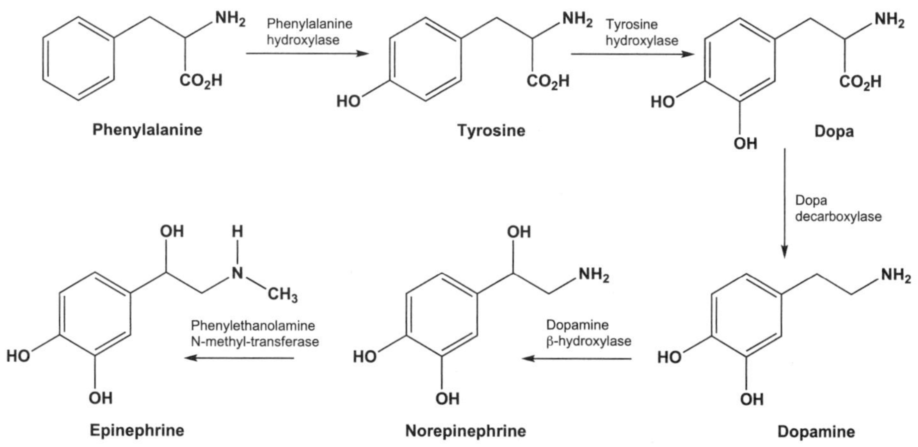

**Figure 15.** *Biosynthesis of catecholamines in the adrenergic system.*

## Catecholamine Metabolism

Following activation of a postsynaptic nerve, catecholamines are removed from the synapse in 2 ways: degradative metabolism and reuptake into the presynaptic cell. Monoamine oxidase (MAO) is the primary metabolizing enzyme of catecholamines. A second enzyme, catechol *O*-methyltransferase, can also inactivate catecholamines in the synapse. The action of both enzymes results in a lower concentration of catecholamine in the synapse. A lower concentration of a neurotransmitter leads to decreased action on postsynaptic nerves. Conversely, inhibition of degrading enzymes results in higher concentrations of catecholamines in the synapse. Monoamine oxidase inhibitors are very useful clinical agents.

Monoamine oxidase degrades catecholamines by oxidative deamination (**Figure 16**). This action effectively removes the catecholamines from the synapse. When the action of MAO is inhibited, more catecholamine is available in the synapse for interaction with the postsynaptic receptor. Two subtypes of MAO are known. The MAO-A form metabolizes predominantly norepinephrine, and MAO-B metabolizes predominantly serotonin.

Several MAO inhibitors have been used to increase the concentration of norepinephrine at its adrenergic sites of action. Tranylcypromine and clorgyline have been used for this purpose (**Figure 17**). Clorgyline is selective for the MAO-A enzyme so that the norepinephrine effect is increased without affecting serotonergic action. Other selective MAO inhibitors are known and are clinically useful. These are discussed in Chapter 12 (Psychotropic Drugs).

## Catecholamine Reuptake

The primary way that catecholamines are removed from the synapse is by binding to reuptake transporters on the presynaptic cell. These proteins relocate the catecholamine back into the presynaptic cell, where it is stored until needed again by the nerve. Because reuptake is the primary means of removing norepinephrine from the synapse, inhibition of this pathway has been shown to be an effective method for sustaining the action of norepinephrine on postsynaptic receptors.

Agents such as tyramine and octopamine behave as *false neurotransmitters* because they mimic the binding of norepinephrine at the reuptake transporter. These agents are transported into the presynaptic cell and into storage vesicles where they displace norepinephrine. The displaced norepinephrine is then released, producing its expected effects on postsynaptic receptors. Tyramine may also have some action as an MAO inhibitor.

True reuptake inhibitors include desipramine and nortriptyline. These molecules bind to the reuptake transporter in place of the neurotransmitter. Because of this action, the neurotransmitter remains in the synapse longer and has a prolonged duration of action at the postsynaptic receptor. Several catecholamine reuptake inhibitors have become popular agents for the treatment of depression. The most well known of these agents, the selective serotonin reuptake inhibitors, are currently among the most widely used and prescribed medications in the United States. These agents are discussed at length in Chapter 12 (Psychotropic Drugs). In addition, cocaine, although not used therapeutically, is a catecholamine reuptake inhibitor (**Figure 18**).

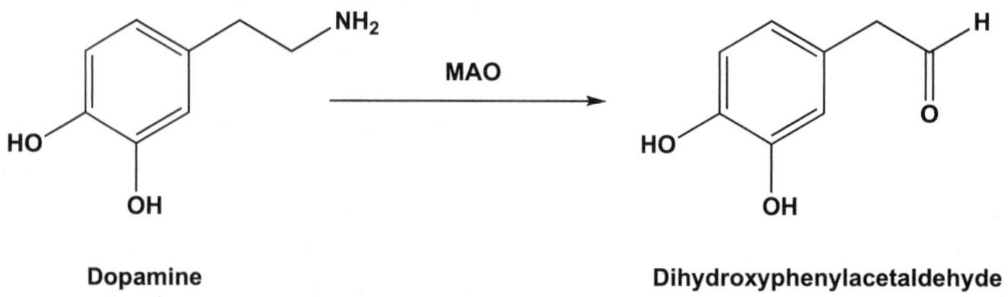

**Dopamine**                    **Dihydroxyphenylacetaldehyde**

**Figure 16.** *Action of monoamine oxidase (MAO). MAO catalyzes the oxidative deamination of several neurotransmitters. The amine is cleaved, leaving an aldehyde function. By this pathway, dopamine, for example, is metabolized to dihydroxyphenylacetaldehyde.*

**Tranylcypromine**                    **Clorgyline**

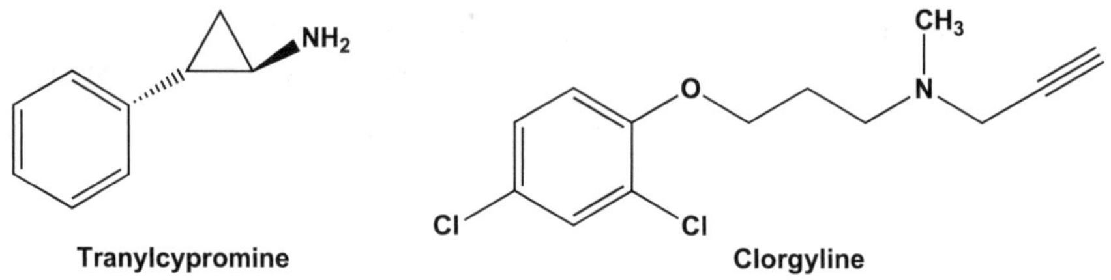

**Figure 17.** *Structures of monoamine oxidase inhibitors.*

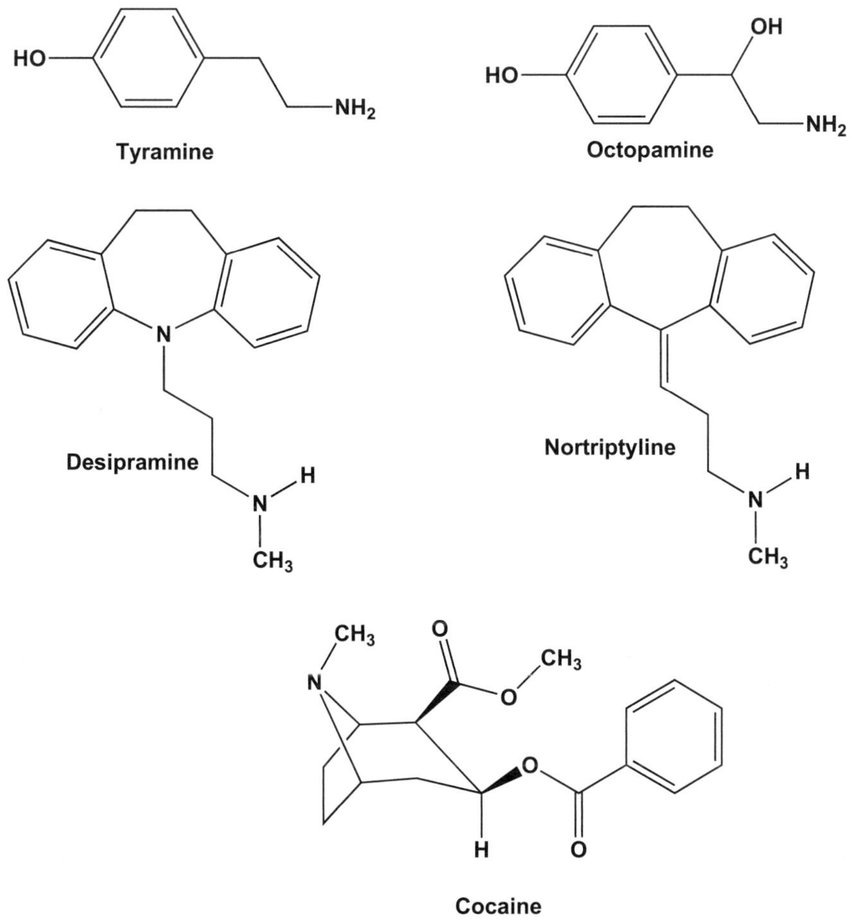

**Figure 18.** *Structures of "true" and "false" reuptake inhibitors.*

## Catecholamine Storage and Release

Once a neurotransmitter is transported back into the presynaptic cell, or following synthesis, it is stored in vesicles where it remains until needed. Several agents are designed to deplete these presynaptic reservoirs of catecholamines, thereby increasing release of neurotransmitter into the synapse. Conversely, agents that inhibit catecholamine release cause decreased stimulation of postsynaptic cells. Many of these agents are nonselective among norepinephrine, dopamine, and serotonin release and, therefore, may have undesired effects.

Reserpine has been used for sedation and the treatment of hypotension (**Figure 19**). Reserpine is thought to block the uptake and storage of biogenic amines. Amphetamine is a stimulant that has many effects, including increasing neurotransmitter release and inhibiting neurotransmitter reuptake.

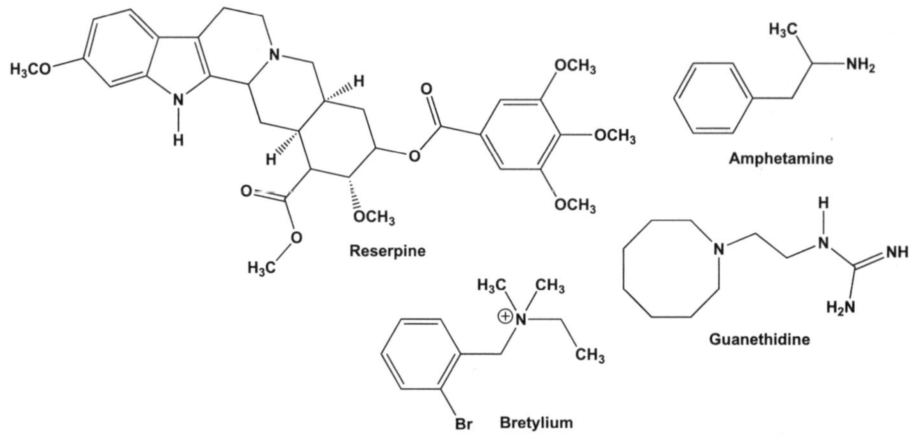

**Figure 19.** *Structures of agents that affect neurotransmitter release.*

Guanethidine and bretylium inhibit neurotransmitter release from the synapse. Guanethidine causes no sedation because it cannot cross the blood-brain barrier. It is used as a hypotensive drug. Bretylium is limited by poor oral absorption and its tendency to induce tolerance. For these reasons, it is used only as a cardiac antiarrhythmic.

## Adrenergic Receptors

Modulation of catecholamine synthesis, metabolism, reuptake, and storage is a nonselective way of altering the response of a catecholamine. A more selective way of changing the adrenergic response is by competing with the endogenous neurotransmitter (epinephrine or norepinephrine) for binding at the postsynaptic receptor sites. There are 2 families of adrenergic receptors: $\alpha$ and $\beta$. Both types of adrenergic receptors belong to the GPCR family. Adrenergic receptors were among the first to be studied, and, therefore, several classes of molecules and their pharmacological effects are well characterized.

## $\alpha$-Adrenergic Receptors

Two subtypes of $\alpha$ adrenergic receptors are known: $\alpha_1$ and $\alpha_2$. The $\alpha_1$ receptors are located on the postsynaptic nerve cell, whereas the $\alpha_2$ receptors are located on the presynaptic nerve cell. Epinephrine and norepinephrine are equipotent at the $\alpha_1$ and $\alpha_2$ receptors. In general, the $\alpha$ receptors are excitatory and constrict uterine, vascular, and intestinal smooth muscle. Agonist potencies for $\alpha$ receptors are as follows: epinephrine > norepinephrine > isoproterenol.

Clonidine binds to the $\alpha_1$ and $\alpha_2$ receptors and acts as a nonselective agonist. Phenylephrine and methoxamine, also $\alpha$ agonists, have been used as vasoconstrictors for the treatment of hypotension and nasal decongestion (**Figure 20**).

## α₁ *Receptor Agents*

α₁ antagonists act as peripheral vasodilators and can be used to treat hypertension. These compounds include WB-4101 and prazosin. Phentolamine is a nonselective α₁ and α₂ receptor antagonist (**Figure 21**).

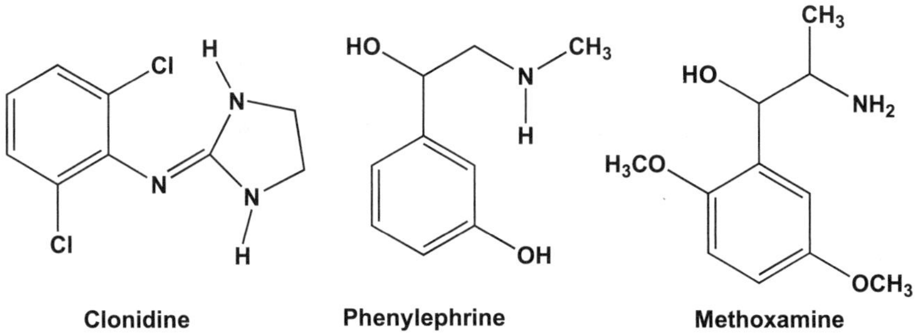

**Figure 20.** *Structures of α agonists.*

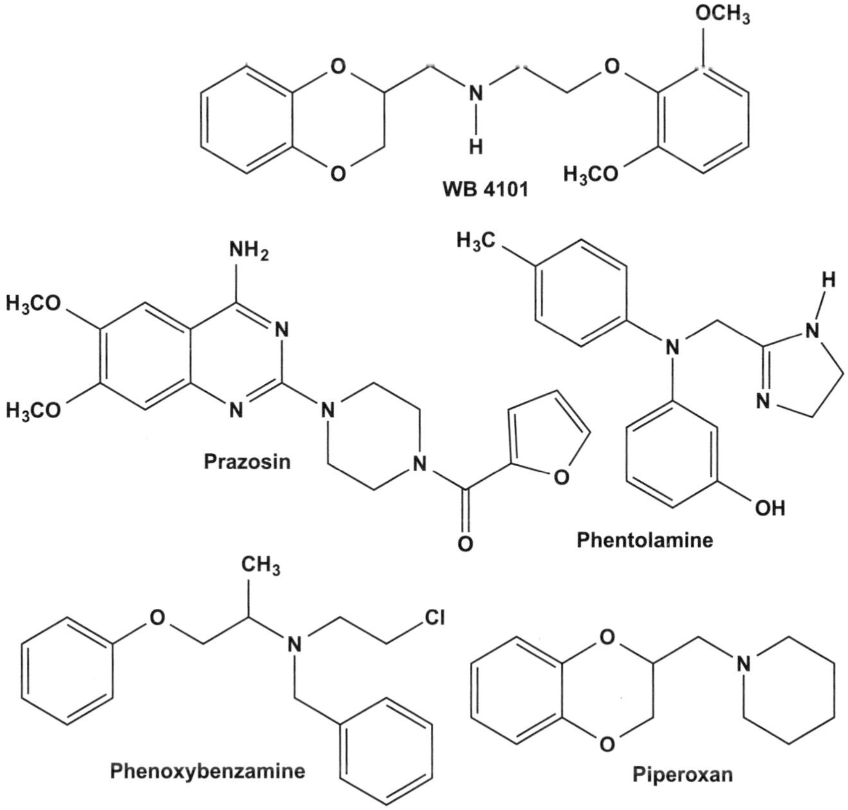

**Figure 21.** *Structures of α₁ agonists.*

Phenoxybenzamine belongs to the class of compounds known as nitrogen mustards. These compounds have a unique way of inactivating $\alpha_1$ receptors by binding irreversibly to them (**Figure 22**). The administered molecule acts as a prodrug that is rapidly converted to the aziridinium ion, the active compound. The aziridinium ion can react with any nucleophile in the body, such as one found in $\alpha_1$ receptors. Unfortunately, the molecules can react with many other nucleophiles as well, making them very nonselective.

### Structure-Activity Relationships of $\alpha_1$ Receptors

Several structural features will make a molecule more active at the $\alpha_1$ receptors versus the $\alpha_2$ or $\beta$ adrenergic receptors. Some important features of these molecules are as follows:

- Hydroxyl groups on the phenyl ring, in general, are necessary for adrenergic activity. Loss of the 3-OH group decreases activity at the $\alpha$ and $\beta$ receptors. Loss of the 4-OH group increases activity at $\alpha_1$ receptors. The 3-OH group is more important than the 4-OH group for $\alpha_1$ activity. Furthermore, the 3-OH group can be replaced by a sulfonamide, amino, or hydroxymethyl group with retention of $\alpha_1$ activity.
- A 2-carbon linker chain between the ring and the amine is nearly essential for $\alpha_1$ activity. The stereochemistry at the branch position is also important for activity. Molecules that bind at the $\alpha_1$ receptors must have the sterioisomeric 'R' configuration.

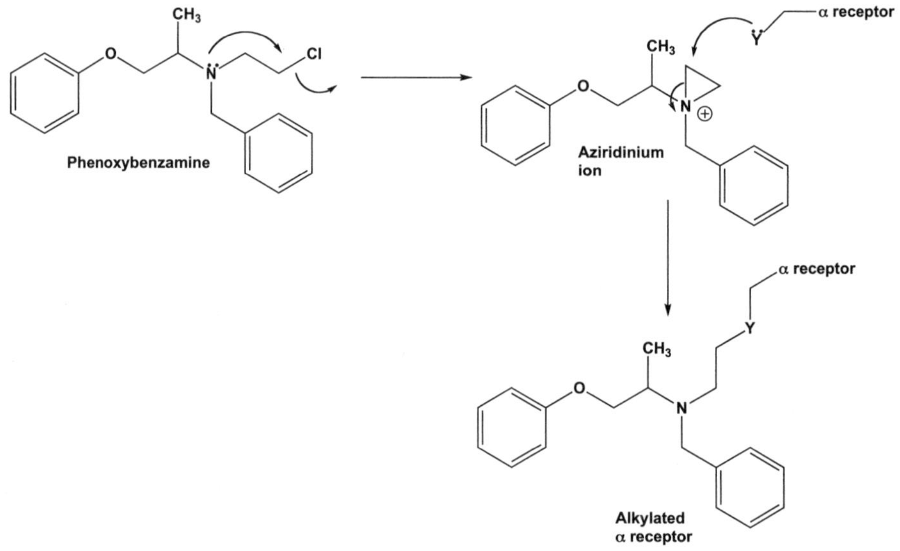

**Figure 22.** *Mechanism of action of phenyoxybenzamine, a nitrogen mustard. Phenoxybenzamine autoalkylates to form a positively-charged aziridinium ion. This highly reactive intermediate reacts quickly with a nucleophilic center in the a receptor, leading to an alkylated, inactive, receptor.*

- To retain $\alpha_1$ receptor activity, the substituents on the nitrogen atom must be small, either hydrogen or methyl. As the size of the nitrogen substituent increases, $\alpha_1$ activity decreases and $\beta$ receptor activity increases.

### $\alpha_2$ *Receptor Agents*

The $\alpha_2$ receptors are found on presynaptic nerve cells. Agonists acting at these receptors will decrease catecholamine release. Nonselective presynaptic $\alpha_2$ agonists include clonidine and phenylephrine (Figure 20). These agents bind to and act as agonists at the $\alpha_1$ and $\alpha_2$ receptors. Clonidine has been used as an antihypertensive. Naphazoline and guanabenz are selective $\alpha_2$ agonists (**Figure 23**). Naphazoline has been used as a nasal decongestant because it decreases the swelling of nasal mucosa. It is important to note that methyl substituents on the $\alpha$ carbon, as well as the loss of the 3-OH group, increase affinity of these molecules at the $\alpha_2$ receptors.

Antagonists at the $\alpha_2$ adrenergic receptors increase catecholamine release. Yohimbine is a selective $\alpha_2$ receptor antagonist (**Figure 24**). Phentolamine is an antagonist but is nonselective between $\alpha_1$ and $\alpha_2$ receptors.

# $\beta$-Adrenergic Receptors

There are 3 known subtypes of $\beta$ receptors: $\beta_1$, $\beta_2$, and $\beta_3$. These receptors are predominantly known for their effects on the cardiovascular system, through $\beta_1$ and $\beta_2$. Because of this, many of these molecules are described in Chapter 8 (Cardiovascular Agents).

The $\beta$-adrenergic receptor agonists act as bronchodilators. Oftentimes, these molecules are used in respiratory care. Agonist potencies at the $\beta$ receptors are opposite that of the potencies of the $\alpha$ receptors. At the $\beta$ receptors, the potency rank is as follows: isoproterenol > epinephrine > norepinephrine.

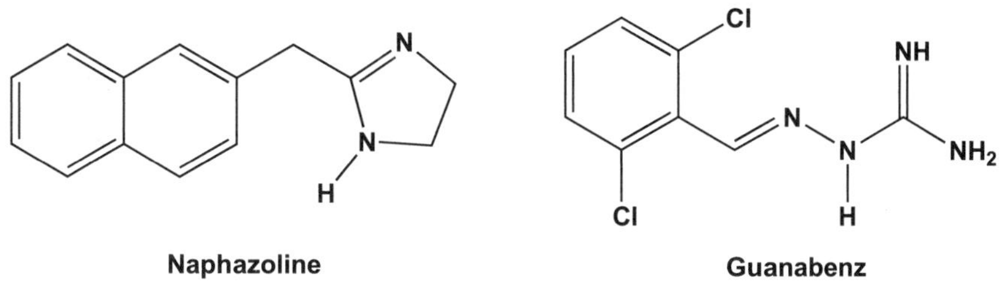

Naphazoline                Guanabenz

**Figure 23.** *Structures of selective $\alpha_2$ agonists.*

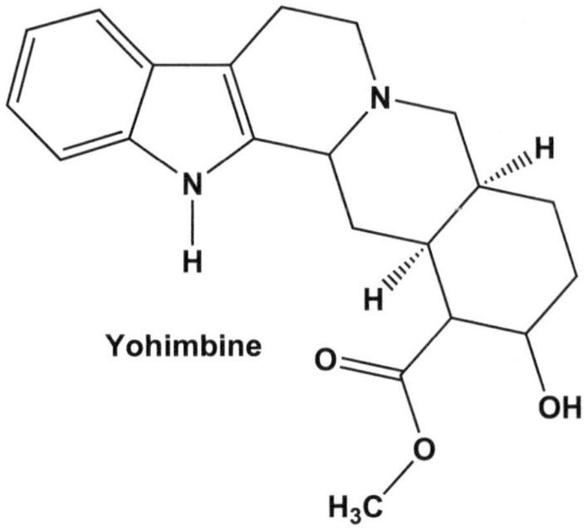

**Figure 24.** *Structure of yohimbine, a selective $\alpha_2$ antagonist.*

Isoproterenol is the prototypical $\beta$ agonist. It affects $\beta_1$ and $\beta_2$ receptors equally. A second $\beta$ agonist is methoxyphenamine. Modifications of the 3-OH group have led to the agonists soterenol and albuterol. Both agonists are more potent at the $\beta_2$ receptors than at the $\beta_1$ receptors. Albuterol is a commonly prescribed therapeutic agent to control asthma. A $\beta_1$ selective agonist is prenalterol (**Figure 25**).

$\beta$ antagonists function as the $\beta$-blockers. These therapeutics are predominantly used for the control of angina, arrhythmia, and hypertension. Antiangina and antiarrhythmic activity is found through the $\beta_1$ antagonists. The $\beta_2$ antagonists cause blood vessel dilation and are, therefore, used to treat hypertension. These agents and their cardiovascular effects are discussed in more detail in Chapter 8 (Cardiovascular Agents).

There are many nonselective $\beta_1/\beta_2$ antagonists (**Figure 26**). Many of these agents are structurally very similar and clinically useful. Sotalol and labetalol are substituted derivatives of 2-amino-phenyl-ethanol. Pindolol, propranolol, and atenolol share a common structural motif in which only the aromatic ring is varied. Metoprolol is a derivative of atenolol.

Oxprenolol is unique in that it is a selective $\beta_1$ antagonist. The only difference between oxprenolol and atenolol is the ethyl ether substituent at the 2-position of the phenyl ring.

### Structure-Activity Relationships of $\beta$ Receptors

Because of their long history, quite a bit of information is known about substituent effects at the $\beta$ receptors. Such structure-activity knowledge helps with designing and predicting activities of $\beta$ receptor ligands. Several key points on the SARs of $\beta$ ligands include the following:

- Nitrogen substituents influence β activity in several ways. A tertiary nitrogen is inactive. A secondary nitrogen with arylalkyl substituents and branched chains increases $β_2$ activity. Larger substituents on the nitrogen atom are necessary to ensure β activity over α receptor activity. The smallest substituent to retain β activity is isopropyl.
- The catechol ring system of the endogenous neurotransmitter ligands can be replaced with other ring systems, and activity is retained.
- Hydroxyl groups on the aliphatic side chain are essential for β activity. The hydroxyl portions of the molecules are responsible for the name endings, eg, albuterol, isoproterenol. Each of these molecules is an alcohol.

Balance between cholinergic and adrenergic receptor stimulation keeps the parasympathetic and sympathetic nervous systems balanced. Inequality between these systems can result in disease of various kinds (eg, cardiovascular, psychological). Similarly, modulations of these systems by appropriate medication can help restore the balance required for good health.

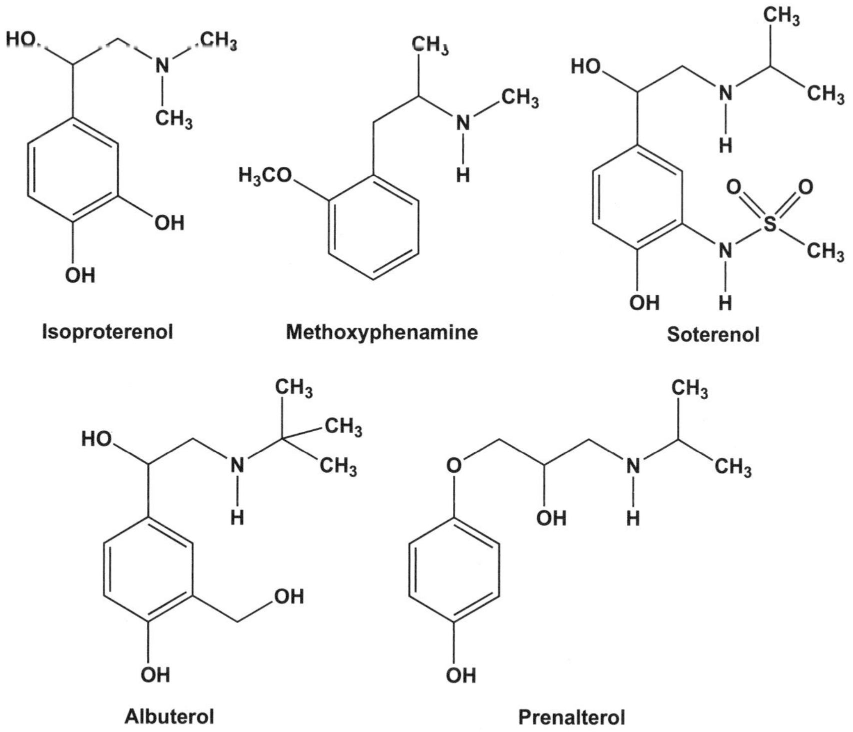

**Figure 25.** *Structures of selective β agonists.*

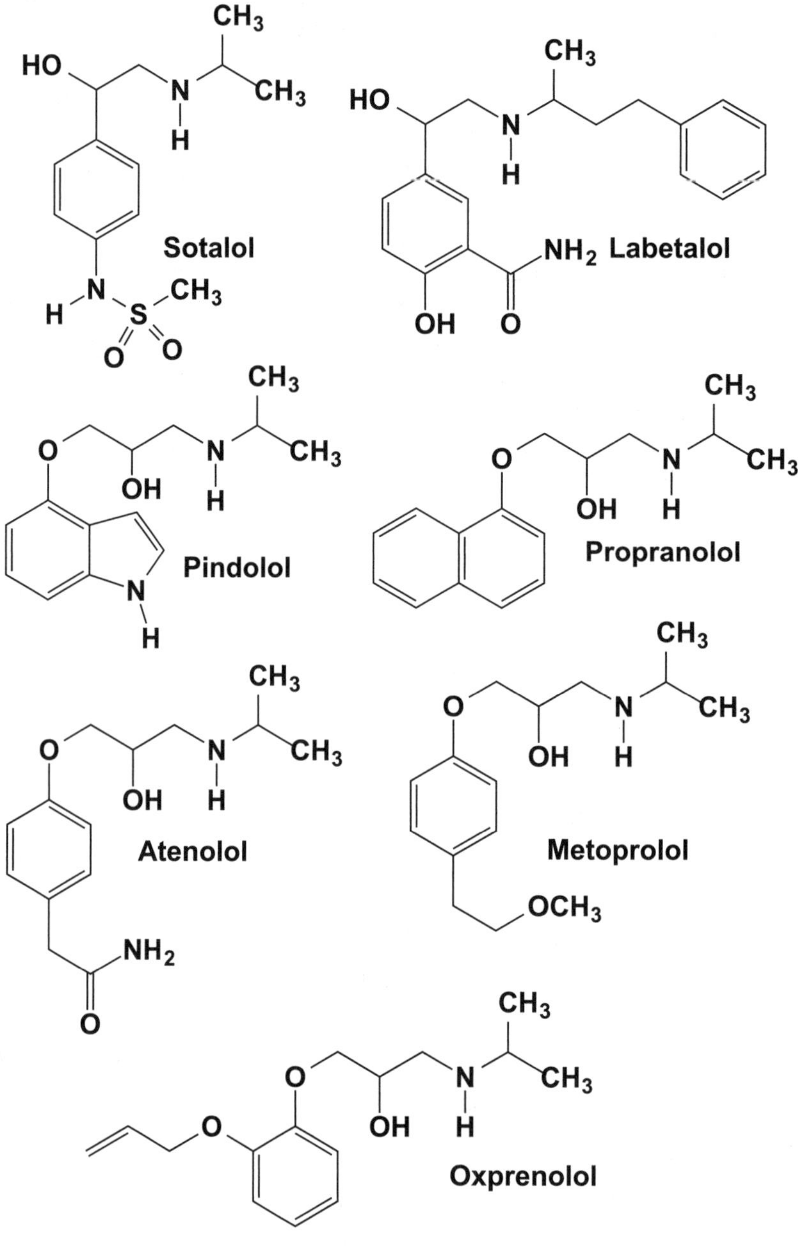

**Figure 26.** *Structures of nonselective β₁/β₂ antagonists.*

## Suggested Reading

Broddle OE, Michel MC. Adrenergic and muscarinic receptors in the human heart. *Pharmacol Rev.* 1999;51(4):651-689.

Cannon, JG. Cholinergics. In: Burger A, Abraham DJ, eds. *Burger's Medicinal Chemistry and Drug Discovery.* Vol 6. 6th ed. Hoboken, NJ: Wiley; 2003:9-108.

Caulfield MP, Birdsall NJM. International Union of Pharmacology. XVII: classification of muscarinic acetylcholine receptors. *Pharmacol Rev.* 1998;50(2):279-290.

Hein L, Kobilka BK. Adrenergic signal transduction and regulation. *Neuropharmacology.* 1995;34(4):357-366.

Kotlikoff M, Kamm KE. Molecular mechanisms of beta-adrenergic relaxation of airway smooth muscle. *Annu Rev Physiol.* 1996;58:115-141.

Westfall, TC, Westfall, DP. Adrenergic agonists and antagonists. In: Brunton LL, Lazo JS, Parker KL, eds. *Goodman and Gilman's The Pharmacological Basis of Therapeutics.* 11th ed. New York, NY: McGraw-Hill; 2006:237-295.

## Discussion Topics

1. What are the physiological effects related to:

   a. cholinergic agents?

   b. adrenergic agents?

2. What is the physiological role of acetylcholine in the body?

3. What are the physiological properties exhibited by muscarinic and nicotinic receptors in the body?

4. What is the role of norepinephrine in the body?

# Chapter 8

# Cardiovascular Agents

*by Umesh R. Desai, PhD, Rami A. Al-Horani, PhD, Akul Y. Mehta, PhD, and May H. Abdel Aziz, PhD*

Cardiovascular disease is the most prevalent disease of the developed and developing world and accounts for the largest health burden of numerous countries. It is estimated that more than 50% of deaths are due to some form of cardiovascular disease. A substantial proportion of these deaths can be prevented through lifestyle modifications coupled with appropriate therapeutic treatment. Cardiovascular drugs can be broadly categorized as follows: (1) antianginals, (2) antiarrhythmics, (3) antihypertensives, (4) anticoagulants, (5) antihyperlipidemics, (6) hypoglycemics, and (7) antithyroid drugs and thyroid hormones. This chapter focuses on the first 4 classes of cardiovascular agents.

## Antianginal Drugs

Antianginal drugs are used to treat angina pectoris. There are 3 classes of agents that relieve anginal pain: *organic nitrates* and *calcium channel antagonists* are indicated in spasmodic and chronic stable angina, whereas β-*adrenergic antagonists* are primarily used for exertion-induced angina. Antianginal agents mainly alleviate the pain by reducing the oxygen requirements of the heart, thereby reducing anginal pain. Each class of antianginal agent uses a distinct mechanism for reducing the heart workload, and, consequently, 2 or more antianginal agents may be simultaneously used to increase the therapeutic effect.

## Organic Nitrates

Organic nitrates (**Figure 1**) are also called *nitrovasodilators*. Amyl nitrite, discovered in 1867, was the first antianginal agent. Several organic nitrates with varying potency are now available for clinical use. Although newer agents such as the calcium channel antagonists and β-adrenergic antagonists have been introduced, organic nitrates remain the drugs of choice for treating spasmodic episodes of angina.

### Chemistry

Nitrovasodilators are small nitrate or nitrite esters of simple organic alcohols. Whereas normal organic esters, eg, RCOOR', are a combination of an organic acid (RCOOH) with an organic alcohol (R'OH), the nitrovasodilators are esters of nitrous ($HNO_2$) or nitric ($HNO_3$) acid with an organic alcohol (**Figure 2**). It is important to note that all nitrate (and nitrite) esters consist of an O—N bond, and not a C—N bond. The name *nitroglycerin* (Figure 1) seems to indicate the presence of a nitro group (NO$_2$) attached to an alkyl carbon, but it is a misnomer and should be more appropriately called glyceryl trinitrate. Also, amyl nitrite consists of an isoamyl group and should be more correctly called isoamyl nitrite.

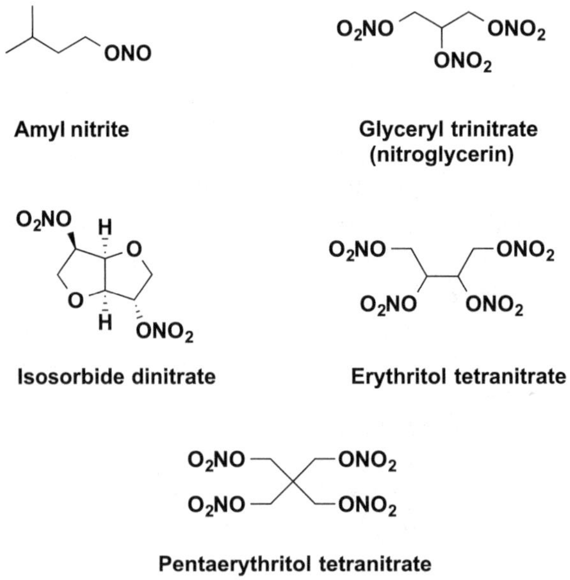

**Amyl nitrite**

**Glyceryl trinitrate (nitroglycerin)**

**Isosorbide dinitrate**

**Erythritol tetranitrate**

**Pentaerythritol tetranitrate**

**Figure 1.** *Organic nitrates are nitrovasodilators and are used as antianginal agents.*

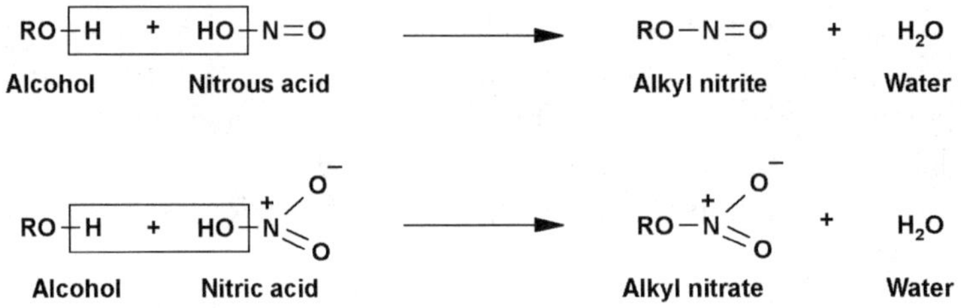

RO—H  +  HO—N=O  ⟶  RO—N=O  +  H$_2$O

Alcohol  Nitrous acid  Alkyl nitrite  Water

RO—H  +  HO—N  ⟶  RO—N  +  H$_2$O

Alcohol  Nitric acid  Alkyl nitrate  Water

**Figure 2.** *Formation of organic nitrates by esterification of nitrous (or nitric) acid with an alcohol.*

As shown in structures in Figure 1, the nitrovasodilators are small uncharged organic molecules. A specific advantage results from this characteristic. Because of their nonpolar nature, these agents exhibit high lipid permeability. Thus, rapid treatment of acute anginal episodes is possible through fast absorption. The severe anginal pain is relieved within minutes. Most agents are fairly volatile, causing some concern in handling. Being esters, nitrovasodilators are susceptible to hydrolysis, and, hence, long-term storage is a concern because of the potential for loss of activity. Preparations of these agents should be protected from moisture. In addition, these nitrate esters also exhibit potential for explosion. Thus, many of the agents are available in diluted forms in the presence of excipients that minimize this hazard.

## Pharmacokinetics

The onset and duration of action of these agents depend on the structure of the molecules. The smallest agent, amyl nitrite, a gas, can be inhaled and, hence, is the one that shows almost instantaneous effect on administration (30 seconds). Although sublingual and oral modes of administration are available, in general, the larger the molecule and more sterically hindered the nitrate group, the longer the onset and the duration of action. Thus, glyceryl trinitrate and isosorbide dinitrate have a shorter onset time ($< 5$ minutes) in comparison with erythritol tetranitrate and pentacrythritol tetranitrate (15–30 minutes). Similarly, the duration of action is 30 to 60 minutes for smaller molecules and 3 to 5 hours for the larger molecules.

## Metabolism

Organic nitrates are rapidly metabolized by first-pass metabolism in the liver and also extrahepatic tissues such as bloodstream, kidneys, lungs, and intestinal mucosa. The metabolism of the organic nitrates is the principal reason for their action as antianginal agents. In this process, the organic nitrates react with cysteine-containing proteins, resulting in the release of nitric oxide, NO, that is responsible for the vasodilating effect on the arteries. Thus, the parent organic nitrates do not have inherent antianginal activity and can be viewed as *prodrugs*, agents that release the therapeutically active entity in the human body. Chemical and enzymatic processes release NO in situ from the nitrovasodilators. Chemical agents such as cysteine react with organic nitrates to form S-nitrosothiols (R-S-NO) that decompose rapidly to release NO, whereas glutathione-nitrate reductase is a specific enzyme that reduces the organic nitrates to nitrites that subsequently release NO nonenzymatically.

## Biochemical Mechanism of Action

**Figure 3** depicts the biochemical events that regulate the contraction and relaxation function of all muscle (smooth, cardiac, and skeletal). The state of muscle (contraction or relaxation) is controlled by the action of myosin-actin pairs of proteins. Depending on whether myosin is phosphorylated, the action of actin results in contraction or relaxation of the muscle. The NO released by nitrovasodilators activates guanylate cyclase, an enzyme that produces cyclic guanosine monophosphate, or cGMP. An increase in the concentration of cGMP, in turn, activates protein kinases that phosphorylate myosin light-chain kinase, thus preventing the phosphorylation of myosin and resulting in muscle relaxation. Muscle relaxation or vasodilation results in reduced workload for the heart, thus easing the anginal pain.

## Calcium Channel Antagonists

Cellular levels of free calcium ions have an important role in the mechanism of muscle contraction. Molecules that block the passage of calcium ions from the outside to the inside of the muscle cell (Figure 3) will also prevent the contraction of muscles, leading to reduced workload and, hence, a lower oxygen requirement. Of 6 types of voltage-gated calcium channels, an L-type channel, named for its long-lasting nature, is principally responsible for the inward current of divalent calcium ions into skeletal, cardiac, and smooth muscle cells. Calcium channel antagonists that bind these L-type channels cause antagonism and are effective as antianginal agents. These agents do not physically block the channel, but bind at specific sites in the open form of the channel.

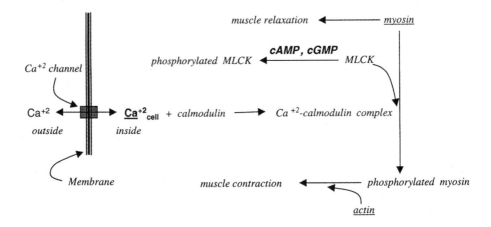

**Figure 3.** *Regulation of muscle contraction and relaxation. Abbreviations: cAMP, cyclic adenosine monophosphate; cGMP, cyclic guanosine monophosphate; MLCK, myosin light-chain kinase.*

## Chemistry

Three classes of calcium channel blockers are currently approved for use in the prophylactic treatment of angina: the dihydropyridines (**Figure 4**); the benzo-1,4-thiazepine, diltiazem (**Figure 5**); and the arylalkylamines (**Figure 6**). No structural similarities exist among the 3 classes of compounds, suggesting that the activity profile of each class is distinct from the others. Nifedipine, amlodipine, and nicardipine belong to the dihydropyridine class of calcium channel blockers (Figure 4). These drugs have a substituted pyridine ring that is partially saturated as a central common feature. Diltiazem belongs to the benzo[*b*-1,5]-thiazepine family, bearing a 7-membered ring containing nitrogen and sulfur atoms fused with an aromatic ring (Figure 5). The arylalkylamines, verapamil and bepridil (Figure 6), have only one thing in common, an amine group substituted with an alkyl and an aryl group. The arylalkylamines have a chiral center, where the dextrorotatory isomer is more active than its counterpart. These drugs are extensively bound to plasma proteins and are metabolized in the liver to form mostly inactive metabolites, which are excreted primarily in urine, except for norverapamil, which retains about 20% of the activity of the parent drug. Norverapamil is formed by removal of the methyl ($CH_3$) group from the tertiary amine of verapamil.

## Pharmacokinetics

Each calcium channel blocker contains an amine group facilitating the preparation of its hydrochloride salt for administration as oral tablets and capsules. Also, these agents have a predominantly hydrophobic structure, explaining their rapid and complete absorption after oral administration. In fact, nearly 75% to 95% of the drug is found in the bloodstream. Most of these agents exist primarily in the protein-bound state (80%-95%) in the plasma, although they are active in the free form. The duration of action ranges from 4 to 8 hours for most agents, except for amlodipine, which has a 24-hour duration of action because of the presence of the chlorine atom.

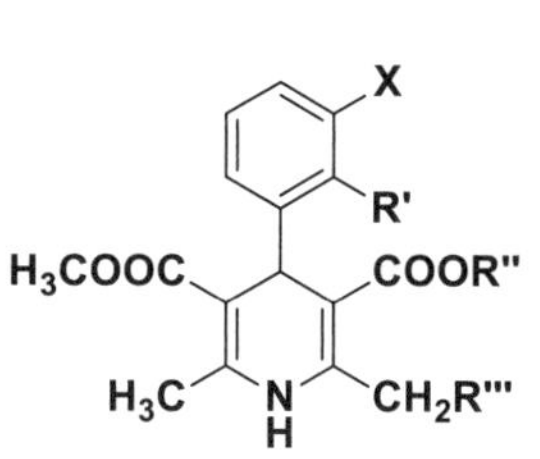

| | R' | R" | R''' | X |
|---|---|---|---|---|
| Nifedipine | -NO$_2$ | -CH$_3$ | -H | -H |
| Amlodipine | -Cl | -C$_2$H$_5$ | -O-(CH$_2$)$_2$-NH$_2$ | -H |
| Nicardipine | -H | -(CH$_2$)$_2$N(CH$_3$)(CH$_2$Ph) | -H | -NO$_2$ |

**Figure 4.** *The dihydropyridines act as calcium channel blockers.*

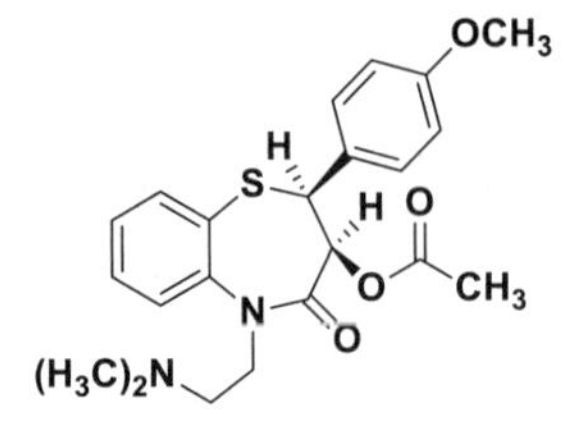

**Diltiazem**

**Figure 5.** *The structure of the calcium channel blocker, diltiazem.*

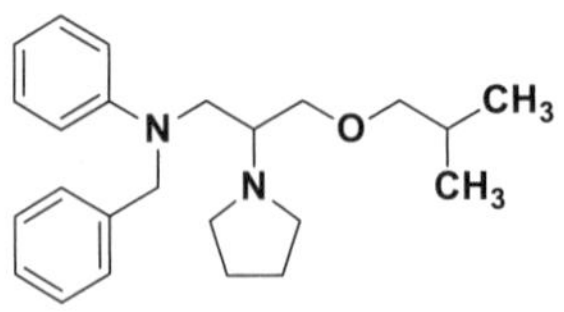

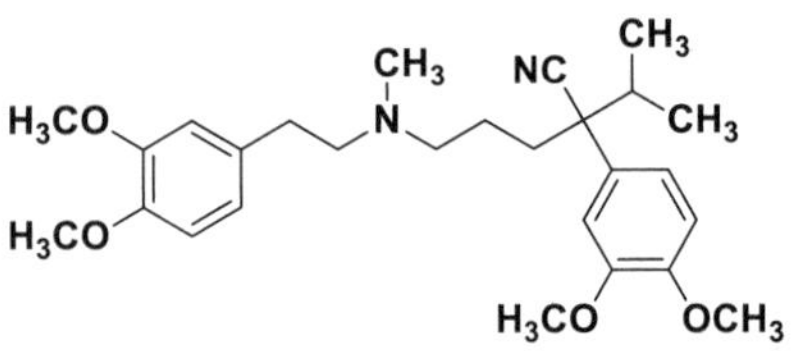

**Bepridil**                    **Verapamil**

**Figure 6.** *The arylalkylamines act as calcium channel blockers.*

## Metabolism

The first-pass metabolism of verapamil, diltiazem, nicardipine, and nifedipine is extensive and results in low bioavailability. Verapamil is converted into norverapamil in which the nitrogen has been *N*-demethylated. Norverapamil is only about 20% as active as the parent active molecule. Extensive *O*-demethylation also occurs, rapidly giving inactive metabolites. Diltiazem is metabolized by the action of esterases to its desacetyl derivative that has only about 50% of the parent activity. Other *N*- and *O*-demethylations result in inactive metabolites. The dihydropyridines are mostly metabolized to inactive species in which the phenyl group has been extensively hydroxylated.

## β-Adrenergic Antagonists

Propranolol (**Figure 7**) is a common nonselective β-blocker of cardiac and bronchial adrenergic receptors. It is typically used for exertion-induced angina that originates from coronary atherosclerosis. Drugs with β-blocking activity slow the heart rate and decrease the force of contraction of muscles; thus, these drugs are useful in treating hypertension and cardiac arrhythmias, in addition to angina. Propranolol is also typically used in combination with organic nitrates or calcium channel blockers to enhance its antianginal efficacy. Some newer β-blockers, such as carvedilol, also have partial $\alpha_1$-adrenergic blocking effects that cause vasodilation. Others, like metoprolol, have antiarrhythmic effects similar to those of propranolol.

### Newer Nontraditional Anti-ischemic Agents

Ranolazine (**Figure 8**) is the first antianginal drug to be approved by the US Food and Drug Administration in more than 25 years. It exhibits a new mechanism of action by inhibiting the slow sodium channel in ventricular heart muscle, leading to the decrease in the inward sodium current. Sodium-calcium exchange is thus reduced, and calcium accumulation in the heart muscle cells is indirectly prevented. Unlike β-blockers, nitrates, and calcium channel blockers, ranolazine does not affect the heart rate or blood pressure.

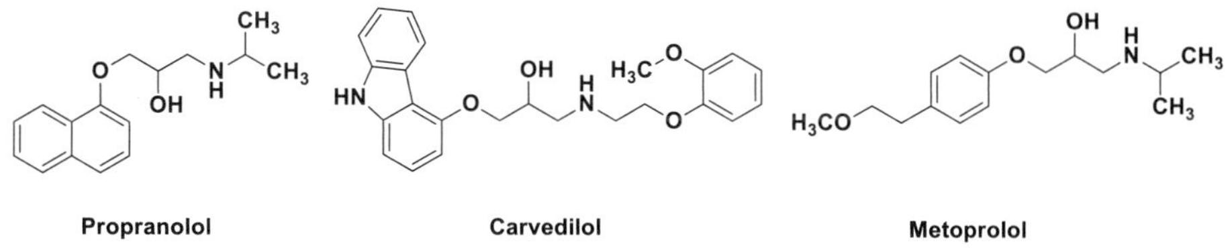

Propranolol          Carvedilol          Metoprolol

**Figure 7.** *β-Adrenergic agents used as β-blockers.*

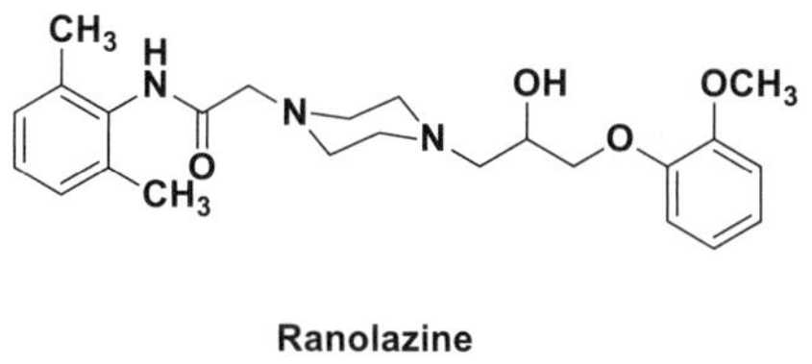

Ranolazine

**Figure 8.** *The structure of ranolazine, an inhibitor of the slow sodium channel in cardiac muscle.*

## Antiarrhythmic Agents

Cardiac arrhythmias can originate from a disturbed origin of the impulse, ie, pacemaker cells. Altered automaticity sometimes develops in the pacemaker cells, resulting in disturbance of the rhythmic beating property arising from optimal membrane depolarization. Disturbed automaticity of pacemaker cells may arise from underlying diseases such as hypertension, atherosclerosis, hyperthyroidism, and lung disease. Other forms of arrhythmias, called ectopic arrhythmias, may be caused by generation of impulses in cells other than pacemaker cells. The underlying causes of ectopic arrhythmias are myocardial ischemia, excessive myocardial catecholamine release, and the toxic effects of cardiac glycosides. Arrhythmias are also produced when the electrical impulse does not die down completely before the beginning of phase 0 (**Figure 9**). In such circumstances, a fraction of previous impulse that remains at the end reenters and reexcites the heart muscles, prematurely giving rise to asynchronous depolarization. This is the characteristic form of premature heartbeat. Reentrant arrhythmias are common in coronary atherosclerosis.

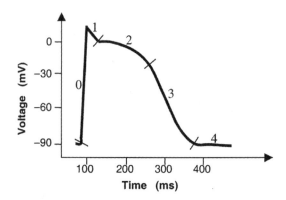

**Figure 9.** *A representation of the membrane action potential (upper trace) and an electrocardiogram (lower trace). Phase 0 corresponds to rapid depolarization (inward movement of $Na^+$ ions), whereas phases 1 through 4 are repolarizations through movement of $K^+$, $Ca^{2+}$, and $Cl^-$ ions. Repolarization is completed during phase 4, the resting phase. The duration of action potential is the total time for the 0-3 segment.*

# Classes of Antiarrhythmic Drugs

The Vaughan Williams classification remains the most widely accepted system to categorize antiarrhythmic drugs. This system classifies the antiarrhythmic agents based on their mode of action and, consequently, on their electrocardiogram effect (**Table**). Drugs with class I properties are generally local anesthetics and block the sodium influx during phase 0 of the action potential. Therefore, these drugs tend to decrease the maximal rate of cardiac depolarization and, accordingly, slow the impulse conduction by their direct effect on the cardiac plasma membrane. All agents in this class bind to the fast sodium channels, which exist in 3 distinct states, referred to as resting, opened, and closed. The affinities of class I agents for these 3 states are different, resulting in differential effects on the duration of action potential. Thus, class I drugs are further subclassified into 3 subclasses (IA, IB, IC) based on their effect on the duration of action potential (QT interval, Figure 9). Class IA drugs increase, class IB drugs decrease, and class IC drugs do not change the duration of action potential. Particularly, class IC agents have slow association-dissociation channel kinetics; thus, they have the most potent sodium channel blocking effects.

   Class II drugs are β-adrenergic blocking agents that stabilize the membrane or block adrenergic-enhanced phase 4 depolarization. These agents decrease the neurologically initiated automaticity. Thus, the effects of ectopic pacemaker cells are depressed, resulting in slowing of the heart rate.

**Table.** *Classes of antiarrhythmic drugs.*

| Class | Drug | Mode of Action |
|---|---|---|
| IA | Quinidine, procainamide, disopyramide | Decreases MRD; lengthens duration of action potential |
| IB | Lidocaine, tocainide, mexiletine, phenytoin | Decreases MRD; shortens duration of action potential |
| IC | Encainide, flecainide, moricizine, propafenone | Decreases MRD; no effect on duration of action potential |
| II | β-Adrenergic blockers (eg, propranolol) | Suppresses adrenergic-induced automaticity |
| III | Bretylium tosylate, amiodarone, dronedarone, celivarone, sotalol, ibutilide, dofetilide, azimilide | Many mechanisms; lengthens duration of action potential |
| IV | Calcium channel blockers (eg, diltiazem, verapamil) | Inhibit slow $Ca^{+2}$ channel; lengthen duration of action potential |

Abbreviation: MRD, maximal rate of depolarization.

Class III drugs prolong the duration of action potential without altering the maximal rate of depolarization or the resting potential. Several reports classify the drugs belonging to this class as potassium channel blockers; however, drugs in this class have been found to act through many mechanisms that involve calcium, potassium, and chloride transport. Accordingly, several other reports appropriately classify them as inhibitors of repolarization.

Class IV drugs are calcium channel blockers with antiarrhythmic activity. These agents block the slow movement of calcium ions during phase 2, which leads to lengthening the duration of action potential.

### Class I: Local Anesthetics, Sodium Channel Blockers

Class IA drugs include quinidine, procainamide, and disopyramide.

Quinidine (**Figure 10**) is a dextrorotatory diastereoisomer of quinine. Quinidine and quinine are obtained from many species of the *Cinchona* plant. Structurally, quinidine is composed of a quinoline ring and the bicyclic quinuclidine ring system. Thus, quinidine contains 2 basic nitrogen atoms, of which the quinuclidine nitrogen is more basic, with an acidic constant (pKa) of about 11. Quinidine is a prototypic antiarrhythmic drug that reduces the sodium ion current by binding to the open ion channel, resulting in depression of automaticity of ectopic foci. It is used to treat supraventricular and ventricular ectopic arrhythmias, atrial and ventricular tachycardia, atrial flutter, and atrial fibrillation.

Quinidine is available as water-soluble sulfate, gluconate, or polygalacturonate salt. Each has slightly different physical and biological absorption properties. Quinidine sulfate is an oral preparation that also can be used intramuscularly. It is rapidly absorbed from the gastrointestinal (GI) tract, and onset of action begins in about 30 minutes. Quinidine gluconate is soluble in water and is mostly used in emergencies when rapid response may be needed that makes oral administration of quinidine sulfate ineffective. Quinidine polygalacturonate gives more stable and uniform blood levels of quinidine.

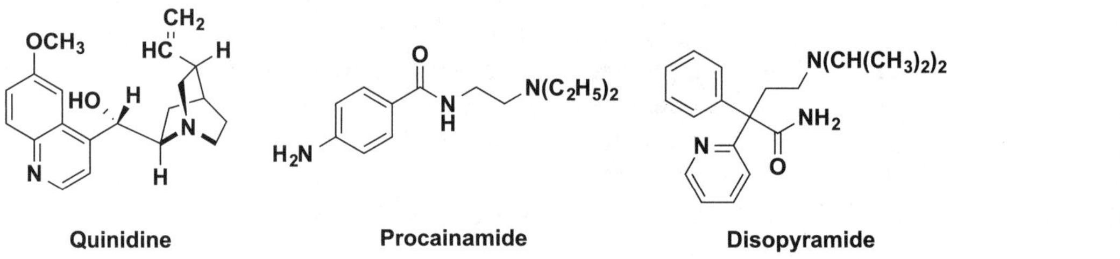

Quinidine · Procainamide · Disopyramide

**Figure 10.** *Class IA antiarrhythmic drugs.*

Procainamide and disopyramide (Figure 10) have emerged as major antiarrhythmic drugs with a mechanism of action similar to that of quinidine. Chemically, procainamide is a *p*-aminobenzamide derivative, whereas disopyramide is a butamide derivative. Both are orally bioavailable, rapidly absorbed from the GI tract, and moderately bound to serum proteins. Metabolism of procainamide results in *N*-acetylprocainamide that has only one-fourth the activity of the parent drug, while half of disopyramide oral dose is excreted in urine unchanged and the other half undergoes *N*-dealkylation through hepatic metabolism. The *N*-dealkylated metabolite of disopyramide retains 50% of its parent antiarrhythmic activity. Most adverse effects of disopyramide are attributed to its antichlolinergic activity.

Some of the class IB drugs are lidocaine, tocainide, mexiletine, and phenytoin. Lidocaine and tocainide are aniline-amide derivatives, whereas mexiletine is an ether derivative (**Figure 11**). Lidocaine has a tertiary amine, and tocainide and mexiletine have a primary amine, which results in a measurable difference in their pKa values (7.7 for tocainide, 9.5 for lidocaine) and affects the degree of the protonated form of these drugs present in the blood. The ether bond of mexiletine imparts greater chemical stability in comparison with tocainide.

Lidocaine was initially introduced as a local anesthetic, but is now routinely used intravenously for treatment of arrhythmias arising from acute myocardial infarction and cardiac surgery. In fact, it is usually the drug of choice for emergency treatment of ventricular arrhythmias. It binds to the active and inactive sodium channels with nearly equivalent affinity, causing depression in diastolic depolarization and automaticity. Lidocaine does not bind to serum proteins to a substantial extent because of its positive charge at the physiological pH. It undergoes extensive first-pass metabolism, which prevents its oral administration. The monoethylglycinexylidide metabolite, resulting from partial de-ethylation of the terminal tertiary amine, is an effective antiarrhythmic agent. Lidocaine has a short half-life of 15 to 30 minutes. Lidocaine solutions containing epinephrine are used only for local anesthetic purposes.

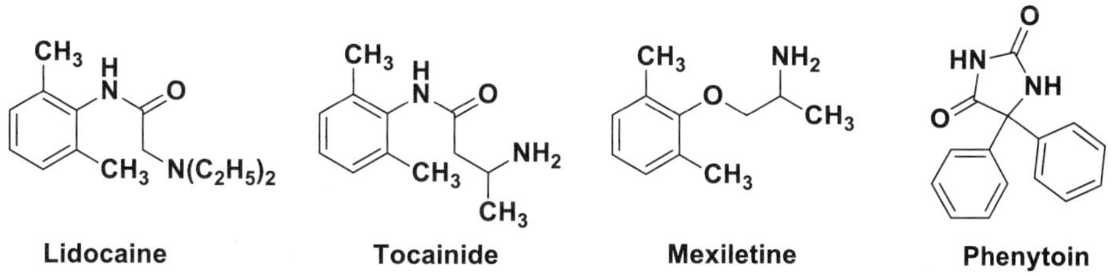

**Figure 11.** *Class IB antiarrhythmic drugs.*

Tocainide is not subject to first-pass metabolism because of its low hepatic clearance, and, consequently, it is orally bioavailable. It has a plasma half-life of 12 hours, and nearly 50% of the drug is excreted unchanged in urine. It is important to note that it has 2 enantiomers, of which the R isomer is nearly 4 times as potent as the S isomer. It is used orally for the treatment of ventricular ectopy and tachycardia.

Mexiletine has a prolonged half-life on oral administration of nearly 14 hours. Metabolism of mexiletine produces *p*-hydroxy and hydroxymethyl derivatives that are not active as antiarrhythmic agents.

5,5-Diphenylhydantoin (phenytoin, Figure 11) has been used traditionally in the control of generalized tonic clonic seizures (formerly known as grand mal seizures). Phenytoin is structurally analogous to the barbiturates but does not have their sedative effects. Phenytoin is clinically used in treatment of digitalis-induced arrhythmias, and its action is similar to that of lidocaine. Phenytoin may be administered orally; however, it is absorbed slowly. It is extensively plasma protein bound (~90%), and the elimination half-life is between 15 and 30 hours. Parenteral administration is limited to intravenous administration, particularly as a phosphate ester (fosphenytoin).

Class IC antiarrhythmic drugs include encainide, flecainide, moricizine, and propafenone. Encainide and flecainide (**Figure 12**) depress the rate of depolarization and increase the length of refractoriness. Both are benzamide derivatives with local anesthetic properties. Encainide is extensively metabolized into 2 active metabolites. The metabolites 3-methoxy-$O^4$-demethyl-encainide and $O^4$-demethyl-encainide are as potent as and more potent than encainide, respectively. Both metabolites can persist in plasma for as long as 12 hours, whereas encainide has a half-life of only 2 to 4 hours. This pharmacokinetic profile leads to a high risk of proarrhythmic adverse effects, which may have been the reason for the withdrawal of this drug from the market. Metabolism of flecainide results in a meta-*O*-dealkylated product with 50% less activity than the parent drug. Flecainide in the acetate form can be given orally to treat ventricular arrhythmias.

Moricizine (Figure 12) is a phenothiazine derivative, oral class IC antiarrhythmic agent that blocks sodium channels. Moricizine has higher affinity for the inactivated state than the activated or resting state of the sodium channels. It is used exclusively for life-threatening ventricular arrhythmias.

Propafenone (Figure 12) can be chemically classified as a phenyl propanone. Although this drug contains a chiral center, it is sold as a racemic mixture. The R and S enantiomers exert a sodium channel blocking effect, but the S isomer also exerts a β-adrenergic effect. The S isomer produces a nearly 40-fold greater antiarrhythmic effect than does the R enantiomer. Metabolism of both enantiomers produces 5-OH metabolites that are as active as the parent compounds. This drug has been primarily proven for ventricular and supraventricular arrhythmias. The drug has poor bioavailability (20%) due to first-pass metabolism and has a short half-life.

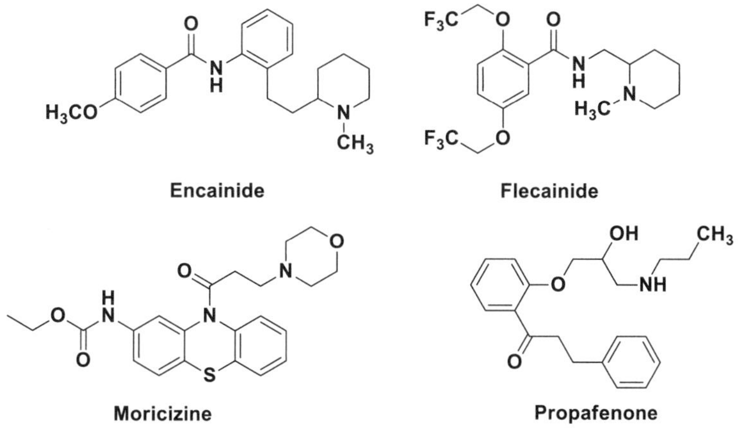

**Figure 12.** *Class IC antiarrhythmic drugs. Note that encainide has been withdrawn from the market.*

### Class II: β-Adrenergic Blockers

Propranolol (Figure 7), a naphthaleneoxy propylamine derivative, is the prototype of class II antiarrhythmics. Both stereoisomers of propranolol are active, with the S isomer the most potent enantiomer. It is a nonselective β-adrenergic blocker and is used for the treatment of supraventricular arrhythmias, including atrial flutter, paroxysmal supraventricular tachycardia, and atrial fibrillation. Propranolol is also effective for the treatment of digitalis-induced ventricular arrhythmias.

### Class III: Potassium Channel Blockers, Inhibitors of Repolarization

Bretylium tosylate (**Figure 13**) is a quaternary ammonium salt that is extremely soluble in water and alcohol. Bretylium tosylate is an adrenergic neuronal blocking agent that accumulates in the neurons and displaces norepinephrine. Because of this action, it was used earlier as an antihypertensive agent, but its use was discontinued because of the development of tolerance and pain-related adverse effects. It prolongs the effective refractory period but does not affect the rate of depolarization and, hence, is classified as a class III agent. The precise mechanism of action of bretylium tosylate remains to be elucidated.

   Amiodarone and dronedarone (Figure 13) are chemically classified as benzofuran derivatives, and each contains a terminal tertiary amine. An important difference is that amiodarone contains a diiodinated aromatic ring, whereas dronedarone is noniodinated. The iodine atoms introduce thyroid-specific adverse effects for amiodarone. Hypothyroidism occurs in up to 11% of people taking amiodarone. In addition, amiodarone inhibits enzymes of the oxidative system and, hence, interferes with the normal metabolism of many other drugs. Thus, it is used primarily in hospital settings, especially for life-threatening ventricular arrhythmias. Amiodarone and dronedarone exert effects across all Vaughan Williams classes. Amiodarone lengthens the effective refractory period. The drug has a very slow onset of action (days) and is eliminated very slowly from the body, with a half-life of approximately 1 month following oral doses. The lipophilicity of dronedarone is decreased because of the methane-sulfonamide moiety, resulting in faster elimination in comparison with amiodarone. Dronedarone is effectively absorbed after oral absorption; however, its bioavailability is only about 15% because of the extensive first-pass effect. The oral bioavailability may be increased by concurrent administration of the drug with a high-fat meal.

Chemically, sotalol is a phenylethylamine derivative, whereas ibutilide is a phenyl-butylamine derivative (Figure 13). Both contain a methane-sulfonamide group, and both are sold as racemic mixtures. Only the d(+) enantiomer of sotalol has class III activity, whereas the l(−) isomer has class II (β-adrenergic blockade) and class III (potassium channel blockade) activity. Thus, the 2 isomers slow the heart rate in slightly different ways. Sotalol is used orally as prophylaxis for and treatment of the recurrence of life-threatening ventricular arrhythmias. Sotalol is not bound to plasma proteins, and it is excreted unchanged through the renal excretion mechanism.

Ibutilide lacks β-adrenergic blocking activity in comparison with sotalol, and, consequently, it has less potential to promote adrenergic receptor–mediated adverse effects. Because of its extensive first-pass effect, ibutilide must be given as an intravenous infusion as the fumarate salt. It has been approved by the US Food and Drug Administration for the conversion of recent-onset atrial fibrillation and atrial flutter.

Dofetilide (Figure 13) is a bis-methane-sulfonamide derivative. In contrast with sotalol, it exhibits only class III effects without any β-blocking activity. It is more potent and selective than other drugs in class III. It is used orally to suppress atrial flutter and atrial fibrillation. It is well absorbed from the GI tract with almost 100% bioavailability. It binds plasma proteins moderately, undergoes N-dealkylation and N-oxidation hepatic metabolism to inactive metabolites, and is mainly excreted unchanged in the urine.

Structurally, azimilide (Figure 13) is unrelated to any drugs in this class and yet shows class III antiarrhythmic effect by blocking potassium channels. It is an imidazolidin-dione with a chlorophenylfuranyl side chain. A phase 3 study of azimilide was recruiting participants as of January 2013 (ClinicalTrials.gov identifier NCT01464476); the estimated study completion date is August 2014.

### Class IV: Calcium Channel Blockers (Nondihydropyridines)

Diltiazem and verapamil (Figures 5 and 6, respectively) were discussed earlier in this chapter as calcium channel blockers. In addition to their antianginal effects, these drugs also have antiarrhythmic properties. Pharmacologically, both drugs block the slow inward movement of calcium ions, resulting in relaxation of arterial smooth muscle and vasodilation and decreased contractility in cardiac myocytes. These agents also slow the atrioventricular node conduction and increase its refractoriness. Clinically, supraventricular tachycardia is the major arrhythmic indication for diltiazem and verapamil. These drugs can also reduce the ventricular rate in atrial fibrillation and atrial flutter.

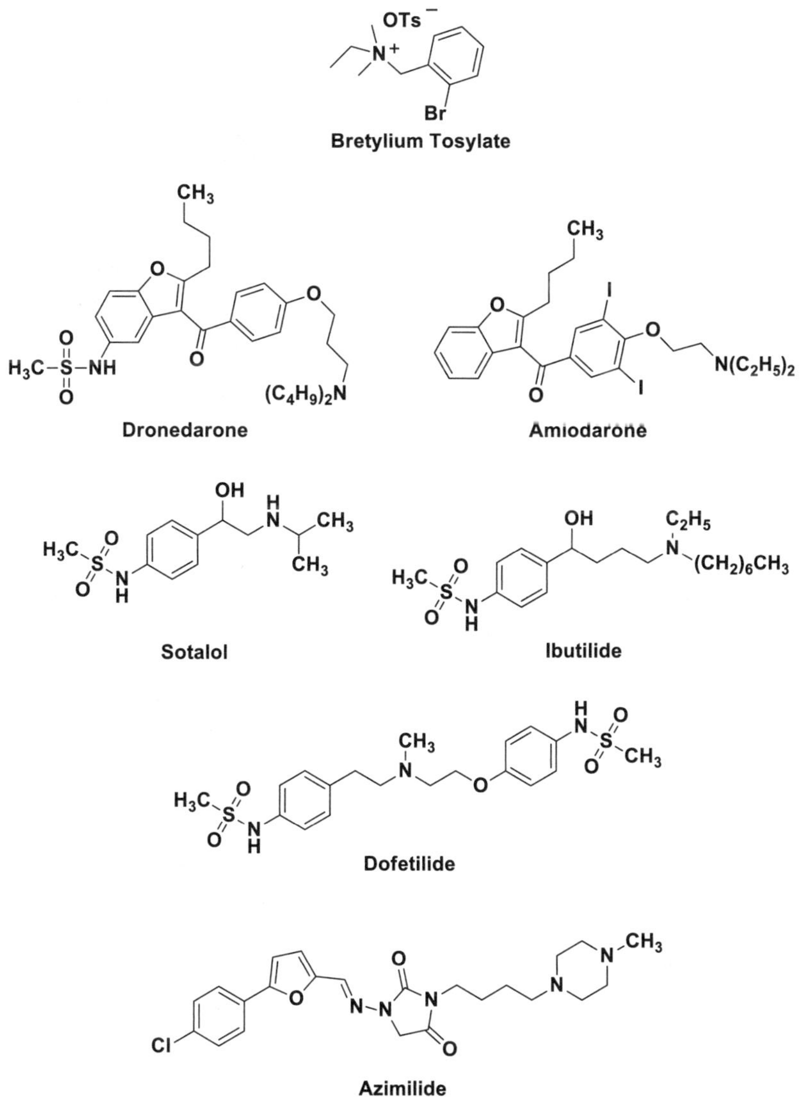

**Figure 13.** *Class III antiarrhythmic drugs. Note that a phase 3 study of azimilide was recruiting participants as of January 2013 (ClinicalTrials.gov identifier NCT01464476); the estimated study completion date is August 2014.*

## Antihypertensive Agents

Hypertension is a known major risk factor for many cardiovascular diseases such as stroke and myocardial infarction. It has been estimated that globally more than 1 billion people are affected by hypertension, with nearly 40 million people affected in the United States alone. Consistently high blood pressure can damage the brain, eyes, and kidneys.

Hypertension is usually classified into 2 types: primary (or essential) and secondary (nonessential). *Primary hypertension,* due to a nonidentifiable cause, is the most common type and occurs in 95% of people who have hypertension. Genetic factors seem to have a role in this hypertension and include genes that regulate a system known collectively as the renin-angiotensin system (RAS) and genes that regulate the sympathetic nervous system.

*Secondary hypertension* has known causes and can be treated independently and even reversed. This type of hypertension is generally seen during temporary conditions, such as pregnancy; cirrhosis; kidney diseases; and Cushing disease. Other causes include certain medications; lifestyle choices, such as drinking alcohol or excessive drinking of caffeinated drinks such as coffee; and obesity. Temporary hypertension also results from physical stress and exercise.

## Targets for Drug Therapies

Hypertension can be combated in a number of ways. Some of the targets include the following:

1. The RAS is responsible for the production of angiotensin II and angiotensin III, which in turn constrict arterioles, causing a rise in the blood pressure. Inhibitors of the RAS are useful antihypertensive drugs.

2. The sympathetic nervous system is responsible for the release of adrenaline and epinephrine, which are neurotransmitters that constrict blood vessels, resulting in increased peripheral vascular resistance. Blocking the effect of these neurotransmitters on the β-receptors present on the blood vessels through the use of β-blockers is a useful strategy for treating hypertension.

3. Voltage-gated calcium channels are responsible for the muscle contractions in the heart and blood vessels. The entry of calcium induces contraction of the blood vessels and heart, thereby increasing the pressure, which can be effectively prevented by calcium channel blockers.

4. Salt reabsorption in the kidneys is responsible for the increase in the volume of fluids in the blood vessels, thereby enhancing blood pressure. This increase in the volume is due to the simultaneous reabsorption of fluids from the kidneys along with salt to maintain osmotic homeostasis. Salt reabsorption can be prevented by the use of diuretic drugs, which causes the body to excrete water and salt.

A discussion of β-blockers and calcium channel blockers was presented earlier in the chapter. Inhibitors of the RAS, diuretics, and direct-acting vasodilators are described in the following paragraphs.

# The Renin-Angiotensin System

The RAS (**Figure 14**) is a cascade of enzymatic reactions, which lead to the release of the peptide hormones, angiotensin I and angiotensin II. These peptides are capable of acting on the angiotensin receptors present in the blood vessels and cause vasoconstriction. The angiotensin secreted is also capable of stimulating the adrenal cortex to release aldosterone, a mineralocorticoid hormone responsible for the increased reabsorption of sodium and water.

Reduction of the blood pressure or lowering of the sodium excretion causes a release of the enzyme renin from the kidneys. The enzyme renin then acts on angiotensinogen (released from the liver) to produce angiotensin I, which is activated by angiotensin-converting enzyme (ACE) to produce angiotensin II. Angiotensin II binds to angiotensin receptors, resulting in an increase in the blood pressure. Angiotensin II mainly acts on the arterioles, causing vasoconstriction. It also acts on the kidneys, causing a constriction of the glomerular arterioles, and reduces the glomerular filtration rate, which increases fluid retention. The hormone also stimulates the $Na^+/H^+$ exchangers located in the renal tubules, causing increased reabsorption of sodium. Finally, it stimulates the adrenal cortex to release more aldosterone, and vasopressin, the antidiuretic hormone, both of which increase the blood pressure. Thus, inhibiting the RAS is important. Three targets have been used for antihypertensive effects: Renin, ACE and the angiotensin receptor. Of these, ACE inhibitors have been used most frequently to reduce hypertension.

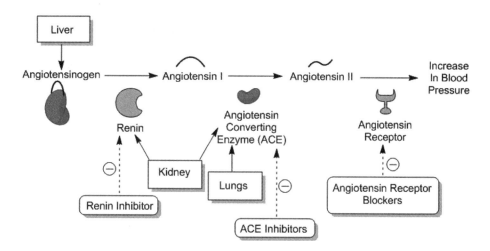

**Figure 14.** *The renin-angiotensin system (RAS) of blood pressure control. Angiotensinogen is released by the liver. With a rise in blood pressure, renin is released by the kidney, followed by a release of angiotensin-converting enzyme (ACE) by the kidney and lungs. Renin inhibitors block the RAS early in the pathway, and ACE inhibitors inactivate the enzyme and prevent the formation of angiotensin II, which is the key peptide of the RAS. Angiotensin receptor blockers block the activity of angiotensin II at the sites where the peptide shows its effect and thereby block the increase in blood pressure.*

## Angiotensin-Converting Enzyme Inhibitors

This class of antihypertensives works by inhibiting ACE and preventing the formation of angiotensin II. The ACE inhibitors have names ending with "pril" and are structurally classified into 3 classes.

### Class I: Thiol- and Carboxylate-Containing Drugs

Captopril and zofenopril (**Figure 15**) contain a carboxylic acid functional group in their structure, which is recognized by the cationic site arginine in the active site of ACE, but it is not approved. The thiol group was introduced in captopril to increase the binding to zinc of ACE, but it causes side effects such as rash and loss of taste. Zofenopril, on the other hand, has protected thiol groups, which reduces the side effects. Captopril reduces hypertension and is useful in myocardial infarction, congestive heart failure, and even preservation of renal function in diabetic nephropathy. Captopril has a relatively short half-life and poor pharmacokinetic properties. With many adverse effects and poor pharmacokinetics, captopril has reduced patient compliance. Zofenopril has been found to be more effective than enalapril and even atenolol for reducing hypertension. The adverse effects observed in the use of zofenopril are also less severe than with other ACE inhibitors. Zofenopril has been used in other countries for its cardioprotective properties, but it is not approved for use in the United States.

### Class II: Aminophenyl Butyric Acid- and Ester-Containing Drugs

This group of drugs contains the 2-(S)-aminophenylbutyric acid functional group (**Figure 16**). These drugs contain 2 carboxylate functional groups, of which 1 interacts with the cationic arginine in the active site. All ester forms of the butyric acid are converted to the active acid form following absorption and metabolism by the liver, kidney, and intestinal enzymes. Hence, it is important for people

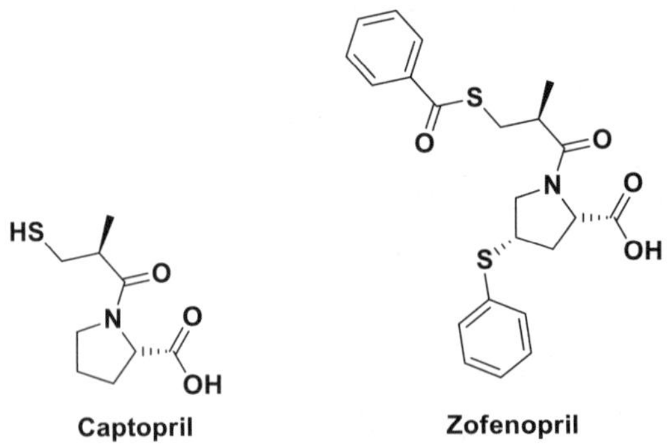

**Captopril**          **Zofenopril**

**Figure 15.** *Class I angiotensin-converting enzyme inhibitors. Note that zofenopril is not approved for use in the United States.*

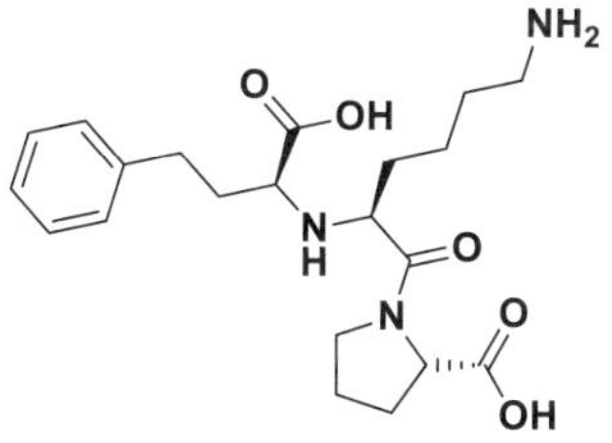


Lisinopril

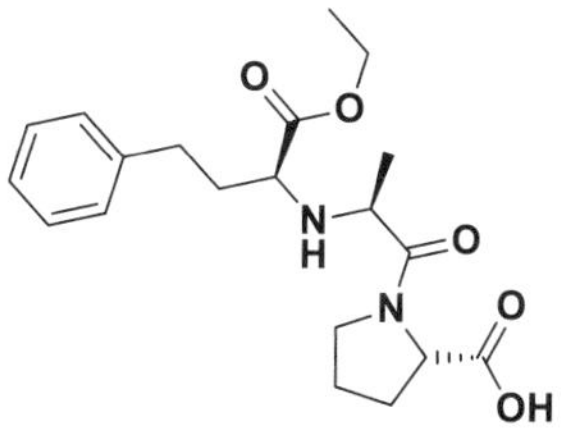


Enalapril

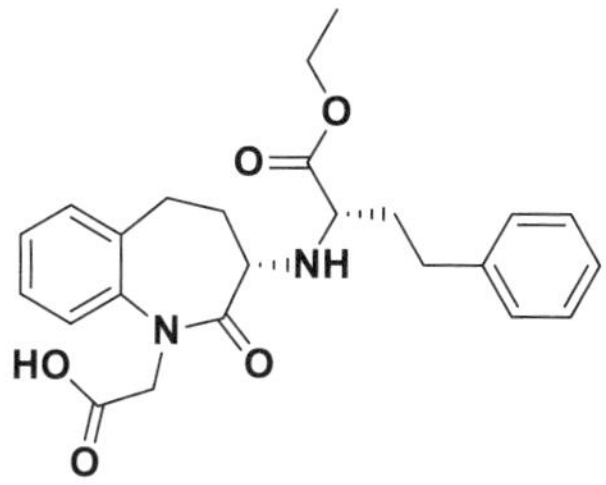


Benazepril

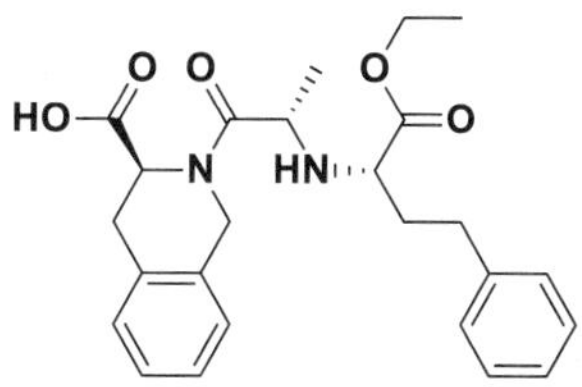


Quinapril

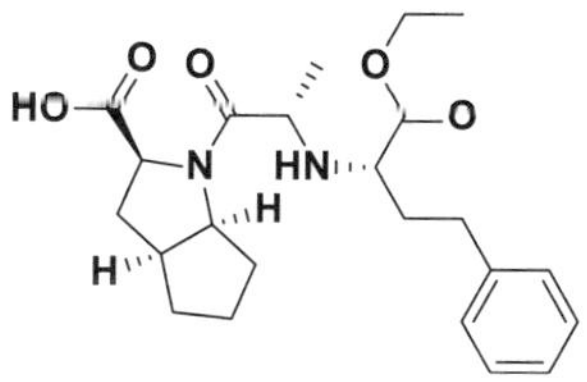


Ramipril

**Figure 16.** *Class II angiotensin-converting enzyme inhibitors.*

who take these drugs to have active enzymes in these organs; these drugs are contraindicated generally in people with impaired renal and liver function. The ester form of the drug is particularly long lasting because it must be hydrolyzed by nonspecific esterases. These drugs are generally used in mild to moderate hypertension states.

Lisinopril (Figure 16) is so named because it contains a lysine group in its structure, benazepril because of its benzazepine ring, and quinapril on account of its isoquinoline structure. Except for lisinopril, all other agents are prodrugs because their butyric acid is protected as an ester moiety. The cleavage of the ester group produces the active form. Enalapril was the first dicarboxylate containing an ACE inhibitor, but its poor bioavailability led to its conversion to the prodrug form.

Lisinopril is primarily used in congestive heart failure and myocardial infarction and is also useful in preventing renal and retinal complications in diabetes. Dosing is dependent on the creatinine clearance. Enalapril has been shown to substantially lower the death rates in systolic heart failure. Renal impairment, however, results in the substantial accumulation of enalapril, and, therefore, in such conditions, the dosage must be reduced. Benazepril has been shown to have kidney-protective properties and slows the progression of kidney diseases. Quinapril has been known to cause angioedema and is therefore not widely used. Ramipril is useful mainly as a preventive drug for myocardial infarction and stroke and also to reduce the risk of cardiovascular events during surgical procedures.

### Class III: Phosphonate-Containing Drugs

Fosinopril (**Figure 17**) is the only phosphonate-containing inhibitor of ACE. Because of its poor oral bioavailability, the phosphonate group in fosinopril had to be protected with a lipophilic side chain.

## Adverse Effects of Angiotensin-Converting Enzyme Inhibitors

The most common adverse effect of ACE inhibitors is persistent dry cough. This cough is believed to be due to an increased bradykinin level, which can also occasionally lead to angioedema. The ACE is also responsible for the breakdown of bradykinin, and, thus, inhibiting it causes an increase in the bradykinin level in the body. If the adverse effect is severe, alternative treatment with angiotensin receptor blockers (see below) is sought. In some cases, renal impairment is also seen, although the reason remains unknown. The ACE inhibitors can also cause hyperkalemia due to a decreased aldosterone level. Potassium supplements are advisable.

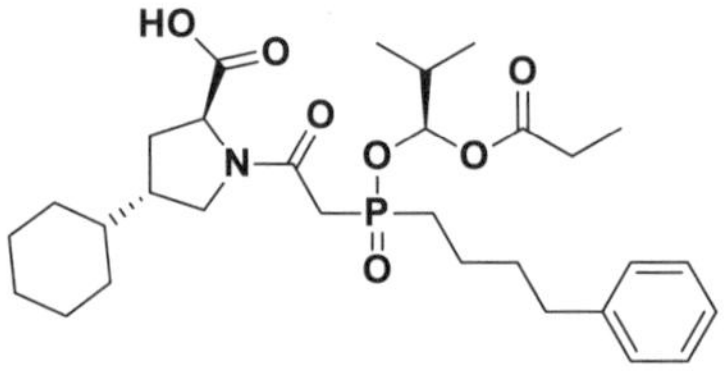

**Fosinopril**

**Figure 17.** *A class III angiotensin-converting enzyme inhibitor, fosinopril.*

## Renin Inhibitors

Renin is an aspartic protease, a rate-limiting enzyme of the RAS. It cleaves angiotensinogen to angiotensin I, a primary catalytic step, which makes inhibition of renin a major strategy in the reduction of hypertension. Other drugs that target the RAS also induce feedback mechanisms to increase renin production, which compensate for the inhibition. However, inhibiting renin directly is devoid of such feedback. The discovery of this enzyme and its role had been known for many years; however, no drugs were designed until recently.

Aliskiren (**Figure 18**), a peptidomimetic drug, binds to the S3bp binding pocket of renin, which is near the active site. Aliskiren is also observed to have renal-protective effects, which are independent of its antihypertensive effects in people with diabetes. On the downside, aliskiren has been known to cause hyperkalemia, particularly when used with ACE inhibitors; angioedema; and hypotension. Other adverse effects observed with aliskiren include gout and kidney stones. Coughing is also observed, although it is not as severe as compared with coughing during use of ACE inhibitors.

## Angiotensin II Receptor Antagonists

This class of antihypertensives works by inhibiting the angiotensin receptors present on the blood vessels. They are also known as angiotensin receptor antagonists, or "sartans" (**Figure 19**). They are mainly useful in hypertension, diabetic nephropathy, and congestive heart failure. Sartans are particularly useful in people who cannot tolerate ACE inhibitors. Valsartan has been one of the most prescribed angiotensin receptor antagonists and has also been indicated for post–myocardial infarction treatment. It is being currently investigated for the treatment and prevention of Alzheimer disease.

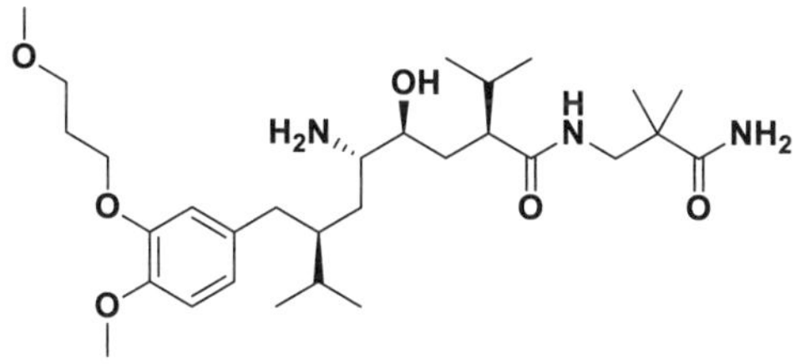

**Aliskiren**

**Figure 18.** *The structure of aliskiren, a renin inhibitor.*

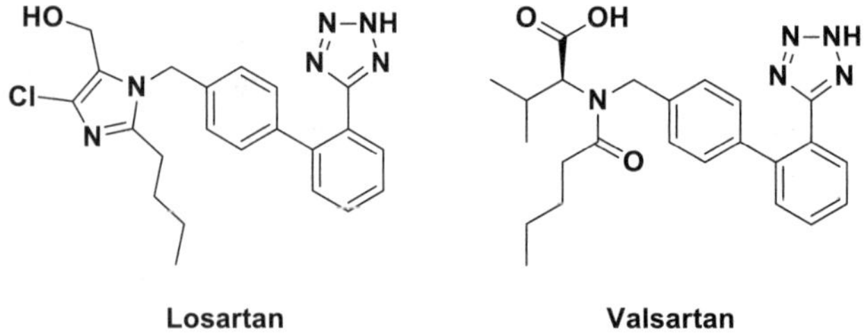

**Figure 19.** *Angiotensin II receptor antagonists.*

Structurally, these drugs generally contain a tetrazole group, and losartan also contains an imidazole ring. The biphenyl linker in both helps binding to the receptor. Losartan, a competitive agonist at the angiotensin II type I receptor, has been seen to decrease the total peripheral resistance and cardiac venous return. Because losartan blocks angiotensin receptors, plasma renin levels increase because of the removal of the negative feedback of the angiotensin II. Mostly, these drugs are well tolerated. Common adverse effects include hyperkalemia due to reduced aldosterone release; angioedema in rare cases; muscle cramps; back pain; insomnia; decreased hemoglobin levels; renal impairment; and nasal congestion.

# Diuretics

Kidneys are the main organ of excretion of fluids, small molecules, and ions to maintain homeostasis. If the volume of fluids increases in the blood, the blood pressure increases. Hence, eliminating this excess volume helps in reduction of blood pressure. About one-fifth of the total blood volume is filtered into the nephrons of the kidneys; however, almost 99% of this volume of fluid is reabsorbed and only a small volume is excreted as urine. The amount of water reabsorbed is related, in turn, to the amount of ions that are reabsorbed as the body absorbs the appropriate amount of water to maintain homeostasis. Diuretics can be classified into a number of subtypes based on their targets of action or their structures. Each class of diuretics acts on different parts of the nephron.

## Class I: Carbonic Anhydrase Inhibitors

These drugs inhibit the action of carbonic anhydrase, an enzyme found in the proximal convoluted tubule of the nephron. Carbonic anhydrase is an enzyme that catalyzes the reversible conversion of bicarbonate to carbon dioxide and water. The bicarbonate that is excreted recombines with the hydrogen ions in the kidneys to be converted back to carbon dioxide and water, which are reabsorbed by the renal tubule. By inhibiting the carbonic anhydrase, the bicarbonate is not reabsorbed into the blood, which increases urine bicarbonate concentration, leading to diuresis. Although useful for diuresis, carbonic anhydrase inhibitors are used primarily for the treatment of glaucoma and sometimes for epilepsy. The diuretic action caused by carbonic anhydrase inhibitors is generally compensated by the distal segments of the nephron and, hence, is not very effective.

Acetazolamide (**Figure 20**) is the prototype drug for the carbonic anhydrase inhibitors. Structurally, the drug has a thiadiazole ring along with a sulfamoyl group, which sits in the active site of the carbonic anhydrase. Acetazolamide exerts diuretic action slowly, and the dose must not be increased if there is no loss of edema fluid. The most common adverse effect of acetazolamide is numbing and tingling in the fingers and toes. There can be taste alteration, especially for carbonated drinks. Blurring of vision is also observed in some people, possibly due to reduced intraocular pressure. These drugs can cause metabolic acidosis because they reduce the reabsorption of bicarbonate ions, which might precipitate kidney stones. Dehydration caused by these diuretics could result in headaches and electrolyte imbalance, so there is a need to drink sufficient fluids.

## Class II: Loop Diuretics

The loop of Henle reabsorbs a large amount of sodium from the filtrate via the $Na^+/K^+$-ATPase transporter, which is present on the anti-luminal membrane. This transporter moves 3 $Na^+$ ions out of the cell of the nephron to the interstitium and 2 $K^+$ ions in the opposite direction. As a result, there is a deficiency of sodium in the cell, which is compensated by another $Na^+/K^+/Cl^-$ cotransporter channel present on the luminal membrane of the cell cotransporter, which transports 1 $Na^+$, 1 $K^+$, and 2 $Cl^-$ ions from the lumen into the cells of the nephron. The return of the $K^+$ and $Cl^-$ ions down the concentration gradient is achieved via their respective channels. As a result, there is continuous movement of sodium ions from the lumen into the interstitium, causing sodium reabsorption into the body and out of the urine. Loop diuretics act by blocking the $Na^+/K^+/Cl^-$ cotransporter. Even though the sodium-potassium exchange begins with the $Na^+/K^+$-ATPase transporter, the sodium deficit cannot be compensated by the $Na^+/K^+/Cl^-$ cotransporter, which implies that the overall reabsorption of sodium will be reduced. Enhanced excretion of sodium results in diuresis.

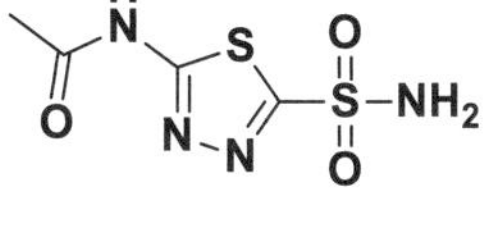

**Acetazolamide**

**Figure 20.** *The structure of acetazolamide, a class I diuretic, inhibiting carbonic anhydrase.*

Furosemide (**Figure 21**) is a phenyl sulfonamide–type of loop diuretic, which is primarily used for the treatment of hypertension and the edema associated with renal impairment, heart failure, and hepatic cirrhosis. It is also useful in the treatment of hypercalcemia because it causes excretion of calcium ions as well. There have been some reports of ototoxicity when using furosemide.

Unlike furosemide, ethacrynic acid (Figure 21) is not a sulfonamide, and, thus, it can be used by people with sulfa allergies. Structurally, it is a phenoxyacetic acid derivative that, in addition, contains a ketone and a methylene group. On entering the body, a cysteine adduct of the drug is formed, which, in turn, is the active form of ethacrynic acid. Hence, it may be considered a prodrug. Ethacrynic acid can cause hypokalemia, ototoxicity, and liver damage.

### Class III: Thiazide Diuretics

Thiazide diuretics are a class of diuretics that prevent the reabsorption of $Na^+$ in the distal convoluted tubule. Unlike the loop of Henle, the distal convoluted tubule has a $Na^+/Cl^-$ cotransporter to replace the $Na^+$ deficit caused by the $Na^+/K^+$-ATPase transporter. The potassium and chloride ion concentrations are restored by their respective channels. Thiazide and thiazidelike diuretics block the $Na^+/Cl^-$ cotransporter, resulting in the net excretion of the $Na^+$. While the thiazide diuretics have a benzothiadiazine molecular structure, the thiazidelike diuretics lack this structure but show similar physiological effects.

Chlorothiazide (**Figure 22**) contains a benzothiadiazine ring with a sulfonamide group. It is generally useful in the hospital setting to manage excessive fluids in congestive heart failure, peripheral edema, and hypertension. The presence of a sulfonamide group is a contraindication for the use of chlorothiazide in people with sulfa allergies. Adverse effects often include hypokalemia and dehydration.

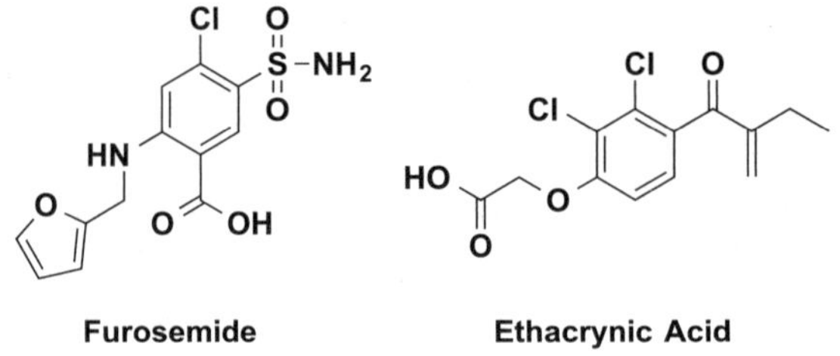

**Furosemide**          **Ethacrynic Acid**

**Figure 21.** *Class II: loop diuretics.*

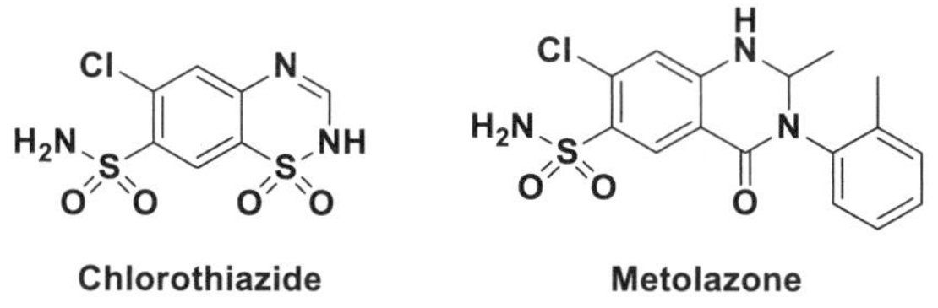

**Figure 22.** *Class III: thiazide diuretics.*

Metolazone (Figure 22) contains a tetrahydroquinazoline ring, in place of the benzothiadiazine ring, and, hence, it is a thiazidelike diuretic. It is also a sulfonamide and can give rise to allergic reactions. It is used primarily for treating edema associated with congestive heart failure, but is also useful in chronic kidney failure and nephrotic syndrome and is very potent in reducing hypertension. Metolazone can result in hypokalemia, dehydration, aplastic anemia, angioedema, agranulocytosis, and pancreatitis.

### Class IV: Potassium-Sparing Diuretics

Potassium-sparing diuretics are a class of drugs that produce diuresis without the secretion of $K^+$ into the urine. Epithelial sodium channels (ENaCs) are sodium ion channels present in the distal convoluted tubule and the collecting tubules of the nephron. Here, reabsorption of sodium occurs without an anion, thus creating a lumen-negative electrical gradient. This gradient favors the secretion of potassium and hydrogen ions. Inhibition of $Na^+$ reabsorption by blocking the ENaCs leads to diuresis without the concomitant loss of potassium. These diuretics have 2 basic mechanisms of action: (1) direct inhibition of ENaCs by amiloride and triamterene and (2) aldosterone antagonism, such as by spironolactone and eplerenone.

Amiloride and triamterene (**Figure 23**) are positively charged drugs and can enter and inhibit the ENaCs directly. These drugs can cause kidney stones and may lead to depletion of sodium, folic acid, and calcium. Serious adverse effects include heart palpitations, tingling and numbness, sore throat, rashes, and back pain. The possibility of hyperkalemia also exists. Amiloride is the best tolerated drug in this class of diuretics.

Spironolactone and eplerenone (**Figure 24**) are steroid derivatives. They inhibit the binding of aldosterone to the ENaCs and the activation of the ENaCs by aldosterone. The onset of action of spironolactone may take a few days. Eplerenone is more selective compared with spironolactone and, hence, has fewer adverse effects. As is common with this class of drugs, the possible adverse effects include hyperkalemia, renal impairment, hepatic impairment, and altered renal function.

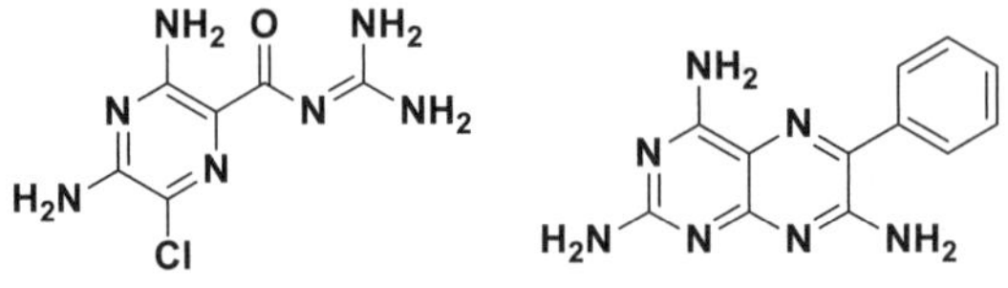

Amiloride Triamterene

**Figure 23.** *The structure of amiloride and triamterene.*

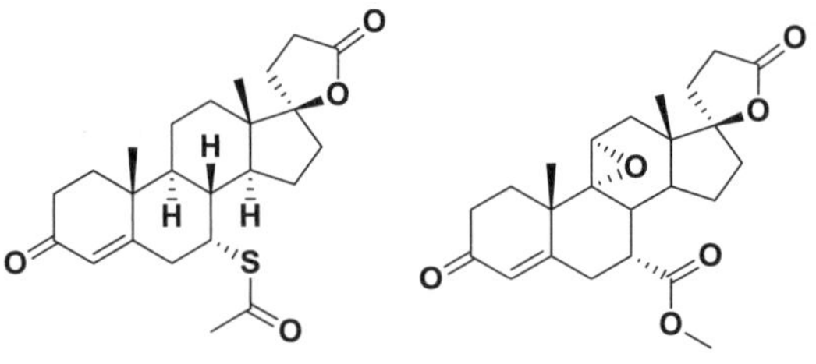

Spironolactone Eplerenone

**Figure 24.** *The structure of spironolactone and eplerenone.*

### *Class V: Osmotic Diuretics*

Certain compounds, such as mannitol (**Figure 25**), are filtered by the nephron, but mannitol is not reabsorbed. This lack of reabsorption increases the osmolality of the filtrate, causing more water to be excreted by the kidneys and leading to diuresis. The use of this class of diuretics is generally not favored.

## Direct-Acting Vasodilatory Drugs

Drugs that directly induce dilation of the smooth muscle cells (SMCs) are useful in treating hypertension. These drugs include hydralazine, sodium nitroprusside, calcium channel blockers, and potassium channel agonists.

Hydralazine (**Figure 26**) is useful in the treatment of moderate to severe hypertension and is used in combination with other antihypertensive drugs. Hydralazine decreases the action of secondary messenger inositol triphosphate, thereby increasing the amount of guanosine monophosphate levels in the SMCs. This action, in turn, causes limited calcium release from the sarcoplasmic reticulum, causing relaxation and dilation of the SMCs, which reduces resistance to blood flow and decreases blood pressure. In addition, it improves renal blood flow, which proves to be very useful for people with renal dysfunction. Its exact mechanism remains unknown. Hydralazine is a stable yellow solid with low water solubility (~3%). It reaches peak plasma concentration within 1 hour and is rapidly metabolized by hydroxylation, glucuronidation, and *N*-acetylation.

Sodium nitroferricyanide (or sodium nitroprusside, Figure 26) is one of the most potent blood pressure–lowering drugs, but its use is restricted to emergencies because of its short duration of action. Dilation of arterial and venous SMCs occurs. The exact mechanism remains unknown, but most probably it decomposes and releases NO, which results in nonspecific dilation of blood vessels.

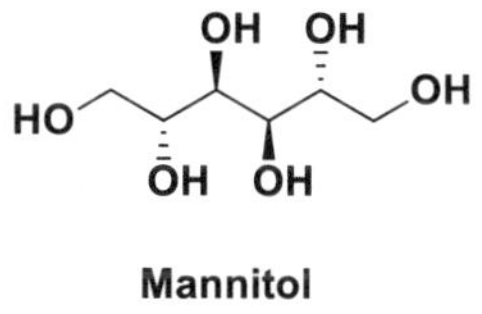

**Mannitol**

**Figure 25.** *A class V osmotic diuretic, mannitol.*

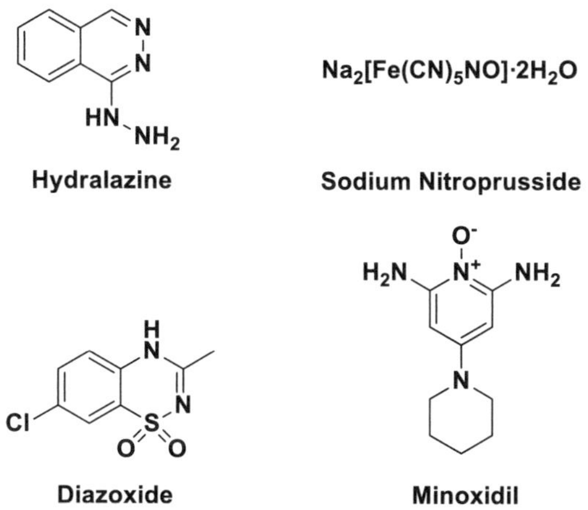

Na$_2$[Fe(CN)$_5$NO]·2H$_2$O

**Hydralazine**     **Sodium Nitroprusside**

**Diazoxide**     **Minoxidil**

**Figure 26.** *The structures of several direct-acting vasodilatory agents.*

Diazoxide and minoxidil (Figure 26) are potassium channel agonists that decrease the concentration of calcium ions in the cells and, thus, reduce the excitability of the SMCs. Both lower the peripheral vascular resistance; however, minoxidil requires activation by sulfotransferase to minoxidil sulfate before it becomes functionally active. Diazoxide must be injected intravenously (pH 11.5), which converts the drug to its soluble form. The drug is highly protein bound and can displace other drugs. Minoxidil is useful in severe hypertension that is difficult to control with other antihypertensive drugs.

## Anticoagulation

The blood circulatory system has to be self-sealing, otherwise continued blood loss from even a small injury would be life threatening. Under normal circumstances, bleeding is rapidly stopped by hemostasis. Technically, hemostasis is a combination of many processes arising from physical and chemical interactions between soluble components of the plasma, the vascular bed, and cellular material. The final result of these interactions is the formation of a thrombus, a highly cross-linked insoluble mass containing cells, enzymes, and other proteins at the site of injury that stops blood loss and ingress of microbes into the vasculature. Intravascular thrombosis can be caused—without external injury—by vascular injury and by blood hypercoagulability.

## Physical and Chemical Forces Involved in Clotting

On injury to the vascular wall, the subendothelial cells are exposed, setting off a series of responses. First, a reduction in blood flow occurs through vasoconstriction, which allows platelet adhesion to the cells at the site of injury (**Figure 27**). Simultaneously, certain chemicals that facilitate platelet activation and aggregation are released. Platelet aggregation leads to the formation of a plug in which a mass of platelets are held together by physical noncovalent forces. The platelet plug is susceptible to rupture by shearing forces due to rapid blood flow. Stabilizing this platelet plug is the formation of fibrin, a 3-dimensional, covalent, polypeptide network, which is the end result of chemical processes forming the coagulation cascade. Molecules that do not allow platelets to aggregate and, thus, prevent clotting, especially in the arteries, are called antiplatelet agents. These include aspirin, dipyridamole, and ticlopidine. Molecules that disintegrate a preformed clot constitute *fibrinolytic agents*. A typical example in this category is the enzyme, streptokinase.

The chemical forces involved in clotting include a series of chemical reactions mediated by proteins, enzymes, calcium ions, and phospholipid surfaces. The series of steps mimics a cascade of events that is traditionally described as a bifurcated process consisting of intrinsic and extrinsic pathways. The intrinsic pathway uses factors soluble in the plasma only, whereas the extrinsic pathway consists of some factors that are insoluble in the plasma, eg, membrane-bound factors (factor VII).

The distinguishing feature of the coagulation cascade is that activation results in an enzyme that converts the proenzyme (zymogen form) in the next step to an active enzyme. The newly formed enzyme then acts further down the cascade to greatly amplify the initial activation signal. These reactions occur in the presence of $Ca^{+2}$ ions and on an appropriate phospholipid membrane.

The intrinsic and extrinsic coagulation pathways merge at the formation of factor Xa (Figure 27), which, in turn, cleaves prothrombin at 2 sites to yield the key enzyme of the clotting cascade, thrombin. Thrombin has numerous properties, chief among them are coagulation and anticoagulation activities. Under appropriate conditions, thrombin cleaves fibrinogen, which constitutes nearly 2% to 3% of plasma protein. Fibrinogen cleavage results in soluble fibrin monomers that spontaneously aggregate to form a soft clot. This aggregate is rapidly converted to a more stable "hard clot" by the covalent cross-linking of neighboring fibrin molecules in a reaction catalyzed by factor XIIIa (fibrin-stabilizing factor). The process of 3-dimensional cross-linking that occurs in the polymeric fibrin formation traps numerous cells, including red blood cells and platelets.

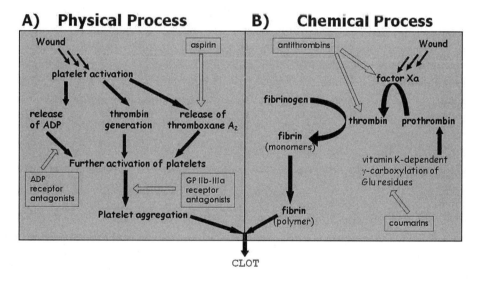

**Figure 27.** *Key elements of clotting consisting of physical and chemical processes. Both processes are more complex than depicted here and are not completely independent, as shown here. There is significant cross-talk between the two, exemplified by thrombin that is involved in the activation of platelets. Inhibitors of clotting are shown in boxed text with arrows indicating their site of action. From Desai UR. New antithrombin-based anticoagulants. Med Res Rev. 2004;24(2):151-181 with permission. Abbreviations: ADP, adenosine diphosphate; GP, glycoprotein; Glu, glutamic acid.*

## Anticoagulants

*Anticoagulants* are molecules that prevent blood clotting by inhibiting the chemical process of proteolytic formation of the 3-dimensional fibrin polymer. These agents include the heparins (heparin, low-molecular-weight [LMW] heparin, fondaparinux), warfarin, the hirudins (desirudin and bivalirudin) and the peptidomimetics (argatroban and dabigatran).

Anticoagulants are indicated in myocardial infarction, venous thrombosis, peripheral arterial embolism, pulmonary embolism, and many other conditions. Anticoagulants are also used in blood transfusions, extracorporeal blood circulation, and dialysis procedures. The following discussion pertains to the structural, functional, and physicochemical aspects of clinically used anticoagulant drugs.

## The Heparins

*Heparin* is a strongly acidic, high-molecular-weight mucopolysaccharide with rapid anticoagulant effects. Heparin, prepared from porcine lung or intestinal mucosa, is a mixture of molecules of varying molecular weights and chemical structures. It is a linear polysaccharide composed of alternating residues of glucosamine and uronic acid that are linked in a 1→4 manner (**Figure 28**). A typical preparation of heparin may have polysaccharide chains in the range of 10 to 100 monosaccharide residues corresponding to an average molecular weight ($M_R$) range of 3,000 to 30,000. The uronic acid residues may be of the β-D-glucuronic or α-L-iduronic type. The β-D-glucosamine residues are typically sulfated ($-OSO_3^-$) or acetylated ($-COCH_3$) at the 2 position. The available hydroxy groups, such as the 2-OH in iduronic acid and the 6-OH in β-D-glucosamine, may be sulfated. The numerous negatively charged groups ($-COO^-$ and $-OSO_3^-$) that span the length of the linear polysaccharide give a strongly acidic character to this molecule. In fact, heparin is the strongest acid in the body. Thus, heparin is a drug with massive structural microheterogeneity and polydispersity. The polyanionic character of heparin is probably the single major source of its numerous adverse effects.

Low-molecular-weight heparins (Figure 28) obviate some of these adverse effects. Low-molecular-weight heparins, prepared by chemical or enzymatic depolymerization or by chromatographic resolution of full-length heparin have an $M_R$ range of 3,000 to 8,000 with an average of 5,000 corresponding to about 15 monosaccharide residues. Reduction in the $M_R$ substantially reduces their negative charge density, thereby lowering their nonspecific interactions with plasma proteins and cells. However, the chemical and enzymatic methods used to prepare LMW heparins may introduce additional structural variations to increase the heterogeneity of the commercial preparations.

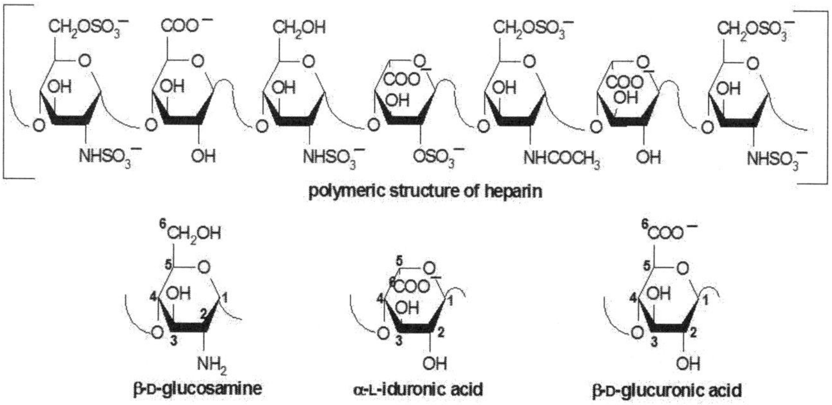

**Figure 28.** *Structure of the polymeric heparin sequence and its constituent monosaccharide residues. Unfractionated heparin has an average molecular weight of 15,000 Da, whereas low-molecular-weight heparin is about 3 to 5 times smaller.*

The key structural unit of heparin is a unique pentasaccharide sequence (**Figure 29**). This sequence is also the basis of fondaparinux, a synthetic drug introduced into clinical use in 2001. The generic 5-residue heparin pentasaccharide sequence consists of 3 D-glucosamine and 2 uronic acid residues. The central D-glucosamine residue contains a unique 3-$O$-sulfate moiety that is rare outside of this sequence. Four sulfate groups on the D-glucosamines (Figure 29) are critical for retaining high anticoagulant activity. Elimination of any one of them results in a dramatic reduction in the anticoagulant activity. Removal of the unique 3-$O$-sulfate group results in complete loss of the anticoagulant activity. Removal of sulfate groups other than the critical ones seems to insignificantly affect anticoagulant activity. Only a third of the chains in commercial heparin preparations have this unique pentasaccharide sequence. Thus, more than two-thirds of heparin chains are probably not active as anticoagulants. The LMW heparin preparations may have considerably varying proportions of chains with the active site.

## Properties of Heparin

Because of its highly acidic sulfate groups, heparin (or LMW heparins) exists as a polyanion at physiological pH. The heparin polysaccharide chain is degraded by gastric acid and must, therefore, be administered intravenously or subcutaneously. Because of its smaller size, LMW heparin is more bioavailable when given subcutaneously. Heparin is typically not given intramuscularly because of the danger of hematoma formation. Peak activity of heparin is reached within minutes of administration and is found to last 2 to 6 hours after intravenous administration and 8 to 12 hours after subcutaneous administration.

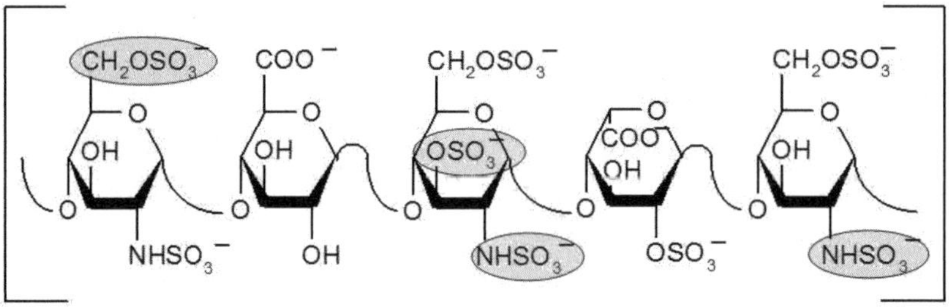

**Figure 29.** *Structure of the pentasaccharide sequence of heparin that binds to antithrombin. Negatively charged groups highlighted in ovals are critical for high-affinity binding and activation of antithrombin for accelerated inhibition of factor Xa and thrombin. Synthetic fondaparinux is derived from this high-affinity heparin pentasaccharide sequence.*

Fondaparinux has a much longer half-life ($\sim 16$ h) because it remains bound to the antithrombin present in plasma. Heparin is relatively nontoxic and can be safely used in pregnancy because it does not cross the placental barrier. Heparin overdose or hypersensitivity may result in excessive bleeding. If hemorrhage occurs, the anticoagulant effect of heparin can be reversed in minutes by administration of protamine sulfate, an LMW protein that has multiple positively charged groups. In contrast, fondaparinux activity cannot be reversed with protamine sulfate. In fact, no effective antidote for fondaparinux is available, which generates substantial risk in case of accidental bleeding. In addition to bleeding complications, unfractionated heparin has substantial intrapatient and interpatient dose variability, which requires frequent laboratory monitoring. The inconsistent response is due to differences in the bioavailability and from heparin binding to proteins in the plasma and on cells. Some of these heparin-binding proteins are acute phase proteins, which are typically elevated in very ill patients, thus reducing heparin efficacy. In addition, heparins do not neutralize clot-bound thrombin, thus raising the possibility of reactivating clotting at a later time. Finally, heparin-induced thrombocytopenia (HIT) is a potentially lethal complication of heparin therapy that may be associated with thrombosis. Heparin-induced thrombocytopenia involves a substantial drop in the platelet count after the initiation of therapy.

## Biochemical Mechanism of Heparin Action

The anticoagulant action of heparin occurs through *antithrombin,* a glycoprotein that exists in plasma at a fairly high concentration ($\sim 2$ μmol/L). Antithrombin is an inhibitor of many proteases of the coagulation cascade, especially thrombin and factor Xa, under physiological conditions. Thus, antithrombin prevents the conversion of fibrinogen to fibrin, thereby inhibiting clotting. However, the rate of inhibition of both of these enzymes by antithrombin is rather slow

(**Figure 30**). Heparin, containing the unique 5-residue sequence, forms a high-affinity complex with antithrombin. The formation of the antithrombin-heparin complex increases the rate of inhibition of factor Xa and thrombin some 500- to 4,000-fold (Figure 30). Heparin chains devoid of the pentasaccharide sequence cannot bind antithrombin tightly and, hence, do not increase the inhibition of the critical coagulation enzymes. The fact that the heparin-antithrombin complex inactivates proteolytically active molecules, thrombin and factor Xa, suggests that heparin action is instantaneous. Accelerated inhibition of factor Xa and thrombin shuts down the coagulation process and is the primary reason for the clinical use of heparin as an anticoagulant.

## The Coumarins and Indanediones

The most common coumarin is warfarin (**Figure 31**), which was discovered in the 1930s while trying to identify a coagulant. Coumarin and 1,3-indanedione are small, aromatic, water-insoluble scaffolds. While coumarin contains a lactone moiety, 1,3-indanedione contains 2 ketone groups. Introduction of a 4-OH substitution in the coumarin structure and a 2-aryl substitution in the 1,3-indanedione structure improves the water solubility of these scaffolds because of resonance stabilization of the anion formed under alkaline conditions (**Figure 32**).

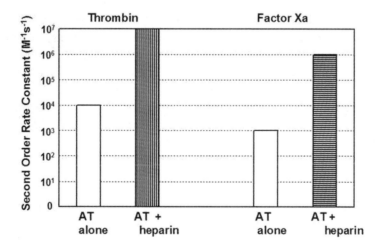

**Figure 30.** *Heparin accelerates the rate of antithrombin (AT) inhibition of procoagulant enzymes. The second-order rate constant increases from approximately $10^3$ and $10^4$ for factor Xa and thrombin, respectively, with antithrombin alone to ~$10^6$ and $10^7$ in the presence of heparin. Note the logarithmic scale on the y-axis. See text for details.*

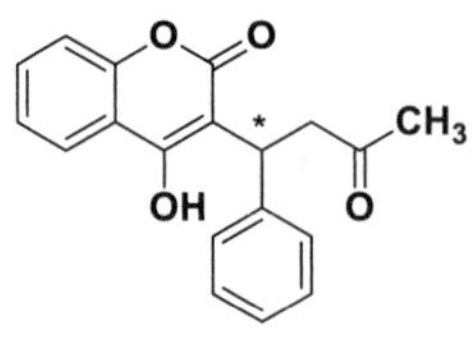

Warfarin
* Chiral center

**Figure 31.** *Structure of warfarin.*

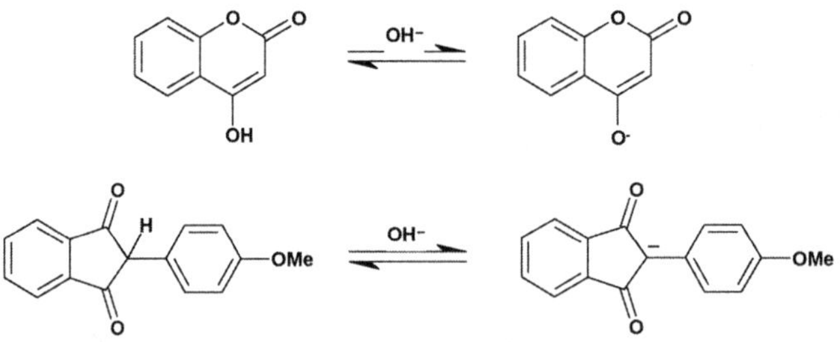

**Figure 32.** *Weakly acidic property of 4-hydroxycoumarins and 2-aryl-1,3-indandiones.*

Neither coumarin nor 1,3-indanedione have anticoagulant activities. However, the 4-OH and 3-alkyl substitutions in the coumarin ring and the 2-aryl substitution in the 1,3-indanedione ring confer anticoagulant activity. The coumarin derivatives are used to treat thrombophlebitis, pulmonary embolism, and coronary thrombosis. Some coumarins have been used as rodenticides.

The coumarins are the most often used oral anticoagulants. Another character-istic of the coumarins is that they have a very slow onset of action. They typically exert their effects in vivo only after about 24 to 48 hours, and their duration of action is also much longer, about 1.5 to 5 days. The reason for this difference in activity lies in their biochemical mechanism of action.

### Biochemical Mechanism of Action of Coumarins

Coumarins and 1,3-indanediones are competitive inhibitors of vitamin K in the biosynthesis of prothrombin. They prevent the formation of prothrombin that contains 10 γ-carboxyglutamic acid residues that are crucial for the optimal activity of thrombin formed by the action of factor Xa.

For thrombin to be fully functional as a clotting enzyme in the presence of $Ca^{+2}$ and phospholipids, it should have 10 γ-carboxyglutamic acid (Gla) residues in its *N*-terminal end. These Gla residues bind several $Ca^{+2}$ ions under physiological conditions, resulting in a specific conformation of the molecule that is important for fibrinogen recognition and cleavage activity.

Under normal circumstances, 10 glutamic acid (Glu) residues in prothrombin are γ-carboxylated to give a prothrombin molecule in a posttranslational modification reaction that is catalyzed by vitamin K (**Figure 33**). Thus, vitamin K is required in the hepatic biosynthesis of prothrombin that contains 10 γ-carboxyglutamic residues. Only this prothrombin molecule containing 10 Gla residues on activation with factor Xa results in a thrombin molecule that is fully functional under physiological conditions.

The 3-dimensional structure of anticoagulant coumarins and 1,3-indanediones resembles vitamin K; thus, they compete for the vitamin K binding site on vitamin K epoxide reductase and vitamin K reductase, resulting in inhibition of γ-carboxylation of the Glu residues in prothrombin. Thus, an abnormal prothrombin is synthesized in the presence of these anticoagulants that, when activated to thrombin, has less than 2% of the proteolytic activity for fibrinogen as normal thrombin. This inhibition of the formation of Gla residues is not restricted to prothrombin alone and is likely to occur for all zymogen forms of the enzymes of the coagulation cascade, thus enhancing the potency of the oral anticoagulants.

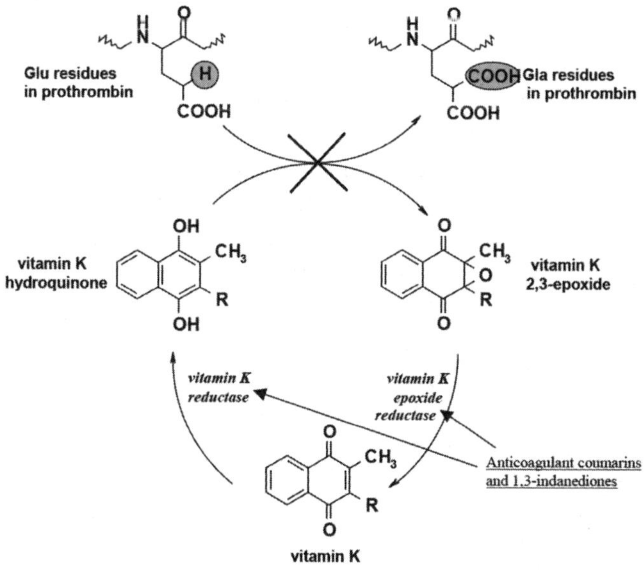

**Figure 33.** *Importance of vitamin K in the γ-carboxylation of glutamic acid (Glu) residues of prothrombin and inactivation of the process by anticoagulant coumarins and 1,3-indandiones. These anticoagulants inhibit vitamin K reductase and vitamin K epoxide reductase, enzymes with an important role in the oxidation-reduction process necessary for γ-carboxylation of prothrombin. Abbreviation: Gla, γ-carboxyglutamic acid.*

Coumarins and 1,3-indanediones do not inactivate thrombin and factor Xa that might have been formed before the administration of the oral anticoagulants. Thus, the antithrombotic effect of these molecules is not observed immediately. The observed slow onset is due to the time required for the body to eliminate predrug prothrombin blood levels (half-life, ~2.5 days). The longer duration of action is because of the time required by liver to resynthesize normal prothrombin following the suspension of oral anticoagulation therapy. Coumarins and 1,3-indandiones interact with certain drugs. For example, the action of oral anticoagulants can be enhanced by phenylbutazone and salicylates and antagonized by barbiturates and vitamin K. Another major risk factor for warfarin therapy is interaction with constituents of food. Spinach and collard greens (or green leafy vegetables) that contain substantial quantities of vitamin K affect the anticoagulant potency of warfarin when consumed in large quantities. Likewise, warfarin taken with cranberry juice, which contains several flavonoids known to bind many CYP isoenzymes, can have metabolic adverse effects.

## The Hirudins

While heparins and coumarins are indirect inhibitors of thrombin, the hirudins are direct thrombin inhibitors (DTIs). *Hirudin,* isolated in 1884 from the leech *Hirudo medicinalis,* is a polypeptide with 65 amino acid residues. Hirudin is the most potent thrombin ligand known to date, with a $K_I$ (inhibition constant) value of about 20 fM. Hirudin binds in an allosteric site of thrombin called anion-binding exosite 1 and in the active site of thrombin, thereby preventing thrombin hydrolysis of fibrinogen, which also has to bind in both of these sites for conversion to fibrin monomers. This process leads to the inhibition of clot formation. Yet, the very high affinity of hirudin for thrombin is problematic because of frequent bleeding episodes in patients during hirudin therapy. To reduce these problems, lepirudin and desirudin were designed, in which 2 residues at the *N*-terminus of hirudin are replaced with leucine-threonine and valine-valine, respectively, and tyrosine 63 does not bear the sulfate group present in native hirudin. Even these 2 hirudin analogs are associated with bleeding issues. Thus, a newer and smaller class of hirulogs, analogs of hirudin, called bivalirudin, was developed. It consists of 4 *N*-terminal residues and 12 *C*-terminal residues of hirudin connected by 4 glycine residues.

The major bleeding issues of the hirudins limit their use to patients with disease refractory to unfractionated heparin and patients with HIT. Another common problem is that they have a narrow therapeutic window. Hirudins also have some immunogenic risk because they are foreign peptides. The very high affinity of hirudin, lepirudin, and desirudin for thrombin makes them essentially irreversible drugs. There is no effective antidote available for reversing these complexes. Bivalirudin (**Figure 34**) binds thrombin with a $K_I$ of 1 to 2 nM, which is much weaker than hirudin. Yet, bivalirudin has a short half-life (25 minutes) because thrombin cleaves its arginine 3–proline 4 bond. Bivalirudin is considered superior to other hirudins because of its more predictable anticoagulant response and its lower immunogenicity. It is also considered a safer anticoagulant for hepatically and renally compromised patients because it can be hemodialyzed.

## The Peptidomimetics

*Peptidomimetics* are small, organic molecules that mimic the key peptide scaffold of a polypeptide therapeutic agent. Argatroban (**Figure 35**) is the first rationally designed, small-molecule, peptidomimetic inhibitor to reach the clinical setting; dabigatran etexilate is currently the only DTI available for oral use. It is a double prodrug form of dabigatran, which is a benzimidazole-based small-molecule inhibitor. Argatroban, approved for use in patients at high risk for HIT, is limited by its short plasma half-life (24 minutes). The 2 DTIs specifically target the active site of thrombin and, thus, function as competitive inhibitors. Thrombin recognizes an arginine at the P1 position, while prefers hydrophobic amino acids such as proline and phenylalanine at the P2 and P3 positions, respectively. (*Note:* The amino acid residue on the N-terminal side of the scissile bond is identified as P1 residues. Residues following the P1 residue on the N-terminal side of the scissile bond are called P2, P3, and so on.) The peptidomimetics typically contain a guanidine (or an amidine) moiety to mimic the P1 arginine side chain and an organic scaffold such as an alicyclic, aromatic, or heteroaromatic ring connected through amide or sulfonamide linker(s) to mimic the proline and phenylalanine residues at the P2 and P3 positions.

**H$_2$N-D-Phe-Pro-Arg-Pro-Gly-Gly-Gly-Gly-Asn-Gly**

|

**HOOC-Leu-Tyr-Glu-Glu-Pro-Ile-Glu-Glu-Phe-Asp**

**Bivalirudin**

**Figure 34.** *The sequence of bivalirudin. Abbreviations: Asp, aspartic acid; Glu, glutamic acid; Ile, isoleucine; Leu, leucine; Phe, phenylalanine; Pro, proline; Tyr, tyrosine.*

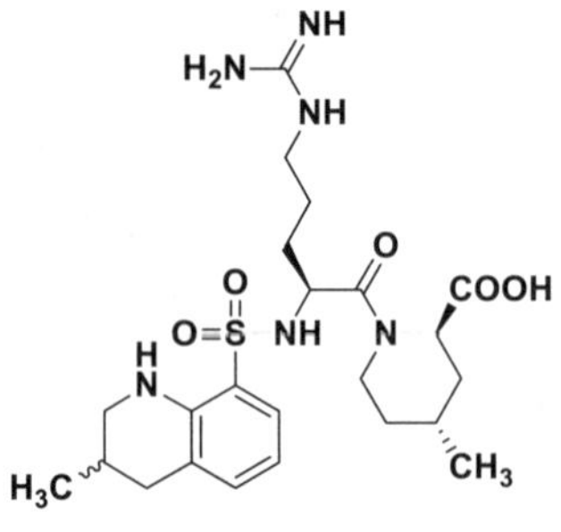

**Argatroban**

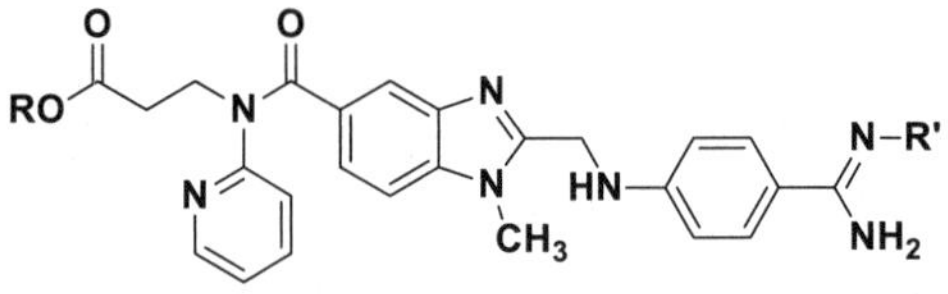

**Dabigatran etexilate R = -CH$_2$CH$_3$; R' = -COO-(CH$_2$)$_5$-CH$_3$
Dabigatran      R= -H;  R' = -H**

**Figure 35.** *Selected peptidomimetics that act as thrombin inhibitors.*

## Suggested Reading

Barrow JC, Duffy JL. Voltage-gated calcium channel antagonists for the central nervous system. *Annual Reports in Med Chem.* 45:3-18. doi: 10.1016/S0065-7743(10)45001-0.

Bauer KA. Selective inhibition of coagulation factors: advances in antithrombotic therapy. *Semin Thromb Hemost.* 2002;28(suppl 2):15-24.

Brown NJ, Vaughan DE. Angiotensin-converting enzyme inhibitors. *Circulation.* 1998;97:1411-1420.

Casu B, Lindahl U. Structure and biological interactions of heparin and heparan sulfate. *Adv Carbohydr Chem Biochem.* 2001;57:159-206.

Casu B, Torri G. Structural characterization of low molecular weight heparins. *Semin Thromb Hemost.* 1999;25(suppl 3):17-25.

Hirsh J, Dalen J, Anderson DR, et al. Oral anticoagulants: mechanism of action, clinical effectiveness, and optimal therapeutic range. *Chest.* 2001;119(1 suppl):8S-21S.

Kurup A, Garg R, Carini DJ, Hansch C. Comparative QSAR: angiotensin II antagonists. *Chem Rev.* 2001;101:2727-2750.

Piepho RW. Overview of the angiotensin-converting-enzyme inhibitors. *Am J Health Syst Pharm.* 2000;57(suppl 1):S3-S7.

Racine E. Differentiation of the low-molecular-weight heparins. *Pharmacotherapy.* 2001;21(6 Pt 2):62S-70S.

Siama K, Tousoulis D, Papageorgiou N, et al. Stable angina pectoris: current medical treatment. *Curr Pharm Design.* 2013;19(9):1569-1580.

Staessen JA, Wang J, Bianchi G, Birkenhager WH. Essential hypertension. *Lancet.* 2003;361:1629-1641.

## Discussion Topics

1. Describe the targets and effects of the following cardiovascular drugs:

   a. antianginal drugs

   b. antiarrhythmic drugs

   c. antihypertensive drugs

   d. anticoagulant drugs

2. Several agents prescribed as cardiovascular agents have multiple modes of action. Discuss agents falling into this category and which effects predominate.

3. As a healthcare provider, you must be aware of adverse effects your patients may have as a result of taking common medications. Discuss what these effects are and how you would moderate those effects.

4. Discuss what effects certain foods might have when combined with therapy, eg, anticoagulant therapy with warfarin.

5. In 2008, a major issue arose in relation to the contamination of clinically used heparin with oversulfated chondroitin sulfate. Discuss the possible structural reasons for contamination of heparin not being detected early enough.

6. The widely used drug sildenafil is an inhibitor of phosphodiesterase, which preserves the levels of nitric oxide in the bloodstream, resulting in muscle relaxation. Why is sildenafil not used as an antianginal agent?

# Chapter 9

# Anesthetic Agents
*by Nicole Damico, CRNA, MSNA, Michael D. Fallacaro, CRNA, DNS, and Lemont B. Kier, PhD*

Anesthetic agents are drugs that produce a loss of sensation in preparation for a surgical or invasive procedure that would be expected to produce pain, irritation, or discomfort. These drugs may be classified according to their route of administration and the generality of their effect. Three classes of anesthetic agents are discussed in this chapter: volatile anesthetics, intravenous induction agents, and local anesthetics.

The purpose of *volatile anesthetics* is to affect the response of the whole body to a procedure. These agents are also classified as complete, general, or nonspecific agents. The state of general anesthesia is characterized by unconsciousness, amnesia, analgesia, and immobility. The actions of this class of molecules are nonspecific. Volatile anesthetics are commonly referred to as anesthetic gases and are, with the exception of nitrous oxide, actually volatile liquids. Once vaporized, these agents are administered by inhalation and, ideally, excreted almost entirely by exhalation.

*Intravenous induction agents* are administered parenterally to induce, but not necessarily maintain, an anesthetic state and are mostly derived from the barbiturate, phencyclidine, and benzodiazepine structural families. In contrast with volatile anesthetics, induction agents act at discrete receptors and are eliminated by traditional metabolic pathways.

*Local anesthetics* are the third class of anesthetic drug molecules. These drugs produce regional anesthesia without having the central nervous system (CNS) effects of general anesthesia. Local anesthetics are administered by a variety of routes for the purpose of suppressing sensation in well-defined areas. Like intravenous induction agents, they act by influencing a specific receptor and are eliminated by metabolism and excretion. The use of local anesthetics allows a patient to remain conscious during the procedure.

Each class of anesthetic agents fulfills a special role in the practice of anesthesia. By using knowledge of the actions of these agents, clinicians can customize the route, duration, and depth of anesthesia for each clinical situation. The historical and mechanistic details of each class are presented, along with examples of drugs used in each class.

## Volatile Anesthetic Agents
Volatile anesthetics are a unique class of drugs because of their route of administration. Also known as general or nonspecific agents, they are intended to produce a partial or total loss of sensation throughout the body. Consciousness is

lost as well, in a dose-dependent manner. Volatile anesthetics act by depressing nervous function mediated through the CNS.

## Historical Background

The historical view of these drugs is of interest because it portrays a sequence of observation, discovery, development, and improvement that is characteristic of all drug categories in common use today. Humphrey Davy made an early observation in 1800 that nitrous oxide could alleviate painful sensation. This discovery opened the possibility of managing pain by the use of an inhaled gas. Soon thereafter, nitrous oxide was used in surgical procedures. In 1868, Edmund Andrews, a surgeon, introduced the use of oxygen along with nitrous oxide, pioneering the way to the current use of this combination.

The first use of ether (ie, diethyl ether) was by Crawford Long in 1842, who used this chemical for a minor operation. The use of ether as an anesthetic agent for major surgery began in 1846 at Massachusetts General Hospital, Boston, under the administration of a dentist, William Morton. For nearly 80 years, ether reigned as the anesthetic of choice, the standard to which all other substances holding anesthetic properties was compared. In time, however, disadvantages of ether became evident. The shortcomings of the early agents were initially overlooked because the management of pain was regarded as a near miracle. Eventually, as chemical knowledge and skills increased, it became possible to seek alternative volatile anesthetics in the search for molecules with improved characteristics.

The primary concerns with the use of ether stemmed from its flammability, irritation of the throat, the resulting excessive secretions, and the slow recovery time. These qualities eventually led to the demise of the use of ether and became the stimulus for further development of better inhalants. To find a better anesthetic, the ether structure was modified by the addition of halogen atoms. It was recognized that adding fluorine atoms decreased the flammability of the anesthetic with concomitant improvement in the pharmacokinetics of the drug. In 1956, the halogen-containing molecule, halothane, was introduced by Bryce-Smith, O'Brien, and Johnstone. A series of halogenated drugs followed that alleviated many of the problems with ether and other early anesthetics. The use of these agents led to the development of the class of agents currently in use.

Experiences with early anesthetic agents helped to identify the ideal characteristics used to guide the design of better drugs. These characteristics include the following:

- Nonflammable
- Production of adequate muscle relaxation
- Production of rapid and uncomplicated anesthesia
- No cardiovascular side effects
- Nontoxic
- Chemical and metabolic stability
- Sufficient potency for adequate induction and recovery oxygen supply
- Wide safety margin

# Stages of Anesthesia

In clinical use, volatile anesthetic drugs may produce 4 sequential stages of anesthesia. Historically, the signs and stages of anesthesia were first described by Guedel in his work with ether in 1937 and later enhanced by Gillespie in 1944. Each stage is a function of the concentration, time, administration technique, and molecular structure of the anesthetic used.

*Stage 1–Analgesia.* This stage involves mild cortical center depression in which procedures may be performed that do not require muscle relaxation. Not all anesthetics produce profound analgesia, but the common attribute among them is a loss of sensitivity to pain.

*Stage 2–Delirium.* This stage is characterized by excitement due to central depression of motor centers, leaving the autonomic nervous system dominant. Such effects as urinary incontinence and increases in heart rate, blood pressure, and respiratory rate are seen in this stage.

The first 2 stages of anesthesia are called the *induction period.* Ideally, these stages are rapidly traversed to avoid the problems associated with them and to enter the stage where most surgeries are performed, Stage 3.

*Stage 3–Surgical anesthesia.* Four sublevels, or planes, of anesthesia characterize this stage:

        Plane 1: Loss of spinal reflexes
        Plane 2: Decreased muscle reflexes
        Plane 3: Paralysis of intercostal muscles
        Plane 4: Disappearance of muscle tone

*Stage 4–Respiratory paralysis, premortem.* This stage indicates a toxic overdose involving severe cardiovascular and respiratory depression and, obviously, is to be avoided.

# Pharmacokinetics and Pharmacodynamics of Volatile Anesthetics

Volatile anesthetic agents are administered by using various anesthesia delivery systems that regulate oxygen and carbon dioxide flow while vital signs such as respiration and blood pressure are monitored. The administration, distribution, metabolism, and excretion of all drugs follow pathways and kinetics that are controlled by the structures of the individual molecules. In the case of volatile anesthetics, entry into the CNS is the objective of any such agent. The general process is illustrated in **Figure 1**.

Inhalation of an anesthetic agent brings it to the alveoli in the lungs where it diffuses through the thin membranes of the capillaries surrounding the alveoli and enters the blood. Once in the circulating blood, the gas is available to diffuse from the arterial system, through the blood-brain barrier (BBB), into the CNS tissue. The gas exhibits its anesthetic effect in the CNS tissue according to a number of hypotheses. The reversal of this process leads to exhalation of the gas.

**Figure 1.** *Passage of an anesthetic gas into and out of the central nervous system (CNS).*

Each step in this scheme represents the arrival, accumulation, and departure of the anesthetic gas in an anatomical region of the body. These regions can be viewed as compartments. As the agent accumulates in a compartment, a tension (or gradient) builds that drives the agent to leave that compartment and pass through a membrane to the next compartment. This tension between 2 compartments will continue to exist until there is equilibrium between them. The rate at which equilibrium is reached depends on the rate of administration and concentration of the agent in that compartment. In addition, the rate of diffusion depends on the chemical structure of the gas, being faster with increased hydrophobic character of the molecule.

To maintain a relatively constant concentration of gas in the appropriate CNS areas, each compartment shown in Figure 1 should have approximately the same tension. The alveolar anesthetic concentration, when all compartments are in equilibrium, is a good descriptor of the state of tension of the gas in the CNS. By monitoring the concentration of anesthetic gas in the alveoli, an estimate can be made of the CNS concentration and the need to increase or decrease the delivery rate. The rate at which the alveolar concentration, $F_A$, approaches the inspired concentration, $F_I$, expressed as the ratio of these 2 concentrations, reflects the speed with which the agent enters the CNS. This ratio for several anesthetic agents is shown in **Figure 2**.

The alveolar concentration required to achieve anesthesia is one way of comparing the potencies of anesthetic agents. An understanding of the relative potency of anesthetics enables clinicians to correlate the uptake and distribution of anesthetics with their pharmacodynamic effects. Potency is commonly expressed in terms of the minimum alveolar concentration (MAC) of the anesthetic compound. For inhaled anesthetics, the MAC is the alveolar concentration of anesthetic at 1 atmosphere (atm) that prevents movement in 50% of subjects in response to a painful stimulus. Factors that increase the MAC include increased central neurotransmitter levels from substances such as monoamine oxidase inhibitors, amphetamines, cocaine, ephedrine, and levodopa. Hyperthermia and hypernatremia have also been associated with an increased MAC. Factors demonstrated to decrease MAC include age older than 30 years, metabolic acidosis, induced hypotension (mean arterial pressure <50 mm Hg), hypothermia, hyponatremia, pregnancy, and substances such as other anesthetic agents, narcotics, ethanol, and barbiturates. Several values of MAC are shown in **Table 1**.

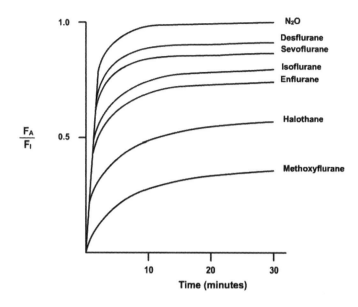

**Figure 2.** *The idealized alveolar concentration–inspired concentration ($F_A/F_I$) ratio for several anesthetic agents.*

**Table 1.** *Physical properties of volatile anesthetics.*

| Anesthetic | MAC (volume %) | Boiling point (760 mm Hg) | Vapor pressure (mm Hg, 20°C) | Liquid density (g/mL, 20°C–25°C) | Vapor/liquid (mL) |
|---|---|---|---|---|---|
| Desflurane | 6.0 | 24 | 664 | 1.45 | 211 |
| Enflurane | 1.7 | 57 | 175 | 1.52 | 198 |
| Halothane | 0.8 | 50 | 243 | 1.87 | 227 |
| Isoflurane | 1.2 | 49 | 238 | 1.50 | 196 |
| Methoxyflurane | 0.2 | 105 | 23 | 1.49 | 208 |
| Nitrous oxide | 104 | −88 | − | − | − |
| Sevoflurane | 1.7 | 59 | 160 | 1.51 | 181 |

Abbreviation: MAC, minimum alveolar concentration.

**Figures 3 and 4** show that the relative solubility of the gas in blood influences the onset, potency, and duration of the anesthetic effect. If the gas is quite soluble in the blood, ie, hydrophilic, it will quickly dissolve in the alveolar capillary blood. However, the gas will not partition through the BBB very quickly because the BBB is relatively lipophilic. The gas will tend to remain in the blood, and the onset of the anesthetic effect will be slow. Once the gas passes through the BBB and into the relatively hydrophilic brain tissue, it will tend to dissolve and remain longer in the brain. Thus, the anesthetic effect is relatively long. This effect is portrayed in Figure 3.

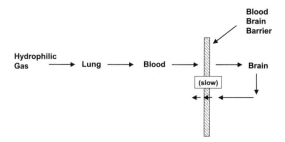

**Figure 3.** *A hydrophilic gas is rapidly soluble in blood, slowly passes the blood-brain barrier (BBB) and is slow to enter the brain. It remains longer in the brain, returning slowly through the BBB. The effects are a slow onset and long recovery.*

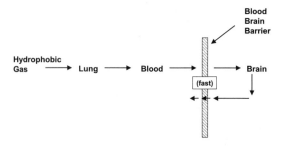

**Figure 4.** *Dynamic behavior of a hydrophobic/water-insoluble gas. The gas rapidly crosses the blood-brain barrier (BBB), entering and leaving the brain quickly.*

In contrast, a volatile molecule that is not very soluble in blood, ie, hydrophobic, preferring solubility in lipoid media, exhibits different behavior. In this case, the molecule will pass the BBB rather quickly, being more soluble in that medium than in the aqueous blood. A rapid onset of activity in the brain is to be expected. However, the molecule will quickly return through the BBB and be excreted (Figure 4). The duration of action is, therefore, shorter than in the case of a hydrophilic drug. The physical property of partitioning strongly influences the temporal characteristics of the volatile anesthetic agents.

## The Hydrophilic or Hydrophobic Character of Molecules

A hydrophilic molecule has a strong affinity with water because both molecules have relatively polar atoms. Examples of hydrophilic molecules include low-molecular-weight alcohols and amines. A hydrophilic molecule will have a corresponding aversion to bonding with lipoid molecules, such as alkanes and fats. A hydrophilic molecule will be surrounded by water molecules (hydrated) in the presence of water; hence, it is easily dissolved in this solvent. It will not be soluble to a great extent in a hydrophobic solvent such as hexane or benzene. **Figure 5** shows a hydrophilic molecule in the presence of water.

In contrast, a hydrophobic molecule will not be associated strongly with a polar solvent like water. It will tend to remain unattached or be associated with a hydrophobic solvent. **Figure 6** depicts this relationship between water and a hydrophobic molecule. These physical attributes of anesthetic gases and volatile liquids manifest in the clinical characteristics that dictate their use. The hydrophilic and hydrophobic states of anesthetic gases are quantified by a series of partition coefficients (the ratio in which a substance distributes between 2 or more partitions or phases) as shown in **Table 2**.

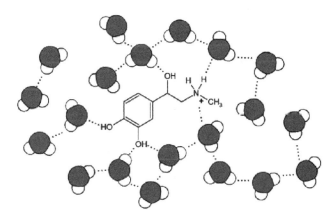

**Figure 5.** *Epinephrine is a hydrophilic drug and forms many bonds with water, making a solution.*

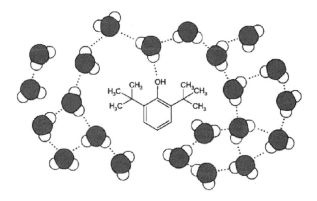

**Figure 6.** *Propofol is a hydrophobic anesthetic agent and forms few bonds with water.*

**Table 2.** *Partition coefficients of selected volatile anesthetics at 37°C*

| Anesthetic | Blood-Gas | Brain-Blood | Fat-Blood | Oil-Gas |
|---|---|---|---|---|
| Desflurane | 0.42 | 1.29 | 27.2 | 18.7 |
| Enflurane | 1.91 | 1.4 | 36 | 98.5 |
| Halothane | 2.54 | 1.9 | 51 | 224 |
| Isoflurane | 1.46 | 1.6 | 45 | 90.8 |
| Methoxyflurane | 12 | 2.0 | 49 | 970 |
| Nitrous oxide | 0.47 | 1.1 | 2.3 | 1.4 |
| Sevoflurane | 0.69 | 1.7 | 47.5 | 53.4 |

## The Second-Gas Effect

It has been observed that administration of a high concentration of a gas promotes an increase in the alveolar concentration of a second gas. This *second-gas effect* is particularly prominent when nitrous oxide is used as the initial, high-concentration anesthetic agent and enhances the uptake of a second volatile anesthetic agent. To achieve an alveolar tension in the lung, a balance between delivery of anesthetic by ventilation and uptake of anesthetic by blood and tissues must be considered. The principle of the concentration effect states that the greater the inspired concentration of a gas, the more rapidly the alveolar partial pressure of that gas approaches the inhaled partial pressure. This greater inspired partial pressure offsets uptake in the blood and speeds the rate at which the alveolar tension increases.

The concentration effect results from an augmentation of tracheal gas inflow. The effect reflects a concentration of the inhaled anesthetic in a smaller lung volume because of the rapid uptake of all gases in the lung. At the same time, anesthetic delivery via tracheal inflow is increased to fill the vacuum produced by the uptake of gases by the pulmonary vascular system. As alveolar ventilation increases, more anesthetic is delivered to the alveoli, thus diminishing the inspired-to-alveolar concentration difference. In essence, 2 complementary methods exist to increase anesthetic delivery and "deepen" the anesthetic: (1) increase the inspired concentration of the agent, and/or (2) increase alveolar ventilation.

## Mechanism of Anesthesia

The exact details of the action of volatile anesthetics at the molecular level are unknown. These agents do not act at a distinct receptor, but are nonspecific. It is known that volatile anesthetics have a prominent role in the excitatory and inhibitory cells governing the critical balance that we know as consciousness. In general, anesthetic agents inhibit transmission among nerves in the CNS. Two types of nerves are targets for anesthetics and, indeed, many of the depressants used in therapy. The first of these nerve types are the excitatory or pyramidal cells. The neurotransmitters for these types of nerve cells are glutamate and acetylcholine. The transmission of these molecules across the synapse to the NMDA receptor results in an excitatory response from these cells. The second system involved is the inhibitory pathway, mediated primarily by the neurotransmitter γ-aminobutyric acid (GABA). Binding of GABA to these cells results in decreased nervous transmission.

General anesthetics act by inhibiting excitatory cells and reinforcing inhibitory cells. These effects are not directly on the nerve receptors mediated by glutamate, NMDA, or GABA. They are nonspecific in that their structures do not contain pharmacophores that prescribe a specific drug-receptor pattern. The action of the volatile anesthetics is a function of their physical properties, specifically their hydrophobic-hydrophilic character. How this property manifests is the subject of much study. A unitary hypothesis supported by the Meyer-Overton rule of lipid solubility postulates that all inhalation agents share a common mechanism of action at the molecular level. Another theory is the lateral phase separation theory which postulates that cell membrane conductance disturbances lead to inhibition of synaptic function.

A proposed theory for the mechanism of action of the volatile anesthetics focuses on the landscape around receptors, particularly those mediated by GABA and glutamate. It is proposed that the anesthetic effect is not due to a direct encounter of the volatile anesthetic agent with these receptors, but is influenced in some way by a change in the rate of diffusion of the neurotransmitters to these sites. The protein side-chain landscape of these receptors provides a mosaic of varying hydrophobic-hydrophilic influences on water near the protein surface. This landscape may facilitate the 2-dimensional diffusion of neurotransmitters to the receptor via pathways (or chreodes) through water cavities created by the varying hydrophobic-hydrophilic states among the side chains. The effect of the volatile anesthetic drugs may be due to a possible disruption of this normal diffusion, leading to an inferior level of neurotransmitter-receptor encounters, producing the effects of anesthesia.

## Early Volatile Anesthetic Agents

Diethyl ether (**Figure 7**) is a low-boiling-point (34.6°C) member of the class of symmetrical alkyl ether compounds, characterized by the presence of an ether group between 2 equivalent alkyl fragments. Diethyl ether is commonly referred to as "ether." It is quite volatile, having a vapor pressure of 291 mm Hg at 20°C. The lone pair electrons of the ether oxygen atom are accessible to water and other proton donors. Because of this accessibility, ether and other low-molecular-weight alkyl ethers are slightly water soluble. At 25°C, ether is soluble up to about 6% in water. Air-ether mixtures of more than 1.85 volumes percent are explosive. When shaken under absolutely dry conditions, ether can generate enough static electricity to start a fire. The disadvantages of ether fall into 2 categories: safety and adverse effects. The safety of ether is a major concern because of its flammability and explosive properties under certain circumstances. Careful management of equipment and procedures can minimize this risk, but ether always poses a potential hazard. The second set of problems involves the effects of ether in the body. Ether produces a slow induction and a prolonged recovery. It may be irritating to the respiratory tract, causing excessive secretions, and it may cause nausea and vomiting. Ether is no longer used clinically as an anesthetic, but its structure is the basis for many of the currently used anesthetics.

Another pioneering event in the history of pain management was the discovery of chloroform as an anesthetic. The biological problems associated with this molecule, however, put it in the same category as ether, both becoming prototype molecules on which progress toward better compounds was made. The primary problem with chloroform is its narrow safety margin. There are potential problems with liver and kidney toxicity at moderate doses due to extensive metabolism of the molecule. The circulatory effects of chloroform include arrhythmia and hypotension. Chloroform is quite irritating to the respiratory tract and mucous membranes. Chloroform is a haloalkane–a dense liquid boiling at 61°C–and is unreactive and nonflammable. It is soluble in water only to 0.5 volumes percent. Chloroform is no longer used as an anesthetic, but the fact that this haloalkane is nonflammable has led to subsequent anesthetics having halogen atoms in their structures.

Nitrous oxide, a gaseous anesthetic agent, has a low potency. Therefore, nitrous oxide is often used with other agents as a second gas. Known as "laughing gas," it first found use in dentistry and childbirth and is now the only inorganic anesthetic gas in clinical use. Long-term use, in which it is misused as a "recreational drug" for example, may lead to impairment in DNA synthesis and the inhibition of methionine synthase. Nitrous oxide is a natural constituent of the earth's atmosphere. It is stable and relatively inert at room temperature but supports combustion. It is soluble at 2 atm and 20°C in 1.5 L of water. It is distributed to all body tissues and equilibrates rapidly. At higher doses, nitrous oxide can injure the hematopoietic system, fetus, brain, liver, and kidneys.

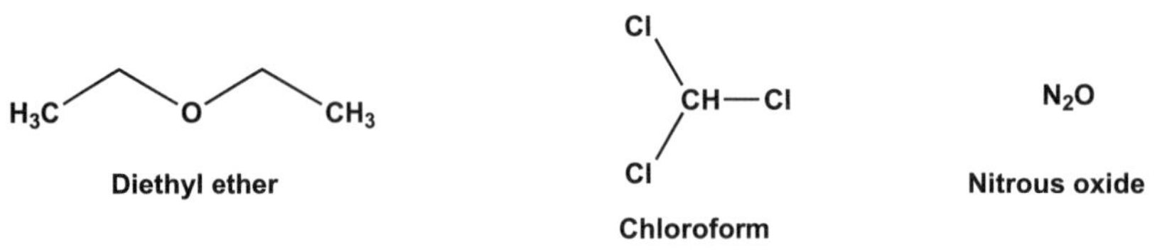

**Figure 7.** *Structures of early anesthetic agents.*

# Structure-Activity Analyses Leading to Haloethers and Haloalkanes

The flammability of ether, plus its unfavorable time course and recovery characteristics, encouraged the search for improved anesthetic agents. It was observed that chloroform was useful as an anesthetic agent and that it was not flammable, but chloroform was irritating and toxic to the liver. The possibility of improving ether and lower-order alkanes was considered in the light of these 2 early anesthetic drugs. Incorporation of halogen atoms into the alkane and ether structures accomplished 2 goals: (1) elimination of flammability and (2) increased potency and more rapid action because of the hydrophobic character and reduced blood solubility. Of the halogens, fluorine, chlorine, and bromine were explored as substituents. It was found that the length of the molecule should be approximately 4 atoms and that the molecular shape should be roughly elliptical with a length-to-width ratio of about 1.5.

The addition of halogen atoms to the basic alkane or ether molecule increases the hydrophobic character of the molecule. The higher the atomic weight of the halogen, the greater the hydrophobicity of the resulting molecule. A blend of 2 or 3 different halogen atoms, singly or in multiples, has been extensively studied for potency, safety, and response characteristics. The improvement of the properties of these agents due to the addition of halogen atoms is somewhat offset by the fact that some of the haloalkanes and haloethers are not entirely eliminated from the body during exhalation. Some are metabolized in the liver to products that may themselves produce toxic effects under some circumstances. Improving elimination by exhalation has been another target in the design of improved anesthetic gases. Several individual haloalkanes and haloethers are discussed here, and their properties are summarized and compared in Tables 1 and 2.

Halothane, a halogenated alkane, was introduced in the 1950s and has become the reference standard inhalation agent. It is nonflammable, has high potency, and has a ratio of blood-to-gas partitioning of 2.54. It is stable in the presence of soda lime but is slowly decomposed by light to hydrochloric acid, phosgene, and other halogenated products. Thymol, used as a preservative in halothane, slows the oxidative decomposition of the agent. Halothane is moderately volatile, with a boiling point of 56°C. The induction is rapid, and the recovery period is short. Halothane is largely eliminated by exhalation with 20% elimination via liver metabolism. The metabolism of halothane is shown in **Figure 8**.

There is a low incidence of hepatic necrosis when halothane is used. However, in the absence of oxygen, the agent is oxidized by the liver P-450 enzyme system primarily to trifluoroacetic acid in a reductive metabolic process that can result in hepatotoxic end products. Although it is extremely rare, "halothane hepatitis" has been reported in select populations, including persons exposed to multiple halothane anesthetics, persons with preexisting liver disease or sepsis, and persons exposed to hepatocytic hypoxia.

There is a somewhat narrow safety margin with halothane use, with side effects being hypotension and respiratory depression. Halothane gives moderate muscle relaxation and increases cranial blood flow. It is an especially potent bronchodilator, and it sensitizes the myocardium to catecholamine-induced arrhythmias. It is used with nitrous oxide or opioids on occasion.

Methoxyflurane, a halogenated methyl ethyl ether, has relatively low volatility, boiling at 105°C. It is blood soluble; hence, induction is slow and the excitatory phase and recovery are prolonged. However, methoxyflurane is the most potent of the volatile anesthetics. It is stable in the presence of soda lime and is not flammable or explosive. Methoxyflurane gives very good analgesia and good muscle relaxation. About 70% is metabolized in the liver, giving the products shown in **Figure 9**. The fluoride ion contributes to renal failure. An additional metabolite, oxalic acid, may lead to renal damage because of its chelating properties and free fluoride ion production.

Enflurane is a halogenated ether and a volatile liquid with a boiling point of 57°C. The blood solubility is less than that of halothane. It can be supplemented with a short-acting barbiturate. There is a low frequency of cardiovascular effects with enflurane use. Enflurane is chemically stable and excreted by exhalation, with about 5% metabolized according to the scheme shown in **Figure 10**. Defluorination occurs far less frequently with enflurane than with methoxyflurane. Furthermore, enflurane is unlikely to cause renal dysfunction. At high doses, CNS side effects can include clonic-tonic activity. Hence, enflurane should be avoided in people with epilepsy.

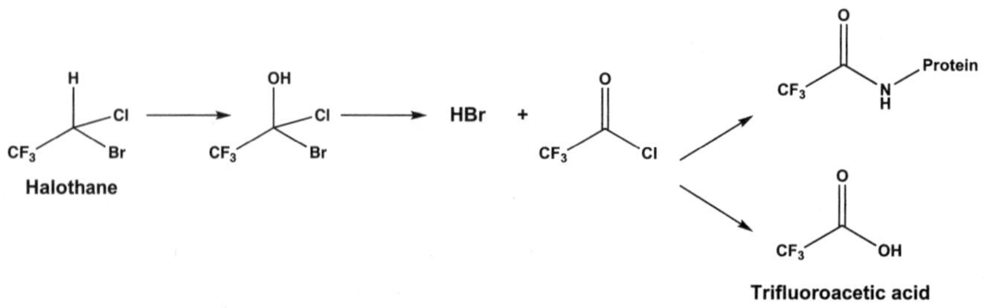

**Figure 8.** *The metabolism of halothane.*

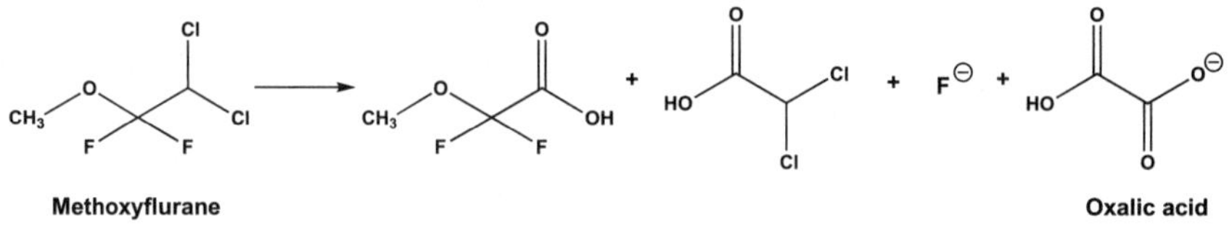

**Figure 9.** *Metabolic products of methoxyflurane.*

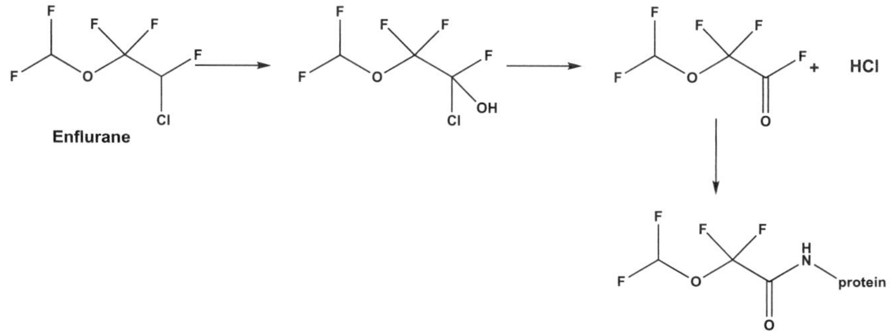

**Figure 10.** *The metabolism of enflurane.*

Isoflurane is a fluoro-chloro ether and has a boiling point of 48°C to 49°C (**Figure 11**). An isomer of enflurane, isoflurane has similar clinical properties. Isoflurane produces minimal cardiac depression. The dose-dependent respiratory depression seen with isoflurane is similar to that seen with other volatile anesthetic agents. The incidence of clonic seizure activity is absent, and isoflurane relaxes skeletal muscles. No kidney or liver damage has been reported with the use of isoflurane. Isoflurane is less soluble in blood than is halothane; hence, it partitions favorably into lipoid tissue. Isoflurane has a rapid onset of activity (7-10 minutes) and may be used with inductive agents. The odor of isoflurane may limit its inhalation rate. Isoflurane is chemically stable, nonflammable, and metabolized only 0.2%, thereby obviating many of the organ toxicity–related side effects resulting from this class of compounds. The (+) stereoisomer of isoflurane is about 50% more potent than the (–) isomer, supporting proposed mechanisms involving a specific receptor target.

Desflurane was more recently introduced as an ultra–short-acting, general anesthetic agent. It has similar characteristics to those of isoflurane, the difference being the substitution of a fluorine atom for a chlorine atom found on isoflurane. Desflurane has low blood solubility; hence, it produces rapid induction and recovery. The vapor pressure of desflurane is 681 mm Hg at 20°C, and it boils at room temperature at higher altitudes. A custom-heated and pressurized vaporizer has been developed to deal with these physicochemical properties. Very little of the administered dose is metabolized; hence, the toxicity is low (**Figure 12**). Desflurane is a potent anesthetic with a rapid onset (1-2 minutes) and elimination, primarily because of its very low solubility and high vapor pressure.

Sevoflurane is an anesthetic agent similar to desflurane. Sevoflurane is a volatile liquid with no pungent odor and a blood-gas solubility of 0.69. The low solubility of sevoflurane permits rapid onset of action (within 2 minutes) and elimination. These properties make sevoflurane well suited for inhalational induction of anesthesia, hence its widespread use in pediatric patients. Because of its moderate vapor pressure (160 mm Hg at 20°C), sevoflurane can be used in a conventional, nonheated vaporizer. There is some decomposition of sevoflurane in soda lime, producing a potentially nephrotoxic end product in animal models. About 5% of the administered drug is metabolized in the liver, with no reported adverse renal effects in humans (**Figure 13**).

## Intravenous Induction Agents

When inducing anesthesia, it is desirable to move the patient through the excitatory stage of anesthesia into the anesthetic stage as quickly as possible. This need is often accomplished by intravenously administering an induction agent that passes into the CNS rapidly to act at key receptors, producing the desired state. These induction agents are less useful for prolonged anesthesia. Induction agents also reduce the levels of general anesthetic agent required for prolonged anesthesia. Several classes of drugs are used as intravenous induction agents and are described in the following paragraphs.

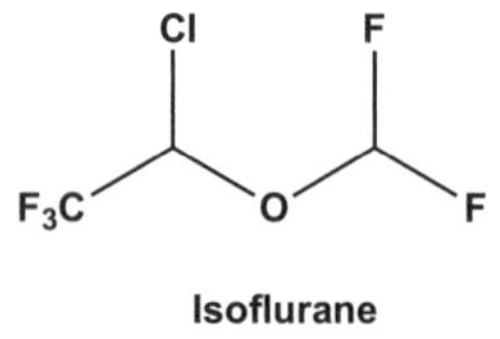

**Figure 11.** *The structure of isoflurane.*

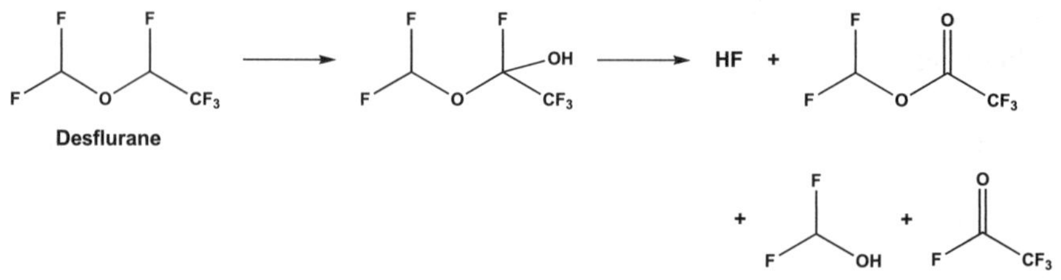

**Figure 12.** *The metabolism of desflurane.*

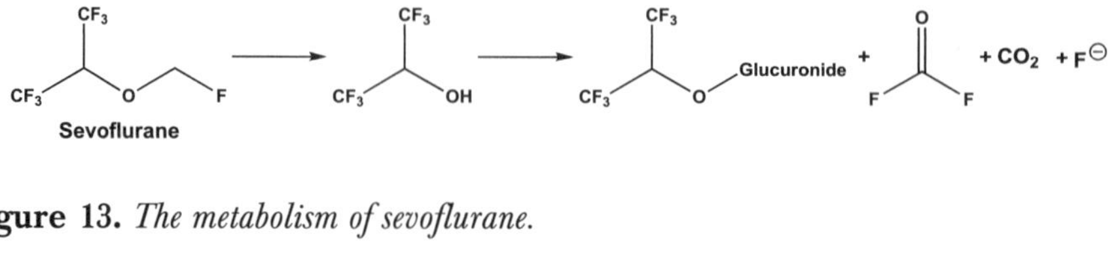

**Figure 13.** *The metabolism of sevoflurane.*

# Barbiturates

Barbituric acid is formed from the condensation of urea and malonic acid. This compound has no intrinsic CNS depressant activity. Drugs that are derivatives of barbituric acid are categorized as barbiturates. Barbituric acid is acidic by virtue of its ability to tautomerize to an enolic form (**Figure 14**). The enolic tautomer is moderately acidic and is responsible for the salt-forming ability of the molecule.

# Mechanism of Action

The mechanism of action of barbiturates is linked to postsynaptic enhancement of GABA, an inhibitory neurotransmitter in the CNS. Barbiturates result in the enhancement of chloride ion movement into the nerve cells through ion channels. This movement of chloride results in the hyperpolarization of nerve cells.

# Structure-Activity Relationships

Modifications of the barbiturate structure produce changes in properties that make these molecules selectively useful for different clinical situations. Substitutions on the barbituric acid molecule that influence the relative hydrophobicity or hydrophilicity of the molecule result in different rates of absorption into the CNS and through cell walls. Any structural change that leads to an increase in the hydrophobicity of barbiturates produces a more rapid onset of action and a shorter duration of action. Two common structural changes that result in more hydrophobic molecules are used:

1. The replacement of the 2-keto oxygen atom of the barbituric acid molecule with a sulfur atom produces thiobarbiturates. Thiobarbiturates have higher lipophilicity, a more rapid onset, and a shorter duration of action than oxybarbiturates.

2. By replacing both hydrogen atoms at position 5 with alkyl, aryl, or arylalkyl groups, sedative-hypnotic activity is produced. These derivatives of barbituric acid are known as oxybarbiturates, or as true barbiturates. Insoluble in water, oxybarbiturates are soluble in nonpolar solvents such as chloroform and oil. Alterations in side-chain length will affect potency, onset time, and duration of action.

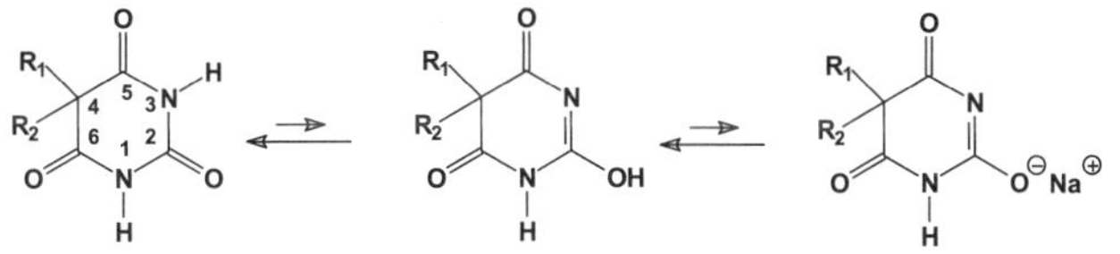

**Figure 14.** *Keto-enol tautomerism of barbituric acids. The presence of the enolic tautomer (far right) imparts acidity to this class of molecules.*

The ultra–short-acting barbiturate methohexital has a more rapid onset of action and a shorter duration than phenobarbital (**Figure 15**). The popularity of methohexital is not as great as that of the thiobarbiturates because it can cause excitatory movements on induction, pain on injection, hiccough, and seizures. The addition of a methyl group at N-3 confers some convulsant activity, such as involuntary muscular movement. Methohexital is used primarily for the induction of anesthesia. The spontaneous muscle movements following administration may be influenced by the total amount of drug given and the rapid rate of injection. Hepatic removal of methohexital is 3 times greater than that of thiopental. Hence, hepatic blood flow is a major determinant in methohexital clearance from the body. The pharmacokinetics of thiopental and methohexital are similar. Redistribution is the most important determinant in the termination of effects for both drugs. Methohexital is 2.5 times more potent than the thiobarbiturates, whereas the incidence of pain on injection is 5% compared with 1% to 2% for the thiobarbiturates.

Thiopental and thiamylal are the 2 most widely used inductive barbiturates. Thiamylal is closely related to thiopental in pharmacokinetics and pharmacodynamics. These drugs are identical in terms of potency, onset of action, duration, and respiratory and cardiac effects. The usual induction dose of these agents is 3 to 4 mg/kg. They produce few excitatory symptoms, have a rapid onset (30-60 seconds) and a short duration of action (5-30 minutes), and are associated with little pain on injection. Thiopental and thiamylal have few side effects.

## Pharmacokinetics of Barbiturates

Barbiturates are bound to plasma proteins (primarily to plasma albumin) in a reversible manner. This binding has a substantial effect on the temporal course of action of these drugs because bound drugs are unable to cross the BBB membranes. The greater the amount of unbound drug available, the faster and more extensive the effect produced. Thiopental is approximately 80% protein bound. When competition with other drugs for protein-binding sites

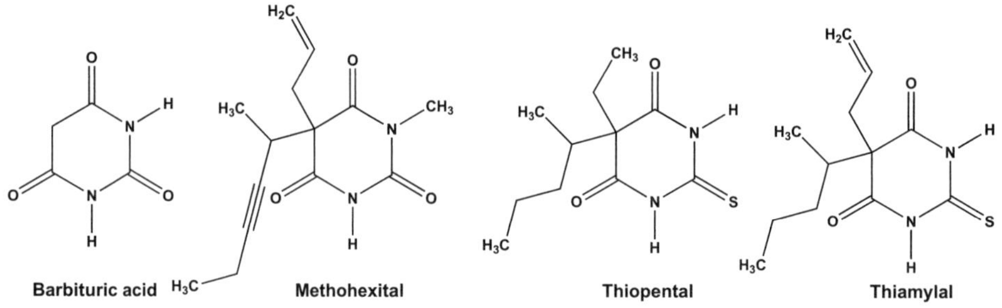

**Figure 15.** *Inductive barbiturates.*

occurs between thiopental and drugs such as naproxen, aspirin, indomethacin, and warfarin, the unbound fraction of thiopental is increased. The greater the amount of free (unbound) drug, the shorter the duration of action. Physiological pH favors the un-ionized fraction of thiopental. The high lipid solubility of thiopental accounts for its rapid movement across the BBB and the quick onset of anesthesia produced. Phenobarbital has lower lipid solubility, a characteristic that accounts for its slower onset of action. **Table** 3 summarizes these attributes for the commonly used intravenous induction barbiturates.

To cross cellular membranes, drugs must be un-ionized and not bound to plasma proteins. The dissociation constant ($pK_a$) of the drug and the pH of the medium determine the proportion of compound that is ionized versus un-ionized. In the extracellular fluid, thiopental is un-ionized (neutral). This un-ionized moiety is able to easily cross the BBB. The $pK_a$ of 7.6 of thiopental is close to the physiological pH of 7.4. Because formation of the un-ionized, pharmacologically active thiopental compound depends on the pH, tissue pH exerts some control over the amount of active compound formed. The $pK_a$ of thiopental is close to physiological pH, so 61% of the compound exists in the un-ionized state at pH 7.4. Intracellular pH is more acidic than extracellular pH, creating a difference in concentration of ionized and un-ionized thiopental on either side of the cellular membrane. Acidosis increases the amount of un-ionized thiopental in the extracellular fluid and allows greater diffusion across membranes into tissues.

Barbiturates are weak acids and are usually combined with anhydrous sodium carbonate to increase water solubility (Figure 14). Barbiturates are reconstituted with water or 0.09% sodium chloride. The resulting solution has a pH of 10.5. If an acidic solution or lactated Ringer's solution is used for reconstitution, the barbiturate will precipitate. Opioids, catecholamines, and muscle relaxant formulations, all of which are acidic, are incompatible with barbiturates because of the required alkalinity of the barbiturate solution. This alkalinity also confers a substantial bacteriostatic property, and a thiopental solution has been shown to remain stable at room temperature for up to 2 weeks.

**Table 3.** *Ionization and protein binding of induction barbiturates.*

| Drug | pKₐ | Un-ionized at normal body pH (%) | Protein bound (%) |
|------|-----|----------------------------------|-------------------|
| Thiopental | 7.6 | 61 | 65-86 |
| Methohexital | 7.9 | 75 | 73 |
| Phenobarbital | 7.3 | 40 | 50 |

Abbreviation: pKa, dissociation constant.

The reason behind the rapid termination of anesthetic effect has been extensively examined. For example, pharmacokinetic models demonstrate that less than 20% of the injected dose of thiopental is lost through metabolism. Redistribution of the drug from the central compartment, not hepatic metabolism, is most likely responsible for lowered plasma and brain concentrations. The most important metabolic pathway for thiopental involves oxidation of the side-chain groups at the C-5 position. This oxidation produces thiopental carboxylic acid, which is not pharmacologically active. Thiobarbiturates can also undergo desulfuration to the corresponding oxybarbiturate (pentobarbital) and further breakdown to inactive metabolites.

## Benzodiazepines

The benzodiazepine drugs share several structural features: (1) the benzodiazepine ring system, (2) nitrogen atoms at positions 1 and 4, (3) a phenyl group at position 5, and (4) an electronegative atom or group of atoms at position 7. Benzodiazepines are used in many clinical situations because of their low incidence of side effects and their multiple pharmacological properties. These activities include sedation, hypnosis, muscle relaxation, antianxiety effects, anticonvulsant effects, amnesia, and, most recently, anesthesia induction. This section focuses on the use of benzodiazepines in anesthesia.

Diazepam, one of the most well-known benzodiazepines, was synthesized in 1959. During the next 2 decades the pharmacological activities of the benzodiazepines were explored. A later benzodiazepine to be developed was midazolam, which was the first molecule of this class to be formulated for anesthesia use. The benzodiazepines available for clinical use have different potencies, pharmacokinetics, and intensities of their associated clinical properties. To date, more than 2,000 benzodiazepines have been synthesized and studied as clinical drug candidates.

Benzodiazepine binding sites are found in the olfactory bulb, cerebral cortex, cerebellum, and substantia nigra, with lesser concentrations in the lower brainstem and spinal cord. Benzodiazepine clinical effects are a result of their occupation of the benzodiazepine receptors within a complex of receptors on the synaptic membrane of the effector neuron. This complex modulates GABA, the major inhibitory neurotransmitter in the CNS. When benzodiazepine binding sites are occupied, the chloride channel opening is increased and neuronal transmission is inhibited.

Diazepam (**Figure 16**) is administered orally, intravenously, and intramuscularly. Diazepam is extremely lipid soluble, a characteristic that promotes extensive tissue distribution. Diazepam is a long-lasting benzodiazepine and has a slow distribution half-life. These properties limit the usefulness of diazepam as an acceptable induction agent. The volume of distribution of diazepam is large, a characteristic of all benzodiazepines, and it binds extensively to plasma proteins. The termination

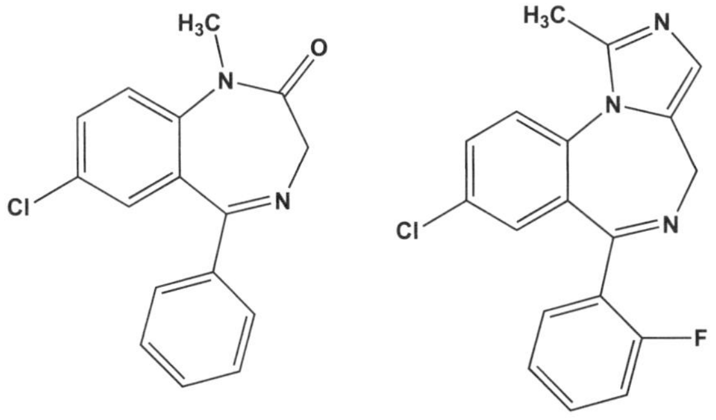

**Figure 16.** *Benzodiazepines used in anesthesia.*

of action of diazepam is caused by redistribution, and its total body clearance is dependent on hepatic metabolism. Diazepam is demethylated to nordiazepam, which is an active metabolite. Although nordiazepam is less potent than the parent drug, it is responsible for a prolonged effect as a result of its slower metabolism. Diazepam is also hydroxylated to give 3-hydroxydiazepam and then demethylated to oxazepam, which is also pharmacologically active. The metabolites of diazepam are excreted in the urine.

Midazolam is shorter acting than diazepam but has similar potency. The chemical structure of midazolam differs from that of the classic benzodiazepines in that it has an imidazole ring. Midazolam is quite lipophilic and acts rapidly. The molecule is quickly metabolized by hepatic microsomal oxidative mechanisms, contributing to its short duration of action. The metabolites do not contribute substantially to the pharmacologic effects of midazolam or its duration of action. The metabolites of midazolam, primarily hydroxylated compounds, are excreted in the urine as glucuronide conjugates.

Oral midazolam is rapidly absorbed and subject to first-pass hepatic extraction. Intramuscular injection produces increased bioavailability of the drug, and peak plasma concentrations are reached within 45 minutes of an intramuscular injection. The pharmacological effects of midazolam include all actions common to benzodiazepines, such as anticonvulsant effects, hypnosis, amnesia, muscle relaxant effects, and anxiolysis.

## Miscellaneous Anesthetic Induction Agents

In the search for the ideal induction agent, phencyclidine and its analogs were introduced into clinical practice. They were deemed unacceptable, however, because they caused serious psychotic disturbances, including hallucinations and delirium. Continued research into the congeners of phencyclidine produced ketamine, which was found to be satisfactory as an inductive agent.

Ketamine is a structural analog of phencyclidine that produces what is commonly referred to as a "dissociative state" of anesthesia. Ketamine (**Figure 17**) produces a state in which the patient is in a catatonic condition and feels separated from the environment and has analgesia and amnesia. This agent is noted to produce hallucinogenic and psychomimetic side effects in some patients. Ketamine is administered intramuscularly or intravenously and reaches peak plasma levels after 10 to 15 minutes.

Ketamine has a $pK_a$ of 7.5 and is partially water soluble. Preparations of ketamine may contain a preservative, benzethonium chloride, at a ratio of 1:10,000. The primary pathway for ketamine metabolism is through the cytochrome P-450 system and involves demethylation to form the metabolite, norketamine. Norketamine has approximately 20% to 30% of the activity of ketamine. Hydroxylation of norketamine occurs at 1 of 2 positions in the cyclohexanone ring to form hydroxynorketamine metabolites. These metabolites form glucuronide conjugates, producing water-soluble compounds for excretion.

Ketamine is 5 to 10 times more lipid soluble than thiopental and is able to cross the BBB quickly to achieve a rapid pharmacologic effect. The distribution kinetics of ketamine are reported to follow a 2-compartment model. Peak plasma concentrations of ketamine are reached within 5 minutes of intravenous injection, and termination of action occurs within 10 to 15 minutes. Ketamine is less protein bound than thiopental, so more drug is immediately available for distribution to the CNS. Brain concentrations decrease rapidly as ketamine is redistributed from the central compartment to peripheral tissue compartments.

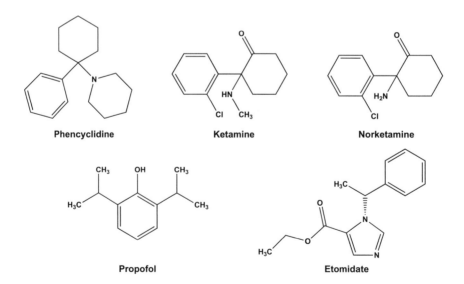

Phencyclidine     Ketamine     Norketamine

Propofol     Etomidate

**Figure 17.** *Structures of miscellaneous anesthetic induction agents.*

Given intramuscularly, ketamine reaches peak plasma concentrations within approximately 20 minutes. After intramuscular administration, more than 90% of the drug is bioavailable. A consideration with the intramuscular route is the delayed onset of anesthesia. Ketamine is known to produce increased cerebral blood flow and cardiac output, and it is a potent bronchodilator. The metabolites of ketamine are excreted renally. Analgesic (subanesthetic) doses of ketamine can be used for painful procedures without causing loss of consciousness and psychic disturbances.

Propofol is 2,6-diisopropylphenol. It is formulated as a milky white solution of 10% soybean oil, 2.25% glycerol, and 1.2% purified egg phosphatide. This composition has been reported to support bacterial growth. It is recommended that aseptic conditions be maintained when syringes are prepared for use. Opened vials and syringes should be discarded if they are not used within 6 hours of preparation. Variable degrees of pain on injection of propofol have been reported.

Propofol is rapidly redistributed from the central to the peripheral compartments, producing a quick initial decline in blood levels. This effect leads to rapid reawakening after sedative and anesthetic doses and is due to the high lipid solubility of the agent. Residual drug undergoes hepatic conjugation and elimination. The effects of propofol can be prolonged in patients with severe liver disease. The kinetics of the drug are also affected by age—elderly people require lower doses and children require higher doses. Drug accumulation can occur with prolonged infusion. Like other induction agents, propofol seems to exert its effect via a GABA-mimetic action. Other actions include a rapid, pleasant recovery and antiemetic and antipruritic effects.

Propofol is widely used for the induction of anesthesia in doses of 0.5 to 2.5 mg/kg. Propofol may be administered by continuous infusion during maintenance of general anesthesia at infusion rates of up to 200 µg/kg/min. Infusion rates of 25 to 75 µg/kg/min are common for intraoperative sedation for a variety of surgical and diagnostic procedures. Use of propofol is especially popular in shorter procedures in ambulatory settings and in monitored anesthesia care. Other uses include sedation for electroconvulsive therapy and cardioversion, facilitation of laryngeal mask airway insertion, and obstetric anesthesia.

Etomidate is an intravenous induction agent that is structurally unrelated to other anesthetics. It is classified as a nonbarbiturate anesthetic, and its effects on the CNS result in a hypnosislike state. Etomidate is a carboxylated imidazole derivative that was synthesized in 1965 and introduced to European anesthesia practice in 1972. No intrinsic analgesic properties are associated with the use of this drug, and it acts by mimicking the CNS inhibitory effects of GABA. Etomidate maintains cardiovascular stability and has a wider margin of safety that seemed to challenge the long-standing role of thiopental as the induction agent of choice in intravenous anesthesia. Side effects, such as pain on injection and myoclonia, however, have somewhat limited a wider acceptance of the drug. Etomidate has 2 isomers, but the (+) isomer is the only one with hypnotic properties.

Etomidate is currently supplied as a 2-mg/mL preparation. Each milliliter of this preparation contains 35% propylene glycol as a solvent and has a pH of 8.1. Etomidate is highly lipid soluble and exists primarily in the un-ionized form in plasma. It is rapidly redistributed and metabolized in the liver by hepatic microsomal enzymes and plasma esterases. Ester hydrolysis is the primary mode of metabolism in the liver and plasma. Etomidate is hydrolyzed to form inactive carboxylic acid metabolites. Approximately 10% of the administered dose can be recovered in bile, 13% can be recovered in feces, and the kidneys eliminate the remainder. Rapid redistribution of etomidate accounts for its extremely short duration of action. The total body clearance of etomidate is 5 times greater than that of thiopental. Rapid distribution and clearance of etomidate, however, make it especially useful in repeated doses and continuous infusions. Etomidate does not accumulate with subsequent dosing. The cardiovascular stability associated with etomidate has led to its extensive use as a sedative-hypnotic infusion agent in critical care units. Etomidate is 15% protein bound, mostly to albumin as with other intravenous anesthetics. Variations in the amount of available plasma protein alter the amount of free drug available to exert pharmacological effects. Disease states that produce alterations in plasma protein content should alert anesthetists to decrease the administered dose.

## Local Anesthetic Agents

Local anesthetic agents produce a loss of sensation or motor function in a discrete area of the body. This action is reversible and permits surgery or an invasion of tissue where a general anesthetic may not be required. Examples of uses for local anesthetics include dentistry, minor surgery, regional anesthesia, and topical relief of itching or pain, burns, bites, and allergic responses. The characteristics of an ideal local anesthetic drug include the following:
- Not irritating to the tissue
- Few or no systemic toxic effects (They usually are absorbed from the site of application.)
- Effective by injection or local application
- Rapid onset and short duration (The action should be long enough for the procedure, but not so long that recovery is slowed.)

In ancient times, the natives of Peru chewed a coca leaf for stamina during long runs through the mountains. The active ingredient in this natural product is cocaine, which is the prototype for most local anesthetic agents.

## Mechanism of Action

Local anesthetic drugs act at sensory nerve fibers to decrease their excitability. They interfere with the flux of sodium ions through membrane channels by binding to an open state of the channel and blocking it or by binding to a closed state of the channel, thus preventing its opening. **Figure 18** shows 2 possible

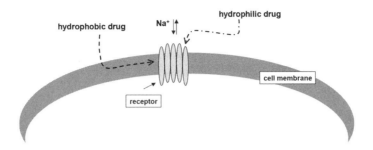

**Figure 18.** *Excitable cell with 2 modes of approach to the receptor. Hydrophilic molecules diffuse through the extracellular media. Hydrophobic molecules pass through the membrane.*

modes of action for local anesthetic drugs. Hydrophilic agents are thought to bind through the extracellular space, whereas hydrophobic molecules are thought to pass through the cellular membrane before binding. Toxic effects associated with local anesthetics are thought to be caused by their interactions with other receptors on excitable cell membranes leading to cardiac, neuromuscular, and CNS effects.

## Structure-Activity Models
Three parts of the local anesthetic molecule are important for activity (**Figure 19**). The hydrophobic fragment of the molecule may be a benzyl or an anilino group. It is desirable to have an amino, alkyl, or methoxy group substituted on the aromatic ring, which produces an electronic effect on the rest of the molecule. This feature facilitates binding to the active site.

   The second important fragment of the local anesthetic is the linker chain. This connecting chain has 1 to 3 carbons and may contain an ester or amide between the alkyl chain and the aromatic ring. The nature of the linkage influences the rate of metabolism of the local anesthetic.

   The third important fragment is the onium group. This group is a substituted amine capable of forming a salt. The salt form of the drug is water soluble and can be used by injection. Some local anesthetics, such as benzocaine, have no amine group in this position but retain anesthetic activity. These molecules approach the receptor in the ion channel by migrating through the lipoid membrane. Local anesthetics with a basic amine (in the ionized form) access the receptor through the hydrophilic channel. Metabolism of commonly used local anesthetics proceeds by ester hydrolysis, if an ester is present, or by enzymatic hydroxylation of the aromatic ring.

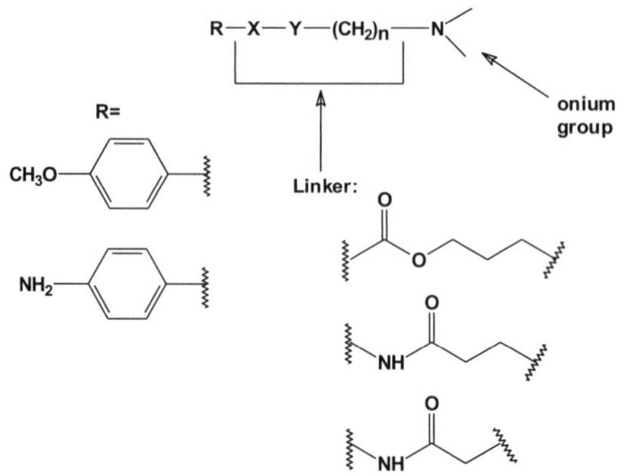

**Figure 19.** *Important fragments of a local anesthetic molecule.*

## Ester-Containing Local Anesthetics

Cocaine (**Figure 20**) is the prototypical local anesthetic agent. It was originally used as an ophthalmic local anesthetic, but had such a propensity for addiction that it is now only minimally used as a topical anesthetic. Several subclasses of local anesthetic drugs have been derived from the cocaine structure.

Benzocaine has no onium group, and so it lacks the necessary water solubility for use in solutions. Benzocaine is formulated as an ointment, aerosol, or paste and is used only in topical applications or in lozenges. It is not used by injection. Benzocaine has been used for ear canal pain and for oral cavity treatment of mucous-membrane soreness. Benzocaine is metabolized by hydrolysis of the ester group.

Procaine has a $pK_a$ of 8.9, thus making it stable and soluble in acidic solutions, facilitating its use by injection. Acidic solutions are stable enough for autoclaving. Procaine is poorly absorbed through the skin but may be used by infiltration. It is sometimes used with a vasoconstrictor such as epinephrine to slow its absorption into the bloodstream, prolonging its effect. In the bloodstream, the ester of procaine is rapidly hydrolyzed, destroying its activity. Toxic effects arise from the presence of procaine in the blood, leading to allergic reactions and sensitivity. Procaine is relatively short acting with a duration of 30 to 60 minutes.

Tetracaine is basic enough to form soluble salts with an acid. It is 16 times more potent than procaine as a local anesthetic. Tetracaine is also longer acting and more stable in solution than procaine. Tetracaine is rapidly absorbed into mucous membranes because of its increased hydrophobic character due to the butyl side chain. It is metabolized by ester hydrolysis. Formulation may be made for topical use by incorporating the free amine form into suitable ointments.

Chloroprocaine is a chloro derivative of procaine with a more rapid onset of action and a shorter duration of action. It has fewer toxic effects than procaine because it is more rapidly metabolized. The half-life in the plasma is less than 1 minute, and side effects are minimal.

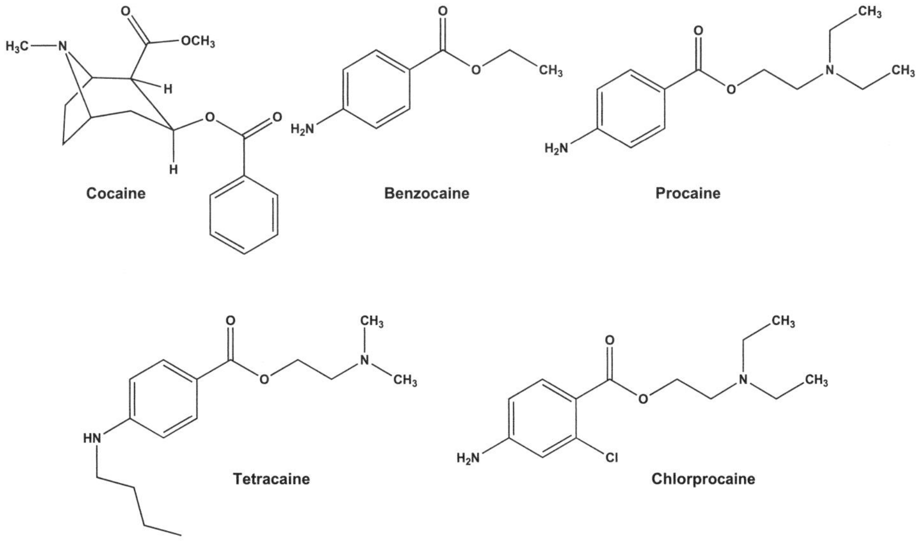

**Figure 20.** *Ester-containing local anesthetics.*

## Amide-Containing Local Anesthetics

This group of local anesthetics (**Figure 21**) replaces the ester on the alkyl linker chain of cocaine with an amide group. The amide group makes these drugs more resistant to hydrolysis, increasing their stability. Several important local anesthetics are in this class.

Lidocaine forms water-soluble salts with acids, forming a solution with a pH of 7.86, making it useful for injection. Lidocaine is resistant to hydrolysis and can be autoclaved. Lidocaine has twice the potency of procaine, but it has more toxic effects. Toxic effects initially manifest as drowsiness, tinnitus, and dizziness. The molecule is metabolized in the liver by *N*-dealkylation with retention of some activity. The metabolites, monoethylglycinexylidide and glycinexylidide, can cause toxic effects. Aside from these metabolites, lidocaine causes few side effects.

Dibucaine is slightly soluble in water; for this reason it is usually used in ointments and suppositories. It is stable and can be autoclaved. Dibucaine is the most potent, the most toxic, and the longest acting of all the generally used local anesthetic drugs.

Mepivacaine is similar to lidocaine in its effects. It is more toxic in neonates because of reduced metabolism; hence, it is not used in obstetrics. The onset of action of mepivacaine is slightly slower than that of lidocaine. Mepivacaine is metabolized in the liver by *N*-dealkylation and aromatic hydroxylation.

Etidocaine is a water-soluble, long-acting drug. It is resistant to heat, so it can be autoclaved. Its profile is similar to that of lidocaine. Etidocaine is more protein bound and has higher lipid solubility than lidocaine. The onset of action of etidocaine resembles that of lidocaine (approximately 3-5 minutes); however, the duration of action of etidocaine is 5 to 10 hours, longer than that of lidocaine. Etidocaine is metabolized by amide hydrolysis.

Bupivacaine is a modification of lidocaine; the difference in structure is in the onium group. Bupivacaine is a potent local anesthetic with a prolonged half-life of approximately 3 hours, which is the longest among the commonly used local anesthetics. The $pK_a$ of bupivacaine is 8.1, higher than that of lidocaine (7.8). Therefore, bupivacaine exhibits higher lipid solubility than lidocaine and increased protein binding. Bupivacaine is useful intraoperatively and in postoperative pain and labor management. Metabolism is by amide hydrolysis. Bupivacaine is more toxic to the cardiovascular system than is lidocaine.

Prilocaine is an intermediate-acting drug, similar to lidocaine. It has negligible cardiovascular effects. Prilocaine is metabolized by amide hydrolysis.

Ropivacaine was designed to lessen the cardiac toxic effects of other amide local anesthetics. The S enantiomer is less toxic than the R enantiomer. It resembles bupivacaine in its profile of action and toxic effects. Ropivacaine has a $pK_a$ of 8.1 but is less lipid soluble than bupivacaine. Ropivacaine is 94% protein bound. Metabolism of ropivacaine leads to 3-hydroxy-ropivacaine and N-dealkylation products.

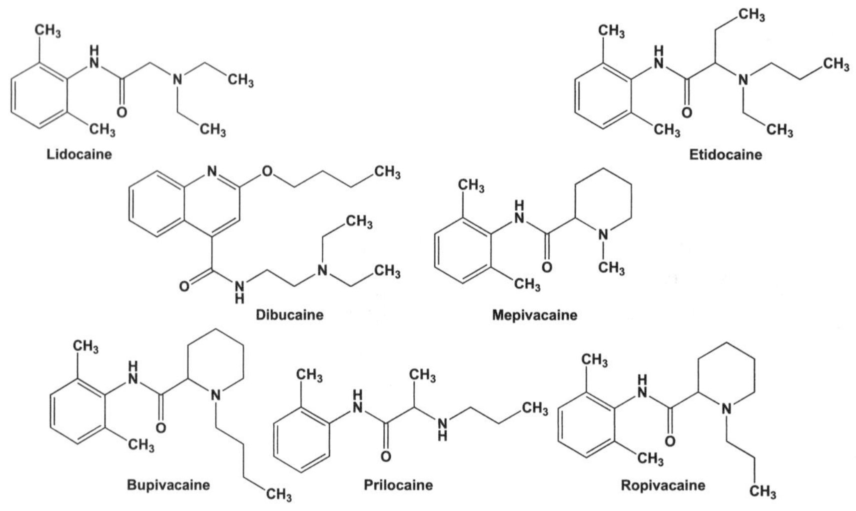

**Figure 21.** *Amide-containing local anesthetics.*

## Suggested Reading

Campagna JD, Miller KW, Forman SA. Mechanisms of actions of inhaled anesthetics. *N Engl J Med.* 2003;348(21):2110-2124.

Ebert TJ, Schmid, PG. Inhaled anesthetics. In: Barash PG, Cullen BF, Stoelting RK, Cahalan MK, Stock MC, eds. *Clinical Anesthesia.* 6th ed. Philadelphia, Pa: Lippincott Williams & Wilkins; 2009:413-443.

Eckenhoff RG. Promiscuous ligands and attractive cavities: how do the inhaled anesthetics work? *Mol Interv.* 2001;1(5):258-268.

Ezekiel MR. *Handbook of Anesthesiology.* Blue Jay, CA: Current Clinical Strategies; 2008.

Kier LB. A review of recent studies relating ligand diffusion, general anesthesia, and sleep. *AANA J.* 2008;76(2):109-112.

Kier LB. A theory of inhaled anesthetic action by disruption of ligand diffusion chreodes. *AANA J.* 2003;71(6):422-428.

Kier LB, Cheng C-K, Testa B. A cellular automata model of ligand passage over a protein hydrodynamic landscape. *J Theor Biol.* 2002;215(4):415-426.

Miller KW. The nature of sites of general anaesthetic action. *Br J Anaesth.* 2002;89(1):17-31.

## Discussion Topics

1. What are the 4 stages of general anesthesia?

2. What are several ideal characteristics of volatile general anesthetic agents?

3. What is the influence of the hydrophilic or hydrophobic character of the general anesthetic agent on the onset and recovery time?

4. What is the role of an inductive agent?

5. What is the second-gas effect?

6. What is the mechanism of action of the local anesthetic agents?

# Chapter 10

# Central Nervous System Depressants
*by Lemont B. Kier, PhD, and Cynthia S. Dowd, PhD*

The sedative, hypnotic, and anticonvulsant drugs constitute a group of drugs that produce a depressant effect mediated through the central nervous system (CNS). These agents are used for their calming effects that can be mild, as in the treatment of insomnia, or extreme, as in the treatment of seizures. Mild sedation with one of these agents is often desired before minor surgical and diagnostic procedures. Many of the drugs discussed in this chapter can be used as sedatives and as anticonvulsants. Adjustment in the dosage will dictate which effect the patient will experience. Lower doses produce sedation, whereas higher doses produce anticonvulsant effects. Benzodiazepines, barbiturates, and hydantoins are the major structural categories of sedatives, hypnotics, and anticonvulsants. These agents, as well as compounds belonging to structurally diverse categories, are discussed in this chapter.

## Sedatives and Hypnotics
The earliest sedative, in fact, one of the first medicinal agents in early records, is ethanol. Clay tablets from more than 4,000 years ago describe fermented grains producing a liquid that gave some relief to the suffering experienced at that time. The active ingredient in the potions was ethanol, used today primarily in beverages. Its use is quite limited in medical practice today because of its addictive potential. However, ethanol (structure follows this paragraph) serves as a model compound from which improved sedatives have been developed.

$$CH_3-CH_2-OH$$

Ethanol acts at the CNS inhibitory pathways that are mediated by the neurotransmitter γ-aminobutyric acid (GABA). Ethanol produces an increase in the chloride ion flux, reinforcing the inhibitory response. Long-term use of ethanol reduces the cell response by lowering the chloride ion flux. At the same time, the excitatory receptors mediated by the neurotransmitter glutamate are inhibited. In the case of a person with alcoholism experiencing withdrawal, there is a rebound in the function of the excitatory neurons, leading to the condition called *delirium tremens.*

Ethanol is metabolized according to the reactions shown in **Figure 1**. One preventive treatment of alcoholism is to give the person disulfiram, a drug that inhibits aldehyde dehydrogenase. The result is an accumulation of acetaldehyde, which produces unpleasant side effects intended to deter the person from further use of alcohol.

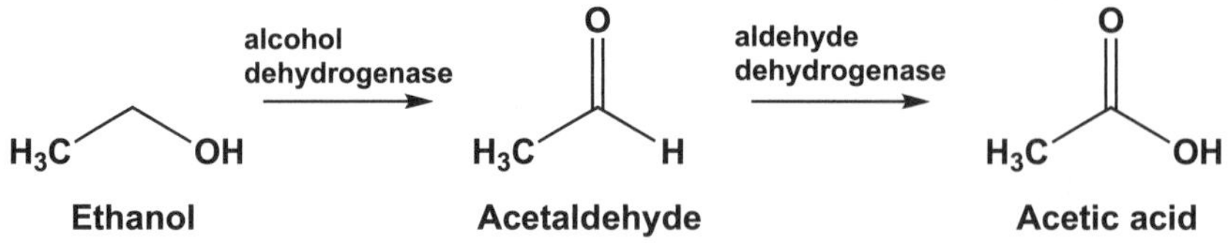

**Figure 1.** *The metabolism of ethanol.*

Because of the potential for ethanol addiction, a number of alternatives were developed for use as sedatives and hypnotics. The design of these newer drugs was based on the structure of ethanol with modifications found from structure-activity studies. For example, it was observed that lengthening the carbon chain of ethanol up to 8 carbons produced a steady increase in potency. Alcohols larger than 8 carbons produced a decline in potency. Branching in the carbon chain of alcohols increased potency. The tertiary alcohol was shown to be more potent than the primary and secondary alcohols (**Figure 2**). The reason for this difference is that the tertiary alcohols are less susceptible to metabolism than the others.

Early observations led to structural changes that resulted in molecules with increased potency as sedatives. Addition of a halogen atom in the alcohol was shown to give greater potency. This effect was shown to be due to slower metabolism and higher lipophilicity, permitting faster accumulation of the molecule in the brain. Similarly, conversion of the hydroxyl group of an alcohol to the carbamate derivative reduced metabolism and gave a more potent molecule. Another modification that improved potency was the introduction of unsaturation in the molecule.

The ureides represent a second class of compounds that have been used historically as sedatives. *Ureides* are derivatives of urea formed by acylation, shown in **Figure 3**. They were used in the treatment of anxiety and nervous tension. The presence of bromine in these compounds, however, presented a problem for long-term use. These drugs are metabolized to produce the bromide ion, which is excreted through the skin as elemental bromine, which produced severe irritation, one of the characteristics of bromism. Compounds of this class are shown in **Figure 4**: carbromal, acecarbromal, and bromisovalum.

Although alcohols, carbamates, and ureides were once used as sedatives, they are not currently used for this purpose. Classes of compounds that are currently used include benzodiazepines, barbiturates, and nonbenzodiazepine GABA receptor ligands. These types of molecules have given insight into the mechanisms of sedation and have refined the treatment protocols to give the desired results with few or no unwanted side effects.

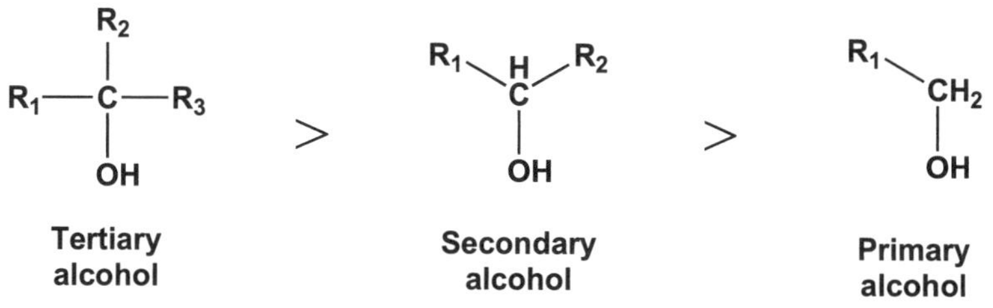

**Figure 2.** *Relative potencies of alcohols as sedatives.*

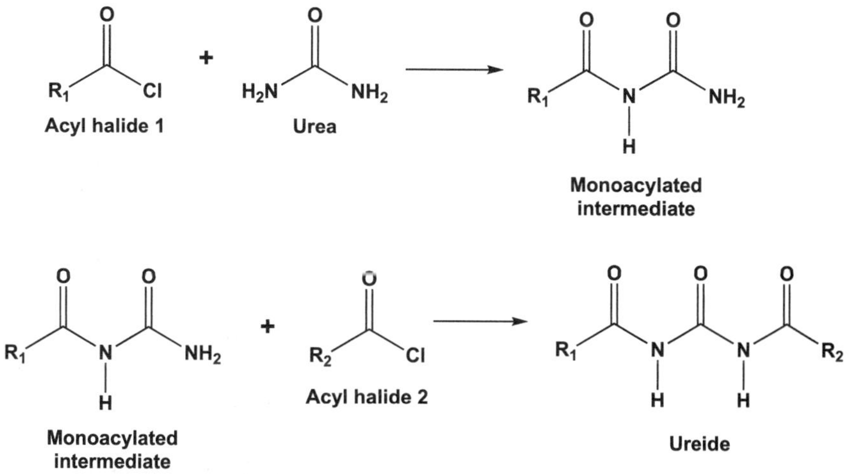

**Figure 3.** *Acylation of urea to produce ureides.*

## Currently Administered Sedatives and Hypnotics

The 3 main classes of compounds currently administered as sedatives and hypnotics are benzodiazepines, chloral hydrates, and barbiturates. These classes are discussed in the following sections.

## Benzodiazepines

The first treatment of choice for mild sedation is often a benzodiazepine. Many of the sleep aids and therapeutics used for preoperative sedation belong to this class of compounds. Benzodiazepines have a lower incidence of respiratory depression compared with barbiturates. However, intoxication associated with

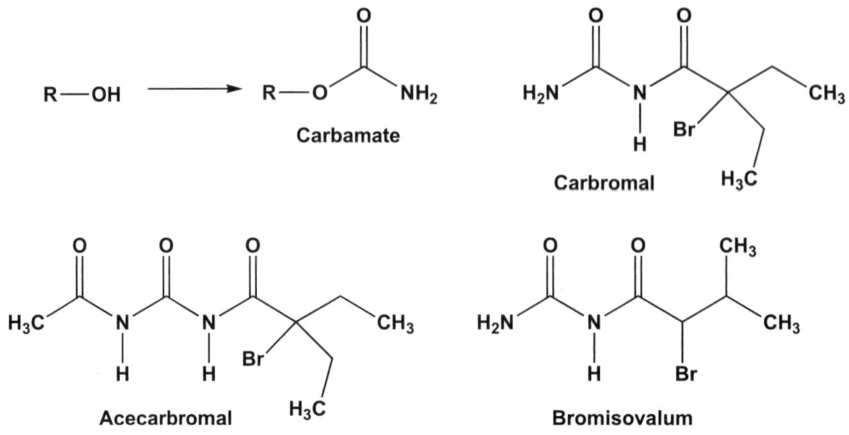

**Figure 4.** *Uriede compounds.*

benzodiazepine metabolites is often a concern. Flumazenil is a benzodiazepine antagonist used as an antidote in cases of benzodiazepine intoxication (**Figure 5**).

Benzodiazepines bind to the α subunits of the GABA receptor. In the presence of a benzodiazepine, the inhibitory effect of GABA is enhanced. This inhibition is due to the increased influx of chloride ions into the cell. Chloride ion influx increases the polarization of the nerve cell so that the ability of the cell to respond to an external (positive) stimulus and promote a nervous signal is decreased. (For a more detailed description of the action of benzodiazepines at the GABA receptor, see Chapter 12.)

Several benzodiazepines are used in the treatment of insomnia. These are typically agents with a rapid onset of action and a relatively short half-life. These agents, shown in Figure 5, include flumazenil, temazepam, flurazepam, triazolam, and estazolam. Typically, these drugs are used for short periods (usually <7 days) and are excreted as glucuronide conjugates.

Midazolam (**Figure 6**) is a short-acting benzodiazepine with a rapid onset of action. It is used as a sedative before surgery. Midazolam has been associated with respiratory depression and arrest; therefore, it is used only in supervised clinical settings. Midazolam is metabolized to 1-hydroxy-midazolam, which is equally as active as the parent drug.

Lorazepam and diazepam are stronger sedatives and can be used as anticonvulsants (Figure 6). Both medications are approved for sedation and relief of tension before surgery and for the treatment of status epilepticus. The onset of action of lorazepam is 30 to 60 minutes (oral dose), and the duration of action is 6 to 8 hours. The onset of action of diazepam occurs almost immediately after administration; however, efficacy in status epilepticus lasts 20 to 30 minutes. Clonazepam is a rapidly absorbed benzodiazepine with a long half-life. It is metabolized by reduction of the 7-nitro group to an amine (Figure 6).

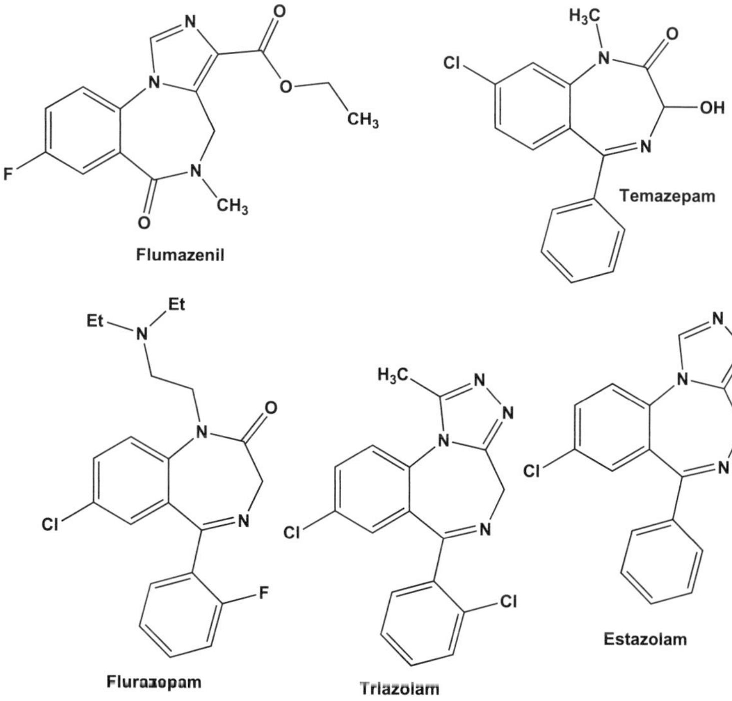

**Figure 5.** *Benzodiazepines used to treat insomnia.*

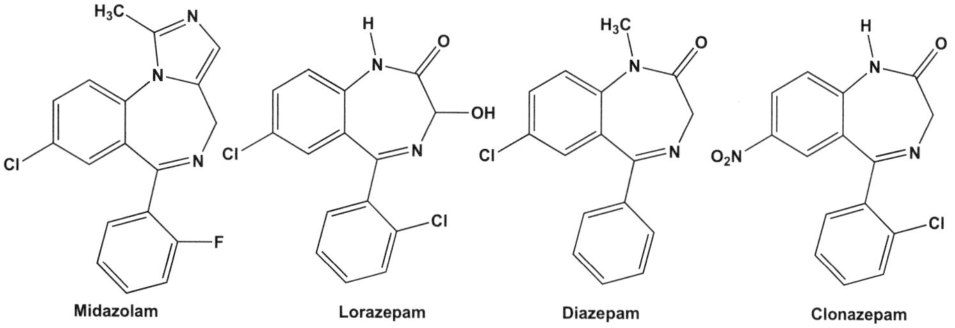

**Figure 6.** *Structures of various benzodiazepines.*

## Chloral Hydrate

*Chloral hydrate* has been used for some time as a sedative and hypnotic. It is an ingredient, along with ethanol, in a notorious cocktail known as a "Mickey Finn," used in the late 1800s to subdue sailors in ports and to take them aboard ships as unwilling crew. In more legitimate limited uses, it is an effective sedative and hypnotic. It produces sleep without interference to rapid eye movement (REM) sleep. It is absorbed from the gastrointestinal tract with a 1-hour onset of action. It has a duration of 4 to 8 hours, long enough for the recipient to wake up in the hold of a ship in the middle of an ocean!

Chloral hydrate (**Figure 7**) acts as a prodrug. It is quickly metabolized in the liver to trichloroethanol, which is the active form of the drug. Chloral hydrate has the same mechanism of action as ethanol. There are no respiratory effects and no analgesia. Some side effects include nausea and vomiting. Chloral hydrate is unstable in basic solutions, in which it decomposes to chloroform and the formate ion.

Triclofos sodium is a modification of chloral hydrate designed to remove some of its side effects. It is rapidly metabolized to trichloroethanol, the active metabolite of chloral hydrate.

## Barbiturates

A number of barbiturates are used as sedatives and hypnotics. Depending on the substituents on the molecule, the drugs may be short-, intermediate-, or long-acting. The rate of metabolism for an individual barbiturate determines the duration of its therapeutic effect. The **Table** lists the structures of various barbiturates according to duration of action for sedative and hypnotic effect. Note that several barbiturates are used both as sedatives and as anticonvulsants.

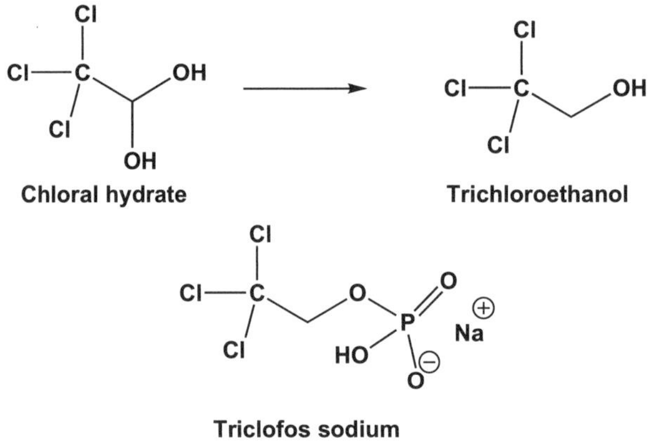

**Figure 7.** *Chloral hydrate and related compounds.*

**Table.** *Barbiturates used as sedatives and hypnotics.*

| Name | R₁ | R₂ | R₃ |
|------|------|------|------|
| **Short Duration (< 3 hour)** | | | |
| Pentobarbital | H | CH₃CH₂CH₂CH—— (with CH₃ branch) | CH₃CH₂- |
| Secobarbital | H | CH₃CH₂CH₂CH—— (with CH₃ branch) | CH₂=CHCH₂- |
| **Intermediate Duration (3-6 hour)** | | | |
| Amobarbital | H | (CH₃)₂CHCH₂CH₂- | CH₃CH₂- |
| Butalbital | H | (CH₃)₂CHCH₂- | CH₂=CHCH₂- |
| Butabarbital | H | CH₃CH₂CH—— (with CH₃ branch) | CH₃CH₂- |
| Talbutal | H | CH₃CH₂CH—— (with CH₃ branch) | CH₂=CHCH₂- |
| **Long Duration (>6 hour)** | | | |
| Mephobarbital | CH₃- | (phenyl) | CH₃CH₂- |
| Phenobarbital | H | (phenyl) | CH₃CH₂- |

Similar to benzodiazepines, barbiturates act through GABA receptors. Barbiturates mediate their effect by enhancing the permeability of inhibitory cellular membranes to chloride ion flow. In the presence of barbiturates, these cells have a higher threshold that must be met for a nervous signal to be propagated.

All barbiturates induce the action of several metabolizing enzymes. For this reason, the metabolism of other medications will be altered in a patient who is also taking a barbiturate. The effects and metabolites of the barbiturate, as well as the other medications, must be carefully monitored. Major side effects of barbiturates include hypotension and respiratory depression.

*Pentobarbital* (See Table) is a short-acting (<3 h) barbiturate with a quick onset of action. It is used as a sedative (low doses) and as an anticonvulsant (higher doses). Pentobarbital is moderately protein bound (35%-55%) and hepatically metabolized by oxidation to inactive metabolites. The half-life of pentobarbital is approximately 15 to 20 hours.

Secobarbital (See Table) is structurally related to pentobarbital, but differs from pentobarbital in one way: The $R_3$ ethyl group of pentobarbital is replaced by an allyl group in secobarbital. Like pentobarbital, secobarbital is short-acting and has a rapid onset of action.

Amobarbital (See Table) has an intermediate duration of action. Like pentobarbital, amobarbital can be used as a sedative and as an anticonvulsant. Orally, amobarbital is used in the short-term treatment of insomnia and for preoperative sedation. Intravenously, amobarbital can be used for the control of seizures or in the treatment of status epilepticus. Tuinal, useful in the treatment of insomnia, is a formulation that contains secobarbital and amobarbital.

Butalbital (See Table), a barbiturate of intermediate duration of action, is present in several formulations. One of the formulations, used for the relief of symptoms due to tension headaches, is a combination of butalbital, acetaminophen, and caffeine. Another formulation contains butalbital, caffeine, and aspirin. These combination drugs are also available with codeine for the treatment of mild to moderate pain with sedation.

Longer-acting barbiturates such as phenobarbital (See Table) are used as sedatives and for the treatment of epilepsy. Both of these molecules have aromatic rings at the $R_2$ position, which is likely the reason for their long action. Phenobarbital is moderately protein bound (20%-45%) and is largely metabolized in the liver to yield hydroxylated and glucuronide-conjugated metabolites. A substantial portion of the delivered drug (20%) is excreted unchanged.

Methohexital and thiopental are very short-acting barbiturates that can be used for sedation during diagnostic imaging (**Figure 8**).

Two drugs derived from the barbiturate structure have been used as sedatives. Methylprylon and glutethimide are modifications of the barbiturate ring. Both drugs have activities that resemble the barbiturates in that they suppress REM sleep, have similar side effects, and may cause dependence. Glutethimide is metabolized by hydroxylation of the phenyl ring and ethyl group.

## Other Sedatives and Hypnotics

Zolpidem (**Figure 9**) does not belong to the structural class of benzodiazepines; however, its site of action is the benzodiazepine site of the GABA receptor. Used for the treatment of insomnia, zolpidem is rapidly absorbed, has a half-life of 2 to 3 hours, and is very highly protein bound (>90%). The drug is metabolized in the liver to inactive compounds.

Zaleplon is structurally related to and has the same mechanism of action as zolpidem. It is rapidly absorbed but less protein bound (approximately 60%). The metabolites of zaleplon (desethylzaleplon and 5-oxo-zaleplon) are rapidly formed and are inactive. Metabolism of zaleplon occurs so rapidly that the half-life of the drug is less than 1 hour.

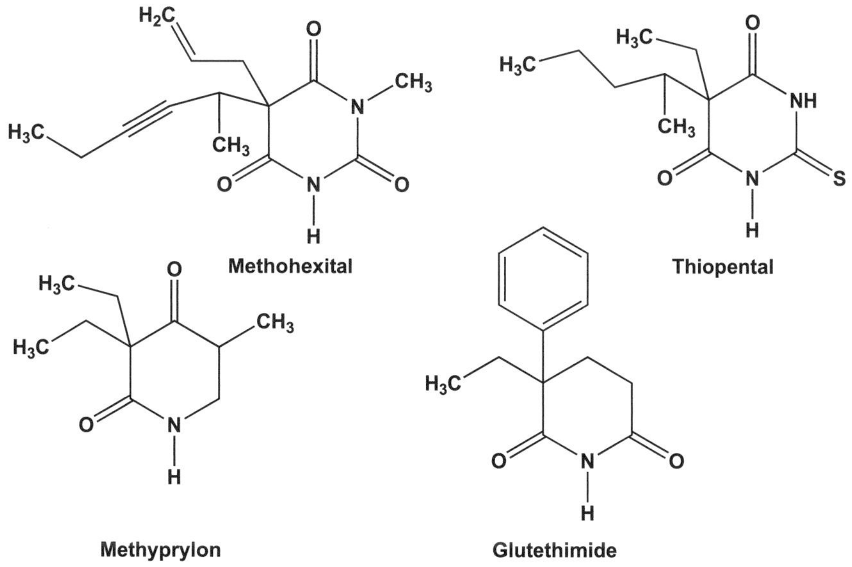

**Figure 8.** *Structures of short-acting barbiturates.*

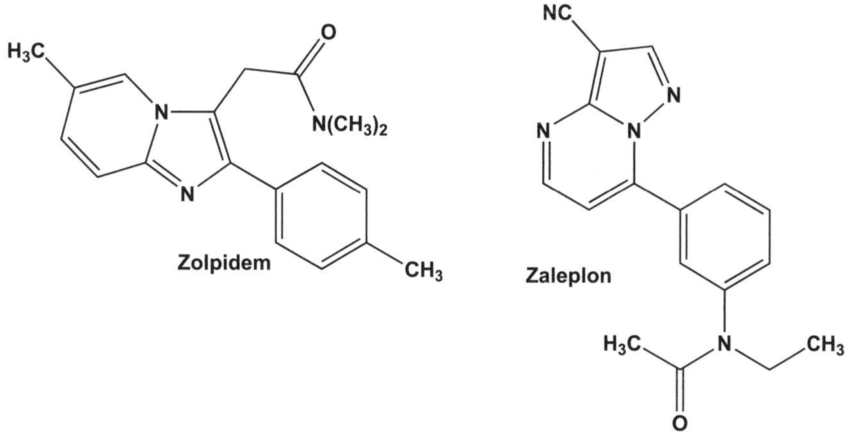

**Figure 9.** *Other sedatives and hypnotics.*

Several other formulations have been used as sedatives, specifically intended to treat insomnia. A formulation of melatonin, vitamin $B_{12}$, and folic acid is marketed for this purpose. Diphenhydramine is an antihistamine that works by inhibiting the $H_1$ histamine receptor. It is found in over-the-counter medications that have been used as sleep aids.

Other drugs used for sedation include promethazine and propofol. Promethazine, which is a phenothiazine, has only 10% of the dopaminergic effects of other neuroleptic phenothiazines. Therefore, extrapyramidal side effects associated with promethazine occur only at higher doses. The combination of promethazine and meperidine is used for sedation (promethazine) with analgesia (meperidine).

Propofol, despite its cardiac side effects (eg, bradycardia, arrhythmia), is used as a preoperative sedative.

## Anticonvulsants

Anticonvulsants are drugs that are used primarily for the treatment of epilepsy. *Epilepsy* is a CNS neuronal pathology characterized by an excessive discharge from the neuronal cells at a central point, followed by spreading of the electrical impulse. The manifestations include motor effects such as twitching, numbness, loss of control, generalized contraction, and possible loss of consciousness. These effects, which may be preceded by an aura or a partial seizure, can be localized or spread throughout the body.

Seizures can be classified as follows:

1. Partial seizures–derived from one focus in the brain (hence, formerly known as focal) and include simple partial seizures (consciousness and memory maintained) and complex partial seizures (loss of consciousness and memory alterations)
2. Generalized seizures–originate from all over the brain and include absence seizures (formerly known as petit mal seizures), generalized tonic-clonic seizures (formerly known as grand mal seizures), atonic seizures ("drop" attacks), myoclonic seizures (one or more brief jerking movements), and tonic seizures (stiffening of muscles; uncommon)

A seizure might involve only one side of the body or might start as a simple partial seizure and progress to generalized tonic-clonic. Among adults, partial seizures occur more often than do other types, whereas among children, absence seizures are the predominant type. Some seizures, known as febrile convulsions, are associated with fever and observed more often in infants and young children. In some cases, the cause of seizures can be identified; in other cases, seizures are idiopathic.

Antiepileptic drugs prevent and control seizures. An ideal anticonvulsant would completely suppress seizures of varying types, produce no sedation, have no undesired effects on the CNS or vital systems, and have a rapid onset with a long duration of action. The most common anticonvulsants are benzodiazepines, barbiturates, and hydantoins. Each of these drug classes acts by raising the threshold required for an excitatory nerve cell to propagate a nervous signal. This effect is mediated by increasing the permeability of the cell membrane to ion flow. The differences among these classes of anticonvulsants arise from their side-effect profiles.

## Benzodiazepines

Many benzodiazepines can be used as sedatives and as anticonvulsants. Lorazepam and diazepam are used for sedation and the treatment of status epilepticus. Clonazepam is a popular antiseizure and antipanic medication (Figure 6). Clorazepate dipotassium (**Figure 10**) is used as adjunct therapy in the treatment of partial seizures. Clorazepate has a carboxylate group on the 7-membered ring that is removed (decarboxylated) during metabolism to give nordiazepam, an active metabolite. This metabolic transformation occurs so rapidly that circulating amounts of the parent compound are negligible. A more detailed description of the family of benzodiazepines can be found in Chapter 12.

## Barbiturates

In addition to their use as sedatives, barbiturates are used as anticonvulsants. Phenobarbital (See Table) is used for children. It has a long half-life in plasma (3-6 days). It is metabolized by oxidation of the phenyl ring. Metharbital (**Figure 11**) is the diethyl derivative of mephobarbital. It is used for general seizures but is more sedating than phenobarbital.

Primidone (Figure 11) is a variant of the barbiturate ring in which a methylene group has replaced 1 carbonyl group. It is effective against all types of seizures except absence seizures. It is metabolized to the barbiturate ring by oxidation of the ring methylene group to give phenobarbital. Pentobarbital (See Table) is used as a sedative and as an anticonvulsant.

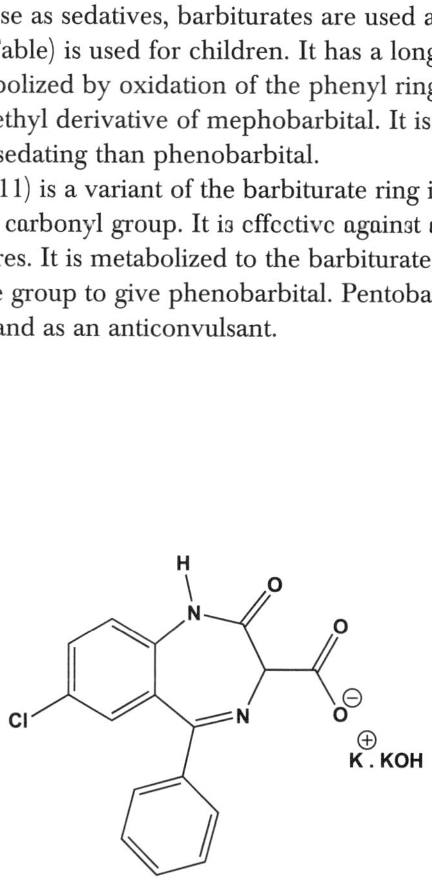

**Chlorazepate dipotassium**

**Figure 10.** *Structure of clorazepate dipotassium.*

Epilepsy can require medication for a long period. The sedative properties of the barbiturates, however, argued against their use for prolonged periods. Therefore, alternative molecules were sought to decrease this side effect. This effort led to a series of derivatives modifying the barbituric acid ring, as shown in **Figure 12**. These molecules are the hydantoins, succinimides, and oxazolidinediones.

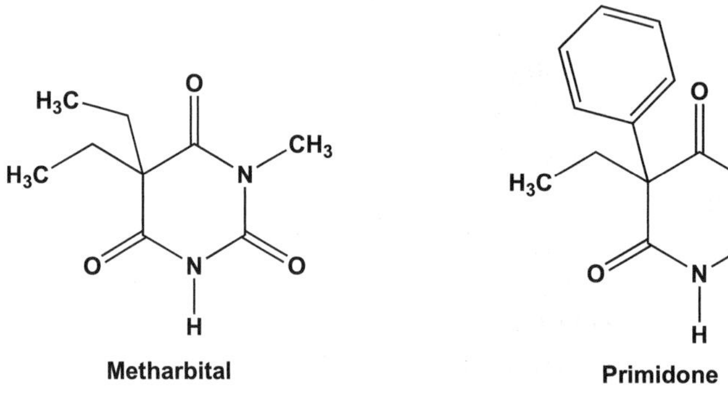

**Metharbital**                    **Primidone**

**Figure 11.** *Barbiturates used as anticonvulsants.*

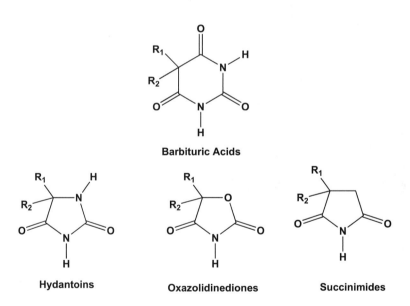

**Barbituric Acids**

**Hydantoins**          **Oxazolidinediones**          **Succinimides**

**Figure 12.** *Ring derivatives of barbituric acid. Hydantoins, oxazolidinediones, and succinimides are 5-membered ring derivatives of the barbituric acid structure. A carbonyl is removed from barbituric acid to form the hydantoin structure. Removal of this carbonyl and replacement of the adjacent amine with an oxygen atom or a methylene group forms the oxazolidinedione and succinimide ring structures, respectively.*

# Hydantoins

Hydantoins are acids by virtue of their ability to exist as the lactim tautomer, as shown in **Figure 13**. This acidic function is necessary for activity. Hydantoins block sodium influx and decrease cell membrane permeability to calcium. These 2 actions lead to decreased neurotransmitter synthesis and release. Therefore, hydantoins stabilize the membrane of a nervous cell, prevent impulse propagation to additional nerve cells, and, thus, decrease the overall nervous response to an external stimulus. Hydantoins are relatively free of the sedative side effects exhibited by barbiturates.

Phenytoin (**Figure 14**) is diphenylhydantoin and is the prototypical hydantoin. Phenytoin is useful in the treatment of many types of seizures and can be administered to older children and adults. Because of the 2 phenyl rings, however, phenytoin has low water solubility and is erratically absorbed when given orally. In addition, phenytoin is more than 90% bound by serum proteins because of the high hydrophobicity of the 2 phenyl rings. Replacement of both phenyl groups by smaller substituents lowers anticonvulsant activity. Modification of the phenyl rings by adding substituents also lowers activity. The plasma half-life is approximately 24 hours. The toxicity is low, but there are side effects such as gastric distress, vertigo, ataxia, skin rash, and anemia. Metabolism occurs via hydroxylation at the *para* position of either one of the phenyl rings, followed by glucuronide conjugation.

Fosphenytoin is a water-soluble prodrug of phenytoin. Endogenous phosphatases act on fosphenytoin to yield 1 molecule of phenytoin and 1 molecule each of formaldehyde and phosphate (Figure 14). The formaldehyde is oxidized to formic acid and excreted. The resulting molecule of phenytoin is responsible for the therapeutic effect. Because metabolism occurs rapidly, fosphenytoin has a half-life of less than 15 minutes. Fosphenytoin can be used as a short-term substitute for phenytoin.

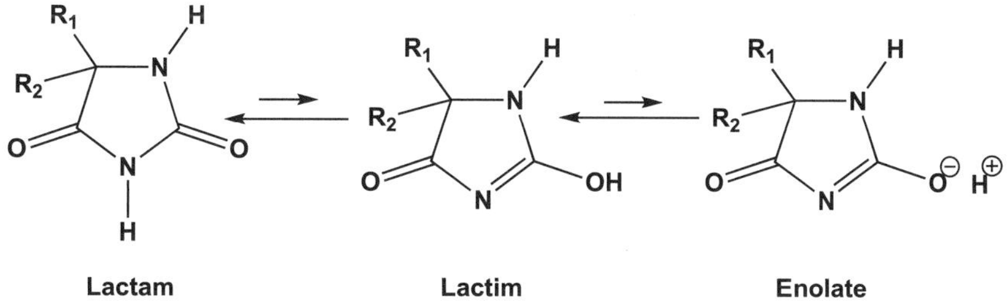

**Lactam**          **Lactim**          **Enolate**

**Figure 13.** *Lactim-lactam tautomerization of the hydantoin ring to yield an acidic function.*

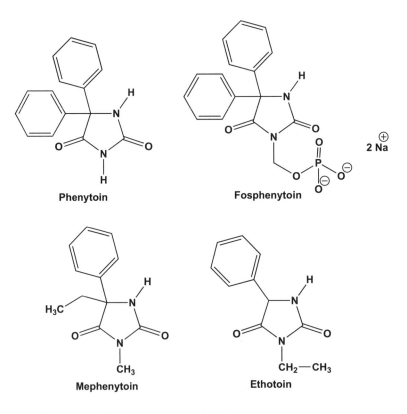

**Figure 14.** *Structures of hydantoins.*

Mephenytoin is a prodrug. The active form results from metabolism of the *N*-methyl group to a hydrogen via *N*-dealkylation. The *N*-methyl group increases absorption and reduces side effects such as skin and blood disorders. Its activity spectrum is similar to that of phenytoin, although it is somewhat more toxic. It is used as a reserve drug or may be combined with phenytoin. Mephenytoin (Figure 14) is currently not available in the United States.

Ethotoin also is a hydantoin prodrug. Metabolism removes the *N*-ethyl group to give the N-H compound, which is active. Ethotoin is further metabolized by oxidation of the phenyl ring to give phenolic metabolites. Ethotoin (Figure 14) is of relatively low potency and is used for generalized seizures.

## Succinimides

Succinimides are analogs of the hydantoins in which a ring nitrogen atom has been replaced by a methylene group (Figure 12). In the CNS, succinimides decrease the threshold of response to convulsive stimuli. The exact mechanism by which succinimides achieve this, however, is unknown. This class of antiepileptic drugs is generally of lower potency than the hydantoins and oxazolidinediones. The major adverse reaction from the use of a succinimide is blood dyscrasias. Milder side effects include dizziness, drowsiness, nausea, and vomiting.

Methsuximide (**Figure 15**) is used in the treatment of seizures that are unresponsive to other forms of therapy. Methsuximide is metabolized by demethylation to the N-H derivative, which is active, and is metabolically inactivated by hydroxylation of the phenyl ring. Ethosuximide is useful for absence seizures, for which it is the drug of choice. It has lower toxicity than the oxazolidinediones. It is metabolized by oxidation of the ethyl group.

## Oxazolidinediones

Oxazolidinediones (**Figure 16**) are derived from the hydantoin structure in which the ring nitrogen atom is replaced with an oxygen atom. Two members of this group are of interest. Trimethadione acts as a prodrug and is metabolized by *N*-demethylation to give the active compound. Trimethadione has been used for nonresponsive patients and was used for patients with absence seizures, but it has not been shown to be useful against generalized seizures. Side effects of trimethadione may include anemia, nephrosis, and dermatological and hematological toxic effects. Paramethadione is similar to trimethadione but is somewhat safer. It is metabolized to the N-H derivative by removal of the methyl group, leading to the active compound. Paramethadione is used for absence seizures.

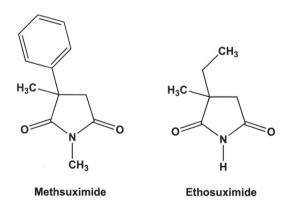

Methsuximide                Ethosuximide

**Figure 15.** *Structures of succinimides.*

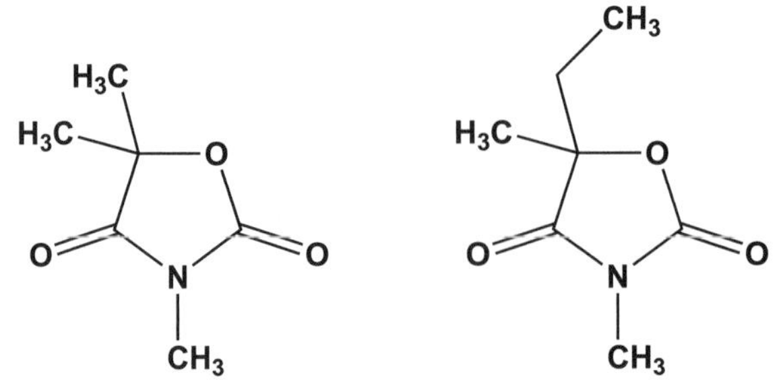

Trimethadione          Paramethadione

**Figure 16.** *Structures of oxazolidinediones.*

## Other Anticonvulsants

Many of the currently used anticonvulsant therapies, such as phenobarbital and phenytoin, are part of large structural classes of molecules with defined activities. Over the years, however, several active molecules that do not belong to the typical anticonvulsant structural classes have emerged. The following compounds (**Figure 17**) represent anticonvulsant agents for which a distinct mechanism of action or structure-activity relationship is not necessarily known, but which warrant attention as effective and important clinical agents.

Carbamazepine is used for generalized and partial seizures. It is 75% protein bound. It must be used with some caution because aplastic anemia and agranulocytosis have been associated with its use. Milder side effects include dizziness, drowsiness, nausea, and vomiting. The mechanism of action of carbamazepine is unknown. Carbamazepine induces the action of metabolizing enzyme CYP3A4 and, thus, induces its own metabolism. This enzyme oxidizes carbamazepine to the 10-11 epoxide, which is active.

Valproic acid is thought to act by increasing the effect of GABA. Hepatotoxicity associated with its use can be fatal, and the drug may be teratogenic. Other adverse effects include nausea, vomiting, hallucinations, pneumonia, and headache. Valproic acid is useful in the treatment of absence seizures, and 30% to 50% of the drug is metabolized by glucuronide conjugation. β Oxidation is an additional metabolic pathway.

Similar to valproic acid, tiagabine and vigabatrin exert their anticonvulsant effects by modulation of GABA effects. Tiagabine is used in the treatment of partial seizures and works by blocking the reuptake of GABA. Tiagabine is rapidly absorbed and greatly protein bound (>95%). It is metabolized by oxidation of the thiophene ring to 5-oxotiagabine, which is inactive, followed by glucuronidation. The half-life is approximately 7 hours. Vigabatrin is an

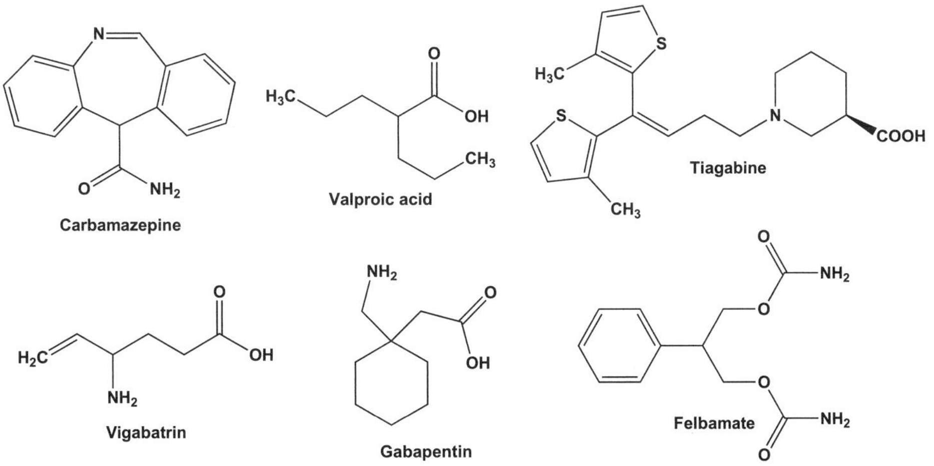

**Figure 17.** *Structures of miscellaneous anticonvulsants.*

irreversible inhibitor of GABA transaminase, the major enzyme responsible for GABA metabolism. Vigabatrin action results in an increase in the concentration of GABA, thus inhibiting the propagation of the seizure. The S(+) isomer is the active form, but it is marketed as the racemate. It is rapidly absorbed and minimally metabolized. The majority of the given dose of vigabatrin is excreted unchanged in the urine.

Gabapentin and felbamate are thought to act via the *N*-methyl-D-aspartate (NMDA) neurotransmitter. Gabapentin was originally designed to be a GABA analog. In subsequent biological testing, however, it was found that gabapentin does not act on any components of the GABA system, but may exert its influence via the NMDA system. Gabapentin is well tolerated with few side effects. The drug is not metabolized in humans, but is excreted in the urine unchanged. Felbamate acts by an unknown mechanism, although binding to the NMDA receptor at the glycine binding site may be involved. Major adverse reactions to felbamate include aplastic anemia and hepatic failure. Because of these side effects, felbamate is used as a backup drug to other antiepileptics. The drug is well absorbed, largely excreted unchanged, and has a half-life of approximately 20 hours.

Several anticonvulsants (**Figure 18**) are thought to exert their effects in part by modulating cation channels of neurons. Lamotrigine, used in the treatment of adult epilepsy, has several effects on the CNS. It inhibits voltage-sensitive sodium channels, inhibits the release of glutamate, and has weak inhibitory activity at serotonergic (5-HT$_3$) receptors. Lamotrigine is metabolized to a glucuronide conjugate that is inactive. It is 55% protein bound and has a half-life of 24 hours. The therapeutic effect of oxcarbazepine may also involve modulation of voltage-sensitive sodium channels. Oxcarbazepine is a prodrug that is reduced metabolically to 10-hydroxy-oxcarbazepine, which is the active compound.

The half-life of the parent molecule is 2 hours, while that of the active compound is 9 hours. Zonisamide is a sulfonamide. The exact mechanism of action of zonisamide is unknown but may involve sodium and calcium channels. The half-life of zonisamide is long (approximately 63 hours) due to its binding to erythrocytes. Because zonisamide is a sulfonamide, side effects associated with this class of compounds can include severe skin lesions (eg, macules and necrosis, as in Stevens-Johnson syndrome) and blood dyscrasias. Zonisamide is excreted largely unchanged.

Topiramate has an unknown mechanism of action that may involve antagonism at α-amino-3-hydroxy-5-methyl-4-isoxazolepropionic acid (AMPA) receptors. It is an adjunct therapy for partial seizures. Topiramate is 10% to 20% protein bound, has good absorption, and is largely (70%) excreted unchanged. Metabolites that occur are inactive. The half-life of topiramate is 20 hours.

Although the activity of levetiracetam has been evaluated at a number of receptor sites, the mechanism of action remains unclear. It is used as an adjunct therapy in adults with epilepsy. Liver metabolism results in hydrolysis of the amide, yielding the inactive carboxylic acid.

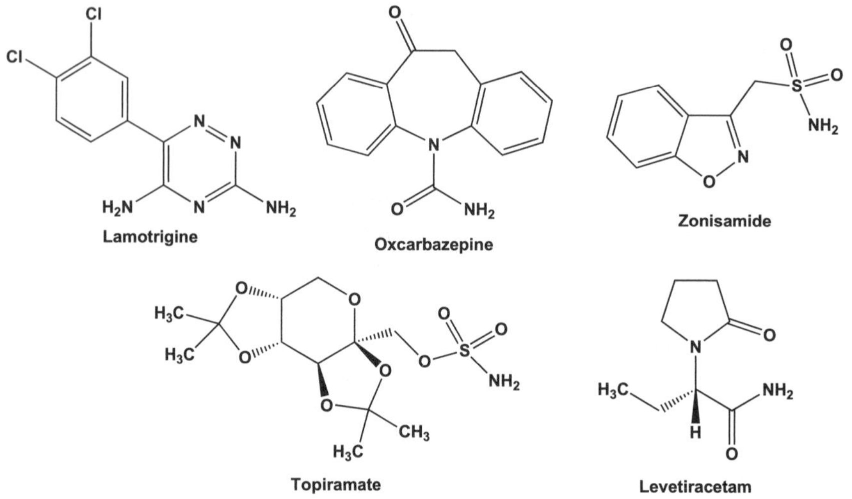

**Figure 18.** *Structures of anticonvulsants thought to exert their effects in part by modulating cation channels of neurons.*

## Suggested Reading

Carter CR, Kozuska JL, Dunn SM. Insights into the structure and pharmacology of GABA(A) receptors. *Future Med Chem.* 2010 May; 2(5):859-875.

Costa E. From GABAA receptor diversity emerges a unified vision of GABAergic inhibition. *Annu Rev Pharmacol Toxicol.* 1998;38:321-351.

Eadie M, Vajda FJE. *Antiepileptic Drugs Pharmacology and Therapeutics (Handbook of Experimental Pharmacology Volume 138).* Berlin, Germany: Springer-Verlag; 1999.

Leach JP, Abassi H. Modern management of epilepsy. *Clin Med.* 2013;13(1):84-86.

Privitera M. Current challenges in the management of epilepsy. *Am J Manag Care.* 2011 Jun;17 Suppl 7:S195-203. Review.

Sigel E, Steinmann ME. Structure, function, and modulation of GABA(A) receptors. *J Biol Chem.* 2012;287(48):40224-40231.

Treiman DM. GABAergic mechanisms in epilepsy. *Epilepsia.* 2001;42 (suppl 3):8-12.

## Discussion Topics

1. What are the mechanisms of action of sedative and hypnotic drugs?

2. What classes of molecules produce the sedative, hypnotic effect?

3. What classes of molecules produce the anticonvulsant effect?

4. What is the mechanism of action of the anticonvulsants?

# Chapter 11

# Analgesic Agents
*by Lemont B. Kier, PhD, and Cynthia S. Dowd, PhD*

Analgesics are a class of drugs used for the alleviation of pain. There are 2 major classes: the opioids, acting in the central nervous system (CNS), and the prostaglandin inhibitors, eg, nonsteroidal anti-inflammatory drugs (NSAIDs). Each of these classes is useful for the relief of pain, although the range of potencies of each puts them in distinct clinical categories. Both classes of drugs are discussed in this chapter.

## Opioids
The discovery of opium and its active component morphine (**Figure 1**) were important events in the search for the relief of pain. Since then, many structural modifications of morphine have produced a class of powerful drugs, the *opioid analgesics*. The opioids are the most important class of analgesics for the relief of severe pain, but they also have a major social impact because of their addiction potential. An important objective of opioid research has been to separate addiction potential from pain relief. Along the way, researchers have gained substantial insight about opioid receptors, their endogenous agonists, and synthetic ligands, resulting in improved treatments for pain management.

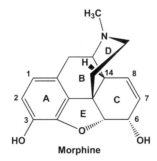

**Figure 1.** *The structure of morphine.*

## The Opioid Receptor Family

Opioid analgesics act on a family of receptors located in the brain, brainstem, and spinal cord. Activation of these receptors mitigates the sensation of pain throughout the body. Endogenous (natural) ligands for the opioid receptors are collectively known as *endorphins*. The term endorphin comes from endo, meaning inside, and morphine, indicating opioid agonist. Endorphins are peptides that are released in response to a painful stimulus. They bind to opioid receptors to decrease a person's perception of the pain. Endorphins include enkephalins, β-endorphins, dynorphins, and neoendorphins (**Table 1**).

The endorphins bind to several subtypes of opioid receptors (**Table 2**). Most clinically available opioid analgesics bind to the μ subtype of receptors and behave as opioid receptor agonists. The drug mimics the action of the endorphins (natural opioid ligands) at the receptor. Effective opioid analgesics act as opioid receptor agonists and decrease the perception of pain.

During studies in which the structure of morphine was varied systematically, it was observed that certain structural modifications produced antagonism in the opioid receptors. These molecules have become useful in treating the effects of opioid overdose. These studies also revealed that some molecules can act as partial agonists *and* as partial antagonists. To date, most molecules examined for clinical opioid activity act at only the μ or at the μ and κ receptors. Ligands that are selective for the κ and δ subtypes exist but are used only as research tools. Currently, there are no clinically useful κ-selective or δ-selective synthetic ligands.

**Table 1.** *Endorphins: Endogenous opioids.*

| | |
|---|---|
| **Enkephalins** | |
| Met-enkephalin | $^+NH_3$–Tyr–Gly–Gly–Phe–Met–$CO_2$ |
| Leu-enkephalin | $^+NH_3$–Tyr–Gly–Gly–Phe–Leu–$CO_2$ |
| **β-Endorphin** | $^+NH_3$–Tyr–Gly–Gly–Phe–Met–Thr–Ser–Glu–Lys–Ser–Gln–Thr–Pro–Leu–Val–Thr–Leu–Phe–Lys–Asn–Ala–Ile–Ile–Lys–Asn–Ala–Tyr–Lys–Lys–Gly–Glu–OH |
| **Dynorphins** | |
| Dynorphin (dyn 1-13) | $^+NH_3$–Tyr–Gly–Gly–Phe–Leu–Arg–Arg–Ile–Arg–Pro–Lys–Leu–Lys–$CO_2$ |
| Dynorphin A (dyn 1-17) | $^+NH_3$–Tyr–Gly–Gly–Phe–Leu–Arg–Arg–Ile–Arg–Pro–Lys– Leu–Lys–Trp–Asp–Asn–Gln–$CO_2$ |
| Dynorphin B (dyn 1-8) | $^+NH_3$–Tyr–Gly–Gly–Phe–Leu–Arg–Arg–Ile–$CO_2$ |
| **Neoendorphins** | |
| α-Neoendorphin | $^+NH_3$–Tyr–Gly–Gly–Phe–Leu–Arg–Lys–Tyr–Pro–Lys–$CO_2$ |
| β-Neoendorphin | $^+NH_3$–Tyr–Gly–Gly–Phe–Leu–Arg–Lys–Tyr–Pro–$CO_2$ |

**Table 2.** *Opioid receptors, ligands, and properties.*

| Receptor Type | Endogenous Ligands (Agonist) | Agonist Properties | Selective Agonists | Selective Antagonists |
|---|---|---|---|---|
| Mu (μ) | Enkephalins | Analgesia, euphoria, respiratory depression, emesis | Morphine and fentanyl analogues | Naloxone, naltrexone |
| $\mu_1$ and $\mu_2$ subtypes | β-endorphin | | | |
| Kappa (κ) | Dynorphins | Analgesia, sedation | None clinically available | None clinically available |
| $\kappa_1$, $\kappa_2$, and $\kappa_3$ subtypes | β-endorphin | | | |
| Delta (δ) | Enkephalins, β-endorphin | Analgesia, respiratory depression | None clinically available | None clinically available |

## Pharmacological Responses to Opioid Analgesics

The opioid analgesics modify the effects of pain impulses in the CNS. They reduce the ability to integrate, interpret, and react to pain. This analgesic effect is often accompanied by sedation, euphoria, and reduced anxiety and suffering. Secondary effects include cough suppression and lowered gut motility, responses that are exploited in antitussive and antidiarrheal drugs, respectively. CNS depression of the respiratory system is an adverse effect associated with overdose.

Clinical and recreational use of opioids can result in physical dependence, tolerance, and addiction. The dependence on opioids manifests when a person experiences withdrawal symptoms after opioid use has ceased. Withdrawal from opioids is characterized by nausea, vomiting, fever, tremors, and nervous excitability. Tolerance to opioids is caused by prolonged use and necessitates higher doses or the use of an alternative analgesic. An important adverse effect of opioid analgesics is addiction. Addiction can develop after prolonged use or a brief exposure, depending on the drug, the dose, and the predisposition of the person. The potential adverse effects of opioid use, balanced with their clinical importance, require close monitoring of opioid therapy.

## Morphine and Related Analogues

Morphine is the major naturally occurring alkaloid in opium and is the prototypical opioid analgesic. Morphine is an amine with properties of a base, having a $pK_a$ of 8.0. At physiological pH, therefore, morphine exists mostly in the protonated form. The un-ionized form is responsible for passage through the blood-brain barrier, whereas the protonated form is thought to be responsible for activity at the receptor. Morphine, being the first isolated opioid, is the reference molecule with which all other opioid analgesics are compared in terms of potency and side effects.

Morphine is metabolized in the liver to 3 major metabolites. The 3-glucuronide metabolite of morphine is inactive and is excreted in the urine. The 6-glucuronide metabolite is active as a μ receptor agonist. In renal failure, the 6-glucuronide metabolite accumulates. Morphine is also metabolized to normorphine by removal of a methyl group (*N*-dealkylation). Normorphine is less active than morphine.

As an analgesic, morphine performs best against dull, constant pain. It has a rapid onset of action and a half-life of 3 to 5 hours. Side effects associated with morphine use are akin to those usually encountered with opioids, such as lowered bowel motility, urinary retention, and some sedation. Respiratory depression, hypotension, nausea, and vomiting can occur. Tolerance is encountered, and, of course, morphine has an addictive potential.

Codeine (**Figure 2**) occurs naturally in the opium mixture extracted from the poppy. It is the 3-methoxy derivative of morphine. The analgesic activity of codeine is due to metabolism of the molecule (by *O*-dealkylation) to morphine, a slow process accounting for its reduced potency. Codeine has approximately 15% of the analgesic effect of morphine. The methoxy group of codeine, however, makes it better absorbed orally. This quality and its antitussive property make codeine useful in a number of mixtures with NSAIDs, such as acetaminophen with codeine. Because of its lower potency, codeine has considerably less addiction potential than morphine and less severe overall adverse effects.

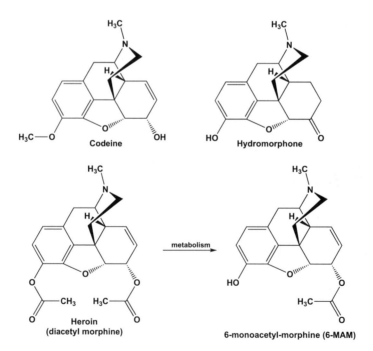

**Figure 2.** *Morphine derivatives.*

Treating morphine with an acetylating reagent produces the 3,6-diacetyl morphine molecule, heroin (Figure 2). Heroin is an illegal substance, but mention is made here because of its prominent use in society. Converting the hydroxyl groups of morphine to acetyl groups makes the molecule more hydrophobic. This conversion enhances its ability to pass through the blood-brain barrier into the CNS, making heroin substantially more potent than morphine. Heroin is metabolized by hydrolysis of the 3-acetyl group to 6-monoacetyl morphine, an active form shown in Figure 2. The addiction potential of heroin is very high.

Reduction of the 7,8-double bond of morphine and oxidation of the 6-hydroxyl group to a ketone produce hydromorphone. These structural changes make the molecule more hydrophobic, enhancing its ability to pass the blood-brain barrier, making it more potent than morphine with a faster onset of action. Hydromorphone (Figure 2) has 3 times the potency of morphine and is correspondingly more addictive. Hydromorphone has a 4 to 5 hour duration of action, and the molecule is eliminated primarily as glucuronide conjugates. The half-life of hydromorphone is 1 to 3 hours.

Alkylation of the 3-hydroxyl group in hydromorphone to give a methoxy group yields hydrocodone (**Figure 3**). This structural change is the same as in the conversion of morphine to codeine, described earlier. This change in both series results in reduced analgesic potency but enhanced antitussive effects. Hydrocodone is an active component, in combination with acetaminophen, in some analgesic drugs.

The addition of a hydroxyl group to the 14-position of hydromorphone leads to oxymorphone. Oxymorphone is more potent than morphine as an analgesic and is longer acting. The addiction potential of morphine, however, remains. Oxymorphone is metabolized by conjugation with glucuronic acid.

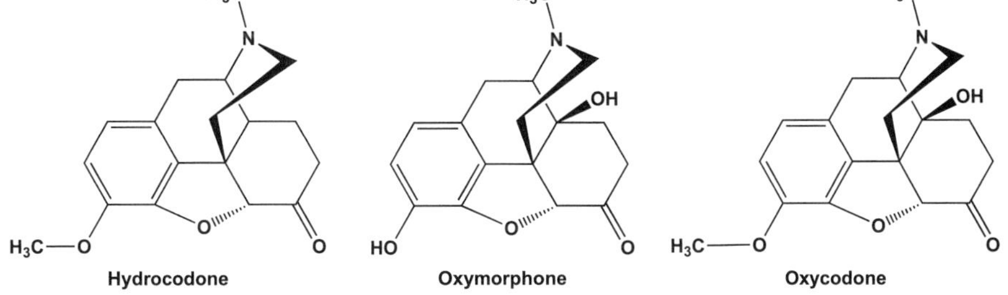

**Figure 3.** *Morphine derivatives.*

Alkylation of the 3-hydroxyl group of oxymorphone to give the methoxy derivative yields oxycodone. These structural changes expectedly lead to weaker analgesic potency but a useful antitussive agent. Oxycodone has a rapid onset of action (10-15 minutes) and a moderate duration of action (3-6 hours). One proprietary form, Oxycontin, a controlled-release formulation, contains a higher dose of oxycodone than is found in other formulations. This form of oxycodone has been used as a drug of abuse because crushing the tablets releases a high dose of the drug. Oxycodone is formulated as combination drugs with aspirin, acetaminophen, and ibuprofen.

## Ring E Modifications of Morphine

The search for an addiction-free opioid analgesic led investigators to systematically modify the multiring structure of morphine. By opening the E ring and putting various substituents on certain positions, some useful drugs were discovered. Levorphanol (**Figure 4**), has 5 times the analgesic potency of morphine but retains the addictive potential. Levorphanol has an onset of action of 10 to 60 minutes, and its effects last 4 to 8 hours. The marketed isomer of levorphanol is the levo form.

The dextro isomer of levorphanol, when converted to the 3-methoxy derivative, is the effective antitussive drug dextromethorphan (Figure 4). It is as effective as codeine with no respiratory depression and a low addiction potential.

## Ring C Modifications of Morphine

Another approach to modify the structure of morphine was the opening of the C ring plus removal of the E ring. These changes produced a series of effective analgesics (**Figure 5**) in the benzomorphan group. Pentazocine is an agonist at the κ receptor and an antagonist at the μ receptor. The levo isomer is the most active. It has only 30% of the potency of morphine and a short onset of action (2-3 minutes). The half-life is 3 to 4 hours, and the molecule is metabolized by oxidation and glucuronide conjugation.

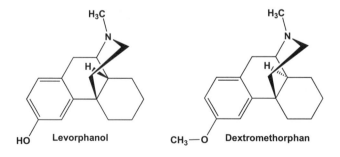

**Figure 4.** *Ring E modifications of morphine.*

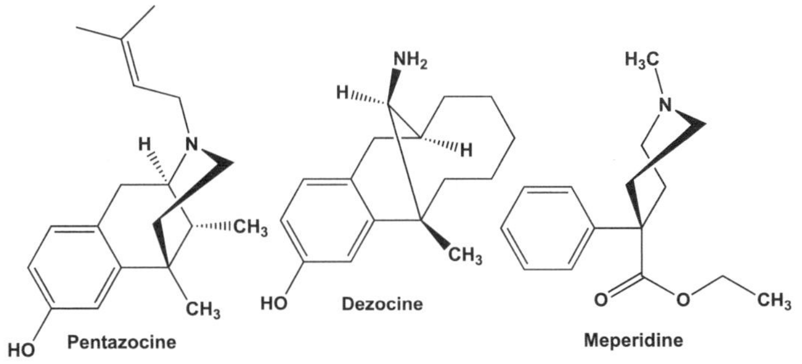

**Figure 5.** *Ring C and ring B modifications of morphine.*

Dezocine is a agonist/antagonist analgesic. Structurally, it differs from the other opioids in that it is a primary amine. The result of this modification is that dezocine binds to both μ and δ opioid receptors. It is comparable to morphine in potency. Dezocine exhibits some respiratory depression in higher doses. The onset of action, duration, and half-life are similar to those of pentazocine.

## Ring B Modifications of Morphine

Opening the B ring in morphine, in addition to the previously described changes in the C and E rings, produced a new series of analgesic drugs. In this group of analgesics, only the A and D rings of morphine remain intact. In addition, the 3-hydroxy group, found in the other morphinelike molecules, is absent.

Meperidine, a simplified morphine structure, has approximately 10% of the potency of morphine. While meperidine (Figure 5) is postulated to bind at the μ receptor in an orientation different from that of other opioid analgesics, it produces the same therapeutic effects as other μ agonists. Meperidine is addictive and has side effects similar to other morphine derivatives. Its analgesic effect is of short duration and rapid onset (5-15 minutes). Meperidine has been extensively used in obstetrics because of its favorable pharmacokinetic profile. It is metabolized by demethylation of the nitrogen atom to give normeperidine. This metabolite is thought to initiate seizures.

## Opioid Antagonists

During the structural modifications of morphine, it was discovered that alkylation of the nitrogen atom with groups larger than methyl produced compounds that antagonized the effects of known opioid drugs. Because of the extreme toxic effects associated with opioid use, the development of molecules to counteract these undesired effects was a breakthrough in analgesic therapy.

The opioid antagonists have the following effects:
- Reversal of the analgesic effect of an opioid drug (ie, observation of the return of pain)
- Precipitation of withdrawal symptoms in a person dependent on opioids
- Reversal of respiratory depression in cases of opioid overdose

Furthermore, the development of opioid antagonists allowed the discernment between the various opioid receptor types and determination of selectivity profiles for opioid analgesics.

Only a small number of pure opioid antagonists have been identified. Clinically, these molecules are used in treating symptoms resulting from opioid overdose. Opioid antagonists can also be used to detect addiction to opioids by producing withdrawal symptoms in the person.

## Pure Antagonists

Naloxone is a derivative of oxymorphone and acts as a pure antagonist. It has an extremely rapid onset of action (<1 minute) and a short duration of action (20-60 minutes). Naloxone (**Figure 6**), is metabolized in the liver and has a half-life of 60 to 90 minutes. Naltrexone differs structurally from naloxone only in the nitrogen atom substituent. It is a pure opioid antagonist with a much longer duration of action than naloxone (24-72 hours). For this reason, naltrexone can be used for long periods of detoxification. Nalmefene is a pure antagonist that is 10-20 times as potent as naltrexone. Nalmefene has an onset of approximately 10 minutes and a half-life of 9 hours.

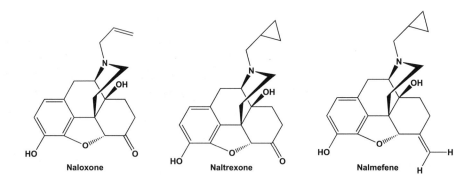

**Figure 6.** *Pure opioid antagonists.*

## Mixed Agonist-Antagonists

Nalbuphine hydrochloride acts as an antagonist at the μ opioid receptors and as an agonist at the κ opioid receptors. Nalbuphine (**Figure 7**) has approximately 25% of the antagonistic activity of naloxone and analgesic potency equal to that of morphine. However, nalbuphine does not have the abuse potential associated with morphine, and there is less respiratory depression.

Buprenorphine acts as a partial agonist at the μ and κ receptors and as an antagonist at the δ receptors. It has been shown that buprenorphine (Figure 7) is more active than morphine, but it does not produce a maximal amount of analgesia. It is extensively metabolized in the first pass by glucuronidation at the 3-position. Respiratory depression is modest. The onset of action is 10 to 30 minutes with a duration of 6 to 10 hours.

Butorphanol is a mixed agonist-antagonist analgesic. It acts as an antagonist at the μ receptors, with one-sixth the efficacy of naloxone as an opioid antagonist. Butorphanol (Figure 7) is a stronger agonist than morphine at the κ receptors, but this difference does not result in a stronger analgesic effect. The onset of action is rapid (<10 minutes), and the duration of action is 3 to 5 hours. Butorphanol results in less respiratory depression than other more effective analgesics. Common side effects are nausea, sedation, and sweating. Pentazocine is also a mixed agonist-antagonist that is used as an analgesic.

## Fentanyl and Related Analogues

Fentanyl and its related molecules (**Figure 8**) are derivatives of propionyl aniline. They are potent analgesics, acting at the μ receptors. The structure of the fentanyl family of compounds is closely related to that of meperidine. The fentanyl group does not have a phenolic hydroxyl group. Such a substituent on these molecules, in fact, greatly reduces analgesic activity.

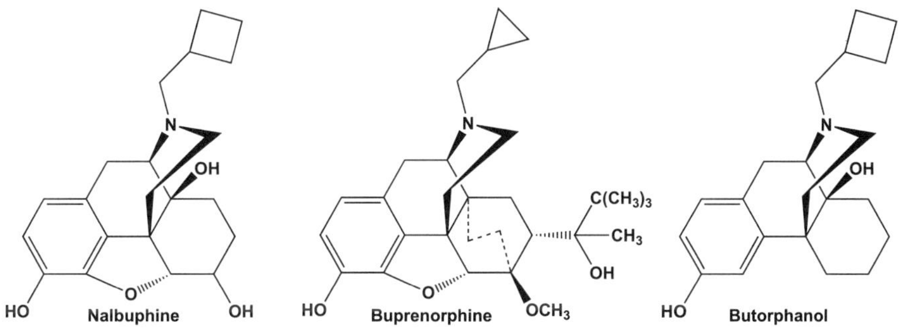

**Figure 7.** *Mixed opioid agonist-antagonists.*

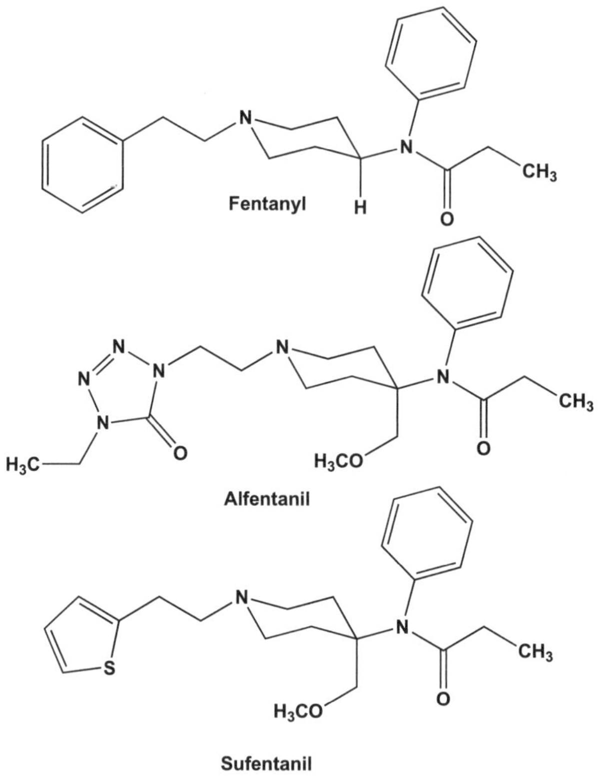

**Figure 8.** *Fentanyl and its derivatives.*

Fentanyl citrate is approximately 100 times more potent than morphine as an analgesic. It is used for moderate to severe pain. Fentanyl is also used as a supplement to general anesthesia, providing analgesia for a short period. Because of its hydrophobic character, fentanyl is highly protein bound (80%-90%) and distributes to muscle and fat tissue. However, the increased hydrophobicity of fentanyl is responsible for the rapid onset of action (1-15 minutes), much faster than that of morphine. Fentanyl has a short duration of action (0.5-2 hours), which increases after repeated administration. The half-life is 2 to 3 hours. Side effects of fentanyl can include respiratory depression and hypotension. Fentanyl results in lower histamine release than morphine and has fewer emetic effects.

Alfentanil has 25% of the potency of fentanyl and a shorter duration (0.5-1 hour). It does not depress the cardiovascular system; hence, it can be used in surgery. It is metabolized faster than fentanyl, accounting for its short duration of activity. Alfentanil has a lower $pK_a$ than other fentanyl derivatives and is, therefore, able to cross the blood-brain barrier faster. Because of this ability, alfentanil has a very rapid onset of action. Metabolism of alfentanil proceeds by dealkylation of the oxygen and substituted nitrogen atoms, yielding inactive metabolites.

Sufentanil is 10 times more potent than fentanyl (1,000 times more potent than morphine) with half of the duration of action. It has a rapid onset of action (1-3 minutes). O-Desmethyl sufentanil is an active metabolite but occurs in such low concentrations that its therapeutic effect is considered negligible.

## Methadone and Related Analogues

The methadone group of drugs (**Figure 9**) resembles the fentanyl and meperidine analgesics in that there is no phenolic hydroxyl group present. Methadone is a μ receptor agonist with a longer duration of action than morphine. The typical duration of action of methadone is 6 to 8 hours; however, the duration is extended with repeated doses. For this reason, it is used to treat opioid addiction. Methadone is orally active with less constipation and fewer emetic side effects than morphine. It is metabolized in the liver by demethylation of the nitrogen atom. The half-life of methadone is 15 to 29 hours.

Levoalpha acetylmethadole (LAAM) is longer acting than methadone (up to 72 hours). Metabolism of LAAM occurs by successive demethylation of the nitrogen atom. Each of these metabolites is active, extending the duration of action of the drug. Cases of arrhythmia were noted with the use of LAAM.

## Opioids Used as Antidiarrheal Drugs

Although most opioids are used as analgesics, some opioids are used clinically as antidiarrheal agents (**Figure 10**). It is thought that these drugs exert their effect by indirectly affecting cholinergic stimulation of peristaltic muscles in the intestine. Opioid release onto cholinergic neurons in the intestine stimulates production and release of acetylcholine, inhibiting peristalsis.

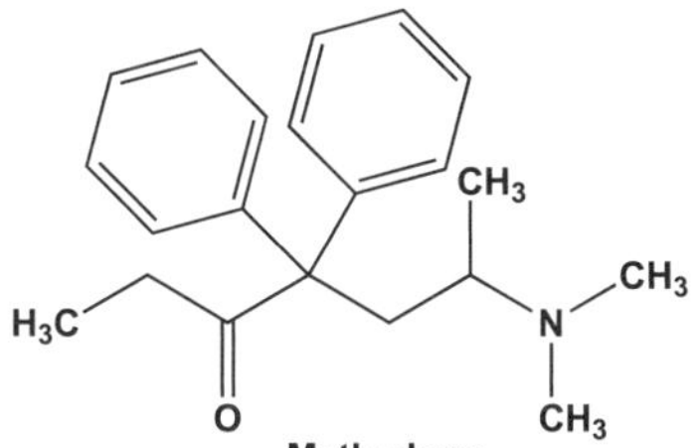


Methadone

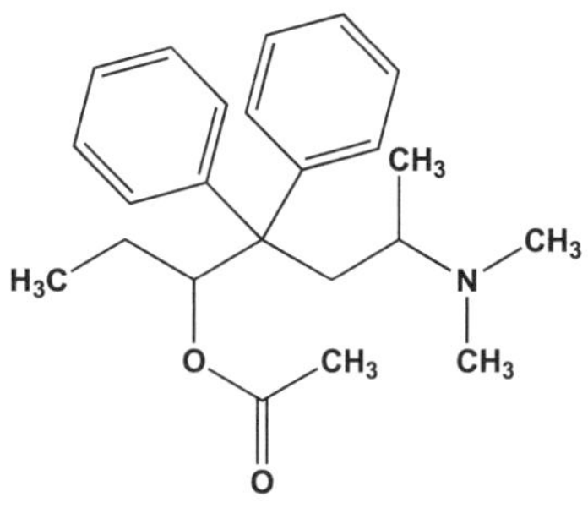


Levoalpha acetylmethadole (LAAM)

**Figure 9.** *The structure of methadone.*

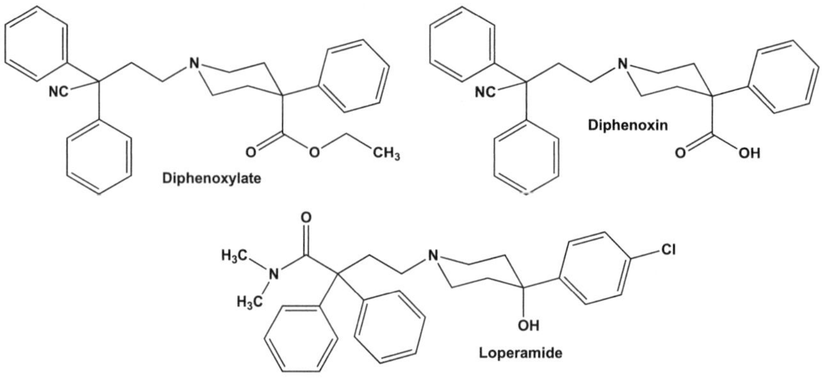

**Figure 10.** *Opioids used as antidiarrheal drugs.*

Because of hydrophilic substituents in these molecules, passage of these drugs through the blood-brain barrier is negligible. Therefore, antidiarrheal doses result in no CNS effects, but higher doses may precipitate withdrawal symptoms and may cause respiratory depression. In children, the blood-brain barrier is not fully formed; hence, passage of drugs into the CNS may occur. Thus, opioid antidiarrheal drugs should be used with caution in pediatric patients.

Diphenoxylate in combination with atropine is an opioid antidiarrheal drug. The presence of atropine in this formulation is to discourage taking excessive amounts of the drug. Atropine, at high doses, results in unpleasant side effects. The onset of action of diphenoxylate is less than 1 hour and therapeutic effects last 3 to 4 hours. Diphenoxylate has a half-life of 2 to 3 hours. The metabolic product of diphenoxylate, diphenoxin, is 5 times more active than diphenoxylate.

Structurally related to diphenoxylate and diphenoxin, loperamide is the active component in an over-the-counter antidiarrheal drug. It does not cross the blood-brain barrier. Loperamide acts to increase transit time, inhibit peristalsis, and decrease electrolyte and fluid loss. The onset of action is less than 1 hour, and the half-life is 7 to 14 hours, substantially longer than that of diphenoxylate.

## Nonsteroidal Anti-inflammatory Drugs (NSAIDs)

The NSAIDs are a mixed set of chemical compounds linked by a common mechanism, the inhibition of enzymes called *cyclooxygenases*. The major advantage of NSAIDs is that they provide relief from moderate pain without the respiratory and emetic adverse effects associated with opioids.

Disease and trauma induce the synthesis of a group of compounds called prostaglandins. Their synthesis in an injured cell begins with arachidonic acid. Injury to the cell mobilizes the activity of the cyclooxygenases to convert arachidonic acid to a number of prostaglandins and related compounds (**Figure 11**). There are 3 types of cyclooxygenases: COX-1, COX-2, and COX-3. These enzymes are responsible for the synthesis of different subsets of prostaglandins. The NSAIDs act by inhibiting the cyclooxygenases, thereby preventing the cascade of prostaglandin synthesis. The effect of this inhibition is the elimination or minimization of the symptoms caused by excess prostaglandin production. The major therapeutic effect of the NSAIDs is thought to be due to inhibition of COX-2, whereas the side effects that occur with NSAID use are thought to arise because of the inhibition of COX-1. With the discovery of COX-3, this enzyme family continues to be the focus of investigation.

Increased levels of prostaglandins have a role in elevated body temperature, maintenance of the protective lining of the gastric mucosa, pain, and increased swelling at the site of injury. The NSAIDs, as COX inhibitors, are designed to inhibit these actions by decreasing prostaglandin synthesis. Antipyretics, typified by acetaminophen, are used to reduce body temperature. Anti-inflammatory drugs, such as celecoxib and rofecoxib, decrease the inflammation and pain associated with chronic conditions such as rheumatoid arthritis and osteoarthritis. Moderate pain is often ameliorated with agents such as ibuprofen and naproxen.

The most pronounced side effects of NSAIDs are heartburn and the risk of ulcers. Certain prostaglandins ($PGI_2$ and $PGE_2$) are responsible for the production of cytoprotective mucus in the stomach. Inhibition of these prostaglandins by NSAIDs lowers this protection from gastric acid, leading to mild dyspepsia, heartburn, and, in more severe cases, ulceration of the stomach or duodenum. This side effect is so prevalent that cessation of use of the particular NSAID is often necessary. Most of the traditional NSAIDs produce this side effect because they inhibit COX-1 and COX-2. The newer groups of NSAIDs, the selective COX-2 inhibitors, do not inhibit COX-1; thus, the effect on gastric protection is minimal.

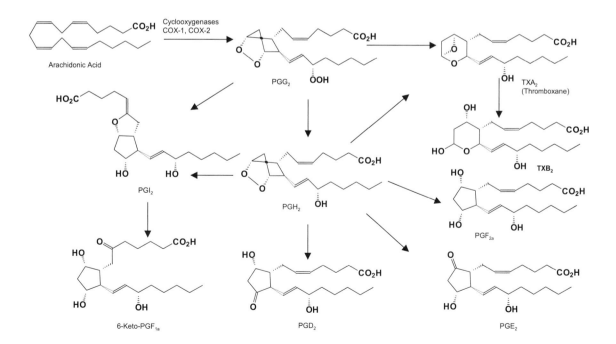

**Figure 11.** *Synthesis of prostaglandins (PG) and thromboxanes (TX). COX indicates cyclooxygenase.*

All NSAIDs, with the exception of choline magnesium trisalicylate (a salt form of salicylic acid) and COX-2 selective NSAIDs, inhibit platelet aggregation. This side effect usually lasts only 1 to 2 days. Inhibition caused by aspirin lasts 4 to 7 days. For this reason, aspirin is often prescribed as prophylaxis against myocardial infarction and stroke. The NSAIDs can also lead to nephrotoxic effects. Therefore, caution is needed in the use of NSAIDs by people with hypertension, renal insufficiency, and/or heart failure.

## Aspirin and Related Salicylates

As early as the 18th century, scientists recognized the antipyretic effect of willow bark. The active ingredient of willow bark, methyl salicylate, yields salicylic acid (**Figure 12**) on hydrolysis. Salicylic acid was used as the lead compound to discover new analgesics. One of the first derivatives was the acetate ester of salicylic acid, aspirin.

Aspirin is rapidly absorbed in the stomach and quickly hydrolyzed to salicylic acid, the active compound. Aspirin has a half-life of 15 to 20 minutes. The therapeutic effect of aspirin lasts 4 to 6 hours. As was later discovered, aspirin works by inhibiting COX-1 and COX-2. The major side effect of aspirin is gastric irritation that can ultimately lead to ulcer formation. To lessen these effects, aspirin has been formulated with buffering agents and enteric coatings. The adverse effects of aspirin can include asthma, urticaria, and tinnitus. Aspirin has been implicated in the hepatic injury observed in Reye syndrome, a severe condition that can arise when young children receive aspirin or salicylate-containing compounds. Aspirin is metabolized in the liver (**Figure 13**). The major excreted form is salicyluric acid, a conjugate with glycine.

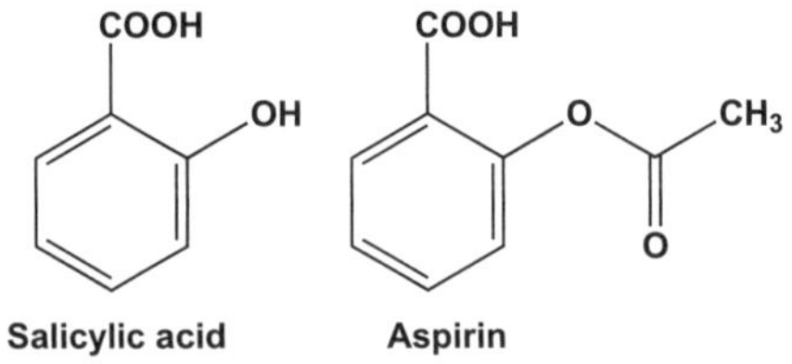

**Figure 12.** *Salicylic acid and its derivative, aspirin.*

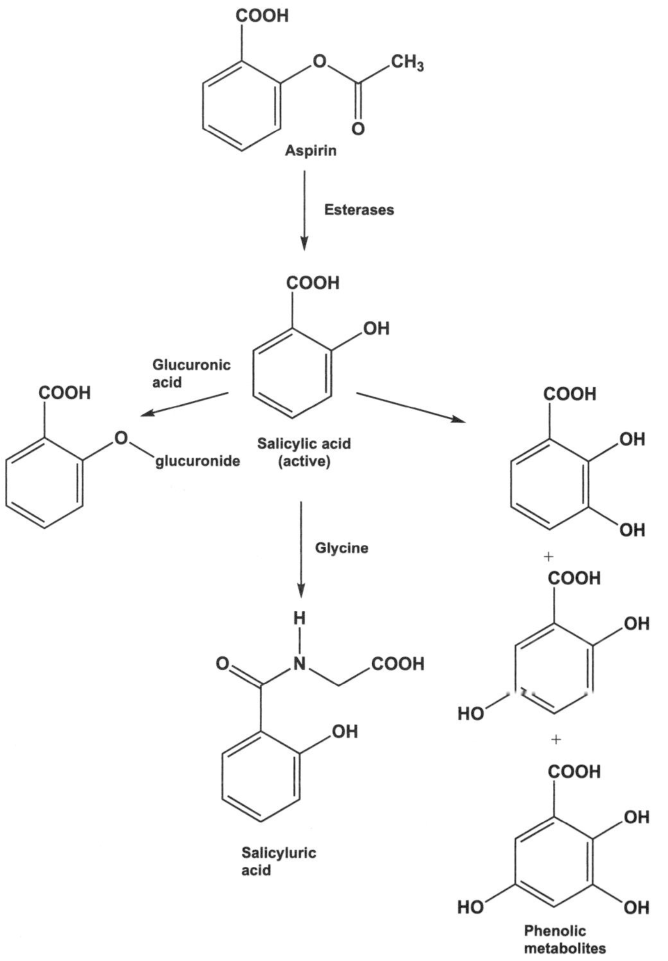

**Figure 13.** *Metabolism of aspirin. Esterases hydrolyze the parent compound to its active form, salicylic acid. Conjugation pathways form glucuronide and salicyluric products. Metabolic hydroxylation results in the formation of various phenolic metabolites.*

The critical structural feature of the salicylates is the acidic carboxyl group. All of the effective salicylates have this feature. Modifications of salicylic acid that have resulted in successful drugs have been those designed to alter absorption and half-life characteristics. The absorption and half-life of a drug molecule can often be improved by the addition of nonpolar groups to increase the hydrophobicity of the molecule. Addition of phenyl or alkyl substituents, for example, can yield molecules with increased membrane permeability (leading to increased systemic absorption) and lower excretion and metabolism rates (leading to increased half-lives).

Diflunisal is a difluorophenyl analog of salicylic acid (**Figure 14**). The difluorophenyl group adds considerable hydrophobic character so that the drug crosses membranes easily. The fluoro groups also reduce the metabolic hydroxylation of the phenyl ring, thereby extending the half-life of the drug. The half-life of diflunisal is 5 to 20 hours, compared with the half-life of salicylic acid of 3 to 5 hours. Increased hydrophobicity also makes diflunisal highly bound by serum proteins (>99%). Diflunisal is metabolized by conjugation with glucuronic acid, which is inactive.

Similar effects can be seen in salsalate, olsalazine, and sulfasalazine, in which the addition of large hydrophobic substituents on the salicylate structure accomplish the same clinical objectives (Figure 14). Salsalate is hydrolyzed in the liver to yield 2 molecules of salicylic acid. In this case, esterification of 2 molecules together allows for efficient absorption, followed by hydrolysis to the active compounds. Olsalazine and sulfasalazine are used in the treatment of irritable bowel syndrome. Both molecules are metabolized in the intestine to give 5-aminosalicylic acid, the active molecule. This molecule has been shown to be active against irritable bowel syndrome and ulcerative colitis.

## Anthranilic Acids

The group of anthranilic acid NSAIDs represents a modification of the salicylic acids in which the phenolic hydroxyl group is replaced by an amine group (**Figure 15**). Examples in this group are mefenamic acid, meclofenamate, and flufenamic acid. The substituent on the amine group is a phenyl ring, imparting a greater degree of hydrophobicity to the molecule. This characteristic facilitates absorption and increased potency. These analgesics inhibit prostaglandin synthesis by inhibiting COXs. Because they inhibit COX-1 and COX-2 at about the same level, they produce the same gastric side effects as the salicylates.

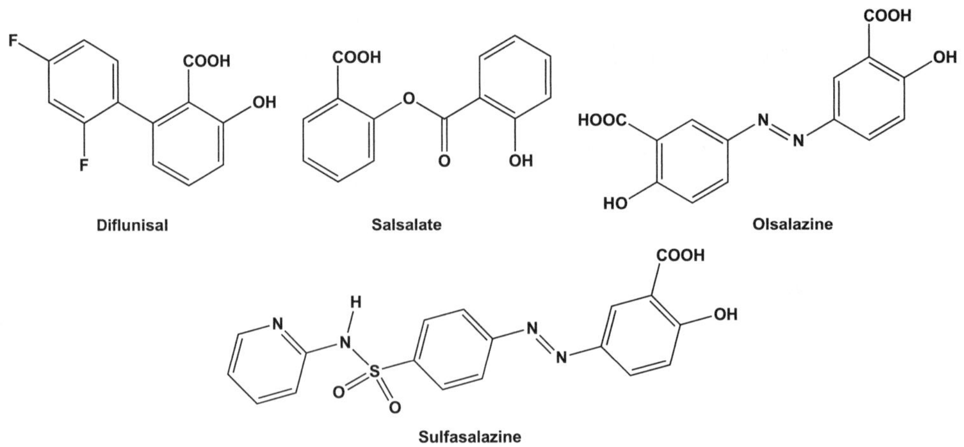

**Figure 14.** *Salicylates related to aspirin.*

# Arylacetic Acids

Arylacetic acids (**Figure 16**) were originally introduced as anti-inflammatory drugs because of the belief that the symptoms were produced by serotonin (5-hydroxytryptamine). The first arylacetic acid derivative was indomethacin, designed to be a serotonin inhibitor. Indomethacin was active in the CNS and caused hallucinations, possibly because it mimicked serotonin at its receptor binding site. To modify the molecule to eliminate the CNS effect, the nitrogen atom of the indole ring was replaced by a bioisosteric feature, a double bond, to form sulindac. Sulindac was found to act as a prodrug. During metabolism, the sulfoxide is reduced to a sulfide, which is the active form of the drug. Alternative metabolism of sulindac leads to the sulfone, which is inactive. Other modifications of the arylacetic acids led to the development of tolmetin, zomepirac, and ketorolac. These drugs work by inhibition of COX-1 and COX-2 to stop prostaglandin synthesis.

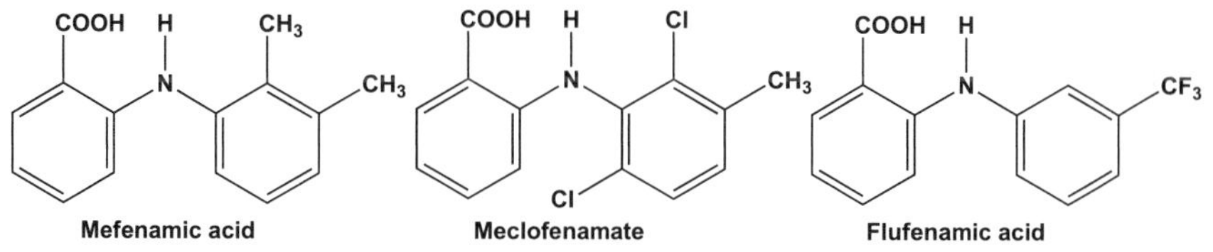

**Figure 15.** *Anthranilic acids.*

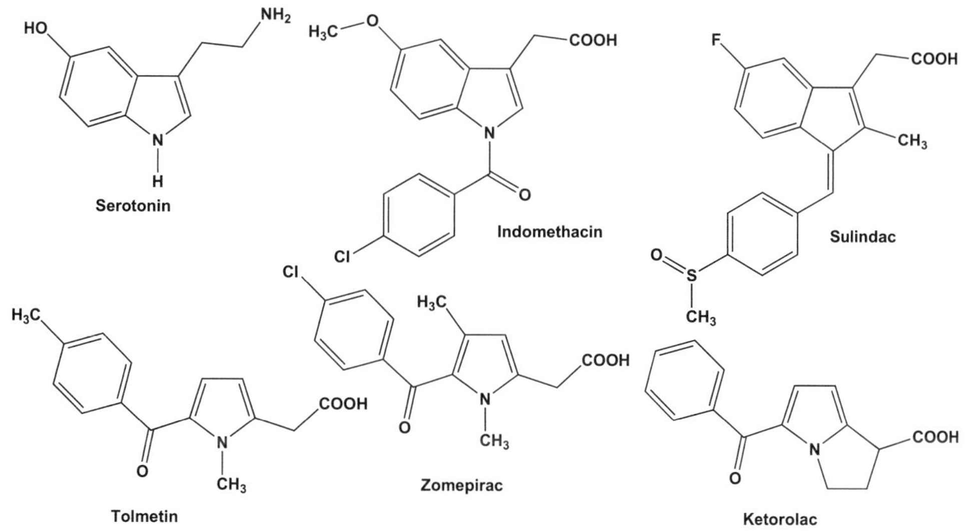

**Figure 16.** *Arylacetic acids.*

## Pyrazoles

A compound introduced more than 100 years ago as a nonnarcotic analgesic was antipyrine. Antipyrine belongs to the group of molecules called pyrazoles because of its 5-membered ring containing a carbonyl and 2 nitrogen atoms (**Figure 17**). Its action and potency equaled that of aspirin, but the finding of agranulocytosis associated with antipyrine ended its use. Despite this result, antipyrine served as a model for further development to achieve a safe NSAID. From these studies, a series of NSAIDs resulted having useful therapeutic effects and safer clinical outcomes.

Phenylbutazone is a structurally related NSAID. It is metabolized by hydroxylation of the phenyl ring to produce another active compound, oxyphenbutazone. A second metabolite, ketobutazone, is formed by the metabolic oxidation of the butyl side chain. All 3 compounds have the same mechanism of action, inhibition of cyclooxygenase with the result of inhibiting prostaglandin synthesis.

Although the pyrazoles lack a carboxylic acid, found in all of the active forms of the drugs so far discussed, they are able to function in the same way at the enzyme active site because of the tautomerization of the diketo ring to form a small amount of an enol (**Figure 18**). The enol is sufficiently acidic to mimic a carboxylic acid at the COX active site. If the hydrogen atom on the 5-membered ring is replaced with a methyl group, keto-enol tautomerism does not occur, and the molecule is inactive.

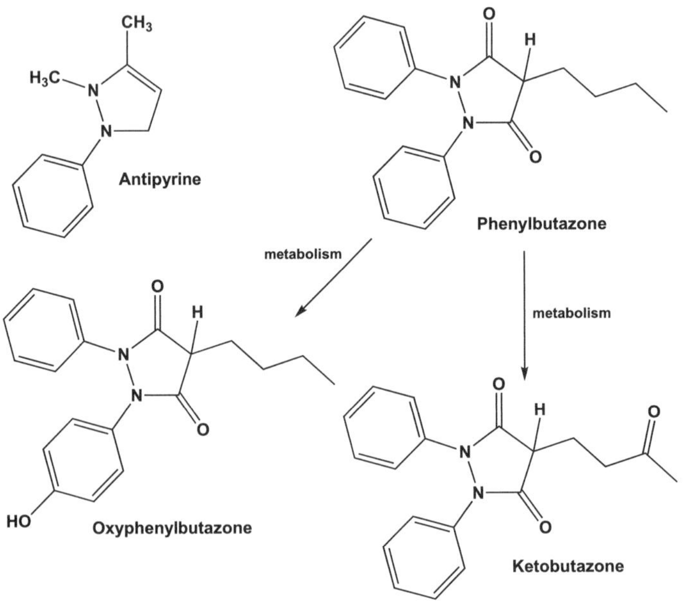

**Figure 17.** *Structures of pyrazole nonsteroidal anti-inflammatory drugs.*

## Propionic Acids

A newer series of NSAIDs has been developed from the 2-arylpropionic acid structure (**Figure 19**). One of the most recognizable members of this group of compounds is ibuprofen. Ibuprofen is rapidly absorbed and has an onset of action of 30 to 60 minutes. With analgesic effects lasting 4 to 6 hours, ibuprofen is metabolized in the liver to inactive compounds. The half-life of ibuprofen is 2 to 4 hours. Naproxen is a propionic acid derivative in which the phenyl ring has been extended to form a naphthyl ring. Compared with ibuprofen, naproxen has a longer duration of action (7 hours) and a longer half-life (12-15 hours). Fenoprofen, ketoprofen, and flurbiprofen are related molecules in this series, in which a second phenyl ring is added via an ether linkage. All of these drugs inhibit COX-1 and COX-2 nonselectively and result in the same side effect profile as seen with other NSAIDs. These drugs are, however, reported to be better tolerated than other NSAIDs. The propionic acid derivatives are very highly bound by serum proteins (97%-99%). They are metabolized by hydroxylation of the phenyl rings and subsequently conjugated with glucuronic acid and eliminated in the urine.

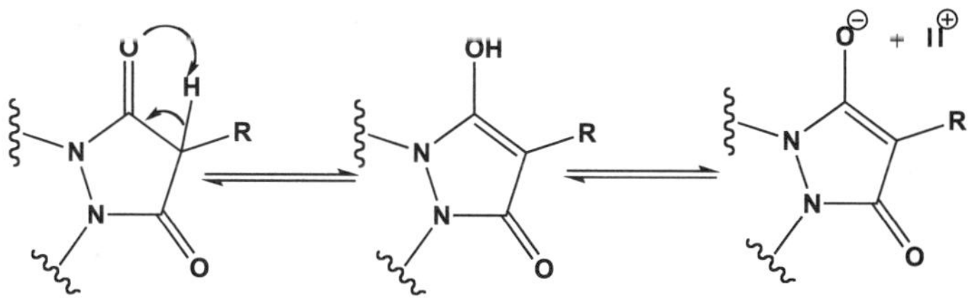

**Figure 18.** *Tautomerism between the diketo and enolic forms of pyrazoles. The enol form of the molecule is acidic and thought to be biologically active.*

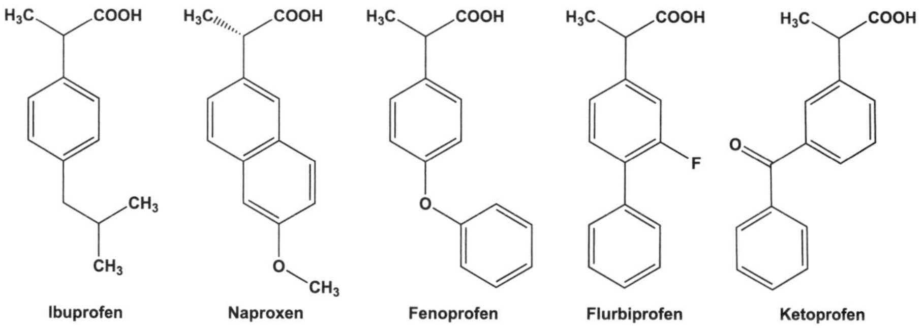

**Figure 19.** *Propionic acids.*

## Selective COX-2 Inhibitors

A small series of molecules has been developed that inhibits only the COX-2 subtype and not COX-1 (**Figure 20**). Because many of the undesirable effects associated with NSAID use are thought to be via COX-1, the selective COX-2 inhibitors show a diminished side effect profile compared with older drugs. Specifically, the gastric side effects experienced with earlier NSAIDs are greatly reduced.

Celecoxib is a substituted pyrazole that has a sulfonamide functionality. Celecoxib exhibits a high ratio of COX-2 to COX-1 inhibition. It is used in the treatment of osteoarthritis and rheumatoid arthritis. It is an effective anti-inflammatory and analgesic drug with modest side effects. Side effects can include epigastric pain, drowsiness, and lethargy. Another drug in this group, rofecoxib, retained the 2 phenyl rings of celecoxib, but the sulfonamide was replaced with a sulfone and the pyrazole ring with an unsaturated lactone. Rofecoxib was used for osteoarthritis and acute pain but was removed from the market in 2004 because of a high risk of cardiovascular side effects.

## Other NSAIDs

Several other NSAIDs are available with selected advantages (**Figure 21**). Piroxicam is a cyclic sulfonamide with an extremely long half-life, 45 to 50 hours, longer than any other NSAID. Nabumetone has a very simplified structure that is reminiscent of the propionic acids. Nabumetone is metabolized in the liver to 6-methoxy-2-naphthylacetic acid which provides the carboxylate group responsible for cyclooxygenase inhibition. The anti-inflammatory activity of nabumetone is substantially better than that of aspirin, but it is less effective as an analgesic. These NSAIDs act by inhibiting the COXs with no selectivity between COX-1 and COX-2. They have the same side effect profile, including gastric distress, as other nonselective NSAIDs.

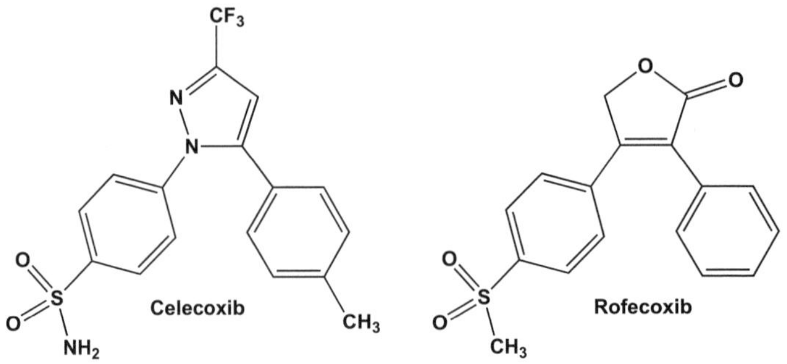

**Figure 20.** *Selective cyclooxygenase-2 inhibitors.*

## Miscellaneous Analgesics

Acetanilide (**Figure** 22) was an early nonnarcotic analgesic compound. It was later removed from use because of toxic effects, but it served as a lead compound in the search for safer NSAIDs in the structural group of aminophenols. One of the members of this group is phenacetin. It was once formulated with aspirin and caffeine as APC or PAC. Phenacetin is metabolized to acetaminophen, a well-known NSAID. Acetaminophen is an effective analgesic and antipyretic, but is weaker than aspirin as an anti-inflammatory drug. Recent research indicates acetaminophen (paracetamol) may act through the TRPA1 sensor protein found on some nerve cells. Pathways where acetaminophen exerts its effects include inhibition of endogenous pyrogens, action on the CNS thermoregulatory center, and depression of the pain response in certain nerves.

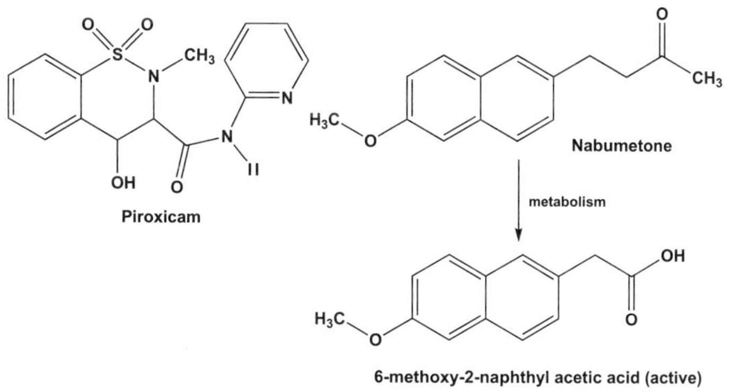

**Figure 21.** *Various nonsteroidal anti-inflammatory drugs.*

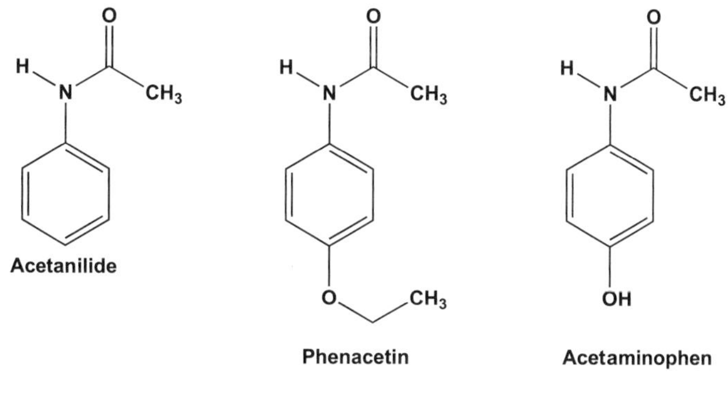

**Figure 22.** *Acetanilide and analogs of aminophenol.*

Acetaminophen is metabolized to glucuronide and sulfate conjugates. Severe toxic effects, related to its metabolism, can occur as a result of acetaminophen overdose. The toxic effects are caused by the saturation of the metabolizing pathways for glucuronidation and sulfation. A reactive intermediate formed by cytochrome P-450 metabolism of acetaminophen reacts with the available glutathione. Following glutathione depletion, this intermediate reacts with any proteinaceous material, leading to toxic effects. The antidote for the toxic effects of acetaminophen is administration of acetyl cysteine, which acts as an effective target for the reactive intermediate and diminishes toxic consequences.

Several molecules are used as analgesics that do not fall into the opioid or the NSAID class of compounds (**Figure 23**). Clonidine is an $\alpha_2$ adrenergic receptor agonist. Stimulation of $\alpha_2$ receptors by clonidine results in a decreased sympathetic response to pain. Clonidine is used as adjunct epidural analgesic therapy for patients who are unresponsive or tolerant to other epidural opiates. The duration of action is 6 to 10 hours, and the half-life is 6 to 20 hours. Hyaluronan derivatives (sodium hyaluronate) are polysaccharides used in osteoarthritis, especially where other forms of analgesia have failed. The formulation is thought to act as a lubricant in the tissues and to ease discomfort. Lidocaine is a local anesthetic and is often used as a topical analgesic. It can be applied before intravenous needle or catheter insertion, immunization, or other procedures requiring needle application. Lidocaine decreases the nerve cell membrane permeability to sodium ions. After this action, the cell cannot meet the threshold required to propagate the nerve signal.

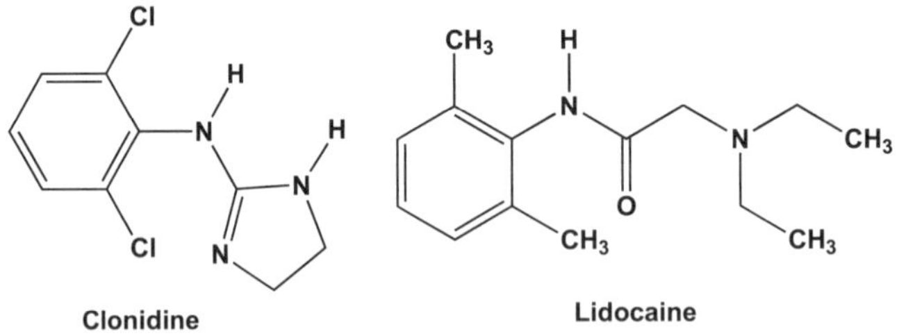

Clonidine

Lidocaine

**Figure 23.** *Miscellaneous analgesics that are neither opioids nor nonsteroidal anti-inflammatory drugs.*

## Suggested Reading

Andersson DA, Gentry C, Alenmyr L, et al. TRPA1 mediates spinal antinociception induced by acetaminophen and the cannabinoid Δ9-tetrahydrocannabiorcol. *Nat Commun.* 2011; Nov 22;551:2-11.

Cox BM. Recent developments in the study of opioid receptors. *Mol Pharmacol.* 2013 Apr;83(4):723-728.

de Leon-Casasola OA. Opioids for chronic pain: new evidence, new strategies, safe prescribing. *Am J Med.* 2013 Mar;126(3 Suppl 1):S3-11.

Waldhoer M, Bartlett SE, Wistler JL. Opioid receptors. *Annu Rev Biochem.* 2004;73:953-990.

Wall PD, Melzak R, McMahon SB, Koltzenburg M. eds. *Textbook of Pain.* 5th ed. New York, NY: Elsevier; 2006.

Yaksh TL, Wallace MS. Opioids, analgesia, and pain management. In: Brunton LL, Chabner BA, Knollmann B, eds. *Goodman and Gilman's The Pharmacological Basis of Therapeutics.* 12th ed. New York, NY: McGraw-Hill Medical; 2011:481-526.

## Discussion Topics

1. What are the 2 major classes of analgesics and their mechanisms?

2. What is the clinical role of opioid antagonists?

3. What is the mechanism of opioids used as antidiarrheal drugs?

4. What are the 4 opioid receptor types and their properties?

5. Discuss the clinical benefits of NSAIDs over opioids.

6. The salicylates are structurally and mechanistically similar to aspirin. Discuss the effect of specific structural changes on metabolism and half-life. Why would this be useful?

7. In general, the NSAIDs are structurally simpler compared with the opioids. Discuss the possible advantages and disadvantages of this observation.

# Chapter 12

# Psychotropic Drugs
*by Cynthia S. Dowd, PhD, and Lemont B. Kier, PhD*

The latter half of the 20th century and the beginning of the 21st century have brought tremendous advances in our knowledge of the brain and how it functions. Even though we are far from knowing the precise details of such complex mechanisms as memory, emotion, and problem solving, we have gained insight into the chemical stimuli responsible for and the influence of chemical substances on certain feelings and behaviors. These insights have resulted in a class of molecules called *psychotropic drugs.*

Psychotropic drugs include several structural classes of molecules that are effective medicines for a range of neurological disorders. Early medications resulted in several unpleasant side effects that limited their use and compliance with medication regimens. More recent advances in our understanding of specific receptor types, however, led to the discovery of second- and third-generation agents with increased potency and lower incidences of side effects. The improved safety profiles of these newer drugs have made the psychotropics one of the most-often prescribed and profitable drug classes.

The psychotropics target specific receptors in the brain and modify the nerve impulses that are sent and received. Because we have some information on which receptors affect a person's behavior, emotions, and mood, drugs targeting these receptors are used to treat disorders affecting these mental processes. The diagnosis of psychiatric disorders remains a complex task and, oftentimes, the same drug is useful for more than a single indication. This chapter, and others in this book, contains several examples of the same drug used for different indications.

This chapter introduces the major classes of psychotropic drugs, their mechanisms of action, and other characteristics such as metabolites and side effects. The major classes of psychotropic drugs discussed are the following:
- Antidepressants
- Anxiolytics (antianxiety drugs)
- Antipsychotics
- Stimulants

## Antidepressants
Depression can manifest itself through several symptoms, including extreme sadness, anhedonia, changes in sleep and eating behaviors, and a decrease in concentration. These symptoms can be severe enough to interfere with a person's normal ability to carry out everyday functions. Treatment of depression can include psychotherapy, pharmacological intervention, and/or electrostimulation.

Evidence indicates that depression can be caused by an imbalance in the levels of serotonin, dopamine, and/or norepinephrine neurotransmitters in the brain. Typically, the level of 1 or more of these neurotransmitters is lower than normal (see Chapter 5 for a general description of neurotransmitters). Pharmacological treatment of depression aims to increase the level of 1 or more of these neurotransmitters. Two of the first-developed classes of agents are monoamine oxidase inhibitors (MAOIs) and tricyclic antidepressants (TCAs). Selective serotonin reuptake inhibitors (SSRIs) have provided a means of intervention that is more effective and results in fewer side effects than either the MAOIs or TCAs.

## Monoamine Oxidase Inhibitors

Monoamine oxidase inhibitors were discovered serendipitously in the early 1950s during the search for a more effective antituberculosis drug. Iproniazid, a derivative of the tuberculosis drug isoniazid, was found to be inactive as an antitubercular agent but was active in tests for treating depression. As was found later, iproniazid is an inhibitor of monoamine oxidase (MAO) and blocks the metabolism of dopamine, norepinephrine, and serotonin. By blocking their metabolism, iproniazid was able to increase the levels of these neurotransmitters in the synapse. Eventually, iproniazid was replaced by other drugs because of its hepatotoxic effects.

In nervous tissue, a neurotransmitter is released from the presynaptic nerve, travels across the synapse, and binds to a receptor on the postsynaptic nerve. Once this second binding event occurs, the nerve impulse travels through the postsynaptic cell and proceeds through the nervous pathway. After binding to the postsynaptic cell, the neurotransmitter must be removed from the synapse to discontinue the transmission of the impulse. The neurotransmitter can be degraded by a metabolizing enzyme or taken back into the presynaptic cell in a process called *reuptake*. One of the enzymes responsible for the metabolism of several common neurotransmitters is MAO.

The MAO catalyzes the oxidative deamination of serotonin, dopamine, norepinephrine, and structurally related molecules. There are 2 forms of MAO: MAO-A, which primarily metabolizes serotonin, norepinephrine, and tyramine; and MAO-B, which primarily metabolizes dopamine. The MAOIs block the action of MAO. Inhibition of MAO keeps the neurotransmitter in the synapse longer, thus prolonging the activation of the postsynaptic receptor. The increased concentration of neurotransmitters in the synapse, particularly serotonin, decreases the symptoms of depression.

The MAOIs have several common side effects that should be noted. The most common side effect of this class of drugs is the "cheese effect," which refers to the hypertension associated with tyramine-containing food, such as cheese. Tyramine is normally metabolized by MAO-A in the digestive tract. However, when nonselective MAOIs are present, tyramine cannot be completely metabolized and, after absorption into the bloodstream, can cause severe hypertension. Because of this effect, people who are taking nonselective MAOIs must follow a diet that limits the consumption of foods containing tyramine, such as cheese.

The MAOIs can also produce hypotension, and many people report dizziness while taking these medications. Changes in blood pressure, which can be fatal, are the most common adverse effects of MAOIs and must be monitored. In addition, many other medications are metabolized by MAO. Therefore, in the presence of MAOIs, the normal metabolism of other medications may be altered, which can lead to undesired, and even fatal, effects. Thus, when taking MAOIs, other medications a patient may be taking must be monitored closely to avoid unwanted drug-drug interactions.

Phenelzine (**Figure 1**) is a useful antidepressant that inhibits MAO-A and MAO-B. On binding to the active site of the enzyme, phenelzine alkylates the enzyme, leading to irreversible inhibition. The side effects of phenelzine include orthostatic hypotension, insomnia, and weight gain. Isocarboxazid is a prodrug in which the amide group is hydrolyzed to the benzylhydrazine. This substance is further converted to the very reactive benzyl free radical, capable of alkylating and irreversibly inhibiting MAO.

Tranylcypromine has a distinctive cyclopropyl ring in its structure. It is an irreversible MAOI in which the enzyme forms a covalent bond with the reactive cyclopropyl group. Tranylcypromine predominantly inhibits MAO-A but also has some MAO-B activity. Side effects of tranylcypromine include orthostatic hypotension, insomnia (more so than with phenelzine), and weight gain (less so than with phenelzine). Tranylcypromine results in more central nervous system (CNS) stimulation than do other MAOIs.

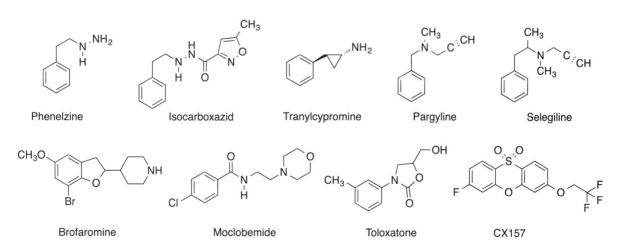

**Figure 1.** *Monoamine oxidase inhibitors.*

Pargyline and selegiline are structurally related inhibitors. Selegiline is a second-generation MAOI that binds irreversibly and selectively to MAO-B over MAO-A. It is used as adjunct therapy for the treatment of Parkinson disease. Metabolites include *N*-desmethylselegiline, which is active, and L-amphetamine and L-methamphetamine, which are inactive as antidepressants. When administered with TCAs, selegiline can produce toxic CNS effects, which are potentially fatal. Other adverse effects include hypertension, syncope, asystole, and diaphoresis. Because it does not bind to MAO-A, selegiline does not produce the cheese effect as nonselective MAOIs do. Adverse reactions have been reported when selegiline is administered with SSRIs.

Several compounds have been shown to bind selectively and reversibly to MAO-A. These agents are called reversible inhibitors of MAO-A (RIMAs) and may give rise to a new generation of MAOIs as antidepressants. The RIMAs have 2 advantages over older MAOIs. The reversible actions of RIMAs do not take as long to wear off as those of irreversible MAOIs. The RIMAs also result in lower pressor effects compared with traditional MAOIs. The RIMAs include bromfaromine, meclobemide, and toloxatone (Figure 1). While these RIMAs are not clinically available, CX157 is a RIMA that is currently in clinical trials for the treatment of depression.

## Tricyclic Antidepressants

In the 1950s, at about the same time as MAOIs were being discovered, TCAs were shown to be useful against depression. For many years, these drugs were the mainstay of antidepressant therapy. Their undesirable side-effect profiles, low differential between therapeutic and toxic dosages, and the advent of SSRIs, however, have led to a decline in the use of TCAs. In addition to depression, these drugs can also be used to treat anxiety.

At the synapse, specialized, membrane-bound proteins on the presynaptic cell transport neurotransmitters back into the presynaptic neuron. These proteins are called *reuptake transporters* or *reuptake pumps*. The TCAs work by binding to these proteins and blocking the reuptake of neurotransmitters into the presynaptic nerve cell. By blocking neurotransmitter reuptake, the TCAs keep the neurotransmitter in the synapse longer. Thus, the net effect of the TCAs (like all antidepressants) is an increased concentration of neurotransmitter in the synapse. The majority of the antidepressant effect of TCAs is thought to be caused by blocking of norepinephrine and serotonin reuptake.

In general, TCAs can produce a panel of side effects. At therapeutic doses, these effects include sedation, weight gain, anticholinergic effects, sexual dysfunction, and the possible increased risk of myocardial infarction. The TCAs have been shown to be fatal at a concentration of as little as 5-fold more than the therapeutic dose. For this reason, overdose can occur easily. Toxic effects from TCAs are generally cardiac arrhythmia, anticholinergic toxicity, and seizure.

Several derivatives of the tricyclic structure shown in **Table 1** have been introduced for their ability to ameliorate the symptoms of depression. Structural modifications of these molecules are found at the 5- and 10-positions of the central ring. In general, the TCAs are not planar but slightly folded around the central ring in a butterfly shape. This shape is necessary for binding effectively to the reuptake receptor.

The TCAs can be divided into 2 groups based on the number of substituents on the basic amine within the R substituent in Table 1. Tertiary amines, such as imipramine and amitriptyline, are not used as primary antidepressants because of their sedative and anticholinergic side effects. These drugs are more often used in combination with SSRIs. They have also been used to treat insomnia and neuropathic pain. The side effects experienced with tertiary amine TCAs can be attributed to their increased affinity for $\alpha$-adrenergic, muscarinic, and histaminic receptors. Secondary amine TCAs, such as desipramine and nortriptyline, have lower affinity for these alternative receptors and, therefore, result in lower incidences of side effects compared with their tertiary homologues. Secondary amines are, therefore, used more often as primary therapy for depression.

**Table 1.** *Tricyclic antidepressants.*

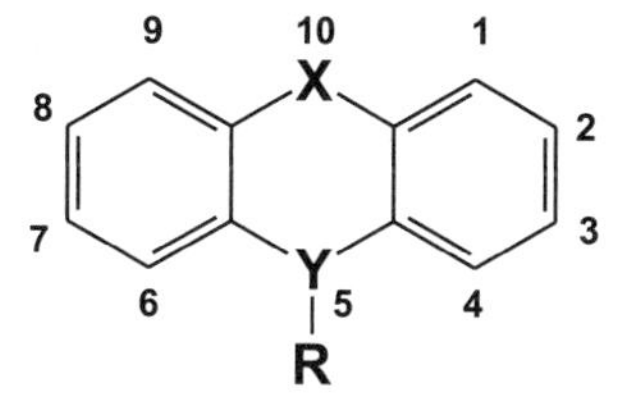

| Name | X | Y | R |
|---|---|---|---|
| Imipramine | $-CH_2CH_2-$ | N | $-CH_2CH_2CH_2N(CH_3)_2$ |
| Desipramine | $-CH_2CH_2-$ | N | $-CH_2CH_2CH_2NH(CH_3)$ |
| Amitriptyline | $-CH_2CH_2-$ | C | $=CHCH_2CH_2N(CH_3)_2$ |
| Nortriptyline | $-CH_2CH_2-$ | C | $=CH_2CH_2CH_2NH(CH_3)$ |
| Protriptyline | $-CH=CH-$ | CH | $-CH_2CH_2CH_2NH(CH_3)$ |
| Trimipramine | $-CH_2CH_2-$ | N | $-CH_2CHCH_2N(CH_3)_2$ $CH_3$ |
| Doxepin | $-CH_2O-$ | C | $=CHCH_2CH_2N(CH_3)_2$ |
| Amoxapine | $-O-$ | $-N=CH-$ | 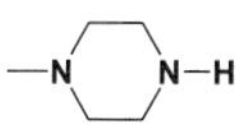 $-N\quad N-H$ |
| Cyproheptadine | $-CH=CH-$ | C | 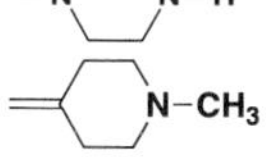 $N-CH_3$ |

Despite its tertiary structure, imipramine is considered the prototypical tricyclic antidepressant. It was introduced in 1957 and was the first TCA to be used. Being a tertiary amine, imipramine does not selectively act on reuptake channels. Its affinity for α-adrenergic, muscarinic, and histaminic receptors gives imipramine an undesirable list of side effects. These effects include sedation, weight gain, and anticholinergic effects. Imipramine is extensively protein bound (>90%) and has a half-life of 15 to 30 hours. The molecule is metabolized in the liver by hydroxylation at the 2-position, yielding 2-hydroxyimipramine. This metabolite is thought to be active in blocking the uptake of catecholamines. Following 2-hydroxylation, conjugation to form the glucuronide occurs, and the resulting inactive metabolite is eliminated in the urine. A second metabolite is formed by *N*-dealkylation to form desipramine, a commercially available TCA.

Desipramine is the *N*-desmethyl derivative of imipramine. One methyl group on the basic nitrogen atom is removed, converting the molecule from a tertiary amine to a secondary amine. As with all secondary amine TCAs, desipramine has lower affinity for α-adrenergic, muscarinic, and histaminic receptors compared with the tertiary amines. It exhibits greater selectivity for reuptake channels and has a lower incidence of cholinergic and sedative side effects. Desipramine has increased selectivity for norepinephrine reuptake sites over serotonin reuptake sites. The major side effect associated with desipramine is orthostatic hypotension. Desipramine is extensively protein bound (>85%) and has a half-life of 12 to 36 hours. It is metabolized in the liver to 2-hydroxydesipramine.

Amitriptyline, a tertiary amine, has higher affinity for histaminic and muscarinic receptors compared with imipramine. Therefore, amitriptyline results in a higher frequency of histaminic and cholinergic side effects compared with imipramine. The drug is highly sedating. Amitriptyline is more than 95% protein bound and has a half-life of 9 to 25 hours. The drug is hepatically metabolized by routes including hydroxylation at the 10-position and *N*-dealkylation of the basic amine to remove 1 methyl group. The dealkylated metabolite, nortriptyline, is active as an antidepressant and is a commonly prescribed TCA.

Nortriptyline is a secondary amine and a common metabolite of amitriptyline. As a secondary amine, it exhibits fewer side effects than its tertiary amine homologues because of decreased affinity at alternative receptor sites. Nortriptyline exhibits more anticholinergic and sedative properties than desipramine. Like desipramine, nortriptyline is more effective at blocking norepinephrine reuptake than serotonin. Nortriptyline results in lower incidences of orthostatic hypotension than does desipramine. As with all TCAs, the drug is extensively protein bound (>90%), and the half-life is 18 to 44 hours. Nortriptyline is metabolized in the liver by hydroxylation in the 10-position, yielding 10-hydroxynortriptyline, a metabolite that is active in inhibiting norepinephrine reuptake.

Protriptyline is a secondary amine with lower incidence of anticholinergic and antihistaminic side effects, as with other secondary amine TCAs. Protriptyline is more than 90% protein bound and has a half-life of approximately 72 hours.

The drug is metabolized in the liver mainly by hydroxylation, followed by glucuronidation. N-oxidation also occurs. The metabolites, none of which are active, are eliminated in the urine.

Trimipramine, a tertiary amine, resembles imipramine in its action and side effects. It is extensively protein bound (~95%) and has a half-life of 9 to 11 hours. It is metabolized by ring hydroxylation followed by conjugation with glucose.

Doxepin, a tertiary amine, is a modification of amitriptyline in which the central ring has been modified with an oxygen atom. It has anticholinergic and sedative properties, much like the other tertiary drugs in this series. It is highly protein bound (>80%) and has a half-life of 11 to 23 hours. Doxepin is metabolized in the liver to yield the N-desmethyl product, desmethyldoxepin, which is active. Doxepin is also available as a topical skin cream that is used to treat itchiness.

Amoxapine, a secondary amine, is used to treat depression and depression in the presence of anxiety. Amoxapine is 80% protein bound and has a half-life of 8 to 30 hours. This drug is metabolized in the liver to 7-hydroxyamoxapine and 8-hydroxyamoxapine, both of which are active. These metabolites inhibit dopaminergic receptors in a manner analogous to that of haloperidol, a "typical" antipsychotic. The adverse effects of amoxapine include extrapyramidal motor system effects and tardive dyskinesia.

Cyproheptadine is an antiserotonergic agent and an antihistaminic agent with sedative effects. It is used for seasonal allergic rhinitis and conjunctivitis. The drug should not be used in newborn or premature infants. Overdose may produce hallucinations, depression, and seizures. There is a possible additive effect with alcohol and CNS depressants.

# Selective Serotonin Reuptake Inhibitors

A marked change in the treatment of depression occurred when certain molecules were designed to have selective affinity for serotonin reuptake transporters (**Figure 2**). Fluoxetine, the prototypical SSRI, was one of the first molecules designed to inhibit serotonin reuptake and avoid inhibition of the reuptake of other neurotransmitters. As such, it was found that fluoxetine and related agents were effective antidepressants, yet lacked the side effects of the MAOIs and TCAs. The SSRIs quickly became the drugs of choice for treating depression.

Although potency and slight selectivity differences may occur among individual SSRIs, the class as a whole has lower affinity for histamine, dopamine, α-adrenergic, and cholinergic receptors compared with TCAs and MAOIs. As a result, SSRIs result in fewer side effects associated with these receptors. The SSRIs are relatively safe during overdose. Common side effects of all SSRIs include changes in sleep patterns and sexual dysfunction. Because SSRIs and MAOIs result in increased synaptic levels of serotonin, caution must be used

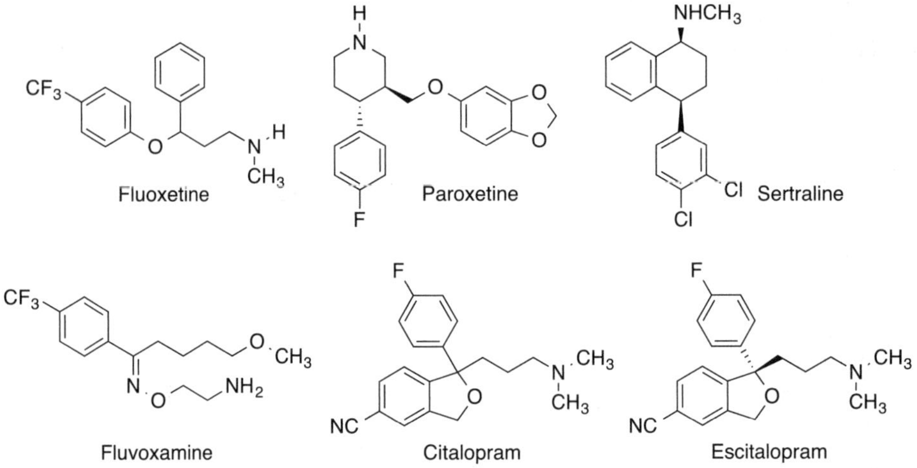

**Figure 2.** *Structures of selective serotonin reuptake inhibitors.*

when giving these drugs in combination. "Serotonin syndrome" occurs when the concentration of serotonin reaches toxic levels. The toxic effects of serotonin syndrome include hyperthermia, muscle rigidity, and rapid changes in mental status and vital signs. In general, all SSRIs are highly protein bound and are metabolized extensively in the liver.

Many SSRIs inhibit 1 or more of the cytochrome $P_{450}$ metabolizing enzymes. $P_{450}$ enzymes are responsible for detoxifying foreign substances in the body, such as medicines, by metabolism. If an SSRI is administered in combination with other medications that rely on $P_{450}$ metabolism, blood levels of each medicine should be monitored. When $P_{450}$ activity is inhibited, the concentration of a drug will not be decreased as quickly as it would normally and will remain high within the body for a longer period.

Fluoxetine is the prototypical SSRI and is one of the most prescribed drugs in the United States. Fluoxetine is used in the treatment of major depressive disorder, obsessive compulsive disorder, and bulimia. It is 95% protein bound. Metabolism of fluoxetine occurs via cytochrome $P_{450}$, yielding the active metabolite norfluoxetine (by removal of the methyl group). The half-life of fluoxetine is 4 to 6 days. The half-life of norfluoxetine is 7 to 15 days. The side effects of fluoxetine include nausea, anxiety, and insomnia. Fluoxetine potently inhibits the $P_{450}$ metabolizing enzyme CYP2D6; therefore, drugs that are metabolized by CYP2D6, such as vinblastine, risperidone, and metoprolol, should not be coadministered with fluoxetine.

Paroxetine, while structurally dissimilar from fluoxetine, has some similar characteristics. Paroxetine is extensively protein bound (~95%), has a half-life of 24 hours, and is metabolized by the liver to inactive metabolites. Like fluoxetine, paroxetine is also a potent inhibitor of CYP2D6. Care must be taken in the coadministration of drugs with this route of metabolism. Paroxetine has a slightly higher affinity at muscarinic receptors than does fluoxetine, resulting in higher frequencies of anticholinergic side effects such as sedation, nausea, and dry mouth. Paroxetine can also cause mild sexual dysfunction.

Sertraline is an SSRI that is used to treat depressive illness. It is 98% protein bound and is metabolized by cytochrome $P_{450}$ in the liver to yield the N-desmethyl analog (desmethylsertraline). The metabolite is active but substantially less potent than the parent molecule. The half-life of sertraline is approximately 26 hours, and, as an advantage, sertraline inhibits CYP2D6 less than does fluoxetine. Common side effects from sertraline include nausea, diarrhea, insomnia, and sexual dysfunction.

Fluvoxamine is widely used in Europe. In the United States, it is approved for treatment of obsessive compulsive disorder. Unlike most SSRIs, fluvoxamine is only 77% protein bound, making more drug available for therapeutic action. No active metabolites are produced from fluvoxamine. Fluvoxamine is a potent inhibitor of CYP1A2, the major metabolic enzyme responsible for degrading drugs such as caffeine, clozapine, and theophylline. Fluvoxamine, therefore, interferes with the normal pharmacodynamics of these drugs. Side effects of fluvoxamine include gastrointestinal upset, sexual dysfunction, nausea, insomnia, and dry mouth.

Citalopram is approved for use in the United States for treatment of depression. This drug mildly inhibits CYP2D6. However, inhibition of CYP2D6 by citalopram is mild compared with that of other SSRIs. Citalopram is metabolized by removal of the methyl group on the nitrogen atom. Removal of 1 methyl group gives desmethylcitalopram. Removal of the second methyl group gives didesmethylcitalopram. Oxidation of the nitrogen atom gives citalopram-*N*-oxide. All of the metabolites are less potent than the parent drug. The side effects of citalopram are similar to those of other SSRIs. Escitalopram is the *S*-isomer of citalopram and is approved for use against major depressive disorder and generalized anxiety disorder. Like citalopram, escitalopram acts as an SSRI.

## Other Antidepressants

Maprotiline (**Figure 3**) resembles the TCAs, but is a TCA, containing 4 rings instead of 3. Because of its slightly different structure compared with the TCAs, maprotiline has a slightly different activity profile. Maprotiline inhibits neurotransmitter reuptake, like the TCAs, but is also thought to desensitize adenylyl cyclase and downregulate β-adrenergic and serotonin receptors. The drug has a half-life of more than 40 hours and is excreted as the glucuronide-conjugated metabolite.

Bupropion was reintroduced for use as an antidepressant in 1989. Use of this drug had been discontinued because a severely increased rate of seizures was reported in some patients with bulimia who took bupropion. The current prescribing information advises caution when considering use by people with

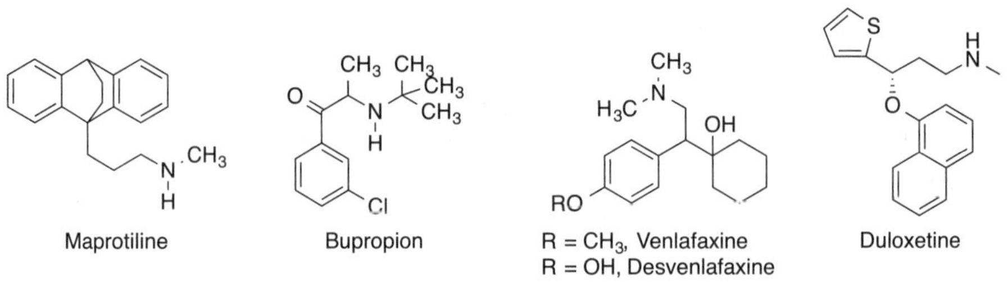

**Figure 3.** *Structures of miscellaneous antidepressants.*

seizure disorders and other CNS conditions; people who use alcohol or sedatives to excess, take over-the-counter stimulants or anorectics, have an addiction to, eg, opiates, or take insulin or oral hypoglycemics; and people who take other medications, eg, other antidepressants, theophylline, or systemic steroids. The mechanism of action of bupropion is not well understood. It is thought to involve weak inhibition of dopamine reuptake and a decrease in norepinephrine activity. The mechanism of action of bupropion is not thought to involve a serotonergic mechanism, so it is not prescribed for anxiety or panic disorders. Bupropion is metabolized to hydroxybupropion, which is active. Bupropion under the trade name Zyban is prescribed to aid in smoking cessation.

Venlafaxine is a potent inhibitor of norepinephrine and serotonin reuptake and a mild inhibitor of dopamine reuptake. This drug has few interactions with histaminic, muscarinic, and adrenergic receptors, making the incidence of side effects low. Venlafaxine is metabolized in the liver to *O*-desmethylvenlafaxine (removal of the methyl group from the oxygen), which is an active molecule. Venlafaxine is not highly protein bound and has a half-life of about 11 hours. Common side effects include nausea, dizziness, insomnia, sedation, constipation, and increased blood pressure. Venlafaxine is also used in the treatment of generalized anxiety disorder. Desvenlafaxine is a commercialized, synthetic version of *O*-desmethylvenlafaxine, the active metabolite. Like its parent compound, it acts as an inhibitor of norepinephrine and serotonin reuptake.

Duloxetine is also an inhibitor of norepinephrine and serotonin reuptake. It was first approved for clinical use in 2004 and is now used for the treatment of major depressive disorder, generalized anxiety disorder, fibromyalgia, and various neuropathies. Structurally it is distinct from other members of this class.

Trazodone (**Figure 4**) is an antidepressant that is thought to mediate its effects through modulation of serotonergic transmission. The drug is approximately 90% protein bound and is metabolized in the liver. The half-life of trazodone is 5 to 9 hours. Sedation is the most common side effect of trazodone, and this effect limits its usefulness. Other side effects include postural hypotension and nausea.

Nefazodone is indicated for depression and has some mechanisms of action different from those of other antidepressants. This drug acts as an antagonist at the $5\text{-}HT_2$ subtype of serotonin receptors, blocks $\alpha_1$-adrenergic receptors, and inhibits serotonin reuptake. Nefazodone has no effect on cholinergic, $\alpha_2$-adrenergic, histaminic, or dopaminergic receptors, decreasing the incidence of associated side effects. Nefazodone is thought to result in less sexual dysfunction than other antidepressants, while it increases rapid eye movement sleep, making it unique among these antidepressant therapies. Nefazodone (Figure 4) is approximately 99% protein bound and is a potent inhibitor of CYP3A4. Because of this inhibition, coadministration of nefazodone with alprazolam or triazolam is contraindicated. Coadministration of nefazodone and cisapride is also contraindicated because of the risk of serious or fatal cardiovascular effects. (Cisapride is available in the United States only via limited-access protocol.) Side effects of nefazodone include dry mouth, constipation, nausea, sedation, and dizziness. The drug may cause liver damage. Nefazodone is metabolized in the liver to the active metabolites meta-chlorophenylpiperazine, hydroxynefazadone, and triazoledione.

Mirtazapine is an antidepressant that acts by inhibition of presynaptic and postsynaptic $\alpha_2$-adrenergic receptors and certain serotonin receptor subtypes ($5\text{-}HT_2$ and $5\text{-}HT_3$). Mirtazapine (Figure 4) has low affinity for $\alpha_1$-adrenergic receptors but very potent antagonist activity at the histamine receptors. Because of its activity at the histamine receptors, mirtazapine is sedating and is used for the treatment of insomnia. The drug is metabolized in the liver by oxidation and demethylation, producing metabolites that are less active than the parent molecule. Mirtazapine has a half-life of 20 to 40 hours and is approximately 80% protein bound. Side effects of the drug include sedation, weight gain, and dry mouth.

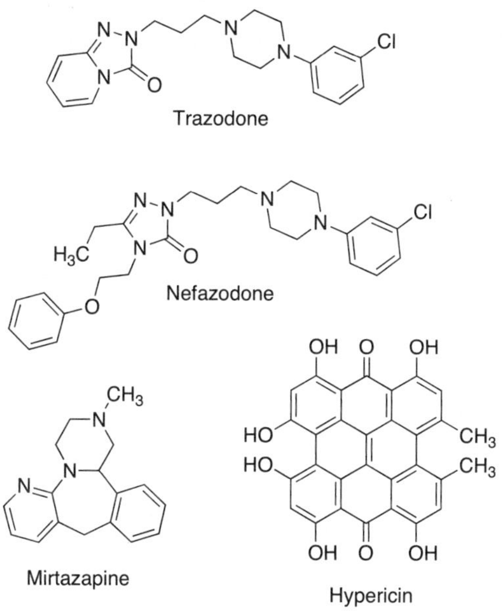

Trazodone

Nefazodone

Mirtazapine

Hypericin

**Figure 4.** *Structures of miscellaneous antidepressants.*

St John's wort *(Hypericum perforatum)* is a plant that is thought to have antidepressant activity. This herbal substance is available without a prescription and is widely used in Europe and the United States. The active component is thought to be hypericin (Figure 4), one of the many naphthodianthrones found in the plant. While the mechanism of action of St John's wort continues to evade investigators, its popularity is sustained. As with many nutritional supplements, the variability of the product consumed, including the active ingredient formulation, can be problematic. Other problems include an unclear picture of side effects, cross-reactivities, and contraindications. Evidence indicates that the effect of this product may be largely related to a placebo effect. Because no requirements exist for standardization, much is left to the integrity of the producer of the product. Clearly, patients should discuss taking this herbal supplement with their physicians. Also, patients should be asked if they are taking this or similar products with antidepressant claims when being interviewed before treatment.

## Anxiolytics

Anxiolytics are drugs used to treat anxiety and tension. *Generalized anxiety disorder* is defined as excessive worry and anxiety that are difficult to control and result in stress or impairment of performing normal functions. Anxiety can arise as a result of improper responses of the neurotransmitters norepinephrine, serotonin, and γ-aminobutyric acid (GABA) to stressful situations. Anxiety can also arise intermittently, such as before surgery or an invasive procedure. Anxiolytics, as a class of drugs, are among the most widely prescribed. Several structural classes of compounds are used in the treatment of anxiety. The major class of anxiolytic drugs is the benzodiazepines. The TCAs, SSRIs, and antipsychotics have also been used therapeutically to treat anxiety. The major drawback in the use of benzodiazepines is their powerful abuse potential. Benzodiazepines are also used as sedatives and hypnotic medications in the treatment of insomnia and seizures (see Chapter 10).

## Benzodiazepines

The general structure of the benzodiazepine molecule is shown in **Table 2**. Benzodiazepines are characterized by the fused benzene and 7-membered ring system, from which the name is derived, along with the phenyl group attached to the 7-membered ring at the 5-position. The differences in the activities of individual benzodiazepines stem from the various substituents on the tricyclic structure.

Benzodiazepines act by binding to GABA (subtype A) receptors on postsynaptic neurons. A GABA$_A$ synapse is shown in **Figure 5**. The GABA$_A$ receptor is composed of 5 subunits that form a channel through the cell membrane. GABA binds to the β subunits and causes the channel to open, which allows chloride

**Table 2.** *Benzodiazepines.*

| Name | R₁ | R₂ | R₃ | R₄ | R₅ |
|------|------|------|------|------|------|
| Chlordiazepoxide | N-1 is –N=; N-4 is (=N→O structure) | —NHCH₃ | —H | —H | —Cl |
| Diazepam | —CH₃ | =O | —H | —H | —Cl |
| Temazepam | —CH₃ | =O | —OH | —H | —Cl |
| Clonazepam | —H | =O | —H | —Cl | —NO₂ |
| Lorazepam | —H | =O | —OH | —Cl | —Cl |
| Nitrazepam | —H | =O | —H | —H | —NO₂ |
| Oxazepam | —H | =O | —OH | —H | —Cl |
| Halazepam | —CH₂CF₃ | =O | —H | —H | —Cl |
| Quazepam | —CH₂CF₃ | =S | —H | —F | —Cl |
| Flurazepam | —CH₂CH₂N(CH₂CH₃)₂ | =O | —H | —F | —Cl |
| Prazepam | (cyclopropylmethyl) | =O | —H | —H | —Cl |

ions into the cell. The additional influx of anions into a nerve cell inhibits cell depolarization and results in a decreased response when subsequent nerve signals are received. Because a decrease in nervous transmission results, GABA is called an *inhibitory neurotransmitter.*

Benzodiazepines bind to the α subunits of the GABA receptor. When a benzodiazepine is bound to the GABA receptor, the action of GABA is reinforced. On GABA and benzodiazepine binding, the anion channel remains open, decreasing cell responsiveness. In other words, when a benzodiazepine is bound to the GABA receptor, a greater inhibitory response occurs at the nerve cell than would be seen by GABA alone.

Benzodiazepines have been shown to be useful in a variety of disorders. In the CNS, they produce a depression similar to the barbiturate action on electrical discharge in the limbic system. As a result, the benzodiazepines are useful in treating or preventing seizures. Circulatory and respiratory depression are rare; hence, benzodiazepines have an advantage over barbiturates. The benzodiazepines are absorbed orally, are protein bound, and are effectively distributed to the brain. This latter effect is modulated by variations made in the benzodiazepine structure. Benzodiazepines may be overused, leading to possible dependence.

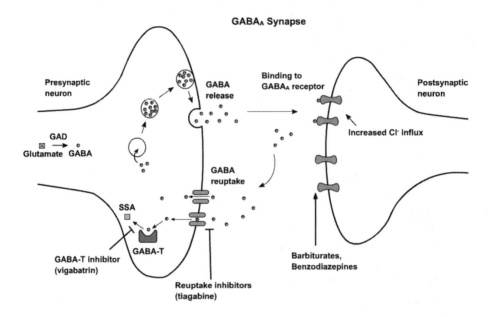

**Figure 5.** *The action of γ-aminobutyric acid (GABA), barbiturates, and benzodiazepines. GABA is synthesized from glutamate in the presynaptic cell by glutamic acid decarboxylase (GAD). Following storage in presynaptic vesicles, GABA is released into the synapse, where it can bind to a GABA$_A$ receptor on the postsynaptic cell. Barbiturates and benzodiazepines also bind to GABA$_A$ receptors, enhancing the action of GABA. GABA can be taken up into the presynaptic cell by specific GABA reuptake transporters. GABA is metabolized in the presynaptic cell by GABA transaminase (GABA-T), yielding succinic semialdehyde (SSA). Many drugs are known to inhibit the action of GABA by acting on specific points in the synapse. The inhibitory action of several drugs is indicated.*

There are not many drug interactions reported, and benzodiazepines are not thought to interfere with the metabolism of other drugs in a substantial way.

Certain structural features of the benzodiazepines are essential for activity or may be systematically modified to achieve graded changes in activity. The 7-position (Table 2) is usually occupied with a substituent other than hydrogen to retard metabolic hydroxylation at this position. Metabolic hydroxylation leads to an easily excreted molecule, reducing the time of residence of an effective drug in the circulating system. The phenyl group at the 5-position imparts hydrophobic character to the molecule, facilitating passage into the CNS. A hydroxyl substituent at the 3-position influences the rate of drug excretion.

Chlordiazepoxide was one of the first benzodiazepines to be used clinically (Table 2). It is absorbed from the gastrointestinal tract, reaching its peak plasma level in 2 to 4 hours. Like most benzodiazepines, chlordiazepoxide is highly protein bound (90%-98%) and has a half-life of 6 to 24 hours. The drug is metabolized in the liver by removal of the methyl group on the exocyclic nitrogen atom. The resulting metabolite, desmethyldiazepam, is active, as are certain other metabolites of this drug such as oxazepam. Desmethyldiazepam and oxazepam are long-acting benzodiazepines, so the activity of the parent drug is extended. The metabolic pathways affecting chlordiazepoxide are shown in **Figure 6**. Side effects include drowsiness and fatigue.

Diazepam, one of the most recognized benzodiazepines, is used in the treatment of anxiety, seizure disorders, and muscle relaxation. Because of the relatively nonpolar character of diazepam, it is easily absorbed and protein bound (97%-98%). It has a half-life of 20 to 50 hours. Diazepam is metabolized to desmethyldiazepam (major metabolite), temazepam, and oxazepam. All 3 of these metabolites are active. Side effects of diazepam include drowsiness, ataxia, rash, and changes in libido and salivation.

Temazepam is used in the treatment of anxiety and panic attacks and as an adjunct therapy for the treatment of depression. The drug is highly protein bound (~96%) and has a half-life of 9 to 12 hours. Most of the drug (80%-90%) is excreted in the urine as inactive, hepatically derived metabolites. Side effects of temazepam include confusion, dizziness, drowsiness, rash, and diarrhea.

Clonazepam is slightly less lipophilic than other benzodiazepines. This factor, due to the presence of the nitro group and only 1 chlorine atom, results in slightly lower protein binding (~85%). Clonazepam is used in the treatment of seizures and panic disorder and is more commonly thought of as an antiepileptic rather than an anxiolytic. The therapeutic effect of clonazepam can begin 20 to 60 minutes after administration. Metabolism of clonazepam by the liver results in glucuronide and sulfate conjugation.

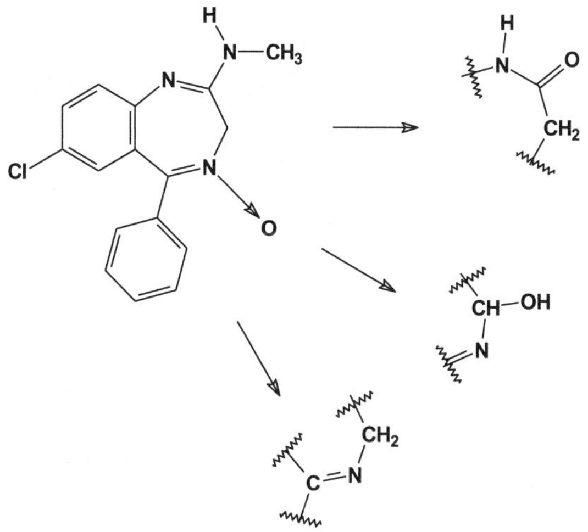

**Figure 6.** *Metabolism of chlordiazepoxide.*

Lorazepam, a dichlorobenzodiazepine with a 3-position hydroxyl group, is used in the treatment of anxiety and status epilepticus. The drug is less lipophilic than other benzodiazepines due to the hydroxyl group and, therefore, results in lower protein binding (~85%). The half-life of lorazepam is approximately 13 hours. Metabolism in the liver results in inactive molecules. Side effects of lorazepam include confusion, hypotension, and dizziness.

Nitrazepam, named for the 7-position nitro substituent, has many of the same characteristics as other members of the benzodiazepine class of compounds. Its decreased lipophilicity results in lower (~87%) binding by serum proteins. The molecule has a longer half-life than other benzodiazepines, approximately 20 to 48 hours.

Oxazepam is used in the treatment of anxiety and ethanol withdrawal. The molecule is highly protein bound (86%-99%) and metabolized in the liver to the inactive glucuronide conjugate via the 3-position hydroxyl group. Half of the dose is excreted in the urine unchanged. The half-life of oxazepam is 2 to 6 hours. Side effects of oxazepam include drowsiness, ataxia, and rash.

Halazepam is one of the few benzodiazepines with a trifluoroethyl substituent. Removal of this substituent, via metabolism, results in desmethyldiazepam, an active metabolite with a long duration of action. The half-life of halazepam is 14 hours. However, desmethyldiazepam has a half-life of 50 to 100 hours, extending the therapeutic effect of the medication. Side effects of halazepam can include drowsiness, tachycardia, hypotension, and confusion.

Like halazepam, quazepam, with a trifluoroethyl substituent, is used for insomnia, rapidly absorbed, and is a long-acting benzodiazepine. The drug is metabolized to 2-oxoquazepam and to N-desalkylflurazepam by removal of the trifluoroethyl substituent. These 2 molecules are active and extend the activity of quazepam dramatically. The half-life of quazepam is 25 to 41 hours. However, its active metabolites have half-lives of 40 to 114 hours. The trifluoroethyl group, as well as the sulfur and halogen atoms, increases the lipophilicity of quazepam. Therefore, these features also result in increased protein binding of the drug (~95%). Side effects of the drug include palpitations, drowsiness, and fatigue, all of which support the insomnia indication, and dermatitis.

Flurazepam is also used for the treatment of insomnia. The large alkyl group makes it highly lipophilic and, therefore, highly protein bound (97%). Onset of action occurs 15 to 20 minutes after administration. The duration of the parent drug is 7 to 8 hours. Metabolism to the active molecules N-desalkylflurazepam and hydroxyethylflurazepam extends the activity of the formulation.

Prazepam, although not available in the United States, is used in other countries for the treatment of anxiety. The drug has a long duration of action (48 hours), but a short half-life (78 minutes). The active metabolites of prazepam, desmethyldiazepam and oxazepam, extend the therapeutic activity of the medication. Side effects of prazepam include hypotension, drowsiness, fatigue, and rash.

## Other Anxiolytics

Although benzodiazepines are the primary structural class of anxiolytics, several other structural classes are approved for this indication as well. Treatment for anxiety can include antipsychotics, such as thioridazine, haloperidol, and olanzapine, or antidepressants, such as venlafaxine and imipramine. Furthermore, there are therapies for anxiety that involve molecules not belonging to any of the aforementioned structural classes.

Meprobamate is a carbamate that belongs to the nonbenzodiazepine hypnotic class of molecules (**Figure 7**). Meprobamate does not act at the GABA receptors. Rather, it is thought to mediate its effects by modulation of the thalamus and the limbic system. Very little of the drug is protein bound, and it has a half-life of approximately 10 hours. The side effects of meprobamate include edema, drowsiness, rash, and syncope. Fatal overdoses have been reported following use of meprobamate, which limits its use.

Hydroxyzine hydrochloride has high antihistaminic properties and is classified as an antiemetic-antihistamine. The drug competes with histamine at histaminic receptor sites ($H_1$) in the gastrointestinal and respiratory tracts and in blood vessels. Because of its rapid absorption, the onset of action of hydroxyzine is 15 to 30 minutes, and the duration is 4 to 6 hours. Much of the drug (45%-60%) is metabolized in the liver to the active molecule cetirizine by oxidation of the alcohol to a carboxylic acid.

Buspirone has high affinity for serotonergic receptor populations and moderate affinity for selected dopaminergic receptor types. Buspirone does not interact at the GABA receptor. The drug is highly protein bound (~86%) and has a slow onset of action. Buspirone is metabolized in the liver to 1-(2-pyrimidinyl) piperazine, which has 20% of the activity of the parent drug. The side effects of buspirone include dizziness, drowsiness, extrapyramidal side effects (caused by dopaminergic activity), and serotonin syndrome. However, an advantage of buspirone over the benzodiazepines is that there is a low potential for abuse.

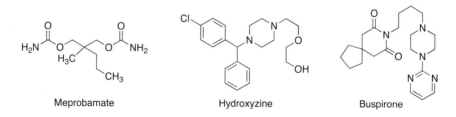

Meprobamate                    Hydroxyzine                    Buspirone

**Figure 7.** *Structures of miscellaneous anxiolytics.*

## *Antipsychotics*

Antipsychotics, formerly also known as neuroleptics, are used to diminish the symptoms associated with schizophrenia, other psychotic disorders, and Parkinson disease. The first antipsychotics were investigated in the 1950s. At this time, a group of phenothiazines, originally interesting because of their antihistaminic activity, were found to decrease the effects of Parkinson disease. This observation led to the development of chlorpromazine and its use as a treatment for mental illness. Since that time, several structural classes of antipsychotics have been developed.

The exact mechanism of action of antipsychotic drugs is not precisely known. Slight differences in activity and side-effect profiles have led to 2 categories of antipsychotic drugs. The typical antipsychotics are older and produce more extrapyramidal side effects. Extrapyramidal side effects are typified by tremors and rigidity. Typical antipsychotics, such as haloperidol, are thought to have activity due to their inhibition of dopamine receptors, which is also responsible for their undesirable side-effect profiles.

The second category of antipsychotics is the atypical antipsychotics. These drugs are newer and have decreased side effects. Atypical antipsychotics, which are equally efficacious in treating mental disorders, generally have lower affinity for dopaminergic receptor subtypes than do typical antipsychotics. Clozapine, the most common atypical antipsychotic, has affinity at the serotonergic and α-adrenergic receptors and low affinity at the dopaminergic receptors. As such, the exact mechanism of action of clozapine is not known. Because atypical antipsychotics such as clozapine do not antagonize postsynaptic dopamine receptors to the same extent as do typical antipsychotics, they result in a lower incidence of extrapyramidal side effects. Other side effects of antipsychotics include sedation and hypotension, resulting from antihistaminic and antiadrenergic activity of the drugs.

## Phenothiazines

The phenothiazines (**Table 3**) were first synthesized in 1883. These molecules were originally used as anthelmintics and later as antihistamines. During this time, it was discovered that some compounds had antiparkinsonian activity. This characteristic led investigators to realize the potential of phenothiazines as antipsychotics. The phenothiazines remain an important component of antipsychotic treatment.

The actions characteristic of the phenothiazines include reduction of initiative and interest, reduced emotion, less agitation and restlessness, and less aggression and impulsiveness. The mechanism of action of the phenothiazines is through binding to and inhibiting dopaminergic receptors. The side effects of phenothiazines include sedation, extrapyramidal effects, and hypotension. Many routes of metabolism exist for these compounds. Hydroxylation at the 7-position and oxidation of the ring sulfur atom are potential routes of metabolism for all phenothiazines. The side chains of individual phenothiazines may be metabolized as well.

Because of their long history, extensive structure-activity relationship information is known about the phenothiazines. It is known that an electronegative substituent must appear at the 2-position for the compound to have antipsychotic activity. The unsubstituted compound (2-H) is inactive. For antipsychotic activity, there must be 3 carbons between the 10-position nitrogen atom and the basic amine. Any molecule with a chain having fewer than 3 or more than 3 carbon atoms separating these nitrogen atoms is inactive. Branching within this chain also results in inactive compounds.

Chlorpromazine is the prototype of the phenothiazine antipsychotics. It is often used as a reference for potency comparisons among many types of antipsychotics. Side effects of chlorpromazine include nausea, vomiting, and hiccoughing. It has some sedative and hypnotic properties because of its adrenergic activity. Metabolism of chlorpromazine in the liver results in an active metabolite, 7-hydroxychlorpromazine. The parent drug is 95% protein bound and has a half-life of 11 to 30 hours.

Triflupromazine has the same structure as chlorpromazine but replaces the chlorine atom of chlorpromazine with a trifluoromethyl group. Triflupromazine has less sedative and hypnotic effects than chlorpromazine. It is more potent and has a lower hypotensive side effect compared with chlorpromazine. Thioridazine

**Table 3.** *Phenothiazines.*

| Name | R | R' |
|------|---|-----|
| Chlorpromazine | $-CH_2CH_2CH_2N(CH_3)_2$ | $-Cl$ |
| Triflupromazine | $-CH_2CH_2CH_2N(CH_3)_2$ | $-CF_3$ |
| Thioridazine | $-CH_2CH_2-$ (piperidine ring, $H_3C$) | $-SCH_3$ |
| Mesoridazine | $-CH_2CH_2-$ (piperidine ring, $H_3C$) | $-\overset{O}{\overset{\|}{S}}CH_3$ |
| Prochlorperazine | $-CH_2CH_2CH_2-N\underset{}{\overset{}{\diagup}}N-CH_3$ | $-Cl$ |
| Trifluoperazine | $-CH_2CH_2CH_2-N\underset{}{\overset{}{\diagup}}N-CH_3$ | $-CF_3$ |
| Perphenazine | $-CH_2CH_2CH_2-N\underset{}{\overset{}{\diagup}}N-\diagup^{OH}$ | $-Cl$ |

has a low incidence of extrapyramidal side effects but some sedative and hypnotic effects. High doses may produce pigmentary retinopathy. Metabolism of thioridazine proceeds by oxidation of the methyl thioether, resulting in the active drug mesoridazine, which once was used to treat alcoholism, schizophrenia, and psychoneuroses. Marketing has been discontinued. Mesoridazine resembles thioridizine but with a lower incidence of pigmentary retinopathy. Other side effects include hypotension, tachycardia, and pseudoparkinsonism.

Prochlorperazine is used for the treatment of nausea, vomiting, and anxiety, in addition to psychotic disorders. The drug has strong antiadrenergic and anticholinergic effects and exhibits a high level of extrapyramidal side effects. It has a low level of sedative and autonomic effects and is more potent than chlorpromazine.

Trifluoperazine is a potent antipsychotic. It has the same structure as prochlorperazine, but the chlorine atom of prochlorperazine is replaced with a trifluoromethyl group. This is the same structural change seen between chlorpromazine and triflupromazine. Trifluoperazine has a high level of extrapyramidal side effects. The sedative and hypnotic activity is low.

Perphenazine has a variable onset with a peak at 30 to 90 minutes and a duration of 1 to 1.5 days. Metabolism occurs in the liver and gastrointestinal tract and elimination through the urine and feces. It is similar to chlorpromazine, affecting all parts of the CNS. It has an antipsychotic effect antagonizing dopamine. Perphenazine is used for the management of psychotic disorders. The side effects include sedation, seizures, hypotension, and tachycardia.

## Thioxanthenes

Thioxanthenes (**Figure 8**) are related structurally to the phenothiazines. In place of the nitrogen atom of the phenothiazines in the central ring, thioxanthenes have an sp$^2$-hybridized carbon atom. Similar halogen and side-chain substitutions are found in phenothiazines and thioxanthenes. The mechanisms of action of these 2 structural classes are also similar. Like phenothiazines, thioxanthenes are thought to exert their antipsychotic effect by the blocking of dopaminergic receptors. The side effects of the thioxanthenes are caused by overinhibition of the dopaminergic receptors and blockade of nondopaminergic receptor types. Chlorprothixene was designed to have fewer extrapyramidal side effects and had properties similar to those of chlorpromazine. Thiothixene is similar to chlorprothixene in its effectiveness and side-effect profile.

## Butyrophenones

The butyrophenones (**Figure 9**) were found as a result of investigating the properties of opioid analgesics. The complex, 4-ring structure of morphine was broken down, yielding molecules related to fentanyl (see Chapter 11). During these investigations, the antipsychotic activity of the butyrophenones was noted. The prototypical butyrophenone is haloperidol.

For antipsychotic activity, the butyrophenones must have a tertiary nitrogen 4 atoms away from a ketone. The carbonyl group must be present for activity. The butyrophenones usually have a fluorine atom at the *para*-position of the benzyl ring. Altering the linking chain of 3 methylene groups by branching, increasing the number of carbon units, or decreasing the number of carbon units decreases potency. The basic nitrogen atom is usually contained in a 6-membered ring, although this structural feature is not necessary to retain activity.

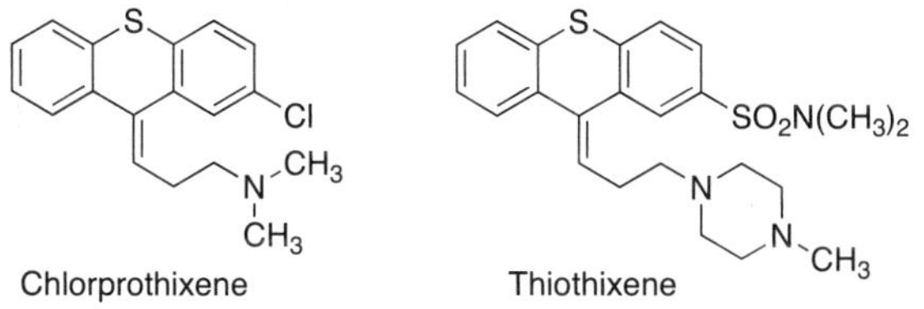

**Figure 8.** *Structures of thioxanthenes.*

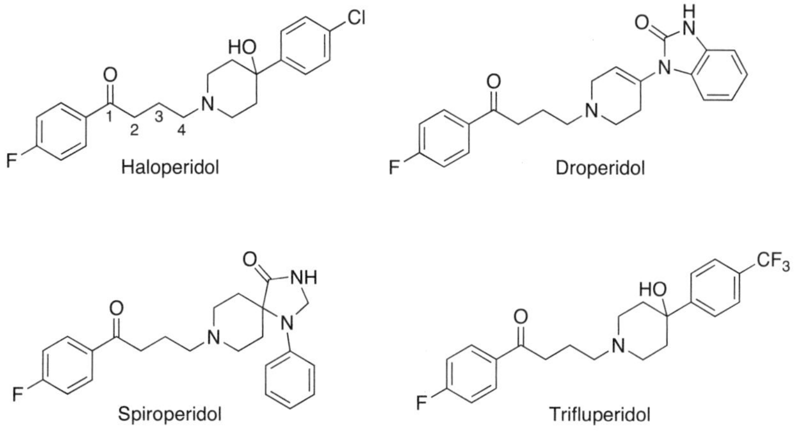

**Figure 9.** *Structures of butyrophenones.*

Haloperidol, originally developed as a fentanyl-like analgesic, was found to have effects resembling those of chlorpromazine. It was structurally modified in an attempt to minimize the addictive characteristics of morphine and related opioids. Haloperidol is useful in treating bipolar disorder and schizophrenia. As the decanoate salt, haloperidol can be injected for efficacy over a 4-week period. Haloperidol is metabolized in the liver to inactive compounds. The inactive metabolite with a reduced carbonyl group can be reoxidized in vivo to form the parent drug. Haloperidol is 90% protein bound and has a half-life of 20 hours. Haloperidol is considered a typical antipsychotic because of its high incidence of extrapyramidal side effects. Haloperidol results in less sedation than chlorpromazine, as well as mild hypotension.

Droperidol is a short-acting antipsychotic that is also used as an antiemetic. Droperidol is sedating, has a half-life of 2 to 3 hours, and is hepatically metabolized. Because of its sedative properties, droperidol is used in combination with the opioid analgesic fentanyl to produce sedation and analgesia prior to invasive medical procedures. Other compounds, structurally related to haloperidol and droperidol and belonging to the butyrophenone class of molecules include spiroperidol and trifluperidol.

## Diphenylbutylpiperidines

The diphenylbutylpiperidines (**Figure 10**) are structurally similar to the butyrophenones. The carbonyl group of the butyrophenones is replaced with a methylene group in the diphenylbutylpiperidine class of molecules. Most of the remaining structural features of the diphenylbutylpiperidines are the same as those of the butyrophenones. In general, the diphenylbutylpiperidines have a longer duration of action than that of the butyrophenones.

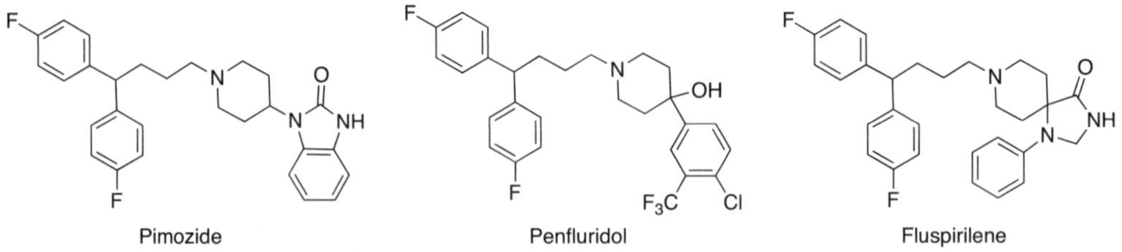

Pimozide          Penfluridol          Fluspirilene

**Figure 10.** *Structures of diphenylbutylpiperidines.*

Pimozide is the only diphenylbutylpiperidine that is approved for use in the United States. Pimozide is used for the treatment of Tourette syndrome and psychoses that do not respond to other forms of treatment. The serum concentrations of pimozide may be increased in the presence of grapefruit juice, although the reason for this increase is unknown. Pimozide results in less sedation than does chlorpromazine but is more likely to cause extrapyramidal side effects. The adverse effects of pimozide include impaired cardiac conduction and potentially irreversible tardive dyskinesia. Penfluridol and fluspirilene are diphenylbutylpiperidines with antipsychotic action, but are not approved for use in the United States. Both of these drugs have long durations of action and the potential for extrapyramidal side effects.

## Dibenzazepines

The treatment of psychotic disorders was revolutionized by the advent of clozapine (**Figure 11**). Clozapine, specifically a dibenzodiazepine with 2 nitrogen atoms in the center ring, was shown to be effective as an antipsychotic, but it did not result in the extrapyramidal side effects that had plagued earlier drugs. As such, clozapine is known as an "atypical" antipsychotic. The mechanism of action of clozapine, however, remains unclear. Clozapine shows weak antidopaminergic activity, in keeping with the proposed mechanism of action of other antipsychotic drugs. However, clozapine also has antiserotonergic and anticholinergic activities. A potential side effect of clozapine that has limited its use is agranulocytosis. Loxapine is structurally similar to clozapine. Loxapine is an effective antipsychotic drug with side effects similar to those of chlorpromazine. It has a low incidence of extrapyramidal side effects. Quetiapine and clothiapine are structurally related dibenzazepines. These compounds replace the oxygen atom of loxapine with a sulfur atom. Quetiapine is approved for use in schizophrenia and bipolar disorder cases. It is also used in children.

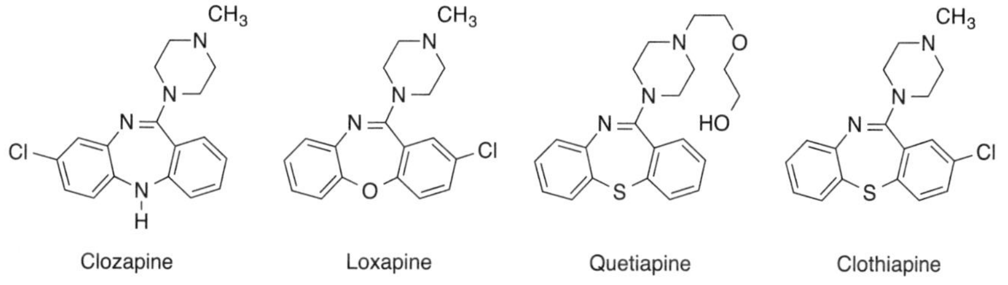

**Figure 11.** *Structures of dibenzazepines.*

## Aripiprazole

Aripiprazole is an atypical antipsychotic that is structurally distinct from other, more developed chemical classes (**Figure 12**). Mechanistically, the drug acts as a dopamine receptor partial agonist, as well as interacting with some types of serotonergic, adrenergic and histaminic receptors. First approved in 2002, it is used for the treatment of schizophrenia, bipolar disorder and major depressive disorder. Hepatic metabolism of aripiprazole is influenced by co-administration of other drugs. Because of this, doses of aripiprazole may require modification when a patient is taking additional medications.

## Lithium

An additional antipsychotic that does not fall into the aforementioned structural categories but deserves mention because of its use is lithium carbonate ($Li_2CO_3$). Lithium is used as a mood stabilizer in the management of bipolar disorders. The mechanism of action of lithium is thought to involve alteration of cation transport, especially of sodium ions, across cell membranes. Because lithium is an inorganic salt, it is not metabolized by the body and is excreted unchanged. The elimination half-life of lithium is 18 to 24 hours, and the molecule is not protein bound. Side effects of lithium include polyuria, tremor, thirst, and nausea.

## *Stimulants*

Although not typically used for the management of psychotropic disorders, stimulants have such a large role in our environment that they cannot be ignored as an important CNS drug class. The most often used stimulant is, of course, caffeine, which is consumed regularly by millions of people around the world. Caffeine is a member of the methylxanthine class of molecules, as is theobromine, the active component in cocoa and chocolate.

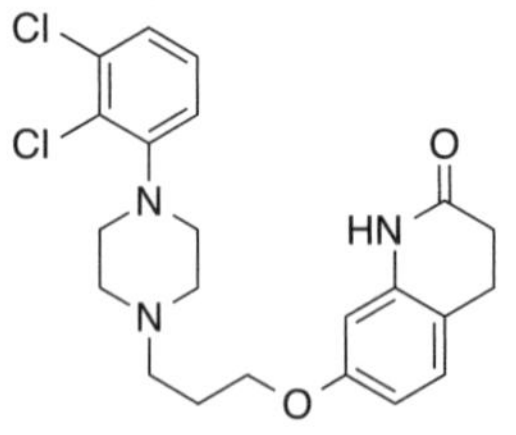

Aripiprazole

**Figure 12.** *The structure of atypical antipsychotic aripiprazole.*

In addition to the socially accepted and legal stimulants, other stimulants are drugs of abuse and are structurally related to amphetamine. Because of their simple structures and ease of synthesis, these molecules are often produced in basement laboratories to be sold illegally. Cocaine belongs to a separate structural class but is also classified as a stimulant. Regardless of the legal or illegal nature of the substance a patient consumes, it is necessary that healthcare providers be aware of the risks associated with all stimulants and their mechanisms of action.

## Amphetamine

Amphetamine, or phenylisopropylamine, is the parent molecule for which this structural class is named. Medically, amphetamine has been used to treat hyperactivity in children and narcolepsy. Amphetamine and related analogs (**Figure 13**) are thought to work by binding to presynaptic dopaminergic receptors and increasing the release of dopamine into the synapse. The molecule is only 20% bound by serum proteins and is excreted largely unchanged. Although an active metabolite of amphetamine, hydroxyamphetamine, is known to arise after consumption, it exists only as a small percentage of the overall dose. Therefore, the activity of this metabolite is not thought to contribute substantially to the overall activity of the drug. There is great potential for overdose with amphetamine. Alternative names for amphetamine include "speed" and "Benzedrine."

A derivative of amphetamine, methamphetamine, is a widely used street drug. It is commonly known as "meth" and "crystal meth." The side effects and abuse potential with methamphetamine are similar to those found with amphetamine. Commercially prepared formulations of methamphetamine hydrochloride are approved for the treatment of attention-deficit/hyperactivity disorder.

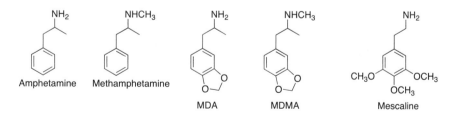

**Figure 13.** *Structures of amphetamine and related analogs.*

Methylenedioxyamphetamine (MDA) is also known as the "love pill" or the "love drug." Effects of this drug include intense euphoria. A drug with similar structure, 3,4-methylenedioxymethamphetamine (MDMA), is the street drug known as "Ecstasy," "E," and "X-TC." The central stimulant activity found in MDMA is thought to be caused by its serotonergic effects. MDMA is thought to increase serotonin release, inhibit serotonin reuptake, and possibly inhibit the biosynthesis of serotonin. These activities result in an overall increase in the concentration of serotonin in the synapse. MDMA, which resembles the structure of the hallucinogen mescaline, has psychedelic properties. Excessive use can lead to paranoia and psychoses.

## Cocaine

The psychological and behavioral effects of cocaine need little introduction. Available illegally, cocaine has a foothold as one of the most popular drugs of abuse despite its potential for overdose and addiction. Legally, cocaine is used as a topical local anesthetic. Cocaine is thought to act via dopaminergic receptors. Like amphetamine, cocaine binds to presynaptic dopamine receptors and increases the release of dopamine in the synapse. Cocaine (**Figure 14**) is rapidly and extensively metabolized to inactive species by hydrolysis of the benzoate ester, to give ecgonine methyl ester, or the methyl ester, to give benzoylecgonine. An active metabolite, ethyl cocaine, is formed in the liver in the presence of ethanol. This metabolic detail heightens the risk of cocaine when it is taken while drinking alcohol.

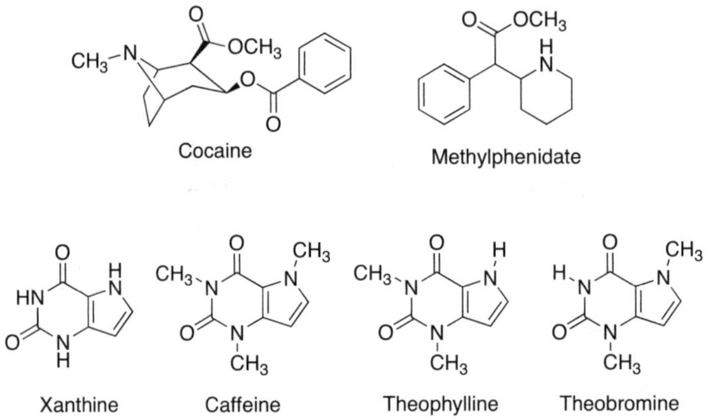

**Figure 14.** *Structures of nonamphetamine stimulants.*

## Methylphenidate

One of the most recognized stimulants is methylphenidate, shown in Figure 14. It is used in the management of attention-deficit/hyperactivity disorder and narcolepsy. Classified as a stimulant, methylphenidate is thought to work by blocking reuptake of dopamine on presynaptic dopaminergic neurons. Metabolism of methylphenidate results in ester hydrolysis to give $\alpha$-phenyl-2-piperidine acetic acid. The half-life of the parent drug is 2 to 3 hours, and it is approximately 15% protein bound. The side effects include nervousness and insomnia.

## Methylxanthines

Methylxanthines (Figure 14) are derivatives of xanthine and are alkaloids found in natural products. They have been used as beverages since ancient times. They include caffeine from tea and coffee, theophylline from tea, and theobromine from cocoa. Caffeine is widely used for its CNS stimulant effect. A cup of coffee contains about 80 to 120 mg of caffeine, whereas a cup of tea or an equivalent amount of a cola beverage contains a somewhat lower concentration. Caffeine functions as a cortical stimulant, producing wakefulness, clear thinking, concentration, and lowered fatigue. Higher doses produce stimulation noticeable as restlessness, anxiety, and nervousness.

The mechanism of action of the methylxanthines is not well understood. They may act by their antagonism of adenosine at the $A_1$ adenosine receptors. The methylxanthines seem indiscriminant in their receptor targeting, which may lead to a variety of side effects from overuse. Theophylline acts as a bronchodilator and is used for the treatment of asthma and chronic obstructive pulmonary disease.

## Applications to Anesthesia

A number of the psychotropic agents discussed in this chapter may have interactions with anesthetic agents when administered concomitantly. Certain psychotropic agents produce an analgesic effect at clinically relevant doses. Accordingly, to evaluate and manage the potential risks associated with anesthesia, clinicians must be well informed of any psychotropic medicines a patient may be taking.

The risk of drug interactions highlight the importance of understanding the medications a patient is currently or has recently been taking. Healthcare providers are urged to become aware of potential problematic situations caused by taking several medications at one time.

## Suggested Reading

Akam E, Strange PG. Inverse agonist properties of atypical antipsychotic drugs. *Biochem Pharmacol.* 2004;6(11):2039-2045.

Birnbach DJ. Interactions in anesthesia: anesthetic management of the drug abusing parturient. *Acta Anaesthesiol Belg.* 2001;52(4):351-356.

Brunton LL, Chabner BA, Knollmann BC. *The Pharmacological Basis of Therapeutics.* 12th ed. New York, NY: McGraw-Hill; 2011.

Cryan JF, Kaupmann K. Don't worry "B" happy! a role for GABA$_B$ receptors in anxiety and depression. *Trends Pharmacol Sci.* 2005;26(1):36-43.

Ezekiel MR. *Handbook of Anesthesiology.* Laguna Hills, CA: CCS Publishing; 2007.

Fischer SP, Healzer JM, Brook MW, Brock-Utne JG. General anesthesia in a patient on long-term amphetamine therapy: is there cause for concern? *Anesth Analg.* 2000;91(3):758-759.

Fowler JS, Logan J, Azzaro AJ, et al. Reversible inhibitors of monoamine oxidase-A (RIMAs): robust, reversible inhibition of human brain MAO-A by CX157. *Neuropsychopharmacology.* 2010; 35(3):623–631.

Mattia C, Coluzzi F. Antidepressants in chronic neuropathic pain. *Mini Rev Med Chem.* 2003 Nov;3(7):773-784.

Naguib M, Koorn R. Interactions between psychotropics, anaesthetics and electroconvulsive therapy: implications for drug choice and patient management. *CNS Drugs.* 2002;16(4):229-247.

Rowlett JK, Platt DM, Lelas S, Atack JR, Dawson GR. Different GABA$_A$ receptor subtypes mediate the anxiolytic, abuse-related, and motor effects of benzodiazepine-like drugs in primates. *Proc Natl Acad Sci USA.* 2005;102(3):915-920.

Stoelting RK, Miller RD. *Basics of Anesthesia.* 5th ed. Philadelphia, PA: Elsevier Health Sciences; 2007.

## Discussion Topics

1. Explain the difference between antidepressants and anxiolytics.

2. What receptors are involved in each of the aforementioned classes of drugs?

3. What are some of the aspects of these drugs related to anesthesia?

# Chapter 13

## Antibiotic and Antiviral Agents
*by Suzanne M. Wright, CRNA, PhD, Cynthia S. Dowd, PhD,
and Lemont B. Kier, PhD*

An infectious process is usually initiated by microorganisms that have invaded the human body through some mechanism such as direct contact, inhalation of solid or liquid droplets in the air, ingestion of contaminated food or water, or through breaks in the skin barrier. Just as microorganisms have been causing infections since the beginning of time, scientists have been searching for effective remedies to combat these infections. The discovery of bacteria, fungi, and viruses as principal offenders in the infectious process has led to a more scientific understanding of microorganisms and, subsequently, the development of effective medicinal therapies.

Early in the 20th century, the modern era of anti-infective therapy began. A pathologist and bacteriologist named Gerhard Domagk earned a Nobel Prize for his development of sulfonamide drugs, such as Prontosil (trade name for the first synthetic antibacterial drug), which are effective against *Streptococcus* infections. Another Nobel Prize winner, German scientist Paul Erhlich, discovered the arsenic-based compound, arsphenamine (also called salvarsan), as a treatment for syphilis, a sexually transmitted disease caused by the spirochetal bacterium *Treponema pallidum*. In 1928, Alexander Fleming, a Scottish biologist, accidentally discovered a *Penicillium* mold, later named penicillin, capable of killing Gram-positive bacteria. Since these monumental discoveries, research has advanced to develop specific medicinal compounds designed to target infections based on their biological cause.

During the last several decades, the discipline of medicinal chemistry has used chemical research techniques to synthesize a large number of new and more effective agents for the treatment of bacterial, parasitic, fungal, and viral infections. Although inclusion of each of these agents is beyond the scope of this chapter, a comprehensive discussion of the common structural classes of antibacterial and antiviral agents is provided.

## Identifying the Cause of Infection

Before initiating the appropriate anti-infective therapy, clinicians must identify the offending pathogen. Proper identification of the infecting microorganism allows for the most appropriate choice of therapeutic agent. Initiating therapy without identification of the causative organism may enable the microorganism to survive exposure to the medication, and the development of resistant strains can ensue. In addition, if the therapy fails to target the specific microorganism, the treatment may be ineffective, as occurs when antibiotics are administered for viral infections.

A microorganism culture obtained from an infected person can provide the necessary information for selecting the most appropriate anti-infective therapy. The cultured organism can be grown in the presence of a variety of anti-infective agents to see which agent is most effective in inhibiting and halting the growth of the microorganism. Tests such as Gram-staining, which involves the use of purple dye and iodine, may also aid in identifying the pathogen. Developed by the Danish microbiologist Christian Gram in 1884, the Gram-staining technique allows the investigator to easily differentiate between groups of bacteria based on the structure of the cell wall of the organism. Nearly all bacteria can be classified as Gram-negative or Gram-positive based on the results of the Gram stain. Because Gram-positive bacteria have a more complex cell wall structure, they are more able to retain the dye. With such tests, identification of the organism is more accurate, and clinicians have the necessary information to select the most effective anti-infective agents for use in treatment.

## Development of Resistance to Anti-infective Therapy

While advances in anti-infective therapy have greatly improved the clinical outcome of patients with bacterial and viral infections, the development of resistant strains of microorganisms has increased remarkably and continues to pose a serious challenge to public health. The presence of antibiotics in everyday items such as soaps, toothpastes, and household cleaners has the potential to do great damage by increasing bacterial resistance to existing antibiotics. Organisms can become resistant to drug therapy by a variety of mechanisms depending on the particular microorganism and the particular drug. Microorganism resistance involves such mechanisms as development of efflux pumps to remove a drug from the interior of its cells, biological mutation of the drug target, and development of enzymes that degrade the drug before its action on the target. Because of the development of drug resistance when using antibiotic and antiviral agents, information on the efficacy of each agent against particular drug-resistant strains of the infecting microorganism is important. Where appropriate, this information is included in the following pages.

## Antibiotic Agents

An *antibiotic* is a drug that is effective in treating bacterial infections. Antibiotics, or antibacterials, can be described as bacteriostatic or bactericidal. A *bacteriostatic agent* inhibits the growth of bacteria so that it grows more slowly than in the absence of the drug. A *bactericidal agent* kills the bacteria.

Several structural classes of antibiotics are available for clinical use. The penicillins were among the first agents used to treat bacterial infections. The development of penicillin revolutionized medicine as it is known today and opened the door to a host of new antibiotic agents. Cephalosporins are structurally related to penicillins and have the same mechanism of action. Newer classes of antibiotics include aminoglycosides, tetracyclines, macrolides, and quinolones. Sulfonamides are an older generation of antibiotics that remain clinically useful despite their undesirable side effects.

## Penicillins

Penicillins are derivatives of 6-aminopenicillanic acid. The common structural feature of all penicillins is the 4-membered cyclic amide ring called the β-lactam ring. Differences among penicillins result from differences among the structures of the side chain on the β-lactam ring. A number of important penicillin structures are shown in **Table 1**. Penicillins in clinical use are naturally occurring and semisynthetic compounds. Penicillin and related analogs are most effective against Gram-positive organisms. Newer penicillin derivatives have shown increased efficacy against Gram-negative species.

Penicillins, when effective, are the drugs of choice for most infections. This class of drugs is effective in treating infections of the upper respiratory tract and genitourinary tract, as well as pelvic inflammatory disease, meningococcal disease, Lyme disease, and tetanus. The most effective route of administration of penicillins is the parenteral route, although large oral doses can work well. Caution is observed when administering penicillins to patients who are allergic to any β-lactam antibiotic because cross-sensitivity may occur.

As a group, the penicillins have considerable protein-binding capacity and are excreted unchanged. Excretion typically occurs via the kidney, so patients with decreased renal function may be expected to retain the drug longer than normal. Penicillin is a common cause of drug allergy, and side effects may include diarrhea, nausea, and/or headache.

## Mechanism of Action

Within bacteria, several proteins named *penicillin-binding proteins* (PBPs) are responsible for cross-linking peptidoglycans to form the bacterial cell wall. The cross-linked structure protects the cell from its hypertonic environment. The β-lactam antibiotics, such as penicillins, work by binding irreversibly to PBPs and disrupting their action. Although this inhibition stops cell wall biosynthesis and is detrimental to the cell, it is thought that the primary bactericidal activity of β-lactam antibiotics arises from the autolytic action of sister enzymes in the bacteria. These enzymes, the autolysins, are responsible for degrading certain portions of the cell wall at well-defined points. Normally, a balance exists between the action of PBPs, which synthesize the cell wall, and autolysins, which degrade it. In the presence of β-lactam antibiotics, however, this balance is shifted in favor of the autolysins. Regulation of autolysin activity, which is to degrade the cell wall, is disrupted, and the bacterial cell lyses and dies.

**Table 1.** *Penicillins.*

| Name | R substituent |
|------|---------------|
| 6-Aminopenicillanic acid | -NH₂ |
| Penicillin G (benzylpenicillin) | |
| Penicillin V (phenoxymethyl penicillin) | |
| Ampicillin | |
| Amoxicillin | |
| Piperacillin | |

| Name | R substituent |
|------|---------------|
| Carbenicillin | |
| Mezlocillin | |
| Ticarcillin | |
| Methicillin | |
| Nafcillin | |
| Oxacillin | |
| Cloxacillin | |
| Dicloxacillin | |

## Penicillin Resistance

A common mechanism for penicillin resistance is the production of enzymes called β-lactamases, one of which is penicillinase. Penicillinase reacts with the carbonyl of the β-lactam ring of these agents and cleaves the amide bond, rendering the molecule inactive. Whereas early penicillin derivatives are susceptible to penicillinase, later modifications of the structure provide resistance. Sterically hindering groups substituted on the β-lactam ring, such as the 2,6-dimethoxy groups in methicillin, confers penicillinase resistance. Whether a drug is resistant to penicillinase is an important component of penicillin therapy. Agents that are degraded by penicillinase are called penicillinase-sensitive, and agents that cannot be degraded by these enzymes are called penicillinase-resistant.

## Penicillinase-Sensitive Penicillins

Penicillin G (Benzylpenicillin is the international nonproprietary name and the British approved name.) and penicillin V (also called phenoxymethyl penicillin) can be isolated from fermentation processes. Penicillin G is the prototype for the penicillin class of drugs. A common problem with penicillin G, however, is the ease of reaction of the β-lactam ring: in aqueous solution, the β-lactam of penicillin G is easily hydrolyzed, which inactivates the drug. Similarly, nucleophilic proteins can react with the β-lactam, producing antigenic compounds. The antigenic compounds can be the basis for penicillin allergies.

The β-lactam ring of penicillin V is more stable than that of penicillin G because of the additional electronegative oxygen atom in the amide side chain. This substituent is thought to decrease the reactivity of the β-lactam bond. The increased stability allows penicillin V to be administered orally, but it has lower antibiotic potency compared with penicillin G.

Ampicillin is a penicillin G analog with an amine group on the side chain. This structural modification produces a drug that is more stable to acid. Because of this feature, ampicillin can be administered orally. Ampicillin has potency equal to that of penicillin G in the treatment of meningococcal, streptococcal, and pneumococcal infections. In addition, the broad-spectrum activity of ampicillin is recognized in its efficacy against *Salmonella* species, *Escherichia coli,* and *Haemophilus influenza* infections. Amoxicillin is structurally related to ampicillin, the only addition being a *p*-hydroxyl group on the benzyl side chain. Ampicillin, along with other antibiotics, has been used prophylactically in surgical patients considered to be at high risk for infectious endocarditis.

Piperacillin is a second derivative of ampicillin. The amine substituent on piperacillin is converted to a complex urea. This antibiotic is equally as effective in the treatment of Gram-positive organisms as ampicillin but has an even greater effectiveness with Gram-negative microorganisms. Piperacillin can be used clinically in the treatment of *Klebsiella pneumoniae* infections. Carbenicillin, mezlocillin, and ticarcillin are 3 additional penicillins that are sensitive to penicillinase activity. The carboxylic acid function of carbenicillin gives it high efficacy against Gram-negative organisms.

## Penicillinase-Resistant Penicillins

Nafcillin is an important penicillin derivative because it represents one of the few derivatives with resistance to penicillinase. Methicillin, which has been discontinued, was the prototypical penicillinase-resistant penicillin. The 2,6-dimethoxy substitution pattern on the benzene ring gave increased steric bulk to methicillin. It was this structural feature that was thought to provide the resistance to penicillinase degradation. This structural change, however, resulted in a substantially lower anti-infective spectrum and decreased potency of the drug. These parameters limited the clinical use of the agent to treatment of *Staphylococcus aureus* and nosocomial staphylococcal cellulitis infections.

Dicloxacillin, oxacillin, and cloxacillin are additional penicillin derivatives that are resistant to penicillinase degradation. In these molecules, the benzene ring in methicillin was replaced by an isoxazole ring. The steric bulk that is important for penicillin resistance is managed by the methyl and halogenated benzyl substituents off the isoxazole ring. These agents are less potent than penicillin G, although both are effective against Gram-positive organisms. They are acid stable and can be administered orally.

## Cephalosporins

As with many anti-infectives, cephalosporins are another antibiotic category with origins in soil. Cephalosporins were first isolated from the genus of fungus called *Acremonium* (formerly known as *Cephalosporium*) and found to be more stable than penicillins against β-lactamase. The agents in this category are natural and semisynthetic compounds. Cephalosporins differ structurally from the penicillins by the type of ring that is fused to the β-lactam ring. The penicillin β-lactam ring is fused to a 5-membered thiazolidine ring, whereas the cephalosporin β-lactam ring is fused to a 6-membered dihydrothiazine ring.

Cephalosporins can be divided into first-, second-, third-, fourth-, and fifth-generation agents. First-generation cephalosporins provide good antimicrobial activity against Gram-positive organisms with moderate effects on Gram-negative bacteria. Second through fifth-generation cephalosporins have increased effects on Gram-negative organisms. Structures of several cephalosporins are shown in **Table 2**.

Infections of the skin, soft tissue, urinary tract, bone, and respiratory system respond well to cephalosporin therapy. First-generation cephalosporins are primarily recommended for treatment of Gram-positive organisms, whereas serious Gram-negative microbial infections respond well to third-generation

**Table 2.** *First-, Second- and Third-Generation Cephalosporins.*

| Name | R$_1$ | R$_2$ | X |
|------|-------|-------|---|
| Cephadroxil | (structure) | -CH$_3$ | -H |
| Cephalexin | (structure) | -CH$_3$ | -H |
| Cefprozil | (structure) | (structure, CH$_3$) | -H |
| Cefixime | (structure) | (structure) | -H |
| Cephalothin | (structure) | (structure) | -H |
| Cefazolin | (structure) | (structure) | -H |
| Cefoxitin | (structure) | (structure) | -OCH$_3$ |
| Cefuroxime | (structure) | (structure) | -H |
| Cefonicid | (structure) | (structure) | -H |
| Cefotetan | (structure) | (structure) | -OCH$_3$ |
| Cefaclor | (structure) | -Cl | -H |
| Cefamandole | (structure) | (structure) | -H |
| Cefotaxime | (structure) | (structure) | -H |
| Ceftriaxone | (structure) | (structure) | -H |
| Ceftazidime | (structure) | (structure) | -H |

cephalosporins. Clinicians should be cautious about the concomitant administration of furosemide and cephalosporins because this combination has been shown to cause enhanced nephrotoxic effects.

In general, cephalosporins are not metabolized and are excreted unchanged. Excretion occurs primarily by glomerular filtration from the kidney. Cephalosporins have substantial binding to serum proteins. Side effects of cephalosporin use include diarrhea, nausea, and vomiting. The half-life of most cephalosporins is 0.5 to 2 hours. Many agents belonging to the cephalosporin class are available for use. Listed in later sections titled "Oral Cephalosporins" and "Parenteral Cephalosporins" are examples of first-, second-, third-, and fourth-generation cephalosporins.

## Mechanism of Action

Cephalosporins are similar to penicillins in that they bind to the PBPs, and their action eventually leads to cell lysis. Also like penicillins, cephalosporins fall under the β-lactam structural class of compounds. These bactericidal agents are carboxylic acids and form water-soluble salts, but they are often unstable in aqueous solutions and must be mixed just before administration. Reactivity of cephalosporins to β-lactamase is modulated by substituents at the C-3 and C-7 positions (Table 2). Many cephalosporins have reactive groups at the C-3 position, which increase susceptibility of the drug to the degrading enzyme. Steric bulk at the C-7 position, however, decreases reactivity with β-lactamase.

## Oral Cephalosporins

First Generation: First-generation cephalosporins are effective in killing Gram-positive organisms but have little activity against Gram-negative organisms. Cefadroxil contains the side chain found in amoxicillin at C-7. This structural group gives cefadroxil increased stability toward hydrolysis and nucleophilic attack; therefore, cefadroxil can be administered orally. Cefadroxil also has a long half-life (1-2 hours) and, therefore, allows for once-a-day dosing. Cefadroxil has a longer half-life than that of cephalexin. Cephalexin has the side chain found in ampicillin, giving resistance to nucleophiles and β-lactamase. Cephalexin can be administered orally. The lack of an ester at the C-3 position also reduces β-lactamase activity. Cephalexin is not metabolized and is excreted unchanged. The half-life of cephalexin is 0.5 to 1 hour.

Second Generation: Second-generation cephalosporins have improved activity against *H. influenzae* compared with oral first-generation cephalosporins. Cefprozil has an amoxicillin side chain at C-7 and a propenyl group at the C-3 position that is conjugated with the double bond in the 6-membered ring. Cefprozil is well absorbed (~95%) and is largely excreted unchanged. Cefuroxime is a second-generation parenteral cephalosporin that is also available in an oral formulation. Others such as cefonicid, cefotetan, and cefaclor have improved Gram-negative activity relative to the first-generation drugs.

Third Generation: Third-generation cephalosporins are more active against Gram-negative organisms than are first- and second-generation oral cephalosporins. However, third-generation oral cephalosporins are less active against these organisms than are the parenterally administered third- and fourth-generation cephalosporins. Third-generation oral cephalosporins retain the increased activity against *H. influenzae* as seen in previous agents. Cefixime is a third-generation oral cephalosporin. It has a C-3 vinyl group and a *cis*-oximinoether at C-7. Both of these structural features contribute to β-lactamase stability.

## Parenteral Cephalosporins

First Generation: First-generation parenterally administered cephalosporins are not active against *H. influenzae* or *Bacteroides* species. Cephalothin, the oldest first-generation cephalosporin, which has been discontinued, had a thiophene ring at the C-7 position that acted as a bioisostere of the benzyl group of penicillin G. In contrast with other cephalosporins, cephalothin was metabolized by deacetylation at the C-3 position. This metabolic route accounted for approximately 25% of the administered drug. The remaining drug was excreted unchanged. The ester at the C-3 position contributed to the susceptibility of cephalothin to β-lactamase.

Cefazolin is an additional first-generation cephalosporin that is administered parenterally. Cefazolin has a longer half-life than that of cephalothin. Cefazolin has a thio-linked thiadiazole ring at the 3-position and a tetrazolylmethyl unit at C-7. The absence of an ester at C-3 makes cefazolin stable to hydrolysis. The prophylactic administration of cefazolin may minimize the incidence of certain postoperative infections in patients undergoing surgical procedures classified as contaminated or potentially contaminated and may be used in surgical patients in whom infection at the operative site could cause a serious complication. It is important to note that cross-hypersensitivity among β-lactam antibiotics has been documented and reported to occur in up to 10% of patients with a history of penicillin allergy.

Second Generation: In general, second-generation parenterally administered cephalosporins are less active against Gram-positive organisms than are first-generation agents. However, second-generation parenteral cephalosporins show increased activity against Gram-negative organisms. Cefoxitin is a useful antibiotic for the treatment of gonorrhea. The methoxy group at the 7-position gives the molecule additional steric bulk, which confers β-lactamase resistance. At the same time, however, cefoxitin treatment has resulted in the induction of β-lactamase activity. Cefuroxime is resistant to β-lactamase with a *syn*-oriented methoxime moiety on the C-7 side chain. Cefuroxime is a treatment for *H. influenzae* meningitis because of its ability to pass into the cerebrospinal fluid. Like cefoxitin, cefuroxime induces β-lactamase activity.

Cefamandole contains a formate ester at the 7-position. The ester is rapidly cleaved in the host, giving the active form of the drug. Cefamandole was especially useful in treating Gram-negative microbes, when compared with first-generation cephalosporins. Of note, cefamandole has an *N*-methylthiotetrazole (NMTT) side chain at the C-3 position. This side chain has been linked to decreased vitamin K activity and a corresponding increase in bleeding. The effect is associated with the release of the 5-thio-1-methyl-1*H*-tetrazole fragment from the C-3 position of the drug.

Third Generation: Third-generation parenterally administered cephalosporins are less efficient against Gram-positive bacteria than are first-generation agents. However, third-generation cephalosporins exhibit increased resistance to Gram-negative β-lactamases. Cefotaxime has a *syn*-methoxime moiety at C-7, which is connected to an aminothiazole ring. Similar to the oral third-generation cephalosporins, cefotaxime is extremely effective in fighting Gram-negative microbes. The C-3 acetyl group is hydrolyzed during metabolism, accounting for 5% to 25% of the administered drug. The deacetylated metabolite retains anti-infective activity. The remainder of the drug is excreted unchanged (30%) or metabolized to inactive compounds.

Ceftriaxone has the same C-7 side-chain fragment as cefotaxime, but has a metabolically stable triazinone group replacing the acetyl group of cefotaxime at the C-3 position. The agent is often administered intra-arterially to treat Gram-negative meningitis. Ceftriaxone has a substantially longer half-life than do other cephalosporins. The half-life of ceftrixone is 5 to 9 hours. Cefotaxime and ceftriaxone are inactive against *Pseudomonas aeruginosa*. Ceftazidime is active against *P. aeruginosa*. Ceftazidime has a pyridinium group at the C-3 position and a substituted oxime on the C-7 side chain. This agent is excreted unchanged and has a half-life of approximately 2 hours. Ceftazidime is resistant to commonly occurring β-lactamases and effective against Gram-negative and Gram-positive organisms.

## Fourth- and Fifth-Generation Cephalosporins

Approved in 2007, fourth-generation cefepime has a larger spectrum of activity than do the third-generation cephalosporins, being active against Gram-positive and Gram-negative organisms. Cefepime is stable to β-lactamase action and results in less induction of these enzymes than other cephalosporins. It is thought that the quaternary ammonium group at the C-3 position enhances the ability of cefepime to cross the cell membranes of Gram-negative organisms, increasing its efficacy.

Structurally-related, fourth-generation compounds are listed in **Table 3**. These compounds retain the quaternary amine at the C-3 position with a significant increase in steric bulk at that position. The fifth generation of cephalosporins is newer and displays improved activity against MRSA. Two examples are shown in Table 3. Both ceftobiprole and cefaroline are active against Gram-positive and Gram-negative bacteria, with improved activity against MRSA. Ceftaroline fosamil was approved for use in 2010. It is a prodrug that is converted *in vivo* to the active metabolite ceftaroline.

**Table 3.** *Fourth- and Fifth-Generation Cephalosporins.*

| Name | R$_1$ | R$_2$ |
|------|-------|-------|
| Cefepime | | |
| Cefclidine | | |
| Cefluprenam | | |
| Cefpirome | | |
| Cefquinome | | |
| Ceftobiprole | | |
| Ceftaroline fosamil | | |

# Aminoglycosides

Introduced in the 1940s, aminoglycosides are broad-spectrum antibiotics and are used to treat infections caused by aerobic Gram-negative bacteria. However, potential toxic effects associated with the use of aminoglycosides often limit their clinical application. Toxic effects associated with the use of aminoglycosides often involve the eighth cranial nerve and the acoustic nerve and can cause vertigo and possible hearing loss. Ototoxic effects may be enhanced with the concurrent administration of other aminoglycosides, furosemide, or ethacrynic acid. Signs and symptoms of ototoxic damage are slow to manifest, thereby minimizing the opportunity to reduce drug levels and effectively treat this complication.

Another important clinical consideration with aminoglycoside use is the potential for symptomatic neuromuscular blockade in certain patient populations. People with Parkinson disease and myasthenia gravis may experience increased muscular weakness when given these agents, although this effect is uncommon. The neuromuscular blockade is believed to be related to the competitive inhibition of calcium ion–dependent acetylcholine release at the neuromuscular junction. Administration of aminoglycosides in the pleural or peritoneal cavity during surgery may intensify the effects of coadministered neuromuscular blockers. Thus, concomitant administration of aminoglycosides with normal clinical doses of neuromuscular blockers could potentially lead to profound neuromuscular blockade.

Aminoglycosides are water soluble at all pH levels, form acid salts, and are not readily absorbed from the gastrointestinal tract. These antibiotics are excreted unchanged in urine. Dosages may be adjusted downward in people with renal impairment to prevent accumulation of toxic levels of the antibiotic. Although care should be taken in assessing adequate renal function before initiating treatment, aminoglycosides are effective in the treatment of infections of the urinary tract, burns, and various types of pneumonia.

# Mechanism of Action

Aminoglycosides (**Figure 1**) constitute a class of antibiotics that have their lethal effect on bacteria by inhibiting bacterial protein biosynthesis. Aminoglycosides bind to the 30S subunit of the ribosome, the site of protein synthesis. Ribosomal binding prevents normal protein synthesis. Because the bacterium is unable to make the proteins necessary for its lifecycle, it dies.

Gentamicin sulfate was one of the first aminoglycosides to effectively treat *P. aeruginosa* infection. Of important clinical note is an incompatibility demonstrated between this agent and β-lactams. Reaction between these antibiotic classes causes *N*-acylation of gentamicin by the β-lactam agent, thus neutralizing both drug molecules. The 2 groups of antibiotics should not be administered in the same solution or in the same part of the body. Gentamicin is not absorbed orally, so the dose must be given parenterally.

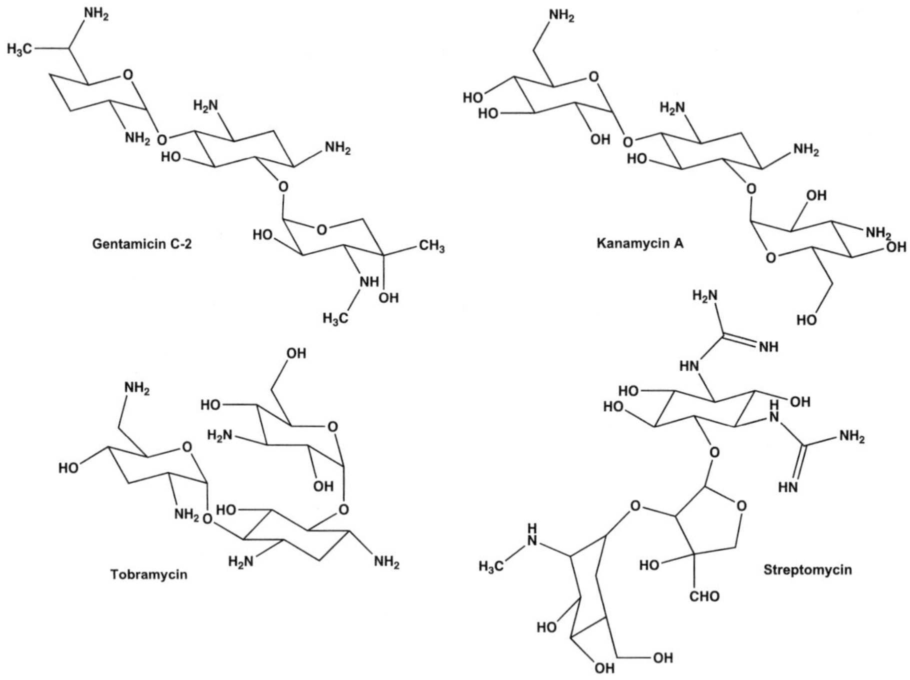

**Figure 1.** *Structures of aminoglycosides.*

Kanamycin sulfate is isolated from *Streptomyces kanamyceticus*. Kanamycin is used in the treatment of Gram-negative infections; however, *P. aeruginosa* is highly resistant. Tobramycin has a much broader spectrum of activity than kanamycin and is less toxic than gentamicin. Streptomycin was developed in the early 1940s for the treatment of tuberculosis. Rarely administered alone today, streptomycin has proven ineffective in treating many of the common microorganisms present in immunosuppressed patients, such as patients with AIDS. Streptomycin remains, however, one of the lead agents in multidrug therapy against tuberculosis.

## Tetracyclines

Tetracyclines are a widely used group of antibiotics. These drugs are effective as broad-spectrum agents. However, because of the frequency of resistance, they are seldom used as first-line agents. Compounds of this class are classified as short, intermediate, and long acting. The structure of the tetracycline antibiotics is based on the structure of tetracycline. Several drugs in this class are shown in **Table 4**. Tetracyclines are most often prescribed for the treatment of acne, infections of the upper respiratory tract and urinary tract (infections due to *E. coli* bacteria), treatment of sexually transmitted diseases, and prophylaxis for malaria.

Chelation, the process by which tetracyclines form salts with inorganic cations, is an important consideration when using tetracyclines. The tetracycline salts are formed because of the electron-rich nature of the tetracyclines that bind to the positive ions. These salts are insoluble at neutral pH levels. Blood levels of tetracyclines are altered in the presence of inorganic cations, and, therefore, the desired pharmacological effect will not be achieved. Because of this characteristic, tetracyclines are incompatible with concurrent administration of products with high levels of cations, such as dairy products high in calcium and antacids rich in iron. Calcium-rich structures of the body, such as the bones and teeth, accumulate tetracyclines. Accumulation leads to permanent discoloration of the teeth. Although not dangerous to a person's health, these side effects can be cosmetically bothersome. To avoid this undesirable side effect, this class of antibiotics is not administered to children.

## Mechanism of Action

Similar to the mode of action for aminoglycoside antibiotics, tetracyclines inhibit bacterial protein synthesis by interfering with the bacterial ribosome. Binding to the 30S subunit of the ribosome prohibits the necessary enzymatic coupling reactions. Consequently, protein synthesis does not occur, and the bacteria cannot survive.

In general, tetracyclines are 40% to 90% bound to serum proteins. Their metabolism typically yields no active compounds, and they have a long half-life of elimination (>10 hours). The well-known tetracyclines vary only slightly in their structures (Table 4). Demeclocycline, minocycline, and doxycycline are commercially available.

**Table 4.** *Tetracycline antibiotics.*

| Name | $R_1$ | $R_2$ | $R_3$ | $R_4$ |
|---|---|---|---|---|
| Tetracycline | -H | -OH | $-CH_3$ | -H |
| Demeclocycline | -Cl | -OH | -H | -H |
| Minocycline | $-N(CH_3)_2$ | -H | -H | -H |
| Doxycycline | -H | -H | $-CH_3$ | -OH |

## Macrolides

Macrolide antibiotics have a very safe pharmacological profile. Agents in this structural class of antibiotics are used to treat some of the more common community-acquired infections. Macrolides are useful in treating infections that are transmitted sexually such as gonorrhea, pelvic inflammatory disease, and chlamydia.

Interactions with other concurrently administered medications are common and often result in alterations in metabolism of the other drug. In particular, there is a much longer half-life and potential for toxic effects with medications such as digoxin, warfarin, methylprednisolone, and theophylline. In general, the side effects of macrolide use include diarrhea, nausea, vomiting, headache, a bad taste in the mouth, and rash.

## Mechanism of Action

Macrolides exert their anti-infective activity on bacteria by inhibiting bacterial protein synthesis. By binding to the 50S ribosomal subunit, macrolides prevent elongation of the growing peptide chain. Drugs of this class feature 1 or more deoxy sugars attached to a lactone ring. These sugar residues usually carry a substituted amino group, giving the molecule weakly basic character.

Erythromycin (**Figure 2**) is produced by a strain of *Streptomyces erythreus*. It is chemically unstable in acid because of internal cyclic ketal formation. This agent is most effective in eliminating Gram-positive cocci, Gram-positive bacilli,

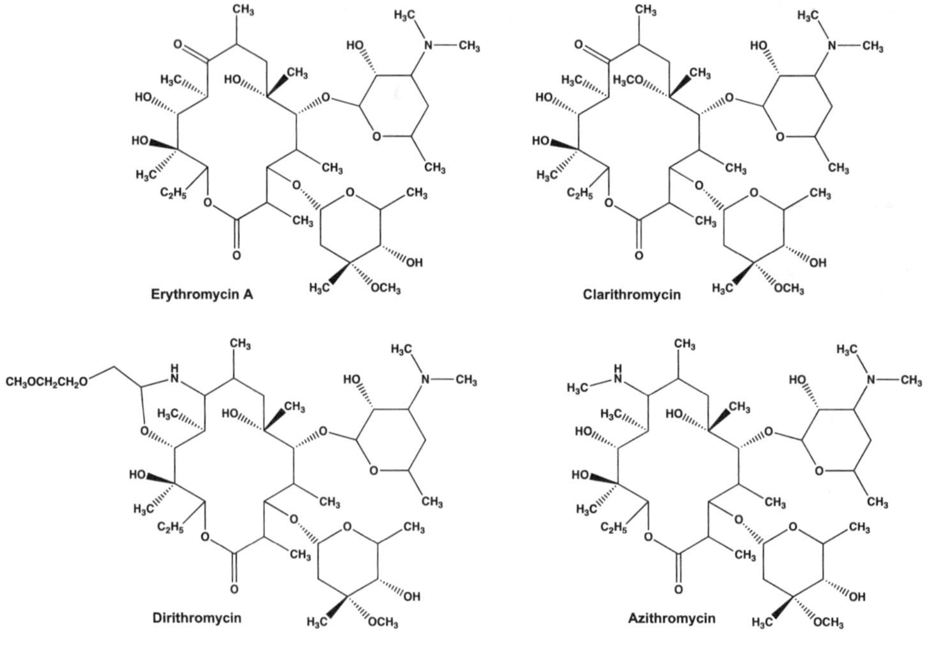

**Figure 2.** *Structures of macrolides.*

and various Gram-negative microbes. Cases of hepatic dysfunction have been results in the formation of 14-hydroxy-clarithromycin, which has twice the activity of the parent drug. An additional macrolide antibiotic that is used clinically is azithromycin. Metabolism of azithromycin does not yield active metabolites.

# Sulfonamides

The advent of sulfonamides in the 1930s had an enormous impact on the treatment of infections. Sulfonamides provided adequate anti-infective activity in a relatively safe and orally effective manner. These agents are bacteriostatic when administered at appropriate doses. These drugs are called sulfonamides because of the common sulfonamide ($-SO_2NH-$) group in their structures.

Sulfonamides are popular drugs for the treatment of urinary tract infections and diseases of the colon, such as Crohn disease. A drawback often limiting the clinical use of sulfonamides is their propensity for adverse effects. Adverse reactions can range in severity from simple rashes and photosensitivity to extreme liver and kidney damage. The most clinically important reaction with the use of sulfonamides is the onset of Stevens-Johnson syndrome, which is characterized by the formation of multiple ulcers and erythema of the eye, mouth, and urethra. Stevens-Johnson syndrome is a rare, but serious, systemic disorder with the potential for death.

# Mechanism of Action

Sulfonamides function by inhibiting dihydropteroate synthase. This enzyme is crucial for the bacterial biosynthesis of folic acid derivatives and DNA. Because folates are necessary intermediates for the synthesis of DNA, sulfonamide inhibition prevents bacteria from multiplying and, ultimately, is lethal to the microorganism. Sulfonamides compete for the active site of the enzyme with $p$-amino benzoic acid

Sulfisoxazole (**Figure 3**) is a sulfonamide with a broad spectrum of antibacterial activity. Absorption is adequate following oral administration, and sulfisoxazole is distributed throughout the body. Resistance to the drug is fairly common and is usually demonstrated by decreased sensitivity to the medication. It is currently available in combination with erythromycin ethylsuccinate.

Sulfamethoxazole is formulated in combination with trimethoprim. The mechanism of action of sulfamethoxazole is the inhibition of dihydrofolic acid synthesis, like other sulfonamides. Trimethoprim is added in the formulation because its mechanism of action is to inhibit dihydrofolic acid reductase. Both pathways are necessary components of the biosynthetic scheme to produce folates. Folates are required for DNA biosynthesis. In this way, sulfamethoxazole and trimethoprim act on different parts of the same necessary pathway to decrease bacterial survival.

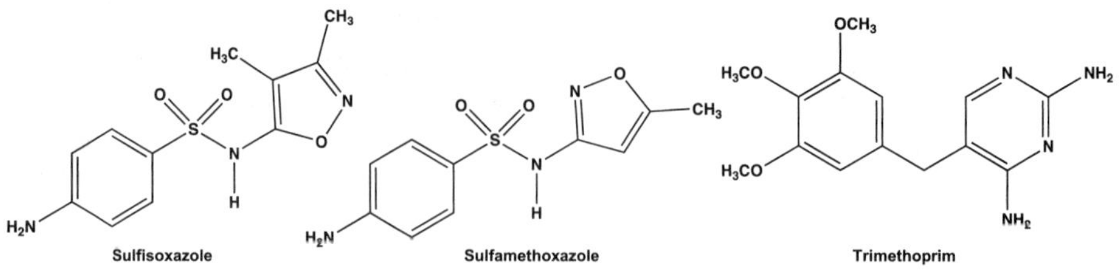

**Figure 3.** *Structures of sulfonamides.*

## Quinolones

Quinolones (**Figure 4**) have gained increased attention because of their activity against pathogens that cause anthrax. This class of antibiotics is not new, however. Quinolones are named for the fused bicyclic (quinolone) ring structure that is the central feature of each analog.

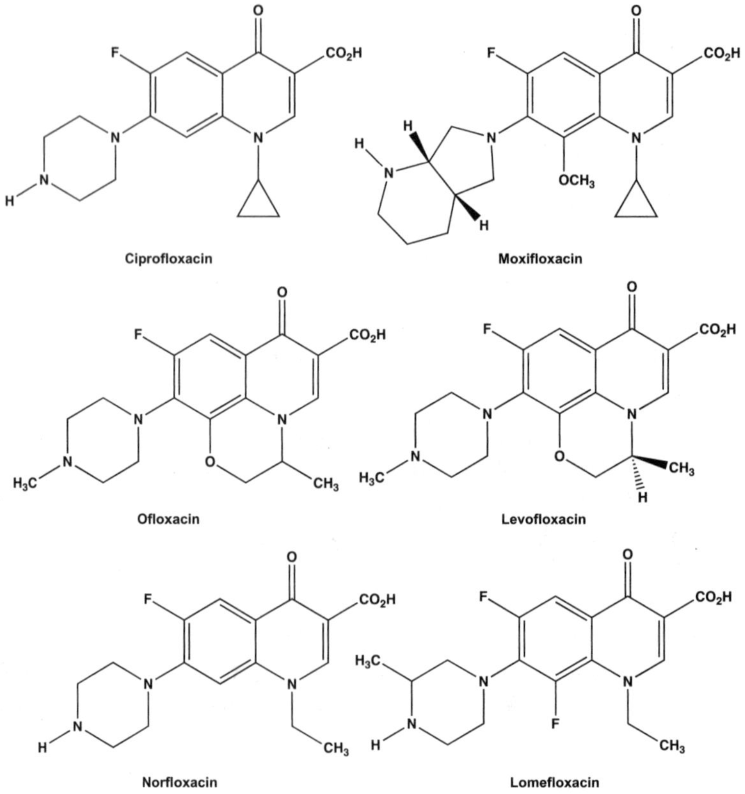

**Figure 4.** *Structures of quinolones.*

## Mechanism of Action

Quinolones exert their action by inhibition of bacterial DNA topoisomerase (ATP-hydrolyzing), which is also called DNA gyrase and type II topoisomerase. This enzyme is involved in DNA replication. Inhibition of the enzyme stops DNA replication so that the bacterial cell cannot divide. This mechanism of action is distinct from that of many of the classes of antibiotics discussed in the preceding sections. Because of this difference, cross-resistance is not seen between quinolones and other categories of antibiotics.

The side effects of quinolones include a proseizure action, particularly in people with epilepsy. Central nervous system disturbances such as hallucinations and insomnia can occur, as can gastrointestinal effects of diarrhea, vomiting, and abdominal pain. Selected quinolones have been removed from use because of extremely toxic profiles (for example, kidney and liver toxic effects). These effects seem to be compound-specific and not general to the entire class of molecules.

Ciprofloxacin is the most widely recognized quinolone and is available in oral and parenteral administration forms. Following oral administration, the bioavailability of ciprofloxacin is good, with approximately 70% to 80% of the medication absorbed. The presence of food in the stomach can decrease absorption of the drug. Up to 35% of the drug is excreted in the feces because of biliary excretion. Approximately 40% to 50% of the drug is excreted unchanged in the urine. The elimination half-life of the drug is 4 hours following oral administration compared with 6 hours following intravenous (IV) administration. The potency and broad-spectrum antibacterial properties, coupled with the wide disbursement of the drug throughout nearly all parts of the body, are reasons this drug is indicated for treatment of numerous infections. Ciprofloxacin is widely used in the treatment of respiratory infections, such as exposure to anthrax, and to treat infections of the skin, bones, and soft tissue. The medication has also been successfully used in the prophylactic treatment of people exposed to *Bacillus anthracis,* a microorganism that causes anthrax. The IV form of ciprofloxacin should not be administered concurrently with drug solutions that are alkaline because of the reduced solubility of ciprofloxacin at a high pH.

Moxifloxacin is a quinolone that may inhibit the bacterial enzyme topoisomerase IV, in addition to DNA topoisomerase (ATP-hydrolyzing). Moxifloxacin is metabolized by the formation of glucuronide and sulfate conjugates. Conversely, the major portion of ofloxacin is unmetabolized and excreted unchanged. Metabolites that are formed (desmethylofloxacin and ofloxacin *N*-oxide) are substantially less potent than the parent drug. Levofloxacin, norfloxacin, and lomefloxacin are structurally related quinolones.

## Miscellaneous Antibiotics

Vancomycin (**Figure 5**) is a glycopeptide that is structurally unrelated to any other class of antibiotics. It is isolated from *Amycolatopsis orientalis* and kills bacteria by inhibiting the biosynthesis of the cell wall. Vancomycin is not

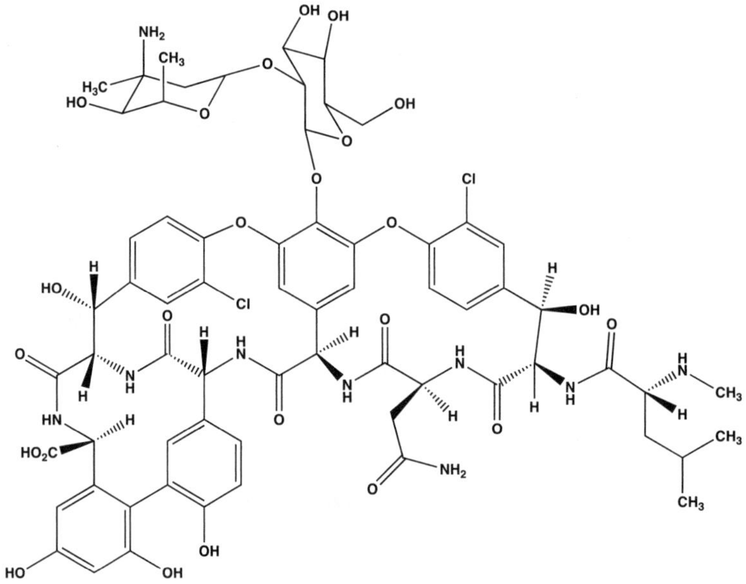

**Figure 5.** *Structure of vancomycin, a glycopeptide that is structurally unrelated to any other class of antibiotics.*

metabolized to an appreciable extent and is eliminated via glomerular filtration by the kidney. Because of this feature, clinicians should be cautious in administering this drug to people with renal impairment. The drug is poorly absorbed when given orally and is typically administered intravenously. Intramuscular administration of vancomycin may cause substantial pain. There have been reported cases of anaphylaxis, nephrotoxic effects, and cardiac arrest following dosing with this agent. An adverse reaction labeled red man syndrome, characterized by rash, angioedema, erythema, and pruritus, has been described after rapid infusion of vancomycin. Red man syndrome should not be considered an allergic reaction. Distribution of this agent is widespread, and load levels are often maintained for up to 12 hours following administration. Vancomycin is clinically very useful because it has been shown to be effective in the treatment of Gram-positive infections that are resistant to other antibiotics. Because of the clinical importance of vancomycin, vancomycin-resistant *Enterococci* (VRE) and vancomycin-resistant *Staphylococcus aureus* (VRSA) are significant health concerns. These infections occur more commonly in hospitals and healthcare settings and continue to be the focus of research.

Lincomycin hydrochloride and clindamycin (**Figure 6**) have the same mechanism of action as erythromycin, despite having very different chemical structures. These agents bind to the 50S subunit of the bacterial ribosome and inhibit protein synthesis. They are effective against aerobic Gram-positive cocci and Gram-negative bacilli. Side effects of lincomycin and clindamycin include

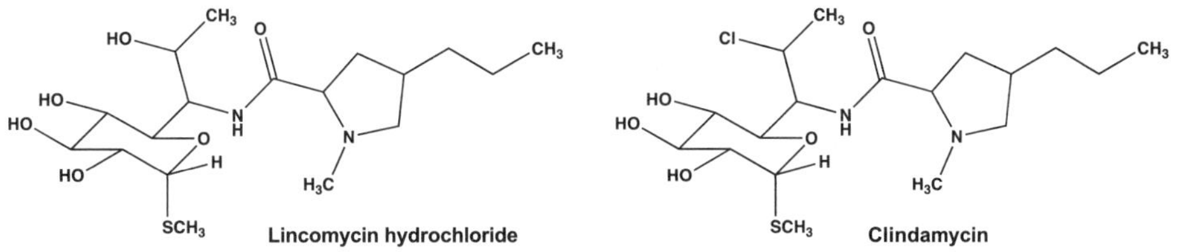

**Figure 6.** *Structures of antibiotics that have the same mechanism of action as erythromycin.*

diarrhea, colitis, and pseudomembranous colitis, which can be fatal. Lincomycin is a naturally occurring agent and is a product of fermentation. It is the starting structure for the semisynthesis of clindamycin. Lincomycin is poorly absorbed compared with its derivative, clindamycin. Clindamycin is more lipophilic than lincomycin and, therefore, is better absorbed after oral administration.

## Antiviral Agents

A *virus* is a microscopic infectious agent composed of a core of nucleic acid surrounded by a protein-based shell. Viruses are cellular parasites and depend on the host cell to continue their lifecycle. Viruses are differentiated according to a number of characteristics that include nucleic acid content, shell composition, and site of replication. It is estimated that more than 60% of the infectious diseases in developing countries are caused by viruses.

Preventing the spread of viruses is seen as the most productive method to inhibit viral infections. Immunizations have been relatively effective in decreasing the incidence of some viral diseases such as polio, rubella, measles, and hepatitis B. Prevention of infection has proven to be more difficult, however, for other viruses such as cytomegalovirus, herpes, and human immunodeficiency virus (HIV). Anesthesia providers are at high risk for acquiring viral infections because of the invasive nature of job-related tasks and procedures that offer an opportunity to come into contact with infected blood and body secretions.

The field of antiviral therapy is expanding at an incredible rate. Much of the increase in antiviral research and drug clinical trials has been brought about because of the HIV epidemic. HIV research has led to new information and novel therapies for treatment of this disease and other viral diseases. The goal of viral research is to develop better antiviral vaccines and more efficient antiviral therapies. This section of the chapter describes therapeutic agents used to treat a variety of viral infections and agents specifically developed to combat HIV.

## Inhibitors of DNA Synthesis (Nucleoside Analogs)

Several agents used to treat viral infections are designed to trick a viral enzyme into using an undesirable substrate. In the process of DNA synthesis, an enzyme called DNA polymerase is used by many viruses to elongate pieces of DNA. This process is necessary to replicate its DNA and form daughter viruses. The natural substrates for DNA polymerase are the 4 DNA nucleosides (adenosine, guanosine, thymidine, and cytidine). Nucleoside analogs inhibit viral replication by mimicking the structure of natural nucleosides. These artificial substrates (ie, the inhibitors) bind to the enzyme in the same manner as do the natural nucleosides. However, the inhibitor cannot be reacted on to continue DNA synthesis, so DNA replication is halted.

Each nucleoside analog is administered as a prodrug and requires conversion to its active form. Once inside the cell, 3 phosphate groups are added to the analog. The triphosphorylated analog is the active form of the drug. In the triphosphate form, the nucleoside analogs trick the viral enzyme and become part of its growing DNA chain, which is quickly arrested. The side effects of nucleoside analogs include fever, rash, diarrhea, nausea, anemia, and leukopenia.

Ganciclovir and acyclovir, once triphosphorylated, mimic deoxyguanosine in the active site of viral DNA polymerase. Although active in stopping DNA synthesis, these molecules (**Figure 7**) are poorly bioavailable. To improve bioavailability, the analogs valganciclovir and valacyclovir were made. Valganciclovir and valacyclovir have a molecule of L-valine added to the structures of the parent compounds. This structural modification greatly increases lipophilicity and, thus, the bioavailability of the parent agents. Valaciclovir is absorbed 3 to 5 times better than acyclovir, and valganciclovir is absorbed 10 times better than is ganciclovir. Once absorbed, the molecules are hydrolyzed (removing L-valine) and triphosphorylated, which converts them into the active compounds. Other nucleoside analogs that are used for viral infections are famciclovir, cidofovir, and idoxuridine. Famciclovir is used to treat herpes zoster (shingles), and cidofovir is used in the treatment of cytomegalovirus infection. Because cidofovir can have nephrotoxic effects, it may be coadministered with probenecid, a medication with nephroprotective properties.

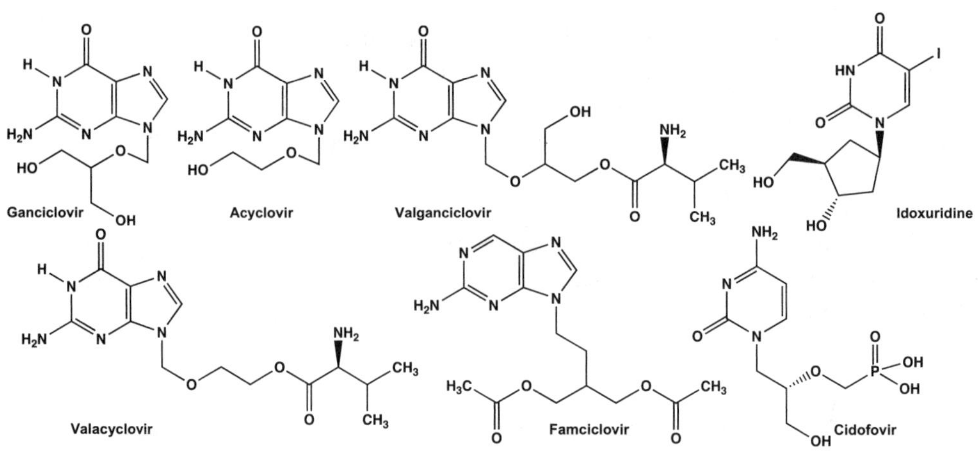

**Figure 7.** *Nucleoside analogs.*

Foscarnet (**Figure 8**) is structurally very different from the antivirals shown in Figure 7 but is also classified as a nucleoside analog. Rather than mimicking the DNA base, foscarnet mimics the pyrophosphate portion of the nucleoside. Foscarnet inhibits RNA and DNA polymerases and is used in the treatment of cytomegalovirus infections in people with AIDS and of mucocutaneous herpes simplex virus infections in immunocompromised people. The molecule is excreted largely unchanged and has a half-life of 3 to 7 hours. The side effects of foscarnet mirror those of other nucleoside analogs.

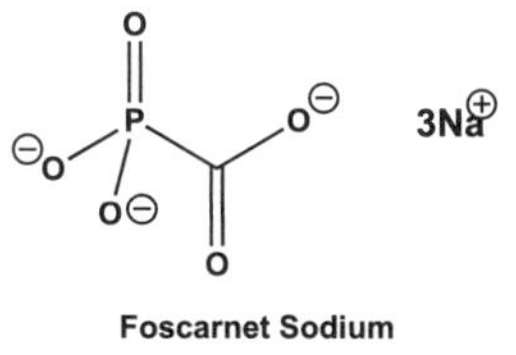

Foscarnet Sodium

**Figure 8.** *Structure of foscarnet, a structurally distinct nucleoside analog.*

# Neuraminidase Inhibitors

A newer class of antiviral agents is the neuraminidase inhibitors (**Figure 9**). These agents are used primarily for the treatment of influenza infections. Neuraminidase is a viral enzyme that cleaves the glycosidic linkage between sialic acid and the adjacent sugar. This bond is part of the attachment that holds a new viral particle onto the parent cell. Once this bond is cleaved, the viral particle is free to infect additional host cells. When this enzyme is inhibited, the viral particles remain attached to their parent cells, and further infection is averted.

Zanamivir and oseltamivir are 2 neuraminidase inhibitors that are commercially available for the treatment of influenza virus infections ("the flu"). Zanamivir is an active molecule that is less than 10% bound and is excreted unchanged. Zanamivir is active only by inhaled, IV, intranasal, and intraperitoneal administration. The molecule is inactive when given orally. Conversely, the ester group of oseltamivir makes this drug orally active. Oseltamivir requires hydrolysis of the ester to give the active form of the drug.

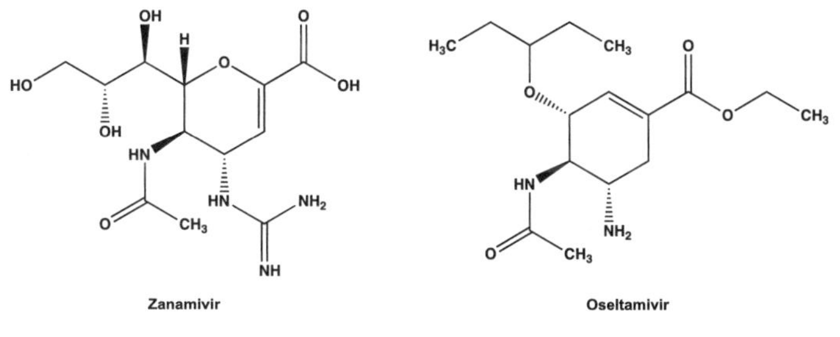

Zanamivir                    Oseltamivir

**Figure 9.** *Structures of neuraminidase inhibitors.*

## Human Immunodeficiency Virus

HIV may have become the most extensively studied virus in medical history. HIV is a retrovirus and, as such, has the enzyme reverse transcriptase (RT). The RT transcribes viral RNA into DNA that is later integrated into the host genome. After infection of host lymphocytes by the virus, a cascade of intracellular events leads to replication of the viral particle. The ultimate result of the viral infection is destruction of the host's immune system. As a result of their compromised immune status, people with HIV infections are susceptible to a variety of diseases. These secondary diseases, called *opportunistic infections,* are what often lead to death.

There are 4 types of therapies approved for HIV treatment. The drugs target specific steps in the HIV lifecycle. They inhibit RT, protease, integrase, and viral fusion. Because HIV easily develops resistance to administered drug regimens, a necessary part of HIV therapy has become the administration of a combination of drugs with complementary modes of action. Inhibitors of RT and protease work together to inhibit viral replication in a synergistic way. These drugs are the basis for highly active antiretroviral therapy (abbreviated HAART). Emerging therapies for HIV will see drug combinations that include RT and protease inhibitors as well as fusion and integrase inhibitors.

## Reverse Transcriptase Inhibitors

The RT is the HIV enzyme responsible for translating the single-stranded viral RNA sequence into single-stranded viral DNA. Once a complementary strand of DNA is made to form the requisite double-stranded DNA, the viral DNA can be incorporated into the host (human) DNA. After this incorporation occurs, the viral genes will be replicated by the cellular machinery of the host. Two classes of molecules have been developed that inhibit RT: nucleoside RT inhibitors (NRTIs) and nonnucleoside RT inhibitors (NNRTIs).

## Nucleoside Reverse Transcriptase Inhibitors

In the active site of RT, nucleosides are added 1 at a time to build the growing single strand of DNA. The NRTIs (**Figure 10**) work by mimicking a natural nucleoside that would be used to make DNA. The NRTIs, however, do not have a 3'-oxygen atom, which is required for DNA elongation. Because of this lack of an oxygen atom, after an NRTI is incorporated into the growing DNA sequence, DNA elongation stops. The virus cannot use this growing strand of DNA, and the synthesis is abandoned. Without successful DNA synthesis, the viral lifecycle cannot proceed. The NRTIs are similar in structure and mechanism of action to the nucleoside analogs described earlier in this chapter. The NRTIs require phosphorylation in vivo to become active, like nucleoside analogs.

Zidovudine is effective against HIV and other retroviruses. Zidovudine is converted to the triphosphate intracellularly, which is the active form of the drug.

The triphosphate acts as a thymidine mimic in the RT active site. Zidovudine is available in oral and IV forms. It is adequately absorbed from the gastrointestinal tract and distributed into most tissues of the body. Approximately 15% of the administered drug is excreted unchanged. Hematologic toxic effects of zidovudine may occur and are evidenced by anemia and granulocytopenia. For these reasons, zidovudine is not given to asymptomatic patients. Zidovudine resistance has been demonstrated in patients undergoing long-term therapy. Zidovudine is available in combination with 1 or more of the following RT inhibitors: abacavir sulfate, efavirenz, lamivudine, and nevirapine.

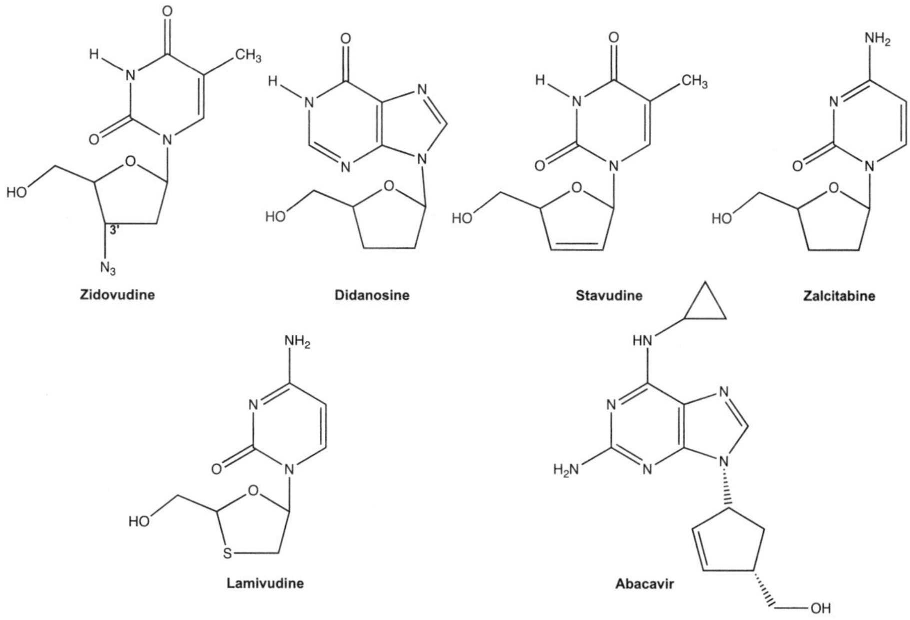

**Figure 10.** *Structures of nucleoside reverse transcriptase inhibitors.*

Didanosine is used for patients with advanced HIV disease who have been undergoing long-term zidovudine therapy and have disease resistant to zidovudine. After intracellular phosphorylation, didanosine mimics deoxyadenosine in the active site of RT. Although didanosine can be administered orally, the bioavailability is low and variable. Therapy using didanosine can lead to serious dose-related adverse effects such as pancreatitis, resulting in abdominal pain and nausea. Peripheral neuropathy has also been described, and patients can experience numbness and pain in the hands and feet. These adverse effects often limit the use of didanosine.

Stavudine is used for adults with HIV infection who have an intolerance for other antiviral therapies or who have had clinical setbacks while receiving other drugs. Similar to zidovudine, stavudine is converted to the triphosphate and mimics thymidine. Stavudine is administered orally and is well absorbed. The primary side effect of stavudine use is peripheral neuropathy. Stavudine is well suited for patients with advanced HIV infection who have immunologic deterioration while receiving treatments.

In addition to the inhibition of RT, zalcitabine also inhibits mitochondrial DNA synthesis, which is responsible for the toxic effects seen with this drug. After conversion to the triphosphate intracellularly, zalcitabine mimics deoxycytidine in the RT active site. The oral preparation of zalcitabine is available orally, and it is well absorbed. Effectiveness is, however, diminished by the presence of food in the stomach. Zalcitabine has an increased incidence of peripheral neuropathy (approximately 30%), and this side effect may occur even more frequently in patients with renal insufficiency. Zalcitabine is commonly administered to patients with advanced HIV and is often given in conjunction with zidovudine.

Other commercially available NRTIs include lamivudine and abacavir. Lamivudine and abacavir are also active ingredients in combination drugs. Just like all NRTIs, these molecules are converted to triphosphates within the cell, the active forms of the drugs. They have the same mechanism of action and side-effect profiles as other NRTIs.

## Nonnucleoside Reverse Transcriptase Inhibitors

A second class of molecules that inhibits RT has been more recently developed. In contrast with the NRTIs, this class of molecules does not mimic nucleosides, the natural substrates for RT. This class of compounds is referred to as NNRTIs (**Figure 11**). Despite this distinction, the mechanism of action of NNRTIs is similar to that of the NRTIs in that they inhibit the action of RT so that DNA synthesis is halted. The NNRTIs inhibit RT by binding to a site separate from the binding site of the NRTIs. Therefore, viral strains that are resistant to the NRTIs are susceptible to the NNRTIs. All NNRTIs result in a similar side-effect profile. These drugs result in high incidences of rash, headache, fatigue, nausea, vomiting, and diarrhea. The NNRTIs are highly bound to serum proteins and often effect changes in their own metabolism and the metabolism of other drugs.

Delavirdine, nevirapine, and efavirenz are commercially available NNRTIs. Delavirdine is approximately 98% bound to serum proteins and has a half-life of 2 to 11 hours. Delavirdine is thought to inhibit its own metabolism by reducing the action of CYP3A3 and 3A4. Conversely, nevirapine induces its own metabolism by increasing the action of metabolic enzymes. Nevirapine is less protein bound than delavirdine (50%-60%) and has a substantially longer half-life (~45 hours). Efavirenz is a highly protein-bound (>99%) member of this class of molecules. The bioavailability of the NNRTIs is typically more than 80%, substantially better than that of the NRTIs. Because of this feature, the NNRTIs can be administered less frequently.

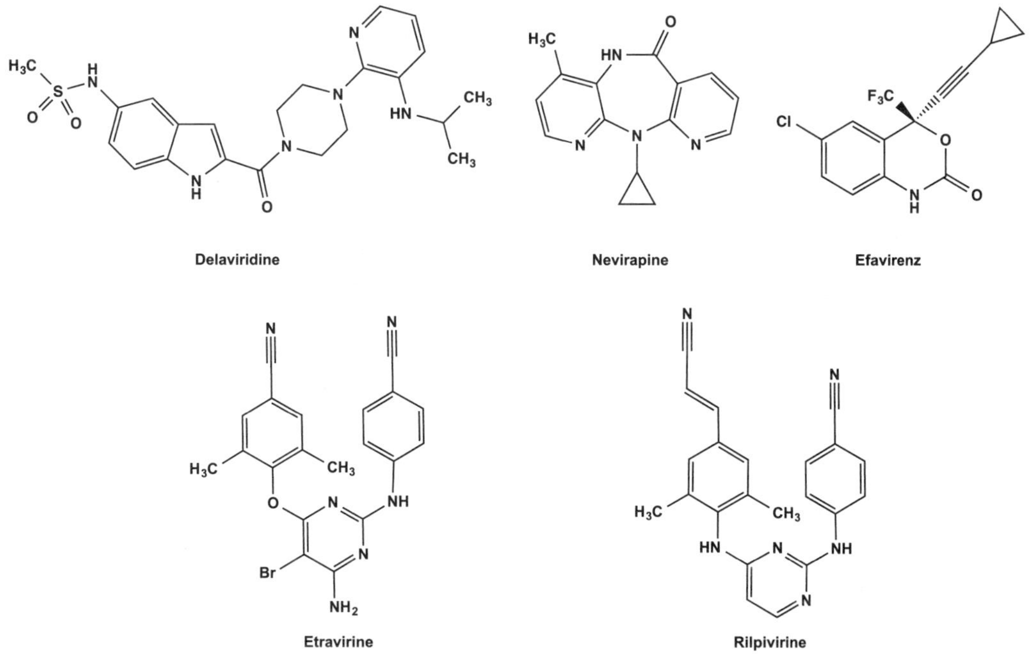

**Delaviridine**    **Nevirapine**    **Efavirenz**

**Etravirine**    **Rilpivirine**

**Figure 11.** *Structures of nonnucleoside reverse transcriptase inhibitors.*

## Protease Inhibitors

An essential enzyme in the HIV lifecycle is HIV protease. The proteins in the HIV genome are synthesized together in a single, inactive polypeptide chain. Protease is responsible for cleaving this polypeptide into smaller fragments, which become the active proteins needed by the virus. Without this cleavage, the virus does not have the tools required to continue its lifecycle. Protease inhibitors (**Figure 12**) work by binding to the active site of HIV protease and mimicking the natural substrates of the enzyme. As such, many protease inhibitors resemble small peptides.

The combination of the NRTIs and NNRTIs with protease inhibitors has enabled patients with HIV to live years longer than originally expected. However, these drugs are not without severe, undesirable effects. Patients taking protease inhibitors have very high (>30%) incidences of dyslipidemia (fat redistribution), rash, nausea, vomiting, and diarrhea. All protease inhibitors are hepatically metabolized, usually by CYP3A4 and 3A3 isozymes. They are very highly protein bound.

Examples of protease inhibitors include amprenavir, indinavir, and saquinavir mesylate. Most protease inhibitors have half-lives of 3 to 5 hours. Amprenivir has a longer half-life (7-11 hours). Ritonavir, nelfinavir, darunavir, and lopinavir are additional examples of clinically available protease inhibitors. Fosamprenavir is

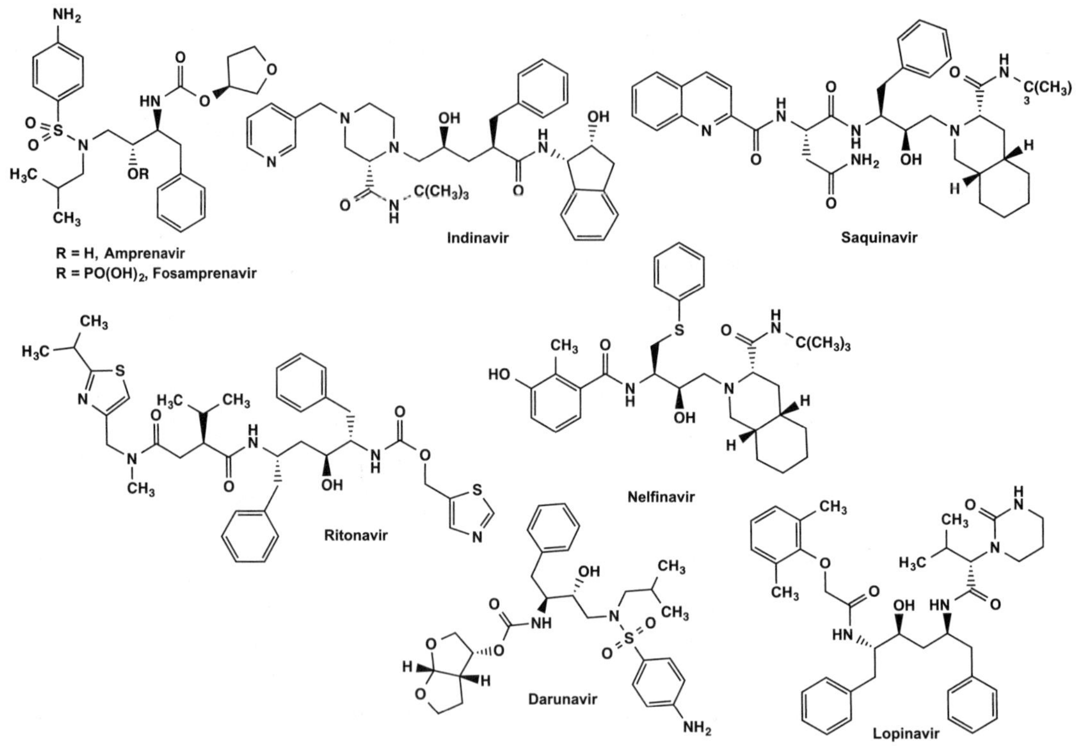

**Figure 12.** *Structures of protease inhibitors.*

a phosphonate prodrug of amprenavir. Removal of the phosphate in the body reveals the active metabolite. This modification is designed to act as an extended-release-form of the drug.

## Fusion Inhibitors

Fusion inhibitors block the entry of HIV into human lymphocytes, their primary target cells. By stopping viral fusion, these agents arrest viral infection at its earliest point.

In 2003, the US Food and Drug Administration (FDA) approved enfuvirtide for the treatment of HIV infection. Enfuvirtide is a linear, 36-amino-acid peptide that binds to the viral glycoprotein, gp41. Required for viral entry into the human cell, gp41 represents one of the first points of attachment between virus and cell. Enfuvirtide is effective against viral strains that are resistant to the NRTIs, NNRTIs, and protease inhibitors. Furthermore, the effect of enfuvirtide is additive to the activities of other (non–fusion-based) HIV therapies. Maraviroc is a small molecule, fusion inhibitor that was approved for use in 2007 (**Figure 13**). This compound binds to CCR5, a receptor on the surface of human cells. By binding to CCR5, HIV is unable to bind to the cell and viral entry is blocked.

## Integrase Inhibitors

For HIV to replicate, it must take over the normal function of CD4 cells. Once reverse transcription of RNA into DNA is complete, HIV must incorporate its DNA into the DNA of the CD4 cell in a process called *integration*. Integrase inhibitors are designed to stop this process by inhibiting the catalytic activity of HIV-1 integrase.

Raltegravir is a 1-*N*-alkyl-5-hydroxypyrimidinone and is the only FDA-approved (2007) integrase inhibitor available for use (Figure 13). Raltegravir is primarily metabolized by glucuronidation and is rapidly absorbed after oral administration; 7%-14% of the drug is excreted unchanged in the urine. Raltegravir is 83% bound to serum proteins and has a half-life of approximately 9 hours. This antiviral drug is indicated in combination with other antiviral agents in the treatment of patients with HIV infection. Raltegravir also shows promise for people infected with HIV infection in whom resistance to RT and protease inhibitors has developed.

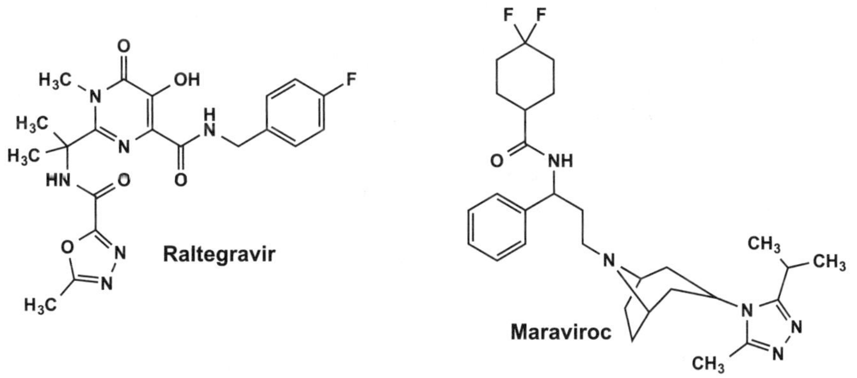

**Figure 13.** *Raltegravir (integrase inhibitor) and maraviroc (entry inhibitor) are approved for use against HIV.*

## Miscellaneous Antiviral Agents

Rimantadine and amantadine have shown antiviral activity against the influenza virus. The mechanism of action of these agents is thought to involve inhibition of the viral uncoating process. Rimantadine is 2 to 3 times more active than amantadine and is metabolized to inactive compounds. The half-life of rimantadine is approximately 24 hours. Amantadine has a half-life of 10 to 30 hours and is eliminated unchanged.

Several protein products are available clinically for the treatment of viral infections. Interferons are natural proteins that have a wide variety of antiviral effects. They are thought to exert their antiviral activity by inhibition of growth, altering gene expression and cell differentiation, and changing the expression of cell-surface antigens. Interferons are used to treat cases of warts and hepatitis, among other viral infections. Palivizumab is an antibody that is used to treat viral infections. Used for the treatment of respiratory syncytial virus infection, palivizumab is thought to inhibit fusion between the virus and the host cell.

Anti-infective agents have an important role in the care of surgical patients and patients undergoing other invasive procedures. As healthcare professionals administering many diverse medications each day, anesthesia providers with a good understanding of the different classes and chemical structure of anti-infective agents are in an ideal position to maximize patient outcomes and improve overall quality of care. Because new antibiotic and antiviral drugs are sure to be discovered, anesthesia providers must continue to apply best evidence regarding the clinical implications of these medications.

## Suggested Reading

Brooks GF, Carroll KC, Butel JS, Morse SA, Mietzner TA, eds. *Jawetz, Melnick & Adelberg's Medical Microbiology*. 26th ed. New York, NY: McGraw-Hill; 2013.

De Clercq E. Recent highlights in the development of new antiviral drugs. *Curr Opin Microbiol*. 2005;8(5):552-560.

Hatziioannou T, Evans DT. Animal models for HIV/AIDS research. *Nat Rev Microbiol*. 2012 Dec;10(12):852-867.

Kong KF, Schneper L, Mathee K. Beta-lactam antibiotics: from antibiosis to resistance and bacteriology. *APMIS*. 2010;118: 1-36.

Koyama N, Inokoshi J, Tomoda H. Anti-infectious agents against MRSA. *Molecules*. 2012 Dec 24;18(1):204-224.

Magnet S, Blanchard JS. Molecular insights into aminoglycoside action and resistance. *Chem Rev*. 2005;105: 477-497.

Zanel GC, Wiebe R, Dialy L, et al. Comparative review of the carbapenems. *Drugs*. 2007;67:1027-1052.

## Discussion Questions

1. What are some of the known mechanisms of action of antibiotics?

2. What are the differences in structure and function between early β-lactamase inhibitors and later generations?

3. What are the benefits of multidrug therapy for a pathogen such as HIV?

4. What is the clinical profile of HIV infection?

# Glossary

**Acid** refers to the ability of a molecule to donate a proton (Brønsted-Lowry acid, A-H) or accept a pair of electrons (Lewis acid).

**Active site** is the site on a macromolecular receptor that includes the points of attraction between the receptor and its substrate. In an enzyme, the active site is the location where the chemical reaction takes place.

**Addiction** is an induced feeling in the body of need and dependence.

**Adiabatic** refers to any change or process where heat is neither gained nor lost.

**Adrenergic receptors** are those receptors responsive to the epinephrine class of molecules.

**Agonist** is a ligand that simulates a receptor's endogenous ligand and activates the receptor.

**Alcohol** is a class of organic compounds with at least 1 hydroxyl (-OH) group attached to a carbon atom (ROH). An example of an alcohol is ethanol: $CH_3CH_2OH$.

**Aldehyde** is a class of carbonyl compounds where the carbonyl carbon is bound to a carbon atom and a hydrogen atom (RC(=O)H). An example of an aldehyde is acetaldehyde: $CH_3C(=O)H$.

**Alkane** is a molecule that is composed only of carbon and hydrogen atoms and where all the carbon atoms are $sp^3$ hybridized. There are no double or triple bonds in the molecule. An example of an alkane is hexane and is denoted $CH_3CH_2CH_2CH_2CH_2CH_3$.

**Alkene** is a molecule that is composed of carbon and hydrogen atoms and where there is at least 1 double (sigma + pi) bond between 2 carbon atoms. For example, 1-hexene is an alkene: $CH_2=CHCH_2CH_2CH_2CH_3$.

**Alkyne** is a molecule that is composed of carbon and hydrogen atoms and where there is at least 1 triple (sigma + pi + pi) bond between 2 carbon atoms. For example, 1-hexyne is an alkyne: $CH\equiv CCH_2CH_2CH_2CH_3$.

**Amide** is a class of carbonyl compounds where the carbonyl carbon is bound to a carbon atom and a nitrogen atom (RC(=O)NHR). The nitrogen atom can be further substituted with 1 or 2 alkyl groups. An example of an amide is acetamide: $CH_3C(=O)NH_2$).

**Amine** is a compound with at least 1 nitrogen atom that is $sp^3$ hybridized and contains 3 bonds to carbon or hydrogen atoms. Amines can be primary (1°, $RNH_2$), secondary (2°, $R_2NH$), or tertiary (3°, $R_3N$). The R groups do not have to be equivalent. An example of an amine is triethylamine: $N(CH_2CH_3)_3$. A nitrogen atom bound to 4 substituents is positively charged and called a quaternary (4°) ammonium ion, such as $N(CH_3)_4^+$.

**Amino acid** is the building block of peptides and proteins. Generally, amino acids refer to α-amino acids, where the alpha carbon atom bears a substituent (R). The general structure for an α-amino acid is: $NH_2CH(R)CO_2H$.

**Analgesic** is an agent that reduces pain.

**Anemia** is a state of low red blood cells in the blood.

**Anesthetic** is a drug that produces some loss of pain and possibly consciousness.

**Angiotensin II receptor antagonists** are a class of antihypertensive drugs that promote vasodilation by blocking angiotensin receptors present on the blood vessels.

**Angiotensin-converting enzyme (ACE) inhibitors** are the drugs of choice to target the Renin Angiotensin System by inhibiting the angiotensin converting enzyme to lower blood pressure for treatment of hypertension.

**Angstrom** (Å) is a unit of measure equal to $1.0 \times 10^{-10}$ meters.

**Anhydride** is a class of organic compounds with 2 carbonyl groups joined by an oxygen atom $(RC(=O)OC(=O)R$ or $(RCO)_2O)$. An example of an anhydride is acetic anhydride: $CH_3C(=O)OC(=O)CH_3$.

**Anorectics** are drugs that exhibit appetite control.

**Antagonist** is a ligand that binds to a receptor and blocks the normal function of that receptor.

**Antiarrhythmic agents** are drugs that are clinically used to treat arrhythmia by targeting different ion channels or receptors implicated in different stages of the cardiac membrane action potential.

**Antibiotic** is a molecule that inhibits or kills bacteria and can be used to clear a bacterial infection.

**Anticoagulants** are molecules that prevent blood clotting by inhibiting the formation of the 3-dimensional fibrin polymer.

**Anticonvulsant** is an agent that prevents or reduces seizures.

**Antidepressant** is the function of a drug that reverses the presence of depression.

**Antiplatelet agents** are molecules that do not allow platelets to aggregate and thus prevent clotting.

**Antipsychotic** is the action of a drug reversing the symptoms of psychotic behavior.

**Anxiolytic** is a class of compounds used to treat anxiety and nervousness.

**Aromatic** refers to a cyclic molecule with alternating single bonds and double bonds or lone pairs of electrons such that the ring has a conjugated system of pi electrons. Aromatic compounds have a generally pleasing aroma. An example of an aromatic compound is benzene.

**Arrhythmia** is the alteration in the normal impulse rhythm that concludes the myocardium contraction. The abnormal alteration could be in the impulse rate, origin, or conduction.

**Autonomic nervous system** is composed of the parasympathetic and sympathetic nervous systems. Its function is generally to maintain control over many involuntary functions such as respiration, heart rate, and digestion.

**Bactericidal agent** is a molecule that kills a bacterial cell.

**Bacteriostatic agent** is a molecule that inhibits bacterial growth.

**Barbiturates** are drugs that are derivatives of barbituric acid, a compound formed from the condensation of urea and malonic acid. The barbiturates methohexital and thiopental are used as intravenous induction agents.

**Base** refers to the ability of a molecule to accept a proton (Brønsted-Lowry base, B:) or donate a pair of electrons (Lewis base).

**β-blockers** is a class of nonselective β-adrenergic antagonists that cause relaxation of smooth muscles of the cardiovascular system, resulting in slower heart rate and decreased force of contraction of muscles thereby allowing its use for hypertension and arrhythmias.

**Biliary excretion** is removal of drugs or metabolites from the plasma into the bile by liver hepatocytes.

**Binding site** is the location on a macromolecular receptor where the complementary forces are sufficiently attractive to fix a ligand or substrate.

**Bioavailability** is the fraction of the dose absorbed relative to the amount administered.

**Blood-brain barrier (BBB)** is the summation of effects that restrict the passage of a drug into the brain.

**Boiling point** is the temperature at which the vapor pressure of a liquid equals the pressure surrounding that liquid.

**Broad-spectrum agents** are drugs that are effective against a wide variety of microorganisms.

**Calcium channel blockers (or antagonists)** are molecules which block the entry of $Ca^{2+}$ into the smooth muscle, thereby reducing the muscle contraction and increasing muscle relaxation. Calcium channel blockers have therefore been used in hypertension, angina and arrhythmia.

**Carbohydrate** refers to a sugar or a molecule bonded to a sugar. Literally, the term means a "hydrate of carbon" as a carbohydrate's molecular formula often dictates 1 water molecule per carbon atom.

**Carbonic anhydrase inhibitors** are a class of diuretics that act by inhibiting an enzyme carbonic anhydrase causing a decrease in reabsorption of bicarbonate from urine to blood, resulting in increased bicarbonate concentration in the urine leading to diuresis.

**Carboxylate** is the negatively charged (anionic) species that results when a carboxylic acid is deprotonated ($RCO_2^-$ or $RC(=O)O^-$). An example of a carboxylate is the acetate ion: $CH_3CO_2^-$.

**Carboxylic acid** is a class of carbonyl compounds where the carbonyl carbon is bound to a carbon atom and a hydroxyl group ($RC(=O)OH$ or $RCO_2H$). The hydroxyl group proton is acidic, giving the carboxylic acid its name. An example of a carboxylic acid is acetic acid: $CH_3C(=O)OH$.

**Catecholamine** is a molecule containing a catechol ring (a benzene ring substituted with 2 adjacent hydroxyl groups), a short alkyl chain, and an amino group. The catecholamine is a common structural motif found in several neurotransmitters including dopamine, norepinephrine, and epinephrine.

**Chiral** refers to a molecule that is not superimposable onto its mirror image.

**Cholinergic receptors** are those receptors responsive to acetylcholine.

**Clearance** is the hypothetical volume of plasma or blood that is completely cleared of a drug per unit time.

**Codon** is a sequence of 3 nucleotides that encode for a specific amino acid.

**Cofactor** is a small, nonsubstrate molecule required by some enzymes to complete a catalyzed reaction.

**Concentration effect** is the observation that the greater the inspired concentration of a gas, the more rapidly the alveolar partial pressure reaches the inhaled partial pressure.

**Conjugate** is a compound formed by the fusion of 2 or more chemical compounds together.

**Covalent bond** is a shared pair of electrons between 2 atoms in a molecule.

**Critical temperature** is the temperature at (or above) which a vapor cannot be liquefied.

**Deoxyribonucleic acid,** or DNA, is a biological macromolecule that carries information needed for the development and function of all cells. The information is stored via a specific linear arrangement (polymer) of nucleotides. DNA is composed of 4 bases: adenine, guanine, cytosine, and thymine.

**Depolarizing agent** is a molecule that binds to a nerve cell receptor and causes an increase in the positive charge inside that cell.

**Diffusion** is the movement of molecules from an area of high concentration to 1 of lower concentration due to the molecules' random motion. It is a process where a mixture of a solvent and solute will become uniformly distributed among each other.

**Dipole** refers to a bond or molecule that has an uneven distribution of electrons. The electron density is greater at 1 portion of the bond (or molecule) than the other. One end (or pole) is electron deficient and bears a slight positive charge. The opposite end is electron rich and bears a slight negative charge. The difference in charge density can be transient (eg, induced dipole) or permanent.

**Dipole-dipole bond (or interaction)** is an attractive force between the complementary regions of 2 dipole bonds/molecules. This attractive force is typically 1-7 kcal/mol.

**Dipole moment** refers to an uneven electron distribution across a bond or molecule. In a bond, a dipole moment develops when the bonding electrons between 2 adjacent atoms are attracted prominently to 1 of these atoms. The uneven electron presence in this bond produces a prominence of electronic charge on that atom.

**Direct-acting vasodilators** are cardiovascular drugs which induce dilation of the smooth muscle cells of the blood vessels, thereby lowering the blood pressure.

**Dispersion force,** see Van der Waals force.

**Distribution half-life** is the time it takes for the concentration of a drug in the plasma to decline by 50%.

**Diuretics** are a class of compounds that promote the removal of water from the body, generally in the form of urine (also called diuresis).

**Double bond** is the sharing of a second pair of electrons between 2 atoms, after a sigma bond is formed. A double bond refers to the bond formed from a sigma and pi bond, and is denoted with 2 lines (=) between the atoms. For example, in "C=O", there is a double bond (sigma + pi) between the carbon and oxygen atoms.

**Drug absorption** is the rate and extent of drug appearance in the systemic circulation.

**Drug-receptor theory** states that a drug exerts its biological effect through binding to a discrete macromolecular receptor.

**Ectopic arrhythmias** are the arrhythmias caused by generation of impulses in cells other than pacemaker cells.

**Effusion** is the process in which individual molecules flow through pores and channels without colliding with other molecules.

**Electron** is a negatively charged particle surrounding the nucleus of an atom. Movement of electrons enables chemical reactions to occur. Shared electrons between atoms define chemical bonds.

**Electronegativity** refers to a property of an atom or functional group to pull electron density toward itself.

**Electrophile,** or "electron loving," refers to the character of a molecule or functional group that is attracted to the electron density of a nucleophile. An electrophile is generally electron deficient.

**Elimination half-life** is the time required for the plasma concentration of a drug to decline by 50%.

**Enantiomer** is 1 of 2 molecules that are not superimposable, but are mirror images of each other.

**Endorphins** are naturally occurring peptides, secreted from the pituitary and hypothalamus glands, having significant analgesic activity, similar to that of morphine.

**Enzyme** is a biological macromolecule that catalyzes a chemical reaction.

**Epilepsy** is a neurological disorder characterized by seizures.

**Epoxide** is a 3-membered ring containing 2 carbon atoms and 1 oxygen atom. Due to the presence of the oxygen atom, the ring is strained and highly reactive toward nucleophilic attack.

**Equilibrium** is a reversible reaction where the forward reaction rate is equal to the reverse reaction rate.

**Ester** is a class of carbonyl compounds where the carbonyl carbon is bound to a carbon atom and an alkoxy group ($RC(=O)OR$ or $RCO_2R$). An example of an ester is ethyl acetate: $CH_3C(=O)OCH_2CH_3$.

**Ether** is a functional group with an oxygen atom bearing 2 carbon substituents (ROR). The alkyl groups may be the same or different. An example ether is diethyl ether: $CH_3CH_2OCH_2CH_3$.

**Euphoria** is an effect in the body producing a feeling of well-being and happiness.

**$F_A/F_I$ ratio** is the ratio of alveolar concentration to inspired concentration of a gas. The rate at which this ratio approaches 1 reflects the speed at which an agent enters the central nervous system.

**Fatty acid** is an alkyl chain connected to a carboxylic acid. Fatty acids are often the building block for certain families of lipids.

**Fibrinolytic agents** are molecules that disintegrate a preformed clot.

**Force** is the change in momentum per unit time.

**Functional group** is a general term that refers to a group of atoms which, collectively, define the chemical or physical properties of a molecule.

**Gamma-aminobutyric acid (GABA)** is an inhibitory neurotransmitter.

**Gene** is a specific pattern of DNA or RNA codons that are required to form a protein.

**Genome** is a group of genes required for an organism.

**Glucuronide** refers to the derivative formed when glucuronic acid reacts with a phenol, alcohol, carboxylic acid or amine.

**Glycolysis** is the enzymatic breakdown of glucose to harvest energy for the cell.

**Haloalkanes** are alkane molecules with halogen atoms incorporated into their structure. Haloalkanes used as volatile (inhaled) anesthetic agents include chloroform and halothane.

**Haloethers** are ether molecules with halogen atoms incorporated into their structure. Haloethers used as volatile (inhaled) anesthetic agents include methoxyflurane, enflurane, isoflurane, desflurane and sevoflurane.

**Halogenation** is a chemical reaction in which a halogen atom is incorporated into a molecule.

**Halogens** are reactive, electronegative elements. The halogens are fluorine, chlorine, bromine, and astatine.

**Heat of vaporization** is the amount of heat (energy) required to vaporize a liquid.

**Heparin-induced thrombocytopenia** is a potentially lethal complication of heparin therapy that may be associated with thrombosis.

**Hepatic failure** is a loss of function in the liver.

**Hepatotoxic** means toxic to the liver.

**Heteroatom** refers to any non-carbon and non-hydrogen atom. In organic chemistry, heteroatom is often used to signify an oxygen, nitrogen, sulfur or a halogen atom.

**Hydrogen bond** is formed between the lone pair electrons on an electronegative atom (electron rich) and a proton attached to an electronegative atom (electron poor).

**Hydrolysis** means breaking apart a molecule (or bond) by the addition of water.

**Hydrophilic,** or "water loving," is a property of a molecule or a part of a molecule that is drawn to water and other polar molecules.

**Hydrophobic,** or "water fearing," refers to the character of a molecule or functional group to repel water and other polar molecules.

**Hydrophobic bonding** is an attractive force between 2 nonpolar (lipophilic) surfaces (0.7 kcal/mol). It results from an entropic gain (increase in disorder) when water is excluded from the system.

**Hypertension** (or high blood pressure) is when the blood pressure is above 140 mm Hg systolic and 90 mm Hg diastolic.

**Hypnotics** are agents that produce a depression greater than sedatives, leading to sleep.

**Hypotension** is a state of lowered blood pressure.

**Induced dipole-induced dipole,** see Van der Waals force.

**Induction agents** are anesthetic drugs that are used to establish, but not maintain, an anesthetic state.

**Inhibitor** is a molecule that prevents binding of an endogenous ligand with the receptor.

**Insomnia** is a state where there is a reduction in the ability to achieve sleep.

**Ion** is a compound that bears a net electrical charge.

**Ion-dipole** is an attractive force between a charged species (ion) of either positive or negative charge and the complementary end of a dipole. An ion-dipole interaction is typically 1-7 kcal/mol.

**Ionic bond** is an attractive force between 2 ions where 1 partner is positively charged and 1 partner is negatively charged. Ionic bonds typically are 5-10 kcal/mol.

**Irreversible inhibitors** are molecules that form a covalent bond with an enzyme or receptor. Binding the receptor in this way significantly slows (or blocks) the receptor's function.

**Ischemia** is the constriction of blood vessels resulting in reduced blood, oxygen and nutrient supply to tissues and muscles.

**Isothermal** refers to any change or process where there is no temperature change.

**Ketone** is a class of carbonyl compounds where the carbonyl carbon atom is bound to 2 additional carbon atoms ($R(C=O)R$). The R groups can be the same or different. An example of a ketone is acetone: $CH_3C(=O)CH_3$.

**Kinase** is an enzyme that adds a phosphate group to a small molecule or protein.

**Kinetic energy** is the energy that an object has due to its motion.

**Laminar flow** is the movement of a fluid where the particles move parallel to one another with no cross-current motion.

**Ligand** is a nonsubstrate molecule that binds to a macromolecular receptor producing a pharmacological effect. The ligand can have 1 of many functional effects including inhibition, agonism, or antagonism.

**Lipid** is a nonpolar, hydrophobic molecule that is soluble in nonpolar, organic solvents and less soluble in polar solvents, such as water. Lipids belong to a variety of structural families and have many important roles.

**Lipophilic,** or "lipid loving," refers to a molecule or functional group that is drawn to hydrocarbons and other molecules that are not water-soluble.

**Local anesthetic agents** are drugs that are used to produce a loss of sensation or motor function in a discrete area of the body.

**Lone pair electrons** are electrons surrounding an atom that do not contribute to covalent bonds. They increase the polarity of functional groups containing oxygen, nitrogen and sulfur atoms, and can accept a hydrogen bond.

**Loop diuretics** are a class of diuretics which target the $Na^+/K^+/Cl^-$ cotransporter in the loop of Henle in order to cause excretion of sodium resulting in diuresis.

**Macromolecule** is a large molecule (MW > 1000 Da) that can act as a receptor for smaller molecules and has a biological function. Examples of macromolecules are DNA, RNA, and proteins.

**Metabolism** is a set of biochemical reactions involved in storing and converting fuel molecules into energy inside a living cell. In pharmacology, metabolism is the conversion of a parent drug into secondary molecules.

**Metabolite** is a chemical compound produced as a result of metabolism or a metabolic reaction.

**Meyer-Overton rule of lipid solubility** is a theory of the mechanism of action of volatile anesthetics proposing that lipid solubility is inversely proportional to anesthetic potency.

**Minimum alveolar concentration (MAC)** is the alveolar concentration of an anesthetic at 1 atmosphere that prevents movement in 50% of subjects in response to a painful stimulus. The MAC of an anesthetic gas reflects the potency of the agent.

**Monoamine oxidase (MAO)** is an enzyme responsible for deactivating certain neurotransmitters by oxidative deamination. MAO is commonly found in the nervous system and inhibition of MAO is used to treat a variety of psychological disorders.

**Monosaccharide** is a simple sugar, or a sugar unit that cannot be broken down to smaller sugar units. Monosaccharides are the building blocks for more complex carbohydrates.

**Muscarine** is a plant-derived natural product that activates a subtype of cholinergic receptors, called muscarinic receptors.

**Myoclonia** is an involuntary muscle contraction.

**Nephrosis** is a kidney disease with lesions and inflammation.

**Neurotransmitter (NT)** is a small molecule released from a neuron on 1 side of a synapse. Binding of the NT to a neuron across the synapse (postsynaptic side) relays a message from 1 neuron to another.

**Nitrovasodilators** are a class of antianginal agents that dilate the vasculature to reduce the symptoms of angina.

**Nomenclature** is a system of naming chemical compounds.

**Noncovalent bond (or force)** is an attractive interaction between 2 molecules or structural features that is weaker than a covalent bond.

**NSAID** is a non-steroidal anti-inflammatory drug.

**Nucleic acid** is the general term used for DNA and RNA, biological macromolecules that are polymers of nucleotides.

**Nucleophile,** or "nucleus loving," refers to the character of a molecule or functional group that is attracted to the electron deficiency of an electrophile. A nucleophile is generally electron rich and often bears a lone pair of electrons and/or a negative charge.

**Nucleoside** is a molecule comprised of a purine or pyrimidine base and a (deoxy)ribose sugar.

**Nucleotide** is a building block of DNA and RNA. It consists of a purine or pyrimidine base, a (deoxy)ribose sugar, and a phosphate. Nucleotides are joined together to form DNA and RNA.

**Oligopeptide** is a small protein made up of 2-20 amino acids.

**Oligosaccharide** is a complex sugar, made of 2-10 simple sugar (monosaccharide) units.

**Opioid** means belonging or related to a chemical class of analgesics related in structure to morphine.

**Opportunistic infections** are secondary infections arising as a result of a weakened immune system.

**Orbital** is the space around the nucleus of an atom in which there is a high probability of finding an electron.

**Organelle** is a subunit within a cell with a specific function.

**Organic nitrates** are class of molecules that contain a nitrite or a nitrate group, which releases nitric oxide in the vasculature.

**Parasympathetic nervous system** is a branch of the nervous system that is responsible for significant involuntary functions such as digestion. The parasympathetic system contains cholinergic receptors responsive to acetylcholine.

**Parenteral** is the administration of a drug by injection.

**Partition coefficient** is the ratio in which a substance distributes between 2 or more partitions or phases.

**Peptide bond** refers to the amide bond joining 2 amino acids. The peptide bond is the foundational unit of a protein.

**Pharmacodynamics (PD)** describes the relationship between plasma concentration of a drug and its pharmacological effect in the body.

**Pharmacokinetics (PK)** describes the relationship between an administered dose of a drug and its observed plasma or tissue concentrations.

**Pharmacophore** is a term introduced by L. B. Kier identifying a pattern of atoms or groups on a ligand that are responsible for its interaction with a receptor.

**Pi ($\pi$) bond** is the sharing of 2 electrons between a pair of atoms after a sigma bond joins them. It results from the overlap of orbitals above and below the bonding axis. Double bonds are composed of 1 sigma and 1 pi bond. Triple bonds are composed of 1 sigma and 2 pi bonds between 2 atoms.

**pKa** is the negative log of the concentration of a dissociable proton in a molecule.

**Placebo effect** is refers to a situation where an inactive treatment (or drug) is effective only because the patient believes it should be effective.

**Polynucleotide** is a polymer of >10 nucleotides.

**Polypeptide** is a large protein made up of >20 amino acids.

**Polysaccharide** is a highly complex sugar, made of >10 simple sugar (monosaccharide) units.

**Potassium-sparing diuretics** are a class of diuretics which produce diuresis without the secretion of $K^+$ into the urine, by blocking the epithelial sodium channels (ENaCs).

**Pressure** is a force applied over an area.

**Primary hypertension (or essential hypertension)** is the most common type of hypertension with no identifiable cause and for which patients can have a genetic predisposition.

**Prodrug** is an inactive agent that must undergo a metabolic chemical change, usually in the body, to form an active drug molecule.

**Prophylaxis** is the role of a drug administered to prevent an occurrence of an undesired physiological effect.

**Prostaglandins** are naturally occurring fatty acid derivatives that have several actions including inhibition of gastric secretion.

**Protein** is a biological macromolecule that is a polymer of amino acids, connected by amide bonds. The linear arrangement of a specific set of amino acids determines the structure and function of the protein.

**Proton** is a positively charged particle in the nucleus of an atom, typically denoted in chemistry as $H^+$. Acids are sources of protons.

**Psychotropic drugs** are those that target specific brain receptors and modify nerve impulses to and from the brain.

**Receptor** is a macromolecule with a specific arrangement of atoms or functional groups that are complementary and attractive to a ligand or substrate.

**REM sleep** is a state of consciousness intermediate between sleep and wakefulness characterized by rapid eye movement (REM).

**Renin angiotensin system (RAS)** is a cascade of enzymatic reactions involving angiotensinogen, renin, angiotensin converting enzyme (ACE), the peptide hormones angiotensin I and II and angiotensin receptors which ultimately leads to constriction of blood pressure causing hypertension.

**Renin inhibitors** are drugs that lower blood pressure by inhibiting renin of the Renin Angiotensin System, which is the rate limiting step.

**Resistance** is the decreased sensitivity of microorganism to a formerly efficacious drug or treatment.

**Reuptake** refers to the passage of a neurotransmitter molecule back into its cell of origin.

**Ribonucleic acid,** or RNA, is a biological macromolecule chemically related to DNA. The information is stored via a specific linear arrangement (polymer) of nucleotides. RNA is composed of 4 bases: adenine, guanine, cytosine, and uracil. RNA has many roles in the cell. One of the most important roles of RNA is translation of DNA's genetic information into proteins.

**Secondary hypertension (or nonessential hypertension)** is a temporary form of hypertension with known causes and can be treated or even reversed.

**Second-gas effect** is the observation that the presence of a high alveolar concentration of 1 gas promotes a rapid increase in the alveolar concentration of a second gas.

**Sedative** is an agent that causes sedation by reducing anxiety.

**Selective serotonin reuptake inhibitor (SSRI)** is a molecule that binds to the serotonin reuptake transporter preferentially over other types of transporters.

**Signal transduction** refers to the process by which a cellular message is passed from 1 place to another: either from 1 cell to another or from outside a cell to inside the cell.

**Single (sigma, σ) bond** is the sharing of the first 2 electrons between 2 atoms. It results from the end-to-end overlap of orbitals, along the bonding axis. Once the orbitals overlap, electrons can be shared between the atoms. A sigma bond is stronger than a pi bond. A single bond is typically denoted by a single line between 2 atoms. For example, in "O H", there is a single bond between the oxygen and hydrogen atoms.

**Solubility** is the greatest quantity of a substance that may be dissolved in another.

**Soluble** refers to a property of a molecule that permits it to disperse throughout a solvent.

**Stereochemistry** is the unique 3-dimensional spatial relationship between substituents bonded to a single atom. The stereochemistry of an atom often imparts unique physical properties and biological activities to the entire molecule.

**Stereogenic center** occurs when 4 different substituents are attached to a single atom, typically carbon.

**Stimulant** is the phenomenon of the reversal of a neutral or depressant state of a system.

**Structure-activity relationship (SAR)** refers to the connection between a ligand's chemical structure and its binding affinity to a receptor, inhibition of a biochemical process, or pharmacological effect.

**Substrate** is a ligand that acts as a starting material for an enzyme. Generally, an enzyme catalyzes a chemical reaction, converting the substrate from 1 substance to another.

**Sulfonamide** is a class of organic compounds related to the amide. The sulfonamide contains a sulfonyl ($SO_2$) group bonded to a nitrogen atom. The sulfonamide ($RSO_2NHR$) appears in several types of drugs and is characterized by a fairly acidic proton on the amide nitrogen atom (pKa = 12-18).

**Sympathetic nervous system** is a branch of the nervous system that is responsible for significant involuntary functions such as the "fight or flight" response. The sympathetic system contains adrenergic receptors responsive to epinephrine and related molecules.

**Synapse** is the space between 2 nerve cells (neurons). Neurotransmitters are released from the presynaptic neuron on 1 side of the synapse and bind to receptors on the postsynaptic neuron on the opposite side of the synapse.

**Tautomers** are isomeric structures of a molecule arising from the movement of a proton between atoms or functional groups.

**Tension** is a gradient between 2 compartments.

**Thiazide diuretics** are a class of diuretics that prevent the reabsorption of $Na^+$ by blocking the $Na^+/Cl^-$ cotransporter in the distal convoluted tubule resulting in excretion of sodium causing diuresis.

**Thioether** is a compound with at least 1 sulfur atom bonded to 2 carbon atoms, denoted R-S-R.

**Thiol** is a compound with at least 1 S-H group.

**Tolerance** is the decline of the effect of a drug in the body, requiring an increased dose to produce the desired effect.

**Transcription** is the process of converting the DNA code to RNA.

**Translation** is the conversion of the RNA message to form proteins.

**Triple bond** results from the formation of 1 sigma and 2 pi bonds between 2 atoms. A triple bond is denoted as 3 lines between the atoms. For example, in "C≡C", there is a triple bond (sigma + pi + pi) between the 2 carbon atoms.

**Turbulent flow** is the chaotic, disordered movement of fluid.

**Valence electrons** are electrons in the outermost shell of electrons surrounding the nucleus of an atom.

**Van der Waals force (or London force)** is a weakly, attractive force (0.5 kcal/mol) between 2 molecules that are not permanent dipoles. When they come into contact with each other, the molecules both adopt a temporary (or induced) dipole configuration.

**Vapor pressure** is the pressure at which a vapor is at equilibrium with its liquid (condensed) state.

**Volatility** is a measure of how readily a substance vaporizes from the liquid phase to the gas phase.

# Index

Note: *f* indicates a figure; *t* indicates a table.

**A**

Abacavir sulfate, 365, 365*f,* 366
Abortifacients, 87
Absence seizures, 284
Acarbose (Precose), 94
Accumulation factor, 172
Acecarbromal, 270
Acetaldehyde, 269
Acetaminophen, 301, 309-310, 309*f*
  cytochrome P-450, metabolism of, 310
Acetanilide, 309, 309*f*
Acetate, 178
Acetazolamide, 223, 223*f*
Acetic acid, 27*f,* 54*f*
Acetoacetyl CoA, 111
Acetonitrile, 27*f*
Acetylcholine (ACh), 56*f,* 175*f*
  action of, at synapse, 177*f*
  binding of molecule of, 84
  binding to acetylcholinesterase, 137*f*
  binding to extracellular membrane, 176
  as ester functional group, 55
  metabolism of, 178-181, 179*f,* 180*f,* 181*f*
  as neurotransmitter, 80, 249
  pharmacophore of, 136
  synthesis and release of, 178, 178*f*
Acetylcholinesterase (AChE) inhibitors, 84, 124, 177*f*
  acetylcholine binding to, 137*f*
  action of, to metabolize acetylcholine, 179*f*
  irreversible inhibition of, 180*f*
  structures of, 181*f*
Acetyl coenzyme A (acetyl CoA), 98, 99*f,* 106-107, 111, 178
Acetyl coenzymes, 98*f*
Acetyl cysteine, 310
Acetylene, 26, 27*f*
*N*-acetylglucosamine residues, 93
*N*-acetylprocainamide, 211
Acetyl salicylic acid, 54*f,* 56*f*
Acid-catalyzed amide hydrolysis, 61*f*
Acid-catalyzed ester hydrolysis, 58*f*
Acids. *See also* Specific acids by name
  Brønsted-Lowry theory of, 64
  conjugate, 64
  defined, 63-66

strong, 65
weak, 65
Aconitase, 106
*cis*-Aconitate, 106
Actinomycin D, 116, 116*f*
Active site, 131, 179
Acyclovir (Zovirax), 94-95, 362, 362*f*
*N*-acylsphingosine, 89
Addiction, 291
Adenine (A), 74, 75*f,* 114
  as ribonucleic acid (RNA) base, 76
Adenosine, 73
Adenosine monophosphate (AMP), 73
Adenosine triphosphate (ATP), 76, 97, 98*f,* 115
  production of, 99*f,* 109*f*
  synthesis of, 109
Adiabatic compression and expansion, 11, 11*f*
Adiphenine, 187, 188*f*
Adipocytes, 87
α-adrenergic, 317
Adrenergic mechanisms of action, 187-192
  catecholamine metabolism, 189, 190*f*
  catecholamine reuptake, 189-190
  catecholamine storage and release, 191-192, 192*f*
Adrenergic receptors, 175, 187-198, 189*f,* 192
  α-adrenergic receptors, 192-195, 193*f*
  ß-adrenergic receptors, 195-197, 197*f,* 198*f*
  mechanisms of action, 187-192
  receptors, 192
  structure-activity relationships of $\alpha_1$ receptors, 194-195
  $\alpha_2$ receptor agents, 195
Adult respiratory distress syndrome (ARDS), 18
Agonists, 132
  muscarinic receptor, 185-186
  potassium channel, 226
Agranulocytosis, 335
Air-entrainment mask, 16
Alanine (Ala), 77
Albuterol, 40, 40*f,* 196, 197*f*
Alcohols (-OH), 38-41, 39*f,* 40*f,* 41*f*
  for attacking esters, 56
  common, 40*f*

defined, 38
metabolism of, 41*f*
potency and, 270, 271*f*
primary, 40
secondary, 40
tertiary, 40
Aldehyde dehydrogenase, 51*f,* 269
Aldehyde oxidase, 51*f*
Aldehydes, 50-51
common, 51*f*
metabolism of, 51*f*
Aldo-keto reductase, 52, 53*f*
Aldoses, 91
Alfentanil, 169, 298, 298*f*
Aliskiren, 221, 221*f*
Alkanes, 29-33
common, 31*t,* 31*tf*
as hydrophobic, 29
metabolism of, 30, 30*f*
naming, 30
types of, 29, 29*f*
Alkenes, 33-36, 34*f,* 35*f*
defined, 33
examples of, 33
metabolism of, 35*f*
naming, 33
oxidation of, 35*f*
stereochemistry of, 34*f*
Alkoxide anions, 60*f,* 125
Alkoxy group, 55
Alkyl chain, 85
Allergenicity, 124
Allosteric inhibition, 132
Allosteric site, 132
Allylic/benzylic carbon, 35*f*
Allylic carbon atoms, 34-35, 35*f*
α-adrenergic receptors, 192-195, 193*f*
Alveolar anesthetic concentration, 244,
245*f*
Alveolar membrane, 17
Alveoli, 17
Alzheimer's disease, 180, 221
α-amanitin, 116
Amantadine, 369
Ambenonium, 179, 179*f*
Ambient temperature, 3
Amide hydrolysis, 60, 266
acid-catalyzed, 61*f*
base-catalyzed, 61*f*
mechanisms of, 61*f*
Amides, 59-61, 59*f,* 60*f*
metabolism of, 60*f*

Amiloride, 225, 226*f*
Amines, 46-47, 46*t,* 56
basicity of, 47
examples of, 46*t*
metabolism of, 49*f*
primary, 46, 47-48, 48*f*
properties of, 47
quaternary, 47, 178
secondary, 46, 48, 48*f*
tertiary, 46, 47, 48*f*
Amino, 125
Amino acids, 76-85. *See also* Proteins
antibodies and, 84
enzymes and, 83-84
nonpolar, 77
structures of, 77*f*
Amino acid transporters, 83
α-amino-3-hydroxy-5-methyl-4-
isoxazolepropionic (AMPA)
receptors, 286
α-amino acids, 76
Aminoglycosides, 94, 119, 343, 353-354,
354*f*
6-aminopenicillanic acid, 343, 344*t*
Aminophenols, 309
Aminophenyl butyric acid- and
ester-containing drugs, 218-220, 219*f*
Amiodarone, 213-214, 215*f*
Amitriptyline, 317, 317*t,* 318
Amlodipine, 205
Ammonia, 46, 47
Ammonium, 46
Amobarbital, 275*f,* 276
Amoxapine, 317*t,* 319
Amoxicillin, 344*t,* 346, 349
*L*-amphetamine, 316
Amphetamine, 191, 192*f,* 337-338, 337*f*
Amphetamines, 244
Ampicillin, 344*t,* 346
Amprenavir (Agenerase), 84, 367, 368*f*
Amyl nitrite, 201, 202, 203
Analgesia, 243
Analgesic agents, 289-310
nonsteroidal anti-inflammatory drugs,
300-308, 301*f*
anthranilic acids, 304, 305*f*
arylacetic acids, 305, 305*f*
aspirin and related salicylates,
302-304, 302*f,* 303*f*
propionic acids, 307, 307*f*
pyrazoles, 306, 306*f*
selective COX-2 inhibitors, 308, 308*f*

opioids, 289-300
  fentanyl and related analogues, 297-299, 298*f*
  methadone and related analogues, 298, 298*f*
  mixed agonist-antagonist, 297, 297*f*
  morphine and related analogues, 291-294
  opioid antagonists, 295-296
  opioid receptor family, 290, 290*t*, 291*t*
  opioids used as antidiarrheal drugs, 298-299, 299*f*
  pharmacological responses to opioid analgesics, 291
  pure antagonists, 296, 296*f*
  ring B modifications of morphine, 295, 295*f*
  ring C modifications of morphine, 294-295, 295*f*
  ring E modifications of morphine, 294, 294*f*
Andrews, Edmund, 242
Anesthesia
  Avogadro's law and, 8-9
  Bernoulli's theorem and, 14-15, 15*f*
  Boyle's law in, 6-7, 9, 12
  Charles law and, 7, 9
  Dalton's law of partial pressures and, 10-11
  delivery of, 1
  Frick's diffusion law and, 18
  Gay-Lussac's temperature/pressure and, 7-8
  Graham's law of effusion and, 18-19
  Hagen-Poiseuille equation and, 14
  Henry's law and, 19
  mechanism of, 248-249
  psychotropic agents in, 339
  stages of, 243
  temperature and, 3-4
  Venturi principle and, 16, 16*f*
Anesthetic agents, 241-266, 260*f*
  classes of, 241
  defined, 241
  early volatile, 249-250, 250*f*
  ideal characteristics of, 242
  intravenous induction agents, 254-262
    barbiturates, 255-258, 255*f*
    sleepiness, 258-262, 259*f*
  latent heat of vaporization, 4
  local, 210-212, 210*f*, 211*f*, 241, 262-266
    amide-containing, 265-266, 266*f*

ester-containing, 264, 265*f*
  mechanism of action, 262-263, 263*f*
  structure-activity models, 263, 264*f*
  partial pressure of, 19
  pharmaceutical properties of, 73
  thermodynamic properties of, 73
  volatile, 5, 241-254
Angiotensin-converting enzyme (ACE) inhibitors, 217, 217*f*, 218-220, 218*f*, 219*f*
  adverse effects of, 220
  aminophenyl butyric acid and ester-containing drugs, 218-220, 219*f*
  phosphonate-containing drugs, 220, 220*f*
  thiol-and carboxylate-containing drugs, 218
Angiotensin I, 217
Angiotensin II, 217
Angiotensin II receptor antagonists, 221-222, 222*f*
Anhydride, 56
Anion-binding exosite, 236
Antagonists, 132, 163
  angiotensin II receptor, 221-222, 222*f*
  ß-adrenergic, 201, 206-207, 207*f*, 213
  calcium channel, 201, 204-206, 204*f*, 205*f*, 206*f*
  muscarinic receptor, 187, 188*f*
  opioid, 295-296
  pure, 296, 296*f*
Anthracyclines, 75
Anthranilic acids, 304, 305*f*
Anthrax, 359
Antiangina, 196
Antianginal drugs, 201-207
  calcium channel antagonists, 204-206, 204*f*
  organic nitrates, 201-204, 202*f*
  ß-adrenergic antagonists, 206-207, 207*f*
Antiarrhythmic agents, 208-215, 208*f*
  classes of, 209-215, 209*t*
Antibiotic agents, 342-361
  aminoglycosides, 353-354, 354*f*
  cephalosporins, 347, 348*t*, 349-352
    fourth- and fifth-generation, 351-352, 352*t*
    oral, 349-350
    parenteral, 350-351
  development of resistance to anti-infective therapy, 342
  identifying cause of infection, 341-342
  macrolides, 76, 356-357, 356*f*
  penicillins, 343-347, 344-345*t*

quinolones, 358-361, 358*f*
sulfonamides, 357, 358*f*
tetracyclines, 354-355, 355*t*
Antibodies, 84
Anticoagulation, 94, 228-238, 230
 anticoagulants, 230
 coumarins, 233-236, 234*f*
 heparins, 230-233, 231*f*
 hirudins, 236-237, 237*f*
 indanediones, 233-236
 peptidomimetics, 237, 238*f*
 physical and chemical forces involved
  in clotting, 228-229, 229*f*
Anticonvulsants, 278-286
 barbiturates, 279-280, 280*f*
 benzodiazepines, 279, 279*f*
 hydantoins, 281-282, 281*f,* 282*f*
 oxazolidinediones, 283, 284*f*
 succinimides, 282-283, 283*f*
Antidepressants, 313-324, 329
 monoamine oxidase inhibitors, 314-316,
  315*f*
 selective serotonin reuptake inhibitor
  (SSRI), 319-321, 320*f*
 tricyclic antidepressants, 316-319, 317*t*
Antidiarrheal drugs, opioids used as,
 298-299, 299*f*
Antihypertensive agents, 216-228
 adverse effects of angiotensin-converting
  enzyme inhibitor, 220
 angiotensin-converting enzyme inhibitor,
  218-220, 218*f,* 219*f*
 angiotensin II receptor antagonists,
  221-222, 222*f*
 direct-acting vasodilatory drugs,
  226-228, 227*f*
 diuretics, 222-226
 renin-angiotensin system, 217, 217*f*
 renin inhibitors, 221, 221*f*
 targets for drug therapies, 216
Anti-infective therapy, development
 of resistance to, 342
Antineoplastic agents, 75
Antiplatelet agents, 228
Antipsychotics, 330-336
 aripiprazole, 336, 336*f*
 atypical, 330
 butyrophenones, 332-334, 334*f*
 dibenzazepines, 335, 335*f*
 diphenylbutylpiperidines, 334-335, 334*f*
 lithium, 336
 phenothiazines, 330-332, 331*t*
 thioxanthenes, 332, 333*f*

Antipyretics, 301
Antipyrine, 306, 306*f*
Antithrombin, 94, 232-233, 233*f*
Antithrombin-heparin complex, formation
 of, 233
Antiviral agents, 75, 361-370
 fusion inhibitors, 368, 369*f*
 human immunodeficiency virus (HIV),
  364
 inhibitors of DNA synthesis (nucleoside
  analogs), 361-363, 362*f,* 363*f*
 integrase inhibitors, 369
 neuraminidase inhibitors, 363, 363*f*
 nonnucleoside reverse transcriptase
  inhibitors, 366, 367*f*
 nucleoside reverse transcriptase
  inhibitors, 364-366, 365*f*
 protease inhibitors, 367-368, 368*f*
 reverse transcriptase inhibitors, 364
Anxiety, 324
Anxiolytics, 324-329
 benzodiazepines, 324-328, 325*t,* 326*f*
Aqueous solubility, 63
Arachidic (eicosanoic) acid, 86*f*
Arachidonic acid, 86, 86*f*
Area under the plasma concentration-time
 curve (AUCx), 144
Arecoline, 186, 186*f*
Argatroban, 230, 237, 238*f*
Arginine (Arg), 77
Aripiprazole, 336, 336*f*
Aromatic compounds, metabolism of, 37,
 39*f*
Aromatic rings, 38*f*
Aromatics, 37-38, 38*f*
Arrhythmias
 ectopic, 208
 reentrant, 208
Arsphenamine, 341
2-aryl-1,3-indandiones, weakly acidic
 property of, 234*f*
Arylacetic acids, 305, 305*f*
Arylalkylamines, 205
Aryloxy group, 55
Asparagine, 77
Aspartic acid (Asp), 77
Aspirin, 38*f,* 54*f,* 56*f,* 302-304, 302*f,* 303*f*
 as carboxylic acid functional group, 53
 drug molecules with aromatic rings, 37
 metabolism of, 303*f*
 as molecule with ester functional group,
  55

Atenolol, 196, 198*f*
Atherosclerosis, 208
Atmospheric pressure, boiling point and, 5
Atoms, 2
  covalent bonds in different, 25, 26*t*
Atracurium, 183, 184*f*
Atropine, 187, 188*f*, 300
Atypical antipsychotics, 330
Autolysin activity, regulation of, 343
Autonomic agents, 175-197
  adrenergic receptors, 187-198, 189*f*
    α-adrenergic receptors, 192-195, 193*f*
    ß-adrenergic receptors, 195-197, 197*f*,
      198*f*
    mechanisms of action, 187-192
    receptors, 192
  cholinergic receptors, 176-187, 176*f*
    acetylcholine metabolism, 178-181,
      179*f*, 180*f*, 181*f*
    acetylcholine synthesis and release,
      178, 178*f*
    mechanisms of action, 177, 177*f*
    muscarinic, 185-187
    nicotinic, 181-184
Autonomic nervous system, 175
Average steady-state concentration, 171
Avogadro's law, 8-9
  usefulness of, 9
Azimilide, 214, 215*f*
Aziridinium ion, 194, 194*f*
Azithromycin, 356*f*
AZT, 75

**B**

Bactericidal agents, 342
Bacteriostatic agents, 342
Barbiturates, 255-258, 255*f*, 274-276, 275*t*,
  279-280, 280*f*
  mechanism of action, 255
  pharmacokinetics of, 256-258
  as sedative, 270
  structure-activity relationships, 255-256
Barbituric acids, 255
  keto-enol tautomerism of, 255*f*
  ring derivatives of, 280, 280*f*
Barometric pressure, 12
Base-catalyzed amide hydrolysis, 61*f*
Base-catalyzed ester hydrolysis, 58*f*
Bases
  conjugate, 64
  defined, 63-66
  paired, 74

Basicity, 47
Benazepril, 219*f*, 220
Benzedrine, 337
Benzene, 37, 38*f*
Benzethonium chloride, 260
Benzocaine, 264, 265*f*
Benzodiazepine binding sites, 258
Benzodiazepines, 258-262, 259*f*, 271-272,
  279, 279*f*, 324-328, 325*t*, 326*f*
  as sedative, 270
  structure of various, 272, 273*f*
  in treating insomnia, 272, 273*f*
Benzoic acid, 53
Benzoylecgonine, 338
Benzyl alcohol, 40*f*
Bepridil, 205, 206*f*
Bernoulli effect, 16
Bernoulli's theorem, 15
ß-adrenergic receptors, 195-197, 197*f*, 198*f*
  structure-activity relationships to
    ß-receptors, 196-197
ß-adrenergic antagonists, 201, 206-207,
  207*f*, 213
  newer nontraditional anti-ischemic
    agents, 207
ß-adrenergic blockers, 207*f*, 213
ß-blockers, 196
  ß-adrenergic agents as, 207*f*
ß-endorphins, 290, 290*t*
Bethanechol, 186, 186*f*
Bile acids, 89
Biliary excretion, 155
Bimatoprost (Lumigan), 87
Binding site, 135, 179
  defined, 123
Bioavailability, 143
Biogenic amines, 191
Biological functions of carbohydrates, 93
Biological macromolecules, 73-95, 132
  amino acids and proteins, 76-85
    antibodies, 84
    enzymes, 83-84
    protein functions, 79
    regulatory proteins, 79-81
    signaling proteins, 85
    structural proteins, 83
    transport proteins, 82-83
  carbohydrates, 90-95
    monosaccharides, 91-92, 91*f*, 92*f*
    oligosaccharides, 92, 92*f*
    polysaccharides, 92, 92*f*

lipids, 85-90
  cholesterol, 89-90
  eicosanoids, 86-87
  fatty acids, 85
  phospholipids, 88-89, 88*f*
  sphingolipids, 89
  triacylglycerols, 87, 88*f*
nucleic acids and polynucleotides, 73-76
  deoxyribonucleic acid (DNA), 73-75, 74*f*
  ribonucleic acid, 74*f*, 76
Biological receptors, 131
Biophase-link model, 165, 165*f*
Biphases, 163
1,3-bisphosphoglycerate, 103
Bivalirudin, 230, 236-237
  sequence of, 237*f*
Bleomycin, 75
Blood
  flow of gases to, 17-19, 17*f*
  pH of, 65, 69
Blood-brain barrier (BBB), 246*f*
  barbiturates and, 256-257
  in children, 300
  volatile anesthetics and, 243, 245
Blood dyscrasias, 283, 286
Blood glucose, 94
Blood transfusions, 230
Boiling point, 63
  atmospheric pressure and, 5
  defined, 5
Bonds
  covalent, 24-28
  dipole-dipole, 126-129, 128*f*
  double, 26, 26*f*, 27, 27*f*
  hydrogen, 29
  ion-dipole, 125-126, 126*f*, 127*f*
  ionic, 125, 125*f*
  multiple, 27, 27*f*
  noncovalent, 124
  single, 25
  triple, 26, 27, 27*f*
  types of, 23
Botulism toxin, 178
Boyle's law, 6-7, 9, 12
  application of, 6
Bretylium, 192, 192*f*
Bretylium tosylate, 213, 215*f*
Brofaromine, 315*f*, 316
Bromine, 251
Bromism, 270
Bromisovalum, 270

3-bromopyruvate, 104, 104*f*
Bronchodilators, 195
Brønsted-Lowry theory of acids, 64
Bulimia, 320
α-bungarotoxin, 184
Bunsen (α) coefficient, 20
Bupivacaine, 266, 266*f*
Buprenorphine, 297, 297*f*
Bupropion, 321-322, 322*f*
Buspirone, 329, 329*f*
Butalbital, 275*f*, 276
2-butanol, 30, 31*f*, 32
2-butene, 33
*cis*-2-butene, 33
Butorphanol, 297, 297*f*
Butyrophenones, 332-334, 334*f*
  structures of, 333*f*

**C**

Caffeine, 321, 336, 338*f*, 339
Cahn-Ingold-Prelog method, 32
Calcium, 80, 134
Calcium channel antagonists, 201, 204-206, 204*f*
  chemistry of, 205, 205*f*, 206*f*
  metabolism of, 206
  pharmacokinetics of, 205
Calcium channel blockers, 214-215, 226
  arylalkylamines as, 206*f*
Cancer drug development, tyrosine kinases in, 81
Captopril, 218, 218*f*
Carbachol, 185-186, 186*f*
Carbamates, 180
Carbamazepine, 284, 285*f*
Carbamoylated enzyme, 180*f*
Carbenicillin, 345*t*, 346-347
Carbohydrates, 90-95
  biological functions of, 93
  drugs related to, 94-95
  monosaccharides, 91-92, 91*f*, 92*f*
  oligosaccharides, 92, 92*f*
  polysaccharides, 92, 92*f*
  variability of, 91
α-carbon atom, 76
Carbon-carbon double bond, 33
Carbon-carbon triple bond, breaking, 26
Carbon-carbon σ bond, 29
Carbon dioxide, 27*f*
  conversion of glucose to, 107, 107*f*
  molecular weight of, 19
Carbonic anhydrase inhibitors, 222-223

Carbon monoxide, 27*f*
Carbon-nitrogen linkage, 78, 78*f*
Carbon skeleton, shapes of, 23
Carbonyl, 49-50, 50*f*, 125
 electronic nature of, 50*f*
Carboxylate anions, 52
 resonance stabilization of, 53*f*
Carboxylates, 52
Carboxylic acids, 41, 52-53, 53*f*, 56
 metabolism of, 54*f*
Carbromal, 270
Cardiac glycosides, toxic effects of, 208
Cardiovascular agents, 201-238
 antianginal drugs, 201-207
  calcium channel antagonists, 204-206,
   204*f*
  organic nitrates, 201-204, 202*f*
  ß-adrenergic antagonists, 206-207,
   207*f*
 antiarrhythmic agents, 208-215, 208*f*
  classes of, 209-215, 209*t*
 anticoagulation, 228-238
  anticoagulants, 230
  coumarins, 233-236, 234*f*
  heparins, 230-233, 231*f*
  hirudins, 236-237, 237*f*
  indanediones, 233-236
  peptidomimetics, 237, 238*f*
  physical and chemical forces involved
   in clotting, 228-229, 229*f*
 antihypertensive agents, 216-228
  adverse effects of angiotensin-
   converting enzyme inhibitor, 220
  angiotensin-converting enzyme
   inhibitor, 218-220, 218*f*, 219*f*
  angiotensin II receptor antagonist,
   221-222, 222*f*
  direct-acting vasodilatory drugs,
   226-228, 227*f*
  diuretics, 222-226
  renin-angiotensin system, 217, 217*f*
  renin inhibitors, 221, 221*f*
  targets for drug therapies, 216
Cardiovascular disease, 201
Carvedilol, 207
Catechol, 42*f*
Catecholamine metabolism, 189, 190*f*
Catecholamine reuptake, 189-190
Catecholamine reuptake inhibitors, 190,
 191*f*
Catecholamine storage and release,
 191-192, 192*f*

Catecholamine synthesis, 188, 189*f*
Catechol *O*-methyltransferase, 189
Catechol ring system, 197
Cation-pi attractive force, 137*f*
CCR5, 368
Cefaclor, 348*t*, 350
Cefadroxil, 349
Cefamandole, 348*t*, 351
Cefazolin, 348*t*, 350
Cefixime, 348*t*, 350
Cefonicid, 348*t*, 350
Cefotaxime, 348*t*
Cefotetan, 348*t*, 350
Cefoxitin, 348*t*, 350
Cefprozil, 348*t*
Ceftazidime, 348*t*, 351
Ceftriaxone, 348*t*, 351
Cefuroxime, 348*t*, 349-351
Celecoxib, 301, 308, 308*f*
Cellulose, 90, 91, 92*f*, 93
Central nervous system (CNS)
 passage of anesthetic gas into and out of,
  243-244, 244*f*
 regulatory proteins in, 79
Central nervous system (CNS) depressants,
 269-286
 anticonvulsants, 278-286
  barbiturates, 279-280, 280*f*
  benzodiazepines, 279, 279*f*
  hydantoins, 281-282, 281*f*, 282*f*
  oxazolidinediones, 283, 284*f*
  succinimides, 282-283, 283*f*
 sedatives and hypnotics, 269-278
  barbiturates, 274-276, 275*t*
  benzodiazepines, 271-272, 273*f*
  chloral hydrate, 274, 274*f*
Cephadroxil, 348*t*
Cephalexin, 348*t*
Cephalosporins, 342-343, 347, 348*t*,
 349-352
 fifth generation, 351-352, 352*t*
 first generation, 347
 fourth generation, 351-352, 352*t*
 oral, 349-350
 parenteral, 350-351
 second generation, 349-350
 third generation, 347, 349, 350
Cephalothin, 348*t*, 350
Ceramides, 89, 90*f*
 structures of, 90*f*
Charge fluctuation forces, 129
Charles, Jacques, 7

Charles' law, 7, 9
Cheese effect, 314
Chelation, 355
Chemical bonds, 26
Children
  blood-brain barrier in, 300
  febrile convulsions in, 278
Chiral molecule, 30, 32, 76
Chitin, 93
Chloral hydrate, 274, 274$f$
Chloramphenicol, 120, 120$f$
Chlordiazepoxide, 325$t$, 326-327
Chloride ion influx, 272
Chlorine, 125, 251
Chloroacetic acid, 67
Chloroform, 85, 250, 250$f$
Chloroprocaine as ester-containing local
  anesthetic agent, 264, 265$f$
Chlorothiazide, 224-225, 224$f$
Chlorpromazine, 330, 331, 331$t$
Chlorprothixene, 332, 333$f$
Cholesterol, 40, 40$f$, 89-90
  structure of, 90$f$, 110$f$
Cholesterol biosynthesis, 99
  drugs that interrupt, 114, 114$f$
  steps in, 111, 111$f$
Cholesterol synthesis, 110-114, 110$f$
  acetyl CoA to mevalonate, 111, 111$f$
  mevalonic acid to squalene, 111-113,
    112$f$
  squalene to, 113, 113$f$
Cholestyramine, 90
Choline, 177$f$
Choline magnesium trisalicylate, 302
Cholinergic mechanisms of action, 177,
  177$f$
Cholinergic receptors, 175, 176-187, 176$f$
  acetylcholine metabolism, 178-181,
    179$f$, 180$f$, 181$f$
  acetylcholine synthesis and release, 178,
    178$f$
  mechanisms of action, 177, 177$f$
  muscarinic, 185-187
  nicotinic, 181-184
  types of, 176
Cidofovir, 362
Ciprofloxacin, 358$f$, 359
Cisapride, 323
*Cis* relationship, 33, 34$f$
Citalopram, 320$f$, 321
Citrate, 106
Citric acid cycle, 104

Claisen condensation, 111
Clarithromycin, 356$f$
Clearance (CL), 155-156
Clearance values, physiological
  interpretation of, 157-161, 158$t$, 160$f$,
    161$f$, 162$t$
Clidinium, 187, 188$f$
Clindamycin, lincomycin hydrochloride
  and, 360-361, 361$f$
Clonazepam, 279, 327
  in treating insomnia, 272, 273$f$
Clonidine, 192, 193$f$, 195, 310, 310$f$
Clorazepate dipotassium, 279, 279$f$
Clorgyline, 189, 190$f$
Clothiapine, 335, 335$f$
Clotting
  inhibition of, 236
  physical and chemical forces involved
    in, 209$f$, 228-229
Cloxacillin, 345$t$
Cloxacillin, 347
Clozapine, 49$f$, 335$f$
  as amines, 48
  anticholinergic activities of, 335
  as atypical antipsychotic, 330
  degrading drug as, 321
Coagulation cascade, 229, 229$f$, 232, 235
CoASH, 104
Cocaine, 56$f$, 191$f$, 338$f$
  as catecholamine reuptake inhibitor, 190
  classification of, 337
  effects of, 338, 338$f$
  as ester-containing local anesthetic
    agent, 264, 265$f$
  as ester functional group, 55
  increased central neurotransmitter levels
    from, 244
Codeine, 292, 292$f$
Codon, 74
Cofactors, 97-98, 104
Colchicine, 83
  inhibition of, 131
Colitis, 361
Combined gas law, 8
Compartmental pharmacokinetics,
  140-141, 140$f$
Competitive inhibition, 132
Complementary, 136
Compounds, 23
Compressed gas in operating room, 1-12
  boiling point, 5
  critical temperature and pressure, 5-6

kinetic energy, 2-3
kinetic theory, 2
   pressure, 3
   temperature, 3-4
   vapor pressure, 4-5
Compressed oxygen, 6
Conjugate acids, 64
Conjugate base, 64
Conjugation, 43*f*, 53, 54*f*, 154
Controlled ventilation, 12
Convulsions, febrile, 278
Coronary thrombosis, 234
Corticosterone, 52, 52*f*, 90
Cortisone, 90
Coumarins, 233-236, 234*f*
   biochemical mechanism of, 234-236
Counterclockwise hysteresis loop, 167, 167*f*
Covalent bonds, 24-28, 123-124
   defined, 24, 26*f*
   in different atoms, 25, 26*t*
   multiple, 25-28, 26*t*
   strength of, 124
Covalent interactions, 124
Critical pressure, 5
Critical temperature, 5
Cross hypersensitivity, 350
Cross-resistance, 359
Cross-sensitivity, 343
Curare, 183
CX157, 315*f*, 316
Cyano, 125
Cyclic adenosine-3', 5-monophosphate (cAMP), 134
Cyclic esters, 186
Cyclic guanosine monophosphate (cGMP), 204
Cycloheptane, 29*f*
Cyclohexane, 29*f*, 37
Cyclooxygenase-1 (COX-1) inhibitors, 300, 301
Cyclooxygenase-2 (COX-2) inhibitors, 300, 301
   selective, 308, 308*f*
Cyclooxygenase-3 (COX-3) inhibitors, 300, 301
Cylinders, Gay-Lussac temperature/pressure in explaining underfilling rationale, 8
CYP1A2, 321
CYP2C9, 154
CYP2C19, 154

CYP2D6, 154, 321
   inhibition of, 321
CYP3A4, 153, 323
CYP isoenzymes, 236
Cyproheptadine, 317*t*, 319
Cysteine (Cys), 44, 77, 203
Cystic fibrosis, 119
Cystosine (C), 75*f*, 114
   as ribonucleic acid (RNA) base, 76
Cytidine triphosphate (CTP), 115
Cytochrome $P_{450}$, 321
Cytochrome $P_{450}$ metabolism
   of acetaminophen, 310
Cytokines, 85
Cytomegalovirus, 361
Cytosine, 73, 74
Cytosine monophosphate (CMP), 73

**D**

Dabigatran, 230, 237, 238*f*
Dalton's law of partial pressures, 10-11
Darunavir, 367, 368*f*
Davy, Humphrey, 242
Dealkylation, 48, 49*f*
*N*-Dealkylation, 265, 318
Decamethonium, 184, 185*f*
Dehydrogenase, 51
Delavirdine, 366, 367*f*
Deletion mutation, 119
Delirium as stage in anesthesia, 243
Delirium tremens (DTs), 269
Demeclocycline, 355, 355*t*
2-Deoxyglucose, 104, 104*f*
Deoxyribonucleic acid (DNA), 73-75, 74*f*
   comparison of ribonucleic acid (RNA) and, 74*f*
   nucleotides of, 73
Deoxyribonucleic acid (DNA) bases, 74
Deoxyribonucleic acid (DNA) polymerase, 84, 362
Deoxyribonucleic acid (DNA) synthesis, inhibition of, 361-363, 362*f*, 363*f*
Deoxyribose, 92
2-Deoxyribose, 92
Depression
   causes of, 314
   treatment of, 313
*N*-Desalkylflurazepam, 328
Desethylzaleplon, 276
Desflurane, 253
   difference between isoflurane and, 5
   metabolism of, 254*f*

Desipramine, 190, 191*f*, 317, 317*t*, 318
Desirudins, 230, 236
Desmethyldiazepam, 327, 328
Desmethyldoxepin, 319
Desmethylofloxacin, 359
*N*-desmethylselegiline, 316
Desvenlafaxine, 322, 322*f*
Dextromethorphan, 294*f*
Dextrose, 90
Dezocine, 295, 295*f*
1,2-Diacylglycerol, 88
Dialysis, 230
Diarrhea, 361
Diazepam, 38*f*
    as benzodiazepine, 258-259, 259*f*, 279,
        327
    as drug molecule with aromatic ring, 37
    with plasma protein binding, 168-169
    in treating insomnia, 272, 273*f*
Diazoxide, 227*f*, 228
Dibenzazepines, 335, 335*f*
    structures of, 335*f*
Dibucaine, 265, 266*f*
Dichloroacetic acid, 67
Dicloxacillin, 345*t*, 347
Didanosine, 365, 365*f*
Didesmethylcitalopram, 321
Diethyl ether, 42, 43*f*, 249-250, 250*f*
    drawbacks to use as drug, 43
Differential pressure gradient, 17
Diffusion, 71
    defined, 17, 18
    Fick's law of, 18
    rate of, 71
Diflunisal, 304, 304*f*
Digoxin, 356
Dihydrofolate reductase, 75
Dihydropyridines, 205
Dihydroxy acetone phosphate, 103
Dihydroxyphenylacetaldehyde, 190*f*
Diisopropylamine, 46*f*
Diisopropylfluorophosphate (DFP), 181*f*
Diltiazem, 205, 206*f*, 214-215
    metabolism of, 206
Dimethylallyl pyrophosphate (DMAPP),
        112
*N, N*-dimethylamine, 46
Dimethylamine, 46*f*
Dimethylethylamine, 46*f*
Diol, 34-35
Dioxolane, 186, 186*f*
Dipalmitoyl lecithin, 88*f*, 89

Diphenhydramine, 42, 43*f*, 277
Diphenoxin, 300, 300*f*
Diphenoxylate, 300, 300*f*
Diphenylbutylpiperidines, 334-335, 334*f*
    structures of, 334*f*
5,5-diphenylhydantoin, 212
Diphenylhydantoin, 281, 282*f*
Diphosphate, 98*f*
Dipole, 27-28, 125
Dipole-dipole bonds, 126-129, 128*f*
Dipole-dipole interactions, 29, 124
Dipole moment, 129
Direct-acting vasodilatory drugs, 226-228,
        227*f*
Direct thrombin inhibitors, 236
Dirithromycin, 356*f*
Disaccharide, 92
Disequilibrium, rate of, 165
D isomers, 76
Disopyramide, 210-212, 210*f*
Dispersion forces, 129
Dissociative state of anesthesia, 260
Distribution, gas uptake and, 19-20
Distribution equilibrium, 147
Distribution half-life, 151
Disulfiram (Antabuse), 41
Diuretics, 222-226
    carbonic anhydrase inhibitors, 222-223
    loop, 223-224, 224*f*
    osmotic, 226, 227*f*
    potassium-sparing, 225, 226*f*
    thiazide, 224-225, 225*f*
DNA. *See* Deoxyribonucleic acid (DNA)
Dofetilide, 214, 215*f*
Domagk, Gerhard, 341
Donepezil, 179*f*, 180
Dopa, 189*f*
Dopa decarboxylase, 84
    inhibition of, 188
Dopamine, 49*f*, 189*f*, 190*f*
    as amine, 48
    imbalance in levels of, 314
    metabolism of, 314
    as natural ligand, 132
    as neurotransmitter, 80, 134
    oxidative deamination of, 314
Dopaminergic receptors, 132
Dose and dosage form, 144
Dosing interval, 157
Double bond, 26, 26*f*, 27, 27*f*
    breaking, 26
    internal, 34

strength of, 27, 27*f*
terminal, 34
Double-bond isomers, 33
Doxepin, 42, 43*f*, 317*t*, 319
Doxorubicin, 75
Doxycycline, 355, 355*t*
Dronedarone, 213-214, 215*f*
   lipophilicity of, 214
Droperidol, 333*f*, 334
Drug absorption, 143-147, 143*f*, 144*f*
   defined, 147
   distribution, 147-152, 148*f*, 149*ft*, 150*t*
   dose and dosage form, 144
   rate of administration, 144-145, 145*f*, 146*f*
Drug accumulation, 157
Drug actions, 132, 133*t*
Drug administration, routes of, 144-147, 145*f*, 146-147, 146*f*
   intramuscular, 146
   intravenous, 146
   rectal, 146
   subcutaneous, 146
   transdermal, 146
Drug binding, 132
   structural requirements for, 135
Drug design, 136
Drug distribution, 147-152, 148*f*, 149*ft*, 150*t*
   defined, 147
   fraction unbound in plasma, 151-152, 153*t*
   half-life, 151
   phase I and phase II metabolism, 153-155, 155*t*
   red blood cell binding, 152
Drug effects on signal transduction, 133-134, 135*f*
Drug exposure (AUC$_x$), 156
Drug metabolism
   defined, 152
   phase I and phase II, 153-155, 155*t*
Drug-receptor binding, molecular forces in, 123-124
Drug-receptor concept, 130-137
   drug actions, 132, 133*t*
   drug effects on signal transduction, 133-134, 135*f*
   pharmacophore, 135-137, 137*f*
   receptors, 131-132, 133*t*
   structural requirements for drug binding, 135

Drug-receptor interactions, 123-137
   concept, 130-137
      drug actions, 132, 133*t*
      drug effects on signal transduction, 133-134, 135*f*
      pharmacophore, 135-137, 137*f*
      receptors, 131-132, 133*t*
      structural requirements for drug binding, 135
   covalent interactions, 124
   molecular forces in binding, 123-124
   noncovalent interactions, 124-130
      dipole-dipole bonds, 126-129, 128*f*
      ion-dipole bonds, 125-126, 126*f*, 127*f*
      ionic bonds, 125, 125*f*
      nonpolar bonding forces, 129-130, 130*f*
Drug-receptor theory, 130
Drugs
   antibodies as, 84
   cholesterol biosynthesis and, 114, 114*f*
   defined, 123
   interfering with glycolysis, 103-104, 104*f*
   irreversible, 124
   oral absorption of, 146
   physical properties of, 63-70
   related to carbohydrates, 94-95
   side effects of, 73
   transcription and, 116
   translation and, 119-120, 120*f*
Drug therapies, targets for, 216
Duloxetine, 322, 322*f*
Dynorphins, 290, 290*t*

**E**

E, 338
Early volatile anesthetic agents, 249-250, 250*f*
EC$_{50}$, 163
Echothiophate, 180, 181*f*
Ecstasy, 338
Ectopic arrhythmias, 208
Edrophonium, 179, 179*f*
Efavirenz, 365, 366, 367*f*
Effect-concentration relationship, 163-164, 164*f*
Effect-time profile, 165-171, 165*f*, 166*f*, 167*f*
Efflux pumps, 83
Effusion
   defined, 18
   Graham's law of, 18-19

Eicosanoids, 86-87
Electron delocalization, 26*f*
Electron-donating groups, 67
  effect of, 67
Electronegativity, 38, 44
Electrons
  lone pair, 25
  valence, 25
Electron transport chain, 108
  oxidative phosphorylation and, 106-109, 107*f*, 109*f*
Electron transport process, 98-99, 103, 109*f*
Electron-withdrawing groups, 67
  effect of, 67
Electrophile, 56
Electrostimulation, 313
Elimination half-life ($t_{1/2}\beta$), 157
Enalapril, 219-220, 219*f*
Encainide, 212
Endogenous ligands, 131
Energy
  kinetic, 2-3, 12, 15
  thermal, 4
Enflurane, 252
  metabolism of, 253*f*
Enfuvirtide, 368
Enkephalins, 290, 290*t*
Enolase, 103
*Enterococci,* vancomycin-resistant, 360
Entgegen (E), 33
Enzymes, 83-84
Ephedrine, 244
Epidermal growth factor receptors, 81
Epilepsy, 278, 280
  treatment of, 276
Epinephrine, 42*f*, 175*f*, 189*f*, 247*f*
  adrenergic receptors and, 175, 187
  equipotent at receptors and, 192
  as molecule with phenolic groups in structure of, 42
  as neurotransmitter, 80
Epithelial sodium channels (ENaCs), 225
Eplerenone, 225, 226*f*
Epoxidation, 35*f*
Epoxide, 34, 113
Equilibrium constant, 65
Erhlich, Paul, 341
Erythromycin, 76, 120, 356-357, 356*f*
Erythromycin A, 120*f*, 356*f*
Erythromycin ethylsuccinate, 357
Escitalopram, 320*f*, 321
Estazolam in treating insomnia, 272, 273*f*

Ester-containing local anesthetics, 264, 265*f*
Ester hydrolysis, 60
  acid-catalyzed, 58*f*
  base-catalyzed, 58*f*
Ester moiety, 219
Esters, 55-56, 55*f*, 56*f*, 57*f*, 58
  metabolism of, 59
  synthesis of, 55*f*
Estradiol, 42, 42*f*, 89-90
Ethacrynic acid, 224, 224*f*, 353
Ethane, 25
  pi ($\pi$) bond in, 26
Ethanol, 27*f*, 40*f*, 269-270, 270*f*
  in alcoholic beverages, 41
  hydrogen bonding in, 128
  potential for addiction, 270
  as primary alcohol, 40
Ethene, 26, 33
Ether, 42-44, 43*f*, 85, 125, 242
  first use of, 242
  metabolism of, 44*f*
Ethosuximide, 283
Ethoxy group, 42
Ethylamine, 46*f*
Ethylene, 26, 27*f*
Ethylmethylamine, 46*f*
Ethyne, 26
Etidocaine, 265-266, 266*f*
Etomidate, 260*f*, 261-262
Etravirine, 367*f*
Excessive myocardial catecholamine release, 208
Exchange mutation, 119
Excretion, 155-157
  biliary, 155
  renal, 155
Extracorporeal blood circulation, 230
Extrapyramidal motor system effects, 319
Ezetimibe, 114
E/Z system, 33, 34*f*

F

Factor Xa, 94, 232
Factor XIIIa (fibrin stabilizing factor), 229
False neurotransmitters, 190
Famciclovir, 362
2-farnesyl pyrophosphate, 112
Fatty acids, 85
  alkyl chain of, 85
  examples of, 86*f*
  oxidation of, 108

Febrile convulsions, 278
Felbamate, 285, 285*f*
Fenoprofen, 307, 307*f*
Fentanyl citrate, 298, 298*f*
  related analogues and, 297-299, 298*f*
Fibrin, formation of, 228
Fibrinogen cleavage, 229
Fibrinolytic agents, 228
Fick's diffusion law, 18
Fifth-generation cephalosporins, 351-352, 352*t*
First-generation cephalosporins, 347
First-pass metabolism, 146
Flammability, 43
Flavin adenine dinucleotide ($FAD^{2+}$/$FADH^+$/$FADH_2$), 98*f*, 99*f*
  adenosine triphosphate energy and, 107
  as cofactor in enzymatic reactions, 98
  as electron shuttle, 108
  TCA cycle and, 104
Flecainide, 212
Fleming, Alexander, 341
Flow
  of fluids, 13
  of gases
    to blood, 17-19, 17*f*
    through tubes, 12-16
  laminar, 13, 13*f*
  radial diameter influence on, 14
  turbulent, 13, 13*f*
Fluctuation, 157
Flufenamic acid, 304, 305*f*
Fluids, flow of, 13
Fluorine, 125, 251
5-fluorouracil, 76
Fluoxetine, 42, 43*f*, 319-320, 320*f*
  as example of selective serotonin reuptake inhibitors, 83
Flurazepam, 328
  for insomnia, 272, 273*f*
Flurbiprofen, 307, 307*f*
Fluspirilene, 334*f*, 335
Fluvoxamine, 320*f*, 321
Fondaparinux, 230, 232
Force(s)
  cation-pi attractive, 137*f*
  charge fluctuation, 129
  defined, 2-3
  molecular, in drug-receptor binding, 123-124
  noncovalent, 124

nonpolar bonding, 129-130, 130*f*
physical and chemical, involved in clotting, 228-229, 229*f*
Formaldehyde, 50
Formyl groups, 51
Fosamprenavir, 367-368
Foscarnet, 363, 363*f*
Fosphenytoin, 281, 282*f*
Fourth-generation cephalosporins, 351-352, 352*t*
Fraction unbound in plasma, 151-152, 153*t*
Fructose, 91
Fructose-1,6-bisphosphate, 103
Fumarase, 106
Functional groups, 23, 28-63, 62
  alcohols, 38-41, 39*f*, 40*f*, 41*f*
  aldehydes, 50-51
  alkanes, 29-33, 29*f*, 30*f*, 31*ft*
  alkenes, 33-36, 34*f*, 35*f*
  alkynes, 36, 36*f*
  amides, 59-61, 59*f*, 60*f*
  amines, 46-47, 46*t*
  aromatics, 37-38, 38*f*
  carbonyls, 49-50, 50*f*
  carboxylic acids, 52-53, 53*f*, 54*f*
  chemical properties of, 23
  defined, 28
  esters, 55-56, 55*f*, 56*f*, 57*f*, 58
  ethers, 42-44, 43*f*
  ketones, 52, 52*f*, 53*f*
  phenols, 42, 42*f*, 43*f*
  $pK_a$ values of, 66, 66*t*
  substituent effects on $pK_a$ values, 67-68
  sulfonamides, 62
  thioethers, 44
  thiols, 44
Furan, 37, 38*f*
Furosemide, 224, 224*f*, 353
Fusion inhibitors, 368, 369*f*

**G**

Gabapentin, 285, 285*f*
Galantamine, 179*f*, 180
γ-aminobutyric acid (GABA), 48, 49*f*, 80, 134, 324-325
  binding of, 249
  ethanol and, 269
  inhibitory effect of, 272
γ-aminobutyric acid$_A$ (GABA$_A$) receptor, 324-325
Ganciclovir, 362, 362*f*
Ganglionic blockers, 183, 183*f*

Gases
    adiabatic compression of, 11, 11*f*
    compressed, in operating room, 1-12
        boiling point, 5
        critical temperature and pressure, 5-6
        kinetic energy and, 2-3
        pressure, 3
        temperature, 3-4
        vapor pressure, 4-5
    distribution and uptake of, 19-20
    flow of
        to blood, 17-19, 17*f*
        through tubes, 12-16
    inspired, 17
    laughing, 250
    laws related to properties of, 6-12
        adiabatic compression and expansion,
           11, 11*f*
        Avogadro's law, 8-9
        Boyle's law, 6-7, 9, 12
        Charles' law, 7, 9
        clinical and practical examples of, 21*f*
        combined gas law, 8
        combining, to form ideal, 9-10
        Dalton's law of partial pressures, 10-11
        Gay-Lussac's temperature/pressure
           law, 7-8, 9
        Joule-Thomson effect, 12
    mass of, 8
    providing, to patients, 12-19
    relationship of temperature and volume, 7
    storage of medical, 5
Gay-Lussac's temperature/pressure law,
    7-8, 9
Generalized anxiety disorder, 324
Generalized seizures, 278
Genetic code, 117*f*
Gentamicin sulfate, 94, 353
3 D-glucosamine, 231
D-glucose, 92*f*
Glucose, 91, 106
    conversion of, to carbon dioxide, 107,
        107*f*
Glucose-6-phosphate, 101
Glucuronic acid, 41
Glucuronidation, 284, 319
Glucuronide conjugate, 43*f*
Glucuronides, 41, 42, 53, 318
L-glutamate, 54*f*
Glutamate, 53, 249
Glutamic acid (Glu), 77
    vitamin K in carboxylation of, 235*f*

Glutamic acid decarboxylase (GAD), 326
Glutamine, 77
Glutathione, 37
Glutathione-nitrates reductase, 203
Glutethimide, 276
D-glyceraldehyde, 91
L-glyceraldehyde, 91
Glyceraldehyde, 91
Glyceraldehyde 3-phosphate, 103
Glyceryl trinitrate, 202, 203
Glycine, 76, 77
Glycinexylidide, 265
Glycogen, 93
Glycolipids, 90
Glycolysis, 93, 98, 100-104, 101*f*, 102*f*
    coupled relationship between
        tricarboxylic acid cycle and, 107*f*
    drugs interfering with, 103-104, 104*f*
    products of, 104
    relationships between tricarboxylic acid
        (TCA) cycle and, 99*f*
Glycolysis pathway
    enzymatic transformations of, 101, 102*f*
    inhibition of, 104*f*
Glycoproteins, 90, 93, 94
Glycosphingolipids, 89
G protein coupled receptor (GPCR)
    family, 79-80, 80*f*, 134, 176
G proteins, 80
Graham, Thomas, 18
Graham's law of effusion, 18-19
Gram, Hans Christian, 342
Gram-staining, 342
Growth hormone, 85
Guanabenz, 195
    structure of, 195*f*
Guanethidine, 192, 192*f*
Guanine (G), 74, 75*f*, 114
    as ribonucleic acid (RNA) base, 76
Guanosine, 73
Guanosine monophosphate (GMP), 73,
    226
Guanosine triphosphate (GTP), 104, 115
Guanylate cyclase, 204

**H**

Hagen-Poiseuille equation, 14
Halazepam, 328
Haloalkanes, structure activity analyses
    leading to, 251-254, 252*f*, 253*f*, 254*f*
Haloethers, structure activity analyses
    leading to, 251-254, 252*f*, 253*f*, 254*f*

Halogen atoms, 125
Haloperidol, 333*f*
  as antipsychotic, 319
  for anxiety, 329
  developed as fentanyl-like analgesic, 334
  inhibition of dopamine receptors by, 330
  as prototypical butyrophenone, 333
Halothane, 29, 30*f*, 242, 251-252
  metabolism of, 252*f*
Halothane hepatitis, 251
Heat of vaporization, 5
α-helical conformation, 79
α-helix, 78
Hemiacetal, 44, 44*f*
Hemicholinium, structure of, 178, 178*f*
Hemoglobulin, 79
Hemostasis, 228
Henderson-Hasselbalch equation, 69-70
Henry's law, 19
Heparin-induced thrombocytopenia (HIT), 232
Heparins, 94, 230-233, 231*f*
  biochemical mechanism of, 232-233, 233*f*
  low-molecular-weight, 230, 231*f*
  properties of, 231-232
Hepatic necrosis, 251
Hepatocytic hypoxia, 251
HER2 receptor, 84
Heroin, 292*f*, 293
Herpes, 361
Hexamethonium, 183, 183*f*
Hexokinase, 101, 104
Hexoses, 91
Highly active antiretroviral therapy (HAART), 364
Hill coefficient, 163
Hirudins, 230, 236-237, 237*f*
Histaminic receptors, 317
Histidine (His), 77
HMG-CoA, conversion of, to (3*R*)-mevalonate, 111
HMG-CoA reductase, 111
Homotropine, 188*f*
Hormones, 81
Hückel rule, 37
Human immunodeficiency virus (HIV)/AIDs, 75, 361, 364
Human immunodeficiency virus (HIV) protease inhibitors, 84
Hyaluronan derivatives, 310

Hydantoin ring, lactim-lactam tautomerization of, 280, 281*f*
Hydantoins, 281-282, 281*f*, 282*f*
Hydralazine, 226-227, 227*f*
Hydrochloric acid, 48
Hydrocodone, 293, 293*f*
Hydrogen bonding, 29, 78, 124, 127-128, 128*f*
  as dipole-dipole interaction, 128
Hydrolysis, 60
Hydromorphone, 292*f*, 293
Hydroperoxyeicosatetraenoic acids, 86*f*
5-hydroperoxyeicosa tetraenoic acids (HPETEs), 87
Hydrophilic character of molecules, 246-248, 247*f*, 248*t*
Hydrophilic gas, 246*f*
Hydrophobic alkanes, 29
Hydrophobic bonding, 129-130
Hydrophobic character of molecules, 246-248, 247*f*, 248*t*
Hydrophobic fragment, 263
Hydrophobicity, 50
Hydrophobic/water-insoluble gas, dynamic behavior of, 246*f*
Hydroxy, 38
ß-hydroxy acid, 114
7-hydroxyamoxapine, 319
8-hydroxyamoxapine, 319
Hydroxyamphetamine, 337
Hydroxybupropion, 322
7-hydroxychlorpromazine, 331
14-hydroxy-clarithromycin, 357
4-hydroxycoumarins, weakly acidic property of, 234*f*
3-hydroxydiazepam, 259
Hydroxyethylflurazepam, 328
2-hydroxyimipramine, 318
Hydroxyl, 125
Hydroxylation, 260, 319, 330-331
Hydroxyl groups, 38, 39-40, 197
4-hydroxy-midazolam, 272
Hydroxy nefazadone, 323
5-hydroxytryptamine (serotonin), 79
Hydroxyzine, 329, 329*f*
Hydroxyzine hydrochloride, 329
Hyoscyamine, 187
Hyperbaric oxygen therapy, efficacy of, 19
Hypericin, 323*f*, 324
Hyperkalemia, 225
Hypernatremia, 244

Hypertension, 208
  primary, 216
  secondary, 216
  temporary, 216
  types of, 216
Hyperthermia, 244
Hyperthyroidism, 208
Hypnotics. *See* Sedatives and hypnotics
Hypothermic bypass, 19
Hypothyroidism, 213

## I

Ibuprofen, 53, 54*f*, 301, 307, 307*f*
Ibutilide, 214, 215*f*
Ideal gas law, combining laws to form,
  9-10
Idoxuridine, 362
Imidazole, 38*f*
Imipramine, 317, 317*t*, 318, 329
Indanediones, 233-236
Indinavir (Crixivan), 84, 367, 368*f*
Indirect effect, 168
Indole, 37, 38*f*
Indomethacin, 305, 305*f*
Induction barbiturates, ionization and
  protein binding of, 257*t*
Infections. *See also specific organism*
  identifying cause of, 341-342
  opportunistic, 364
Inhibited enzyme, 180*f*
Inhibition
  allosteric, 132
  competitive, 132
Inhibitors, 132
  of DNA synthesis (nucleoside analogs),
    361-363, 362*f*, 363*f*
  irreversible, 124, 179
Inhibitory neurotransmitter, 325
Inorganic (monophosphate), 98*f*
Inositol-1,4,5-triphos-phate (IP3), 134
Inositol triphosphate, 226
Insertion mutation, 119
Insomnia, benzodiazepines in treating, 272
Inspired gas, 17
Insulin, 85
Integrase inhibitors, 369
Integration, 369
Interactions
  covalent, 124
  noncovalent, 124-130
Interferons, 85, 369-370
Interferon-γ, 85

Interleukins, 85
Internal double bond, 34
Interpatient variability, 139
Interstitial space, 19
Intramuscular (IM) route of drug
  administration, 146
Intrathoracic pressure, 12
Intravascular thrombosis, 228
Intravenous induction agents, 241, 254-262
  benzodiazepines, 258-262, 259*f*
Intravenous route of drug administration,
  143, 146
Ion channels, 80, 176
  binding of neurotransmitter to, 80
Ion-dipole bonds, 125-126, 126*f*, 127*f*
Ionic bonds, 125, 125*f*
Ion-ion interactions, 125, 125*f*
Ionization, 141
  effect of $pK_a$ on, 69-70
Iproniazid, 314
Irreversible drugs, 124
Irreversible inhibitors, 124, 179
Isoamyl nitrite, 202
Isocarboxazid, 315, 315*f*
Isocitrate dehydrogenase, 106
Isoflurane, 253
  difference between desflurane and, 5
  structure of, 254*f*
Isoleucine (Ile), 77
Isomerization reaction, 101
Isoniazid, 314
Isopentenyl pyrophosphate, 112
Isopropanol, 40, 40*f*
Isopropyl, 197
Isopropylamine, 46*f*
Isoproterenol, 196, 197, 197*f*
Isosorbide dinitrate, 203
Isothermal, 11

## J

Joule-Thomson effect, 12

## K

Kanamycin sulfate, 94, 354
$K_b$, 66
Ketamine, 259-261, 260*f*
Ketobutazone, 306, 306*f*
Keto-enol-tautomerism, 306
α-ketoglutarate dehydrogenase, 106
Ketones, 52, 52*f*, 53*f*
  metabolism of, 53*f*
  structure of, 52*f*

Ketopentose, 91
Ketorolac, 305, 305*f*
Ketoses, 91
ß-ketothiolase, 111
Kidney, salt reabsorption in, 216
Kinase, 101
Kinetic energy, 2-3
    Bernoulli's theorem and, 15
    Joule-Thomson effect and, 12
Kinetic theory, 2-3
    defined, 1, 2
*Klebsiella pneumoniae* infections, 346
Krebs, Hans, 104
Krebs cycle, 104

**L**

Labetalol, 196, 198*f*
ß-lactam antibiotics, 131
ß-lactamases, 346
ß-lactam ring, 343
Lactic acid
    pyruvate conversion to, 101*f*
    pyruvate oxidation of conversion to, 100
Lactim-lactam tautomerization of
    hydantoin ring, 280, 281*f*
Lactose, 90, 91
Laminar flow, 13, 13*f*
Lamivudine, 45*f*, 365, 365*f*, 366
Lamotrigine, 285, 286*f*
Lanosterol, 113
    conversion to cholesterol, 113
Latanoprost (Xalatan), 87
Lateral phase separation theory, 249
Laughing gas, 250
Laws
    Avogadro's, 8-9
    Boyle's, 6-7, 9, 12
    Charles', 7, 9
    combined gas, 8
    Dalton's of partial pressures, 10-11
    Fick's diffusion, 18
    Gay-Lussac temperature/pressure, 7-8, 9
    Graham's law of effusion and, 18-19
    Henry's, 19
    ideal gas, 9-10
    Newton's of motion, 2
    Poiseuille's, 14
    sum of partial pressures, 10
Lepirudin, 236
Leucine (Leu), 77
Leukotrienes, 86, 87
Levetiracetam, 286, 286*f*

Levo-alpha-acetylmethadol (LAAM), 299, 299*f*
Levofloxacin, 358*f*
Levorphanol, 294*f*
Lewis acid, 64
Lidocaine, 59*f*, 62*f*, 211*f*
    as amide-containing local anesthetic,
        265, 266*f*
    as amide group, 59
    as class of IB drug, 211, 211*f*
    decreasing of nerve cell permeability by,
        310, 310*f*
    injection of, 61
Ligand binding, 82*f*
Ligand-gated ion channel, 81*f*
Ligands, 80, 131, 131*t*
    endogenous, 131
Lincomycin hydrochloride, clindamycin
    and, 360-361, 361*f*
Linker chain, 263
Lipids, 85-90
    cholesterol as, 89-90
    eicosanoids as, 86-87
    fatty acids as, 85
    phospholipids as, 88-89, 88*f*
    solubility of, 63
    sphingolipids as, 89
    triacylglycerols as, 87, 88*f*
Lipophilicity, 43, 47, 141, 270
Lisinopril, 219, 219*f*
L isomers, 76
Lithium, 336
Local anesthetic agents, 210-212, 210*f*,
        211*f*, 241, 262-266
    amide-containing, 265-266, 266*f*
    ester-containing, 264, 265*f*
    mechanism of action, 262-263, 263*f*
    structure-activity models of, 263, 264*f*
Lomefloxacin, 358*f*, 359
London force, 129
Lone pair electrons, 25
Long, Crawford, 242
Lonidamine, 104, 104*f*
Loop diuretics, 223-224, 224*f*
Loperamide, 300, 300*f*
Lopinavir, 367, 368*f*
Lorazepam, 279, 328
    for insomnia, 272, 273*f*
Losartan, 222
Lovastatin (Mevacor), 90, 114
Low-molecular-weight heparins, 230, 231*f*
Loxapine, 335, 335*f*

L-serine, 89
L-type channels, 204
Lung disease, 208
Lysergic acid diethylamide (LSD), 59, 59*f*
Lysine, 77

**M**

Macrolides, 76, 343, 356-357, 356*f*
Macromolecule, 131
Major depressive disorder, treatment of, 320
Malate dehydrogenase, 106
Malathion, 180, 180*f*, 181*f*
Maltose, 92*f*
Mannitol, 226, 227, 227*f*
Maprotiline, 321, 322*f*
Maraviroc, 368, 369*f*
Mass
  of gas, 8
  measurement of, 8
Matter, 2
Mecamylamine, 183, 183*f*
Mechanical aerosol delivery systems, reliance on Venturi principle, 16
Meclobemide, 315*f*, 316
Meclofenamate, 304, 305*f*
Mefenamic acid, 304, 305*f*
Melting point, 63
Meperidine, 295, 295*f*
Mephobarbital, 279
Mepivacaine, 265, 266*f*
Meprobamate, 329, 329*f*
Mercaptan, 44
ß-mercaptoethanol, 44
Mescaline, 337*f*
Mesoridazine, 331*t*, 332
Messenger ribonucleic acid (mRNA), 76, 114-115, 117
Metabolic hydroxylation, 303*f*, 326
Metabolic processes, biochemistry of
  fundamental, 97-120, 98*f*
    cholesterol biosynthesis, 110-114, 110*f*, 111*f*, 112*f*, 113*f*, 114*f*
    electron transport and oxidative phosphorylation, 106-109, 107*f*, 109*f*
    glycolysis, 100-104, 101*f*, 102*f*
    transcription, 114-116, 115*f*, 116*f*
    translation, 116-120, 117*f*, 118*f*, 120*f*
    tricarboxylic acid (TCA), 104, 105*f*, 106
Meta-chlorophenylpiperazine, 323
Methacholine, 185, 186*f*
Methadone, 52, 52*f*, 298, 298*f*
  related analogues and, 298, 298*f*

L-methamphetamine, 316
Methamphetamine, 337, 337*f*
Methane ($CH_4$), 27*f*, 30
Methanol, 40, 40*f*
Metharbital, 279, 280*f*
Methicillin, 345*t*, 347
Methionine, 77
Methohexital, 256, 276, 277*f*
  pharmacokinetics of, 256
Methotrexate, 75
Methoxamine, 192, 193*f*
6-methoxy-2-naphthyl acetic acid, 309*f*
Methoxyflurane, 252
  metabolic products of, 252*f*
Methoxy group, 42
Methoxyphenamine, 196, 197*f*
Methsuximide, 283, 283*f*
Methylamine, 46, 46*f*
*N*-methyl-D-aspartate (NMDA) neurotransmitter, 285
Methylenedioxyamphetamine (MDA), 337*f*, 338
3,4-methylenedioxymethamphetamine (MDMA), 337*f*, 338
Methylethylamine, 46
Methyl groups, 67
Methylphenidate, 338*f*, 339
Methylprednisolone, 356
Methylprylon, 276
Methyl salicylate, 302, 302*f*, 303*f*
*N*-methylthiotetrazole (NMTT), 351
Methylxanthines, 339
Metolazone, 225, 225*f*
Metoprolol, 196, 198*f*, 207, 320
(3*R*)-mevalonate
  conversion of HMG-CoA to, 111
  production of, from acetyl coenzyme A (acetyl CoA), 111-112*f*
  production of squalene from, 111-113, 112*f*
Mevalonate kinase, 111
Mexiletine, 211, 211*f*, 212
Meyer-Overton rule of lipid solubility, 249
Mezlocillin, 345*t*, 347
Michaelis-Menten model of enzyme kinetics, 163
Mickey Finn, 274
Microorganism resistance, 342
Midazolam, 259
  in treating insomnia, 272, 273*f*
Miglitol (Glyset), 94
Minimum alveolar concentration (MAC), 244, 245*f*

Minocycline, 355, 355*t*
Minoxidil, 227*f,* 228
Mirtazapine, 323, 323*f*
Misoprostol (Cytotec), 87
Mithramycin, 76
Mitochondria, 108
Mitochondrial RNA (mtRNA), 76
Mixed agonist-antagonist, 297, 297*f*
Mixed triglyceride, 87
Moclobemide, 315*f*
Mole, 9
Molecular forces in drug-receptor binding, 123-124
Molecules, 2, 42
    acid and base characteristics of, 63
    diffusion rate of, 71
    hydrophilic or hydrophobic character of, 246-248, 247*f,* 248*t*
    motion of, 2
    of solids, 2
6-monoacetyl-morphine (6-MAM), 292*f*
Monoamine oxidase-A (MAO-A), 189, 314
Monoamine oxidase-B (MAO-B), 189, 314
Monoamine oxidase (MAO) inhibitors, 189, 244, 314-316, 315*f*
    action of, 190*f*
Monoethylglycinexylidide, 265
Monoethylglycinexylidide metabolite, 211
Monosaccharides, 91-92, 91*f,* 92*f*
    defined, 91
    stereochemistry of, 92*f*
    structure of, 91
Moricizine, 212, 213*f*
Morphine, 42, 42*f,* 48, 49*f*
    related analogues and, 291-294
    ring B modifications of, 295, 295*f*
    ring C modifications of, 294-295, 295*f*
    ring E modifications of, 294, 294*f*
    structure of, 289*f*
Morphine-6-glucuronide, 155
Morton, William, 242
Motion
    molecular, 2
    Newton's laws of, 2
Moxifloxacin, 358*f,* 359
Multiple bonds, 27, 27*f*
    covalent, 25-28, 26*t*
Muscarine, 176, 176*f,* 185
Muscarinic, 317
Muscarinic receptor agonists, 185-186
    structures of, 186*f*
Muscarinic receptor antagonists, 187, 188*f*

Muscarinic receptors, 176
Muscarone, 186, 186*f*
Mutagenicity, 124
Mutation
    deletion, 119
    exchange, 119
    insertion, 119
Myasthenia gravis, 181
    treatment of, 181
Myocardial infarction (MI), 230
Myosin, 203-204

**N**

Nabumetome, 308, 309*f*
Nafcillin, 345*t,* 347
Nalbuphine hydrochloride, 297, 297*f*
Nalmefene, 296, 296*f*
Naloxone, 34, 35*f,* 296, 296*f*
Naltrexone, 296, 296*f*
Naphazoline, 195
    structure of, 195*f*
Naphthalene, 38*f*
Naphthodianthrones, 324
Naproxen sodium, 53, 54*f,* 301, 307, 307*f*
Necrosis, hepatic, 251
Nefazodone, 322-323, 323*f*
Nelfinavir, 45*f,* 367, 368*f*
Neoendorphins, 290, 290*t*
Neomycin, 94
Neostigmine, 179*f,* 180
Neuraminic acid, 94
Neuraminidase inhibitors, 94, 363, 363*f*
Neuroleptics, 330
Neuromuscular junction blockers, 183-184, 184*f*
    PK/PD properties of, 170*t*
Neurotransmitter, 80, 134
    binding of, to ion channel, 80
Neurotransmitter reuptake, blocking, 316
Neurotransmitter reuptake pumps, 82
Nevirapine, 365, 366, 367*f*
Newton, laws of motion of, 2
Nicardipine, 205
    metabolism of, 206
Nicotinamide adenine dinucleotide (NAD/NADH), 98*f*
    energy of adenosine triphosphate (ATP) and, 107
    forming of cellular cofactor, 98
    as high-energy cofactor, 104
    oxidation of, 108
    as product of tricarboxylic acid (TCA) cycle, 109

Nicotinamide adenine dinucleotide phosphate (NADPH), 98*f*

Nicotine, 37, 38*f,* 176, 176*f*

Nicotinic ACh receptors (nAChRs), 176

Nicotinic receptors, 176, 181-184
 ganglionic blockers, 183, 183*f*
 neuromuscular junction blockers, 183-184, 184*f*

Nifedipine, 205

Nitrazepam, 328

Nitrogen mustards, 194

Nitroglycerin, 202, 202*f*

Nitrous oxide, 5-6, 241, 242, 250, 250*f*
 boiling point of, 5
 critical temperature of, 5
 storage of, 5
 use of oxygen with, 242

Nitrovasodilators, 201, 203

Nomenclature, 30

Nonamphetamine stimulants, structures of, 338*f*

Nonbenzodiazepine, 270

Noncovalent bonds, 124

Noncovalent forces, 124

Noncovalent interactions, 124-130
 dipole-dipole bonds, 126-129, 128*f*
 ion-dipole bonds, 125-126, 126*f,* 127*f*
 ionic bonds, 125, 125*f*
 nonpolar bonding forces, 129-130, 130*f*

Nondihydropyridines, 214-215

Nonnucleoside reverse transciptase inhibitors, 366, 367*f*

Nonpolar amino acids, 77

Nonpolar bonding forces, 129-130, 130*f*

Nonrenal clearance (CL$_{nonren}$), 156-157

Nonsteroidal anti-inflammatory drugs (NSAIDS), 86, 300-308, 301*f*
 anthranilic acids as, 304, 305*f*
 arylacetic acids as, 305, 305*f*
 aspirin and related salicylates as, 302-304, 302*f,* 303*f*
 propionic acids as, 307, 307*f*
 pyrazoles as, 306, 306*f*
 selective COX-2 inhibitors as, 308, 308*f*

Nordiazepam, 259, 279

Norepinephrine, 175*f,* 189*f*
 adrenergic receptors and, 175, 187
 as equipotent at receptors, 192
 MAO-A metabolization of, 189
 metabolism of, 314
 oxidative deamination of, 314

Norepinephrine neurotransmitters, 80
 imbalance in levels of, 314

Norfloxacin, 358*f*

Norfluoxetine, 320

Norketamine, 260*f*
 hydroxylation of, 260

Normeperidine, 295

Normorphine, 292

Nortriptyline, 190, 191*f,* 317, 317*t,* 318

Norverapamil, 205, 206

Nuclear hormone receptors, 81, 82*f*

Nucleic acids and polynucleotides, 73-76
 deoxyribonucleic acid, 73-75, 74*f*
 ribonucleic acid, 74*f,* 76

Nucleoside, 73

Nucleoside analogs, 361-363, 362*f,* 363*f*

Nucleoside reverse transcriptase inhibitors, 364-366, 365*f*

Nucleotides, 73

**O**

Obsessive compulsive disorder, 320

Octet, 24

Octopamine, 190, 191*f*

*O*-demethylation, 206

Ofloxacin, 358*f*

Ofloxacin *N*-oxide, 359

Olanzapine, 329

Oligopeptides, 79

Oligosaccharides, 91, 92, 92*f,* 94

Olsalazine, 304, 304*f*

Onium group, 263

Operating room, compressed gas in, 1-12
 boiling point, 5
 critical temperature and pressure, 5-6
 kinetic energy and, 2-3
 pressure, 3
 temperature, 3-4
 vapor pressure, 4-5

Opioid antagonists, 295-296

Opioid receptor family, 290, 290*t,* 291*t*

Opioids, 289-300
 as antidiarrheal drugs, 298-299, 299*f*
 fentanyl and related analogues, 297-299, 298*f*
 methadone and related analogues, 298, 298*f*
 mixed agonist-antagonist, 297, 297*f*
 morphine and related analogues, 291-294
 opioid antagonists, 295-296
 opioid receptor family, 290, 290*t,* 291*t*
 pharmacological responses to opioid analgesics, 291
 pure antagonists, 296, 296*f*

ring B modifications of morphine, 295, 295*f*
ring C modifications of morphine, 294-295, 295*f*
ring E modifications of morphine, 294, 294*f*
used as antidiarrheal drugs, 298-299, 299*f*
Opium, 289
Opportunistic infections, 364
Oral absorption of drug, 146
Oral cephalosporins, 349-350
Orbital, 24
Organic, 23
Organic chemistry, 23-71
  acid and base characteristics of molecules, 63
  definitions of acid and base, 63-66
  pK$_a$ values of important functional groups, 66, 66*t*
  structure and bonding, 24-63
    covalent bonds, 24-28
    diffusion, 71
    functional groups, 28-63
    important physical properties of drugs, 63-70
    water solubility, 70-71
  substituent effects on functional group pKa values, 67-68
Organic compounds, 23
Organic materials, 23
Organic molecules, names of, 30
Organic nitrates, 201-204, 202*f*
  biochemical mechanism of action, 203-204, 204*f*
  chemistry, 201-203, 202*f*
  metabolism, 203
  pharmacokinetics, 203
Organ perfusion, 142
Orthostatic hypotension, 318
Oseltamivir phosphate (Tamiflu), 94, 363, 363*f*
Osmotic diuretics, 226, 227*f*
Ostwald (λ) coefficient, 20
Oxacillin, 345*t*, 347
Oxaloacetate, 106
Oxalosuccinate, 106
Oxazepam, 259, 327, 328
Oxazolidinediones, 283, 284*f*
Oxcarbazepine, 285, 286*f*
*N*-oxidation, 48, 49*f*, 60, 319
Oxidation, 29

Oxidative deamination, 189, 189*f*
Oxidative phosphorylation, 93, 103
  electron transport chain and, 106-109, 107*f*, 109*f*
  production of adenosine triphosphate (ATP) during, 99*f*
2-oxoquazepam, 328
5-oxotiagabine, 284
Oxotremorine, 186, 186*f*
5-oxo-zaleplon, 276
Oxprenolol, 196, 198*f*
Oxybarbiturates, 255
Oxycodone, 293*f*, 294
Oxygen, 27*f*
  compressed, 6
  molecular weight of, 19
  use of, with nitrous oxide, 242
Oxymorphine, 293, 293*f*
Oxyphenbutazone, 306, 306*f*
Oxyphencyclimine, 187, 188*f*
Oxyphenonium, 187, 188*f*

**P**

P$_{450}$ enzymes, 29, 153, 320
Paclitaxel (Taxol), 83
Paired bases, 74
Palivizumab, 370
Palmitic (hexadecanoic) acid, 86*f*
Palmitoyl CoA (coenzyme A), 89
Pancreatitis, 365
Pancuronium, 183
Paramethadione, 283, 284*f*
Parasympathetic action, 175
Parasympathetic nervous system, 175, 176
  neurotransmitters in, 175*f*
Parenteral cephalosporins, 350-351
Pargyline, 315*f*, 316
Parkinson disease, 187
Paromomycin, 94
Paroxetine, 320-321, 320*f*
  as example of selective serotonin reuptake inhibitors, 83
Partial pressures, Dalton's law of, 10-11
Partial seizures, 278
Partition coefficient, 20
Patients, providing gases to, 12-19
*PD*-tolerance, 168
Peak concentration, 172
Peak plasma concentration (C$_{max}$), 143, 143*f*, 144*f*
Penfluridol, 334*f*, 335
Penicillinase, 346

Penicillinase-resistant, 346
Penicillinase-sensitive penicillins, 346-347
Penicillin-binding proteins (PBPs), 343
Penicillin G (benzylpenicillin), 59*f*, 344*t*, 346, 347
Penicillins, 59, 341, 342, 343-347, 344-345*t*
   penicillinase-sensitive, 346-347
Penicillin V (phenoxymethyl penicillin), 344*t*, 346
Pentasaccharide sequence, 231, 232*f*
Pentobarbital, 258, 275, 275*t*, 276, 279
Pentolinium, 183, 183*f*
Pentose, 91
Peptide bond, 59, 77
   planarity of, 78, 78*f*
Peptides, 79
Peptidomimetics, 230, 237, 238*f*
Peripheral arterial embolism, 230
Peripheral neuropathy, 365
Perphenazine, 331*t*, 332
PGA, 86
PGE, 86
PGF, 86
pH
   of blood, 65, 69
   of saliva, 65
   of water, 65
Pharmacodynamics, 163-168
   accumulation factor, 172
   average steady-state concentration, 171
   defined, 139, 139*f*
   effect-concentration relationship, 163-164, 164*f*
   effect-time profile, 165-171, 165*f*, 166*f*, 167*f*
   peak concentration, 172
   tolerance, 168
   trough concentration, 172
   of volatile anesthetics, 243-246, 244*f*, 245*ft*
Pharmacokinetics
   of barbiturates, 256-258
   compartmental, 140-141, 140*f*
   defined, 139, 139*f*
   saturable, 162
   of volatile anesthetics, 243-246, 244*f*, 245*ft*
Pharmacological effects, 132
Pharmacological intervention, 313
Pharmacological responses to opioid analgesics, 291
Pharmacophores, 135-137, 137*f*, 249

Phase I metabolism, 153
Phase II metabolism, 154-155
Phase 1 reactions, 28
Phase 2 reactions, 28
Phenacetin, 309, 309*f*
Phencyclidine, 259, 260*f*
Phenelzine, 315, 315*f*
Phenobarbital, 257
Phenols (Ph-OH), 42, 42*f*, 43*f*
   metabolism of, 43*f*
Phenothiazine neuroleptics, 132
Phenothiazines, 278, 330-332, 331*t*
Phenoxybenzamine, 193*f*, 194, 194*f*
Phenoxybenzamine autoalkylates, 194*f*
Phenoxymethyl, 346
Phentolamine, 193, 193*f*, 195
Phenylalanine, 77, 119
Phenylbutazone, 306, 306*f*
Phenylephrine, 192, 193*f*, 195
Phenyl group, 37
Phenyl rings, 186
Phenytoin, 189*f*, 211*f*
   as class 1B drug, 211, 211*f*
   as prototypical hydantoin, 281, 282*f*
   structure of, 212
Phosphate group, 125
Phosphatidylcholine, 88
Phosphatidylethanolamine, 88
Phosphatidylserine, 88
Phosphodiester bond, 73
Phosphoenolpyruvate (PEP), 103
Phosphofructokinase, 101, 103
Phosphoglucose isomerase, 101
2-phosphoglycerate, 103
3-phosphoglycerate, 103
Phospholipids, 88-89, 88*f*
   dual polarity of, 88-89
Phosphomevalonate, 111
Phosphonate-containing drugs, 220, 220*f*
Phosphorylation, 81
pH scale, 64-65
Physiological interpretation of clearance values, 157-161, 158*t*, 160*f*, 161*f*, 162*t*
Physostigmine, 124, 179*f*, 180, 180*f*
Physostigmine carbamoylate acetylcholinesterase (AChE), 180*f*
Physostigmine inhibition, 180*f*
Pi ($\pi$) bond, 26*f*, 33
Pilocarpine, 186, 186*f*
Pimozide, 335
Pindolol, 196, 198*f*
Piperacillin, 344*t*, 346-347

Piperoxan, 193*f*
Pirenzepine, 187, 188*f*
Piroxicam, 308, 309*f*
PK$_a$, 65
   effect of, on ionization, 69-70
   value of, 65-66, 66*t*
PK/PD abbreviations and symbols,
   173-174
Platelet activation, 228
Platelet aggregation, 86, 228
Platelet-derived growth factor receptors, 81
Platelet plug, 228
ß-pleated sheet, 78
Poiseuille's law, 14
Polar amino acids, 77
Polypeptides, 79
Polysaccharides, 91, 92, 92*f*
P orbitals, overlap of, 26, 26*f*
Postsynaptic nerve, 314
Potassium, 80
Potassium channel agonists, 226
Potassium channel blockers, 213-214, 214*f*
   as inhibitors of repolarization, 213-214,
     215*f*
Potassium-sparing diuretics, 225, 226*f*
Potassium supplements, 220
Pralidoxime, 180, 181*f,* 182*f*
Prazepam, 328
Prazosin, 193, 193*f*
Prenalterol, 196, 197*f*
Pressures
   barometric, 12
   critical, 5
   Dalton's of partial, 10-11
   defined, 3
   intrathoracic, 12
   measurement of, 3
Presynaptic nerve, 314
Prilocaine as amide-containing local
   anesthetic, 266, 266*f*
Primary alcohols, 40
Primary amines, 46, 47-48, 48*f*
Primary ammonium ion, 46
Primary hypertension, 216
Primary structure, 77
Primidone, 279, 280*f*
Primozide, 334*f*
Procainamide, 210-212, 210*f*
Procaine, 61, 62*f*
   as ester-containing local anesthetic
     agent, 264, 265*f*
Prochlorperazine, 331*t,* 332

Prodrugs, 60, 203
Proline, 77
Promethazine, 278
Prontosil, 341
Propafenone, 212, 213*f*
Propantheline bromide, 187
Propantheline chloride, 188*f*
Propene, 33
Propionic acids, 307, 307*f*
Propofol, 247*f,* 260*f,* 261, 278
Propranolol, 40*f,* 198*f*
   alcohol in drug molecules of, 40
   for digitalis-induced ventricular
     arrhythmias, 213
   as nonselective ß-blocker, 206-207, 207*f*
   structure of, 196
Prostaglandin E$_2$ (PGE$_2$), 301
Prostaglandins, 86, 300
   synthesis of, 301*f*
Protease inhibitors, 367-368, 368*f*
Proteins. *See also* Amino acids
   biosynthesis of, 83
   formation of, 74
   functions of, 79
   inhibition of, 119
   joining of amino acids in creating, 77
   quaternary structure of, 79
   regulatory, 79-81
   secondary structure of, 78
   signaling, 85
   structural, 83
   tertiary structure of, 79
   transport, 82-83
Proteoglycan, 93
Prothrombin, 234
Protriptyline, 317*t,* 318-319
Pseudomembranous colitis, 361
Pseudo-steady state, 147
Psychotherapy, 313
Psychotropic drugs, 313-339
   antidepressants, 313-324
     monoamine oxidase inhibitors,
       314-316, 315*f*
     selective serotonin reuptake inhibitor
       (SSRI), 319-321, 320*f*
     tricyclic antidepressants, 316-319, 317*t*
   antipsychotics, 330-336
     aripiprazole, 336, 336*f*
     butyrophenones, 332-334, 334*f*
     dibenzazepines, 335, 335*f*
     diphenylbutylpiperidines, 334-335,
       334*f*

lithium, 336
  phenothiazines, 330-332, 331*t*
  thioxanthenes, 332, 333*f*
anxiolytics, 324-329
  benzodiazepines, 324-328, 325*t*, 326*f*
defined, 313
stimulants, 336-339
  amphetamine, 337-338, 337*f*
  applications to anesthesia, 339
  cocaine, 338, 338*f*
  methylphenidate, 339
  methylxanthines, 339
Pulmonary embolism, 230, 234
Pumps, 82
  efflux, 83
  neurotransmitter reuptake, 82
  reuptake, 82, 316
Pure antagonists, 296, 296*f*
Pyrazoles, 306, 306*f*
Pyridine, 37, 38*f*
Pyrimidines, 74
Pyrophosphate, 98*f*
5-pyrophosphomevalonate, 112
Pyrophosphomevalonate decarboxylase, 112
Pyruvate, 104, 106
  conversion to lactic acid, 101*f*
  oxidation of conversion to lactic acid, 100
Pyruvate dehydrogenase, 104, 106-107, 108

**Q**

Quaternary amines, 47, 178
Quaternary ammonium, 46
Quaternary structure of protein, 79
Quazepam, 328
Quetiapine, 335, 335*f*
Quinapril, 219, 219*f*, 220
Quinidine, 210, 210*f*
Quinidine gluconate, 210
Quinidine polygalacturonate, 210
Quinidine sulfate, 210
Quinolones, 343, 358-361, 358*f*

**R**

Radial diameter, influence on flow, 14
Raltegravir, 369, 369*f*
Ramipril, 219*f*
Ranolazine, 207, 207*f*
Rate of loss, 157

Receptors, 131-132, 133*t*
  biological, 131
  defined, 123
Rectal route of drug administration, 146
Red blood cell binding, 152
Red man syndrome, 360
Reentrant arrhythmias, 208
Regulatory proteins, 79-81
Renal clearance (CL$_{ren}$), 156
Renal excretion, 155
R enantiomer, 212
Renin-angiotensin system (RAS), 216, 217, 217*f*
Renin inhibitors, 221, 221*f*
Repolarization, potassium channel blockers as inhibitors of, 213-214, 215*f*
Reserpine, 191, 192*f*
Resonance stabilization of carboxylate anion, 53*f*
Respiratory paralysis, 243
Respiratory syncytial virus infection, 370
Retrovir, 75
Retrovirus, 364
Reuptake, 314
Reuptake inhibitors, true and false, 191*f*
Reuptake pumps, 316
  action of, 82
Reuptake transporters, 316
Reverse transcriptase inhibitors, 364
  nucleoside, 364-366, 365*f*
Reversible inhibitors of MAO-A (RIMAs), 316
Reye syndrome, 302
Reynolds number, 13
Ribonucleic acid (RNA), 74*f*, 76
  comparison of deoxyribonucleic acid (DNA) and, 74*f*
  messenger, 76, 114-115, 117
  ribosomal, 76, 117
  transfer, 76, 117
  types of, 76
Ribonucleic acid (RNA) bases, 74, 76
Ribonucleic acid (RNA) polymerase, 76
Ribose, 92
Ribosomal binding, 353
Ribosomal RNA (rRNA), 76, 117
Rifampin, 76, 116, 116*f*
Rilpivirine, 367*f*
Rimantadine, 369
Ring B modifications of morphine, 295, 295*f*

Ring C modifications of morphine, 294-295, 295*f*
Ring E modifications of morphine, 294, 294*f*
Risperidone, 320
Ritonavir, 367, 368*f*
Rivastigmine, 180
RNA. *See* Ribonucleic acid (RNA)
Rofecoxib, 301, 308, 308*f*
Ropivacaine, 266, 266*f*

**S**

St. John's wort, 324
Salicylic acid, 302, 302*f,* 303*f*
Salicyluric acid, 302, 302*f*
Saliva, pH of, 65
Salsalate, 304, 304*f*
Salt reabsorption in kidney, 216
Salvarsan, 341
Saquinavir, 367, 368*f*
Sarcoplasmic reticulum, 226
Sartans, 221
Saturable pharmacokinetics, 162
Scopolamine, 187, 188*f*
Secobarbital, 275*f,* 276
Secondary alcohol, 40
Secondary amines, 46, 48, 48*f*
Secondary amine tricarboxylic acid, 317
Secondary ammonium ion, 46
Secondary hypertension, 216
Secondary nitrogen, 197
Secondary structure of protein, 78
Second-gas effect, 248
Second-generation cephalosporins, 349-350
Second-messenger events, 134
Sedatives and hypnotics, 269-278
    barbiturates, 274-276, 275*t*
    benzodiazepines, 271-272, 273*f*
    chloral hydrate, 274, 274*f*
Seizures
    absence, 284
    generalized, 278
    partial, 278
Selective COX-2 inhibitors, 308, 308*f*
Selective serotonin reuptake inhibitors (SSRIs), 82-83, 190, 319-321, 320*f*
    examples of, 83
Selegiline, 315*f,* 316
Serine (Ser), 77
Serotonin, 80, 134, 189
    imbalance in levels of, 314
    metabolism of, 314

oxidative deamination of, 314
Serotonin receptors, 79
    physiological effects of, 79
Serotonin reuptake transporter, 82
Serotonin syndrome, 320, 329
Sertraline, 320*f,* 321
Sevoflurane, 253-254
    metabolism of, 254*f*
Side chain, 76
Sigma ($\sigma$) bond, 25, 26*f*
Sigmoidal $E_{max}$ model, 163
Signaling proteins, 85
Signal transduction
    defined, 133
    drug effects on, 133-134, 135*f*
Simple triglyceride, 87
Simvastatin, 114
Single bond, 25
    strength of, 27, 27*f*
S isomer, 212
S-nitrosothiols, 203
Sodium, 80
Sodium benzoate, 53
Sodium calcium exchange, 207
Sodium channel blockers, 210-212, 210*f,* 211*f*
Sodium hyaluronate, 310
Sodium nitroferricyanide, 227, 227*f*
Sodium nitroprusside, 226, 227*f*
Solids, molecules of, 2
Solubility
    lipid, 63
    water, 63
Solubility coefficients, 19-20
Soman, 181*f*
Sotalol, 196, 198*f,* 214, 215*f*
Soterenol, 197*f*
Spectinomycin, 119, 120*f*
Speed, 337
Sphingolipids, 89
    subclasses of, 89
Sphingomyelins, subclasses of, 89
Sphingosine, 89, 90*f*
    structures of, 90*f*
Spironolactone, 225, 226*f*
Spiroperidol, 333*f,* 334
Spontaneous ventilation, 12
Squalene, 110
    production of, from (3*R*)-Mevalonate, 111-113, 112*f*
    production of cholesterol from, 113, 113*f*
Squalene-2,3 epoxides, 113

Squalene-monooxygenase, 113
*Staphylococcus aureus,* vancomycin-resistant, 360
Starch, 90
Stavudine, 365-366, 365*f*
Stearic (octadecanoic) acid, 86*f*
Stereochemistry
  of alkene, 34*f*
  at stereogenic center, 31*f*
Stereogenic center, 30, 32
  stereochemistry at, 31*f*
Stereoisomers, 76
Steroids, 86, 110
Stevens-Johnson syndrome, 286, 357
Stimulants, 336-339
  amphetamine as, 337-338, 337*f*
  applications to anesthesia, 339
  cocaine as, 338, 338*f*
  methylphenidate as, 339
  methylxanthines as, 339
Streptomycin, 94, 119, 120*f,* 354
  structure of, 94
Strong acid, 65
Structural proteins, 83
Structural requirements for drug binding, 135
Structure-activity models, 263, 264*f*
Structure-activity relationships, 186
Subcutaneous route of drug administration, 146
Substance, boiling point of, 5
Substituent effects on functional group p$K_a$ values, 67-68
Substrate, 131
Succinate, 106
Succinic semialdehyde (SSA), 326
Succinimides, 282-283, 283*f*
Succinylcholine, 184, 185*f*
Succinyl-CoA synthetase, 106
Sucrose, 90, 92*f*
Sufentanil, 298*f,* 299
Sulfa drugs, 62, 62*f*
Sulfamethoxazole, 357, 358*f*
Sulfasalazine, 304, 304*f*
Sulfate conjugate, 43*f*
Sulfate group, 125
Sulfates, 41, 42
Sulfisoxazole, 358*f*
Sulfonamides, 62, 341, 343, 357, 358*f*
  general structure of, 62*f*
  metabolism of, 63*f*
Sulfone, 44, 305, 305*f*

Sulfoxide, 44
Sulfur, electronegativity of, 44
Sulfuric acid, 41
Sulindac, 305, 305*f*
Sum of partial pressures law, 10
Supraventricular tachycardia, 215
Surgical anesthesia as stage in, 243
Sympathetic nervous system, 175, 216
  neurotransmitters in, 175*f*
Synapse, 134
Syphilis, 341
Systemic exposure, 144

**T**

Tacrine (Cognex), 84
Tamoxifen, 34, 35*f*
Tardive dyskinesia, 319
Tautomerism, 307, 307*f*
Temazepam, 327
  for insomnia, 272, 273*f*
Temperature
  critical, 5
  relationship of gas volume and, 7
Temperature compensated vaporizers, 3
Terminal double bond, 34
Tert-butanol, 40, 40*f*
Tertiary alcohol, 40
Tertiary amines, 46, 47, 48*f,* 317
Tertiary ammonium ion, 46
Tertiary nitrogen, 197
Tertiary structure of protein, 79
Testosterone, 89-90
Tetrabutylammonium chloride, 46*f*
Tetracaine as ester-containing local anesthetic agent, 264, 265*f*
Tetracyclines, 119-120, 120*f,* 343, 354-355, 355*t*
Tetraethylammonium chloride, 184, 185*f*
Tetrahydrofolic acid, 75
Tetramethylammonium chloride, 46, 46*f*
Theobromine, 336, 338*f,* 339
Theophylline, 321, 338*f,* 339, 356
Thermal energy, 4
Thiamylal, 256
Thiazide diuretics, 224-225, 225*f*
Thiobarbiturates, 255, 258
Thioether acetyl CoA, 104
Thioethers (R-S-R), 44, 56
  metabolism of, 45*f*
Thioether succinyl CoA, 106
Thiol-and carboxylate-containing drugs, 218

Thiols (-SH), 44, 45*f*, 56
  metabolism of, 44, 45*f*
Thiopental, 276, 277*f*
  pharmacokinetics of, 256
  pK$_a$ of, 257
Thiopental carboxylic, 258
Thiophene, 37
Thioridazine, 329, 331*t*
Thiothixene, 333*f*
Thioxanthenes, 332
  structures of, 333*f*
Third-generation cephalosporins, 347, 349, 350
Threonine (Thr), 77, 93
Thrombin, 229, 229*f*
Thrombin inhibitors, 238*f*
Thrombocytopenia, heparin-induced, 232
Thrombophlebitis, 234
Thrombosis, intravascular, 228
Thromboxanes (TX), 86, 87
  synthesis of, 301*f*
Thrombus, formation of, 228
Thymidine, 73, 75
Thymidine monophosphate (TMP), 73
Thymine (T), 74, 75, 75*f*, 114
Thymol, 251
Tiagabine, 284, 285*f*
Ticarcillin, 345*t*, 347
Time of peak plasma concentration (C$_{max}$), 143
Tobramycin, 354
Tocainide, 211, 211*f*, 212
Tolmetin, 305, 305*f*
Toloxatone, 315*f*, 316
Topiramate, 286, 286*f*
Total body clearance (CL$_{tot}$), 139, 156, 170
Trans-2-butene, 33
Transcription, 74, 100*f*, 114-116, 115*f*
  defined, 99, 114
  drugs that interrupt, 116
Transdermal system of drug
  administration, 146
Transfer ribonucleic acid (tRNA), 76, 117
Translation (protein biosynthesis), 116-120, 117*f*, 118*f*
  conversion of RNA message and, 100*f*
  defined, 74, 114
  drugs that interrupt, 119-120, 120*f*
  occurrence at ribosome, 99
  as process of making protein from DNA, 115*f*
Translation inhibitors, 120*f*

Transporters, 82
Transport proteins, 82-83
Trans relationship, 33, 34*f*
Tranylcypromine, 189, 190*f*, 315, 315*f*
Trastuzumab (Herceptin), 84
Travatan (Travoprost), 87
Trazodone, 322, 323*f*
*Treponema pallidum,* 341
Triacylglycerides, 89
Triacylglycerols, 87, 88*f*
Triamterene, 225, 226*f*
Triazolam in treating insomnia, 272, 273*f*
Triazoledione, 323
Tricarboxylic acid (TCA) cycle, 98, 101*f*, 104, 105*f*, 106
  coupled relationship between glycolysis and, 107*f*
  relationships between glycolysis and, 99*f*
Trichloroacetic acid, 67
Trichloroethanol, 274
Triclofos sodium, 274
Tricyclic antidepressants, 316-319, 317*t*
Tridihexethyl bromide, 187, 188*f*
Triethylamine, 48, 66
Triethylammonium chloride, 48
Trifluoperazine, 331*t*, 332
Trifluoroacetic acid, 252*f*
Trifluperidol, 333*f*, 334
Triflupromazine, 331-332, 331*t*
Triglyceride
  mixed, 87
  simple, 87
Trihexyphenidyl, 187, 188*f*
Triisopropylamine, 46*f*
Trimethadione, 283, 284*f*
Trimethaphan, 183, 183*f*
Trimethoprim, 357, 358*f*
Trimethylamine, 46*f*
Trimipramine, 317*t*, 319
Trinucleotides, 115
Triose, 103
Triphosphorylated analog, 362
Triple bond, 26, 27, 27*f*
Trisaccharide, 92
Trough concentration, 172
Tryptophan (Trp), 77
Tubes, flow of gases through, 12-16
Tubocurarine, 183, 184*f*
Tubular reabsorption, 155
Tubular secretion, 155
Tubulin, 83, 131
  inhibiting polymerization of, 83

Tuinal, 276
Tumor necrosis factor $\alpha$, 85
Turbulence, 15
Turbulent flow, 13, 13*f*
Tyramine, 190, 191*f*, 314-315
Tyrosine, 77
Tyrosine kinases, 81, 189*f*

**U**

Uracil, 114
   as ribonucleic acid (RNA) base, 76
Ureides, 270, 271*f*, 272*f*
Uric acid, phagocytosis of, 83
Uridine diphosphate-glucuronosyltran-
   ferases, 44
Uridine triphosphate (UTP), 115
Uronic acid, 231

**V**

Valacyclovir, 362
Valence electrons, 25
Valganciclovir, 362
Valine (Val), 77
Valproic acid, 284, 285*f*
Valsartan, 221
Vancomycin, 359-360, 360*f*
Vancomycin-resistant *Enterococci* (VRE),
   360
Vancomycin-resistant *Staphylococcus aureus*
   (VRSA), 360
Van der Waals forces, 129
Vaporization as cooling process, 4
Vaporizers, temperature compensated, 3
Vapor pressure, 4-5
   defined, 4
   as temperature-dependent phenomenon, 5
Vascular endothelial growth factor, 81
Vasodilators, 86
Vasodilatory drugs, direct-acting, 226-228,
   227*f*
Vaughan Williams classification, 209, 214
Vecuronium, 183, 184*f*
Venlafaxine, 322, 322*f*, 329
Venous thrombosis, 230
Ventilation
   Boyle's law in controlled, 6-7, 9, 12
   controlled, 12
   spontaneous, 12
Venturi principle, 16, 16*f*
Venturi tube, 15*f*
Verapamil, 205, 206*f*, 214-215
   metabolism of, 206

Vigabatrin, 284-285, 285*f*
Vinblastine, 320
Virus, 361
Vitamin D, 81, 90
Vitamin K, 235, 235*f*
Vitamin K$_1$, 34, 35*f*
Vitamin K binding site, 235
Volatile anesthetic agents, 241-254
   early, 249-250, 250*f*
   historical background, 242
   hydrophilic or hydrophobic character of
     molecules, 246-248, 247*f*, 248*t*
   mechanism of, 248-249
   partition coefficients of selected, 248*t*
   pharmacokinetics and pharmaco-
     dynamics of, 243-246, 244*f*, 245*ft*
   physical properties of, 245*t*
   purpose of, 241
   second-gas effect, 248
   stages of, 243
   structure-activity analyses leading to
     haloethers and haloalkanes, 251-254,
     252*f*, 253*f*, 254*f*
Voltage-gated calcium channels, 216
Volume of distribution, 139, 148, 149*t*,
   150, 150*t*
   of central compartment, 150
   at pseudo-steady state, 151
   at steady state, 150-151

**W**

Warfarin, 230, 356
   risk factor for, 236
   structure of, 234*f*
Water
   hydrogen bonding activity of, 129
   pH of, 65
   solubility of, 63, 70-71
Watson-Crick hydrogen-bonding pattern,
   75*f*
WB-4101, 193
Weak acids, 65
Wilkinson-Shand equation, 159
Willow bark, 302

**X**

Xanthine oxidase, 51*f*, 338*f*
X-TC, 338

**Y**

Yohimbine, 195
   structure of, 196*f*

## Z

Zalcitabine, 365*f,* 366
Zaleplon, 276, 277*f*
Zanamivir (Relenza), 94, 363, 363*f*
Zidovudine (Retrovir), 75, 94-95, 364-365, 365*f*
Zofenopril, 218, 218*f*
Zolpidem, 276, 277*f*
Zomepirac, 305, 305*f*
Zonisamide, 286, 286*f*
Zusammen, 33
Zyban, 322